BOLTZMANN CONSTANT:

$$k = 1.38 \times 10^{-23} \text{ joule/}^\circ\text{K}$$
$$= 8.616 \times 10^{-5} \text{ ev/}^\circ\text{K}$$

PLANCK'S CONSTANT:

$$h = 6.625 \times 10^{-34} \text{ joule-sec}$$
$$= 4.14 \times 10^{-15} \text{ ev-sec}$$

AVOGADRO'S NUMBER

$$A = 6.025 \times 10^{-23} \text{ mole}^{-1}$$

ELECTRONIC CHARGE

$$e = 1.6 \times 10^{-19} \text{ coul}$$
$$= 4.8 \times 10^{-10} \text{ esu}$$
$$= 1.6 \times 10^{-20} \text{ emu}$$

ELECTRONIC MASS

$$m = 9.1 \times 10^{-31} \text{ kg}$$

PERMITTIVITY OF FREE SPACE

$$\epsilon_0 = 8.85 \times 10^{-12} \frac{\text{farad}}{m} \frac{\text{coul}^2\text{-sec}^2}{m^3 - \text{kg}}$$

PERMEABILITY OF FREE SPACE

$$\mu_0 = 4\pi \times 10^{-7} \frac{\text{henry}}{m} \frac{\text{kg} - \text{m}}{\text{coul}^2}$$

CONVERSION FACTORS

$$1 \text{ ev} = 1.6 \times 10^{-19} \text{ joule}$$
$$1 \text{ dyne/cm}^2 = 7.5 \times 10^{-4} \text{ mm Hg (Torr)}$$
$$1 \text{ weber/m}^2 = 10^4 \text{ gauss}$$
$$1 \text{ stat-volt} = 300 \text{ volts} = 3 \times 10^{10} \text{ ab-volts}$$
$$1 \text{ joule} = 10^7 \text{ ergs}$$

FOUNDATIONS OF PLASMA DYNAMICS

Foundations of

PLASMA

E. H. HOLT

Rensselaer Polytechnic Institute, Troy, New York

R. E. HASKELL

Air Force Cambridge Research Laboratories, Bedford, Massachusetts

DYNAMICS

The Macmillan Company, New York

Collier-Macmillan Limited, London

THE MACMILLAN COMPANY, NEW YORK
COLLIER-MACMILLAN CANADA, LTD., TORONTO, ONTARIO

Printed in the United States of America

To Lois and Edie

PREFACE

This book is written as a text in the fundamentals of plasma dynamics. This branch of physics has recently seen a spectacular growth because of its relevance to the nuclear and space age. People in many of the conventional engineering disciplines, realizing the impressive potential importance of the field, are working on a wide variety of applications. Such work is being pursued in industrial and government laboratories and in a variety of university departments. Because much of the work is of recent origin there is a need for basic text material which will serve the practicing engineer and scientist as well as the student. In considering the scope of this book our decision has been to emphasize the fundamental topics of the field. These topics have been treated in depth without bias towards any particular application.

The situation which we have described calls for a book which is essentially self-contained in its subject matter. We have assumed a starting point of three years of college work in science or engineering. In mathematics we assume that the reader has worked with the differential and integral calculus and with vectors treated by the symbolic vector notation. In order to round out this background we discuss the mathematics of Cartesian tensors in Chapter 2; the equations of electromagnetic theory from first principles in Chapter 3; a review of the physics of particle interactions in Chapters 4 and 15; a presentation of kinetic theory in Chapter 5 which includes the definition of all basic quantities; and a treatment of electromagnetic waves in free space in Chapter 11. The pace of the development of these topics is appropriate to the assumed maturity of the reader and the manner of their presentation leads smoothly into the discussion of the various plasma topics.

Plasma dynamics is not an elementary subject. The level of understanding required to work in the field necessitates some involved mathematics. We gave much thought to the question of the appropriate mathematical language to use, and decided that the advantage of using a Cartesian tensor formalism decisively outweighed the disadvantage that this notation would be new to a number of those persons for whom the book is designed. Chapter 2 recounts all that need be known about Cartesian tensors to make the rest of the book comprehensible.

The desire to include adequate steps in all the topics presented has motivated us throughout. The reader will find that the stepping stones are within his stride and, as he follows the discussion and becomes involved in its details through working the exercises, he will have the experience of discovering for himself those insights into the subject which reflect an increasing understanding of it.

The majority of the topics treated in this book are pertinent to a person working in this field irrespective of his particular area of specialization. Accordingly, we present these topics in a unified manner. So, for example, we do not treat plasma physics and magneto-fluid dynamics as separate subjects but rather emphasize the origin of the macroscopic equations in the kinetic theory. This procedure makes clear the assumptions and restrictions of magneto-fluid dynamics. Although we reach what is sometimes considered to be an advanced level in such topics as plasma kinetic theory and waves in plasmas, the step-by-step presentation of these topics is no more difficult to follow than the material in earlier chapters. In fact we have found the material to be within the reach of college seniors.

The book is adaptable to a variety of needs and a few suggestions about its use in teaching may be helpful. They are made in the light of the experience of teaching the material at the graduate and senior year levels to students from the aeronautical, electrical, mechanical and nuclear departments in the school of engineering and from the physics department in the school of science at Rensselaer. The increasing adoption of a unified curriculum for engineering students during the first three years of college has minimized the problems of diversity of background at the senior level.

For a senior course about half the semester will be needed to cover the first six chapters with some material from Chapter 15 in addition. Chapters 7 through 10 can be used in the second half with some sections omitted at the instructor's discretion. Alternatively, a shorter time may be spent on the material of Chapters 8 and 9 and Chapter 10 may be omitted altogether. In this case Chapter 11 may be used to lead into an introductory treatment of waves in plasmas (Chapters 12 and 13) or magneto-fluid dynamics (Chapter 14).

In graduate courses a faster pace through the early chapters (and Chapter 15) will be maintained, so that Chapters 7, 8 and 9 may be covered in depth. Subsequent emphasis may be given to either the kinetic theory of plasmas (Chapter 10) or waves in plasmas (Chapters 11 through 13) or magneto-fluid dynamics (Chapter 14).

We acknowledge gratefully the loving support given by our wives, Lois and Edie; the research sponsorship of the National Aeronautics and Space Administration while we were together at Rensselaer, which enabled us to concentrate on plasma problems; the cooperation of the Electrical Engineering Department at Rensselaer in the preparation of the manuscript, and in particular to Miss Rosana Laviolette and Mrs. Marilyn Santerre for their typing; and the critical comments of students, colleagues and reviewers which have been invaluable.

Troy, N.Y.   E. H. HOLT
Bedford, Mass.   R. E. HASKELL

CHAPTER

CONTENTS

* May be omitted on a first reading and taken up later as appropriate.

I

INTRODUCTION

In olden times men thought of their world as consisting of four substances—earth, air, fire, and water. It is now realized that, from a scientific point of view, modern man must also classify natural phenomena in terms of the behavior of four states of matter—solid, liquid, gaseous, and plasma. The plasma state can be distinguished from the other states of matter in that a significant number of its molecules are in the electrically charged or ionized state. The fact that the two lists can be related to each other is rather intriguing, and in doing this the reader may ponder how far we have come in our ability to describe the world around us.

It is not particularly surprising that it has taken the space age to alert us to the importance of the plasma state of matter. One author has described our situation by saying that we live in a bubble of nearly un-ionized gas, and it naturally follows that the scientist, as an observer of the world in which he lives, should have leaned toward the study of the states of matter common to his environment—the earth, the air, and the water. However the fact is that the "bubble" exists in a sea of plasma!

The distinction between the four states of matter can be expressed in terms of an ascending scale of characteristic energy as we pass from the solid, to the liquid, to the gaseous and, finally, to the plasma state. Let us explore this sequence in more detail.

The atomic theory of matter has made us familiar with the concept of basic particles—atoms, molecules, and groups of molecules—being common to any of the states in which matter can exist. The distinction between the solid, liquid, and gaseous states lies in the difference between the forces, or bonds, joining these constituent particles to each other. Thus the solid state is characterized by a strong bonding between the particles, the liquid state by a weak bonding, and the gaseous state by a lack of bonding between the particles. What causes a substance to be found in any particular state? The temperature of the substance determines its state. In microscopic terms the kinetic energy of the atoms and molecules determines whether the material is in the solid, liquid, or gaseous state. This particle energy opposes the interparticle bond forces and the resultant equilibrium determines the state. Water provides a convenient example. At low temperature the bond between the H_2O molecules holds them tightly against the low energy of molecular motion. The matter is in the solid state—ice. At room temperature the increased molecular energy permits the more widespread movements and currents of molecular motion within the substance, which we associate with the liquid state. Due to a degree of random motion the particles do not all possess the same energy. The more energetic ones escape from the liquid surface and form a vapor above it. As the temperature is increased, a larger fraction of the molecules escapes until the whole substance is in the gaseous state—steam.

For almost a hundred years scientists have been exploring the properties of that state of matter characterized by an even higher mean particle energy. This is the energy necessary to ionize the particles. Sir William Crookes, in 1879, studied electrical discharges in gases and was sufficiently impressed by the novel phenomena observed to conclude that the matter in his discharge tubes existed in a new state—the fourth state of matter. In 1928, Langmuir used the word *plasma* to describe the inner region of an electrical discharge which was not dominated by wall and electrode effects. The word means a mold or form and is also used for the liquid part of blood in which the corpuscles are suspended. In our present usage it means a state of matter containing electrically charged particles.

It is not necessary for every particle to be ionized for us to be involved in plasma phenomena. Just as we saw that there was a transition between the liquid and gas phases due to the distribution of molecular energies, so there is a transition between the ordinary gaseous state and the ionized gaseous state. Sir William Crookes' discharges consisted of gases that were only partially ionized. We need to make two distinctions at this point. First we must consider the criterion that will qualify a partially ionized gas as a plasma.

Second we will distinguish between weakly ionized gases satisfying the plasma criterion and strongly ionized gases.

We have seen that Langmuir restricted the term *plasma* to the part of the discharge remote from the boundaries. The physical significance of this is that particles within the plasma region are not influenced by the boundaries of the discharge. Between the plasma proper and the potential surface which the boundary represents, there exists a transition region called the *plasma sheath*. The sheath region has properties that differ from those of the plasma, and the motions of the charged particles within the sheath are influenced by the potential of the boundary. The sheath particles form an electrical screen between the plasma and the boundary. A simple analogy is that of a person entering a forest. Beyond a certain distance within the forest there are enough trees to screen the edge of the forest from view. If the trees are spaced too far apart and the forest is too small, the person may never lose sight of the fields beyond, and such a group of trees hardly merits being called a forest. Our criterion then is this: to be classed as a plasma a partially ionized gas must have a volume larger than that of a sphere with a radius equal to the screening distance. We will find that the screening distance is a function of the density of the charged particles and their temperature.

Now what special effects occur to distinguish a strongly ionized plasma from a weakly ionized plasma? To answer this question we will assert that in a plasma with a low density of charged particles the effects of the presence of neutral particles overshadows the effects of the interactions between the charged particles. Although there are enough charged particles to satisfy the plasma definition, they are still too sparse in the gas, compared with the much larger number of neutral particles, to interact strongly with each other. The collisions between particles are governed by the laws of force between the interacting particles. Collisions between charged particles obey the Coulomb force law with its dependence upon the inverse of the square of the separation distance. On the contrary, collisions involving at least one neutral particle are governed by forces that are significant only in close proximity to the atom or molecule involved. The dependence upon separation may, for example, be with the inverse fifth power. So as the degree of ionization of the gas increases, the collision behavior of the plasma changes and Coulomb interactions become increasingly important. In the fully ionized plasma all the particles are subject to Coulomb interactions.

The plasma state is, then, characterized by a high mean particle energy. How high? High enough to cause a charged particle density to be maintained that satisfies the plasma criterion (the screening distance criterion). In general the mechanism that maintains the plasma is the ionization of the neutral particles by impact with other particles. When the energy source maintaining the plasma is an applied electric field, the electrons play a dominant role in impact ionization. Other phenomena in which electrons may play a dominant role are the electrical conductivity of the plasma and its interaction with electromagnetic waves. Negative ions play a minor role in plasma phenomena because they can exist only if the energy of the colliding particles is quite low.

I.I THE NATURAL OCCURRENCE OF THE PLASMA STATE

A transient plasma exists in the earth's atmosphere every time a lightning stroke occurs. Because the air is normally nonconducting, potential differences of millions of volts can be generated between clouds and the earth and from one cloud to another, during the time when thunderstorm conditions prevail. The lightning discharge occurs in two phases with what is known as a leader stroke progressing in steps across the potential gap first. This establishes a low degree of ionization in the discharge path, thus providing the conditions for the second phase, the return stroke, to take place. The return stroke establishes a highly conducting plasma path which permits a large current flow and the neutralization of the electrical charge which accumulated in the clouds.

At about 100 kilometers above the surface of the earth we find that the nonconducting property of the atmosphere no longer applies. The sun bathes us in a variety of radiations and the energy in the ultraviolet part of the spectrum is absorbed in the upper atmosphere. In the process of absorption a significant number of air molecules and atoms receive enough energy to become ionized. The resulting free electrons and positive ions are dense enough in the region called the "ionosphere" to satisfy the plasma criterion which has already been mentioned.

Because plasma interacts with electromagnetic waves, the early radio pioneers inferred the existence of the ionosphere when it was found that under certain conditions radio waves were propagated between distant parts of the earth's surface which were far beyond the line of sight. The explanation lay in the refracting properties of the ionosphere for radio waves in a certain range of frequencies. Studies of propagation through the ionosphere are now made also by means of satellites.

Many of the major features of the space within several earth radii of the earth have been established by rocket and satellite studies. This region is called the *magnetosphere* because of the important role played by the earth's magnetic field. The charged particles continually streaming toward the earth from the sun are diverted, and sometimes even trapped, by the earth's magnetic field. The trapped particles are most dense in regions of high latitude and account for the Aurorae. The Van Allen radiation belts consist of electrons and protons with energies extending to several million electron volts which are trapped at equatorial latitudes within several earth radii of the earth. These phenomena are illustrated in Figure 1.1.

The effects of plasma in the universe, which are of major interest, involve the interaction between plasma and magnetic fields. The widespread existence of magnetic fields in the galaxy has been demonstrated by independent measurements. A wide range of field magnitudes has been found, varying from 10^{-5} gauss in interstellar space to 10,000 gauss on the surface of magnetic variable stars. On the surface of the sun the general level of the field may be about one gauss, but in the region of sun spots it is known to rise to several thousand gauss. A highly conducting plasma and a magnetic

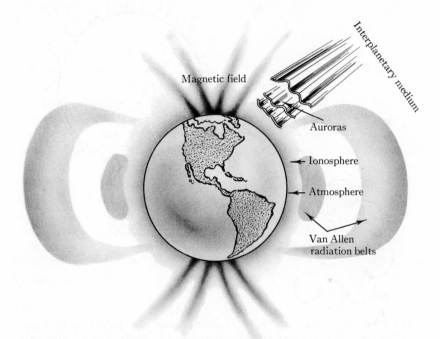

FIGURE 1.1 Plasma in the Magnetosphere (G. H. Ludwig: Proceedings of the NASA-University Conference on the Science and Technology of Space Exploration Vol. 1, Chap. 12. NASA SP-11, 1962)

field tend to remain frozen in whatever condition of intermixing occurs initially. This means that the plasma streaming from a solar flare not only follows the magnetic field but also distorts the field and pulls it along in the stream (Figure 1.2). To understand this effect it is helpful to consider the motion of individual particles in the presence of a magnetic field. We find that the motion transverse to the field is constrained to circular motion around the field lines, whereas the component of motion parallel to the field is unaffected by the presence of the field. Thus the luminous plasma tends to form a visual plot of the magnetic field lines. This basic property of the plasma state is evidenced in the shape of solar prominences, in the luminous filaments observed in the sun's corona, and in the paths followed by the solar plasma as it streams from the sun through the interplanetary gas to the vicinity of the earth. A dramatic example of mutual exclusion of charged particles and magnetic fields is provided by the continuous stream of charged particles coming from the sun, which is called the *solar wind*, as it impinges upon the earth's magnetic field. The geomagnetic field is considerably compressed on the side of the magnetosphere which faces the sun and is elongated on the

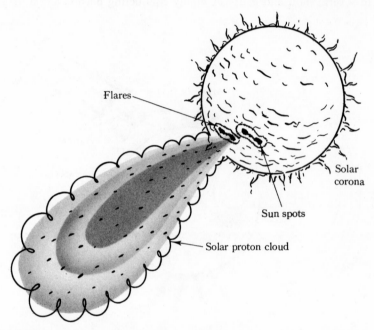

FIGURE 1.2 Plasma Phenomena Associated with the Sun (Adapted from G. H. Ludwig: Proceedings of the NASA-University Conference on the Science and Technology of Space Exploration Vol. I, Chap. 12. NASA SP-11, 1962)

remote side (Figure 1.3). Rocket and satellite measurements have shown that discontinuities occur in charged particle density and magnetic field in the region where the magnetosphere and the solar wind interact.

The study of electromagnetic radiations from space comprises the field of radio astronomy, and several of the observations in this field relate to the properties of plasma. For example, relativistic electrons in a magnetic field will emit synchrotron radiation which has a wide spectrum, while lower energy electrons in a magnetic field will emit cyclotron radiation at the cyclotron frequency and its harmonics. These types of polarized radiation have been detected from gaseous nebulae. Furthermore, as the radiation travels through interstellar space to the earth, its polarization is changed by an amount that depends upon the density of the intervening magnetoplasma medium. Measurements of this effect have been used to calculate this density. The study of the signals received by a radiotelescope from the general direction of the sun has also been used to obtain a plot of the distribution of the plasma density that exists in the vicinity of the sun.

An example of plasma wave propagation is provided in nature by the phenomenon known as *whistler propagation*. Whistlers are detected as an

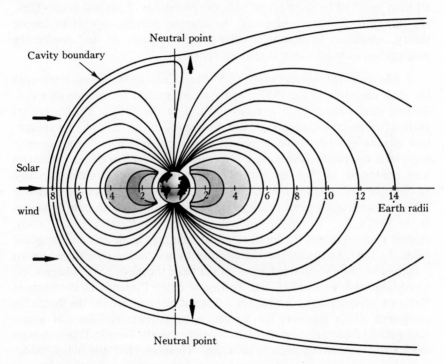

FIGURE 1.3 Distortion of the Magnetosphere by the Solar Wind (G. H. Ludwig: Proceedings of the NASA-University Conference on the Science and Technology of Space Exploration Vol. I, Chap. 12. NASA SP-11, 1962)

audiofrequency signal with a pitch that decreases with time and are generated in a particularly fascinating way. A lightning stroke at a certain point on the earth's surface is the source of a strong burst of radio noise. Some of this noise is in a frequency range that causes it to be guided by the earth's magnetic field. It is thus led back to earth at the remote conjugate point which corresponds to the shape of this field. However in its passage through the magnetosphere the frequency band is dispersed in time by the effect of the magnetoplasma medium. The band of frequencies arrives at the remote point over a period of a few seconds, resulting in the whistle.

1.2 SOME FACTORS IN THE HISTORICAL DEVELOPMENT OF PLASMA PHYSICS

We will discuss the origins of plasma physics in terms of four fields which have all been involved to some extent with the properties of ionized gases. These are electrical discharges in gases, the charged particle aspects of kinetic theory, astronomy in relation to solar plasma phenomena, and, finally, the propagation of radio waves in the ionosphere.

Electrical Discharges in Gases   Michael Faraday made observations of the glow discharge in the 1830's, and Ampere studied the motion of a conducting fluid (mercury) in a magnetic field in the 1850's. Thus a typical plasma (the positive column) and the elements of the modern plasma application of magnetohydrodynamic power generation were part of the scientific scene over one hundred years ago. Experimental researches on gas discharges were continued, in 1869, by Hittorf and, in 1879, by Sir William Crookes, who, as we have already noted, wrote that the phenomena of the discharge tube were sufficiently novel to suggest the existence of a fourth state of matter. In the 1890's, J. J. Thomson, who was a professor at Cambridge University, studied discharges and the motions of cathode rays in electric and magnetic fields. In 1897, he discovered the electron by measuring its charge-to-mass ratio and went on to establish much of the basic theory of gas discharges and gaseous electronics. In 1903, J. S. Townsend of the Clarendon Laboratory at Oxford University was studying spark breakdown and defined the ionization coefficient which accounts for ionization by particle collisions in a gas. Recognizing the ionizing agents as electrons, he thereby identified the dominant mechanism of current growth in a gas. Their epochal researches, which extended over several decades in the case of both men, made Thomson and Townsend the founding fathers of the modern understanding of electrical discharges in gases.

Also in the early 1900's, Langevin developed the theory of ion recombination and mobility, and Townsend himself contributed notably to the field of gaseous electronics by the design of his experiment to measure the ratio D/μ—the diffusion coefficient to the mobility of a charged particle. The theoretical relationship between these quantities was established by Einstein in the early 1900's.

The twenties were notable for the work of Irving Langmuir of the General Electric Research Laboratory. In 1913, Langmuir was working on thermionic emission of electrons into a vacuum and confirmed the law of space charge current limitation discovered by Child in 1911. The importance of space charge effects was to remain as a strong point of his subsequent work on plasmas. This led to a thorough analysis of the space charge sheath which separates the plasma proper from its boundaries. His principal tool in this analysis was the electrostatic probe which became known as the Langmuir probe. In addition to the presence of space charge his probe theory recognized the role of the electron and ion velocity distribution functions in plasma behavior. The Debye-Hückel theory of Coulomb shielding as applied to the ions in electrolytes was published in 1923.

In 1925, Langmuir observed that a beam of electrons in his discharge tube was being scattered much more rapidly than could be accounted for by collisions. To try to explain this "Langmuir paradox," F. M. Penning of the Philips Research Laboratory in the Netherlands looked for and observed high-frequency electrostatic oscillations in a gas discharge in 1926. Tonks and Langmuir subsequently also measured the oscillations, and, in 1929, they derived an equation for the oscillation frequency which is commonly called the *plasma frequency*.

Charged Particle Aspects of Kinetic Theory In 1905, Lorentz applied the Boltzmann theory to the problem of electrical conduction in an electron gas. His notable contribution to kinetic theory was discussed in terms of the theory of metals. In fact it applied to the electron gas constituent of a gaseous plasma, although this was not fully appreciated for many years.

The problem of the form of the electron velocity distribution function in a gas subject to an applied electric field was treated by Druyvesteyn in 1930, and by Morse, Allis, and Lamar in 1935. Inclusion of the effect of thermal motion of the neutral scatterers was added by Davydov, also in 1935, and the high-frequency case was studied by Margenau in 1946. This whole problem is one of considerable importance in gaseous electronics, and it remains the subject of active research. The Boltzmann equation was used by Vlasov in 1938 to discuss plasma electron waves and oscillations. The connection between the Boltzmann equation and the Liouville equation was studied by Bogoliubov and Kirkwood in the forties for dense neutral gases. Recently, progress has been made in applying their work to the ionized gaseous state.

Kinetic theory as a whole developed from the work of Boltzmann and Maxwell and was expounded and added to by Jeans. Although it assumed a crude model of the molecule, kinetic theory was highly successful in describing the statistical behavior of gases that were not in thermal equilibrium with their surroundings. The rather complete development of this specialized branch of physics was highlighted by Chapman and Cowling's famous book (1938) *The Mathematical Theory of Non-Uniform Gases*. There are some glimpses in this work of the complications attendant upon the presence of charged particles in gases, and since that time substantial progress has been made in the development of the Boltzmann equation approach to plasma problems. A milestone in this direction is represented by Allis' article, "Motions of Ions and Electrons," in the *Handbuch der Physik* (1956). This approach provides a foundation for the development of the fluid model of a plasma and, as it also encompasses orbit theory, represents a starting point for a comprehensive discussion of plasma problems. It is from this starting point that we begin the discussion of plasma dynamics presented in this book.

Astronomy—Solar Plasma Phenomena Disturbances in the earth's magnetic field were related to solar flares by Carrington in the 1850's, and Sabine correlated variations in the earth's magnetic field with the sunspot cycle during the same period. Observations of the eclipse of the sun in 1878 drew attention to the resemblance of coronal streamers to magnetic lines of force. In 1889, F. H. Bigelow inferred that the sun was a great magnet from the appearance of the corona at sunspot minimum.

The work of Hale established the modern period in astronomy. In 1908, he inferred that a large magnetic field was associated with sunspots by measuring the Zeeman effect in the sunspot radiations. The thesis that the forms and motions of solar prominences are influenced by the sun's magnetic field was advanced by Deslandres in 1912, and, in 1913, Hale deduced the general magnetic field of the sun from Zeeman splitting. Larmor discussed his dynamo theory of the solar magnetic field in 1919. In 1920, Saha was studying the solar chromosphere, and his theory of equilibrium ionization (the Saha equation) contributed notably to establishing the values of the parameters of the chromosphere and, in particular, its low pressure.

In expounding the theory of geomagnetic storms which result from solar activity, Chapman and Ferraro discussed the mutual interaction of mechanical forces and magnetic forces in ionized gases in the early thirties, and Cowling discussed the frozen field effect in 1933. Alfvén's work on magnetohydrodynamic waves dates from the early forties. Hans Bethe described the theory of the generation of thermonuclear energy in the sun in 1939.

The problem of the treatment of Coulomb interactions between charged particles is interwoven with the development of astronomy. In discussing the motions of stars, Jeans considered the inverse square dependence of the gravitational force of attraction and reasoned that the cumulative effect of many weak encounters would have more effect on the motion of a star than the occasional close encounter. Landau, in 1936, treated the case of multiple, small deflection, Coulomb collisions between charged particles and introduced the Debye screening length as a cutoff parameter.

The Fokker-Planck equation was applied to the treatment of Brownian motion by Chandrasekhar in 1943 and was later applied to multiple Coulomb collisions by Spitzer.

Propagation of Radio Waves in the Ionosphere Balfour and Stewart, in 1878, postulated the existence of the ionosphere to explain the diurnal variations in the terrestrial magnetic field. In 1901, Marconi demonstrated long distance radio communication across the Atlantic ocean, and this was explained, in 1902, by Heaviside and Kennelly in terms of the properties of the ionosphere. They also postulated that the ionosphere is created by ionizing radiations from the sun. In 1925, Nichols and Schelling considered the problem of propagation in a plasma in a magnetic field (the earth's), and the so-called magnetoionic theory was discussed, in 1927, by Breit who also described the technique of ionospheric sounding using pulses of radio frequency energy. Appleton, in 1927, and Hartree, in 1931, clarified the basic theory of magnetoionic radio propagation and derived the equation for the refractive index of the ionosphere which bears their names.

In summary we may identify the two poles of plasma physics history as electrical discharges on the one hand and solar plasma phenomena on the other. The problems of classical electrical discharges were concerned with electrons in strong interaction with neutral particles in the presence of an applied electric field. In contrast, the problems of solar plasma physics are less concerned with electron-neutral particle interactions but involve the interactions between plasmas and magnetic fields.

Our purpose in this section has been to sketch in bare outline some of the roots of plasma physics. We have not attempted to follow more recent developments. However we must mention the Second United Nations International Conference on the Peaceful Uses of Atomic Energy held in Geneva in 1958. At that time the work on controlled thermonuclear fusion, which had hitherto been done in secret, was declassified by mutual agreement amongst the nations concerned. The subsequent open effort to achieve controlled thermonuclear power generation has done much to stimulate interest in the youthful discipline of plasma dynamics.

1.3   PLASMA   APPLICATIONS

We began this book with a definition of plasma as the fourth state of matter, characterized by a high energy density. Bearing in mind that high particle energy, $\frac{1}{2}mv^2$, not only implies high speed (v) but also, according to the kinetic picture of a gas, a high temperature, it appears that we will encounter matter in the plasma state in many diverse pursuits. In fact it is even a little misleading to make a list of the present applications of plasma because this tends to narrow one's perspective. For example, it would be a frustrating task to attempt a brief discussion of the applications of the solid state of matter—a moment's thought will suffice to illustrate the point. Nevertheless we make the excuse that our subject is new, and in presenting a list of applications we may at least indicate the present stage of its development.

Energy Conversion   The most widely publicized plasma applications are energy conversion by means of controlled thermonuclear (fusion) reactions and magnetohydrodynamic (MHD) power generation. In addition the plasma diode is the most promising form of thermionic energy converter. There are also several well-established uses of the plasma of an electrical discharge. We will mention these first.

A glow discharge is present in every fluorescent lamp and the voltage-current characteristic of this type of discharge is exploited in the constant voltage gas tube widely used in electronic circuits. Various types of gas vapor are also used for lighting, mercury and neon being the most common. Two other types of gas tubes, the thyratron and the ignitron, have important applications in electrical power handling, these being switching and rectification, respectively.

The most awesome form of energy in the universe is the fusion reaction which is the source of the energy of the sun. It is in such reactions that the elements are formed—the heavier from the lighter as nuclei collide and fuse together. Here in the heart of the sun is the alchemist's laboratory, and, until recent times, his manipulations and wizardry on earth were to no avail. Now, however, man has contrived to bring about at least the most elemental of the fusion reactions—and possesses the hydrogen bomb. The taming of this energy monster is a sober, scientific, and engineering enterprise to which many laboratories are committed. Let us consider the problem involved.

In order to undergo fusion reactions, nuclei must come very close together in spite of the electrostatic repulsion between them. This means that they must approach each other at high speed. The use of opposing beams of particles is not feasible because for each collision which results in a fusion event many collisions will occur in which the particles are merely scattered. Rather it is necessary to retain the scattered particles by reflecting them back into the heart of the device as many times as necessary until the eventual fusion collision takes place. Such a collection of randomly moving particles fulfils the kinetic theory description of a gas at a certain temperature. The temperature required to produce a significant amount of fusion is over 100 million degrees Kelvin in the case of deuterium.

At such temperatures any gas is fully ionized and thus constitutes a plasma. The controlled fusion problem is, therefore, to create a gas at this high temperature and hold it together long enough for a substantial number of fusion reactions to take place. The resulting energy must then be converted into a usable form. The fact that charged particles interact with a magnetic field provides the only hope of containing such a high-temperature plasma, and magnetic fields of the order of 100 thousand gauss must be used. The work done on this problem indicates that the development of a fusion generator requires a long-range program, and this type of effort is being made at a quite intensive level at a number of laboratories.

The MHD generator illustrates the properties of plasma in motion, as well as the interaction between plasma and the magnetic field. The MHD generator converts the kinetic energy of a flowing plasma into electrical power. The inverse effect is used in the design of the plasma accelerator, a promising aspirant as an engine for space vehicles. The principles of both devices are illustrated by Figures 1.4 and 1.5. Figure 1.4 shows the plasma flow (**v**) along the x_1-axis with an applied magnetic field ($\mathbf{B}_{appl}$) in the x_2-direction. As a result of the interaction between the plasma and the magnetic field, an electric field ($\mathbf{E}_{ind}$) is induced in the x_3-direction. If electrodes are placed in the walls of the channel with an external circuit to permit a current to flow through the plasma because of this electric field, then a current density ($\mathbf{J}_{ind}$) flows across the stream. This, in turn, produces a force ($\mathbf{F}_{ind}$) in the $-x_1$-direction which acts to decelerate the plasma. Thus, because a current passes through an

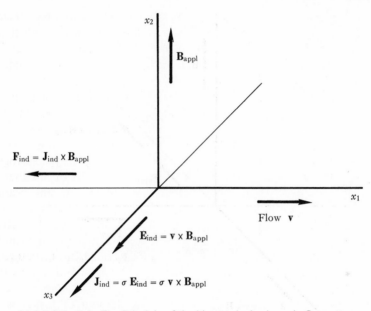

FIGURE   I.4   The Principle of the Magnetohydrodynamic Generator

external load connected across the channel electrodes, the plasma loses kinetic energy.

The plasma accelerator requires both applied electric ($\mathbf{E}_{appl}$) and magnetic ($\mathbf{B}_{appl}$) fields (Figure 1.5). An induced current density ($\mathbf{J}_{ind}$) is present as in the case of the MHD generator, but this is offset by an opposite current density ($\mathbf{J}_{cond}$) driven by the applied electric field. The accelerating force ($\mathbf{F}_{accl}$) which acts on the plasma will be positive if the applied electric field is strong enough, as is shown in the figure.

In contrast to the situation in the fusion work, operating MHD generators can be designed and their actual performance can be reasonably predicted from the theory. Although important problems still remain, the major restraint on their final development is an economical one.

As a final example of an energy converter utilizing the properties of a plasma, we will mention the thermionic generator. The simple diode configuration of this device is shown in Figure 1.6. The cathode is heated so that electrons boil off from the surface, and the anode is cooled. The output voltage is about one volt, and the units commonly have a small diode spacing of about 0.005 inch and an output current of the order of 100 amps. The unit is filled with cesium vapor which becomes ionized, either on contact with the hot cathode or by a stepwise process in the gas. The positive cesium ions neutralize the electronic space charge and permit high currents to flow. The cesium also forms a monolayer on the anode, thus reducing its work function.

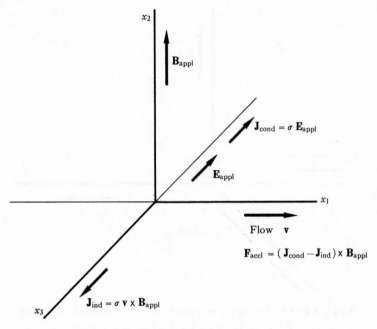

FIGURE 1.5   The Principle of the Plasma Accelerator

By constructing such diodes in a concentric cylindrical geometry around the fuel rods of a nuclear (fission) reactor, some of the nuclear energy can be converted directly into electricity. These converters are being intensively developed in this way as portable power generators, particularly for space missions, and have been proposed to form a topping cycle for the steam turbine in a nuclear (fission) central power station.

Electrical Communications   The two major applications in this area are long-distance radio propagation by refraction in the ionosphere and the communication with a space vehicle during the period of reentry into the earth's atmosphere, when the vehicle becomes covered by a plasma layer.

Long-distance radio propagation is possible over only a fairly well-defined frequency band which ranges from about 3 to 25 Mc (megacycles). At the low-frequency end of the range the wavelength is long compared to

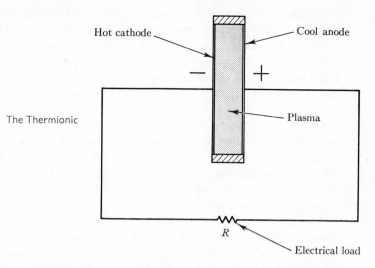

FIGURE 1.6 The Thermionic Converter

the distance over which the electron density changes in the lower ionosphere, and the wave suffers considerable attenuation on being reflected. At the high-frequency end of the range the wavelength is short compared to the characteristic length of the electron density gradient, and the wave can be pictured as a ray that is continuously refracted in the medium. Within the propagation frequency band this refraction causes the ray path to bend over and to reemerge into the troposphere and return to the surface of the earth. However, as the frequency increases, the amount of refraction decreases until the ray path is not bent over sufficiently to return to the earth. This effect is clearly dependent upon the angle of incidence of the radio wave upon the ionosphere. For example, a wave with vertical incidence may be returned up

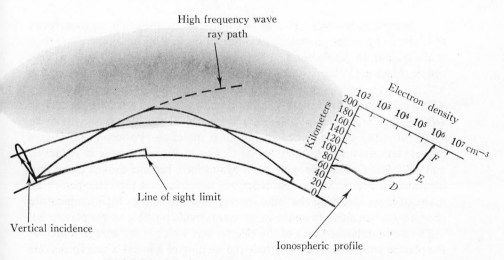

FIGURE 1.7 Ionospheric Refraction of Radio Waves

to a frequency of 6 Mc for a typical condition of the ionosphere, while long-distance communication under the same ionospheric condition may be practical up to 22 Mc. The effect is illustrated in Figure 1.7 which shows also the structure of the ionosphere in a series of plateaus. These are commonly called the *D*, *E*, and *F* layers. Attenuation of low-frequency waves occurs in the *D* layer, and refraction of the upper frequencies occurs mainly in the *F* layer.

The earth's magnetic field affects the wave propagation properties of the ionosphere through the interaction between the circular motion of the electrons of the ionosphere and the motion of the electric field vector of the electromagnetic wave. This latter motion depends upon the polarization of the wave, and, in general, this will be changed by the effect of the magnetoplasma medium.

The reentry communications problem is of increasing importance as manned space exploration comes of age. Low-frequency telemetering channels in a space craft are often interrupted when the vehicle reenters the earth's atmosphere. This is because the signals cannot penetrate the plasma layer which forms around the vehicle during this period.

The study of the formation of the plasma layer around a reentering vehicle is one of great complexity. The vehicle generates a shock wave around its nose, which heats the atmosphere sufficiently to generate the ionization which constitutes the plasma. The properties of the boundary layer, chemical kinetics in a rapidly changing atmosphere, and a large variety of possible ionizing reactions, combined with the complicated shock wave profile, require considerable sophistication in the approach to a solution. Laboratory simulation of the problem involves the use of hypersonic shock tubes which may require major facilities for their operation. This problem has also motivated interest in the study of high temperature air.

Materials Sciences Plasma applications in materials science result from the fact that the arc discharge is the source of a higher temperature than is available from gas flames. Gas flames are limited to about 3000°C, while a simple, hand-held plasma torch, in which an internal arc heats a flow of gas which emerges as a plasma jet, provides a working temperature of 6000°C. When it is remembered that the boiling point of tungsten is 5930°C, carbon 4830°C, and molybdenum 4800°C, it is clear that the plasma torch can be useful in many operations involving such materials. Powerful arc devices provide temperatures of about 30,000°C. Few molecules survive at 10,000°C, and at 30,000°C a high proportion of atoms have become broken down into ions and electrons. Many new reactions take place at these temperatures, many of them involving the ionic species, and the field of high-temperature chemistry is benefiting from the experiments made possible by the plasma jet.

The well-established uses of the electric arc, which is the energy source of the plasma jet, in metallurgy include the melting of a metal which forms one of the electrodes of the arc discharge. This may be done under vacuum conditions in order to prepare a high-purity metal. Electric arc welding is common, and an inert gas atmosphere may be used around the arc and the melted metal, in order to reduce oxidation of the weld.

More recent applications of the plasma jet include the spraying of refractory materials and the high-speed cutting of steel. Small particle powders, either metallic or nonmetallic, can be produced conveniently by vaporizing the raw material in a high-intensity arc in a supercooled vapor state. When the vapor is condensed very rapidly, spheroidal particles in controllable sizes from 10^{-6} to 10^{-5} cm are obtained. New refractory materials can be synthesized in the plasma jet, and sizable single crystals of high melting point metals and compounds are grown by allowing the plasma jet to play on a rod and dropping powder on the hot spot. Several applications exist in extractive metallurgy. In thermal decomposition the arc is mixed with carbon to increase its conductivity, and the resulting rod is used as a consumable cathode in an arc discharge or placed in a graphite crucible to form the anode. A plasma flame consisting mainly of the elemental vapors streams away from the anode, and the various simple oxides condense at different points along the flame. The metallic constituents are recovered from the oxides by subsequent processes. If chlorine gas is injected into the plasma flame, the metal oxides are converted into halides in the vapor state. As the boiling points of many metallic chlorides are widely separated, halogenation facilitates separation by partial condensation in the plasma flame. The plasma environment provides fast reactions, and this technique is set up as a high-speed flow process.

A number of natural and man-made plasmas are compared in terms of their charged particle density and gas temperature in Figure 1.8.

Plasmas in Solids   In describing plasma as the fourth state of matter, we have synonymously used the term *ionized gaseous state*. The only proviso was that the plasma criterion had to be met by the presence of sufficient ionization in the gas. We now mention the occurrence of charged particles in solids under conditions that make plasma theory applicable.

Charged particle concentrations that are high enough and consist of approximately equal numbers of positive and negative charges warrant the designation *plasma*. In two important classes of solids, metals and semiconductors, these conditions are satisfied. Because the motions of atoms and molecules in solids are inherently less chaotic than the motion in gases due to the ordering effect of the lattice, the behavior of the plasmas in these two classes of solids may be expected to exhibit simplicities which are difficult to achieve in gaseous plasmas. This has indeed proved to be the case, and certain types of plasma waves, for example, have been beautifully demonstrated in appropriate solid materials.

Conduction of electricity in metals is due to the motion of electrons within the metal. On the average, one electron per metallic atom is able to move freely. Because the bulk metal remains electrically neutral, the electron gas moves within a positive ion matrix, or mold, and is thus closely analogous to the gaseous plasma situation. The important difference between the two cases is that the distribution of electron velocities in the metal obeys Fermi statistics rather than Maxwell-Boltzmann statistics. The conduction electrons are free to respond to an applied electric field and they have a density of the order of 10^{22} cm^{-3}. The advantages of this type of plasma for research studies are

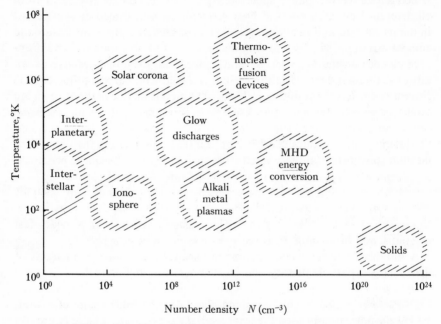

FIGURE   I.8   Temperature and Density Ranges for Various Plasmas.

that its boundaries are well defined, the concentration of charge carriers is accurately known, the types and masses of the charge carriers are known, and the temperature is easily determined.

Conduction of electricity in semiconductors is by means of electrons and positive holes. Energy distributions may follow the Maxwell-Boltzmann statistics of the ionized gaseous state. Calculation of current flow and the diffusion of charges may be made following the procedure for gaseous plasmas. Semiconductors are divided into two types depending upon the nature of the carrier responsible for most of the current carrying capacity at low electric fields. In a p-type semiconductor electrons are the minority carrier and most of the current is carried by holes which have a low mobility in the electric field. In an n-type semiconductor the mobile electrons are the majority carrier.

The density of charged particles in a semiconductor is several orders of magnitude less than the atom density, and it is found that the number of charge carriers increases upon application of an electric field of sufficient strength. The increased density of charge carriers is due to the generation of electron-hole pairs rather than to an increase in the number of either electrons or holes independently. The extra electrons and holes both participate in the subsequent conduction phenomena so that a new type of plasma, as it were, is generated in the semiconductor. The phenomenon of the current pinch, which is well known in gaseous plasmas, has been demonstrated also in these electron-hole plasmas. Electrical breakdown of a semiconductor is explained in terms of impact ionization by electrons just as in the case of gaseous breakdown.

Standing waves in the whistler mode, which was mentioned in Section 1.1, have been demonstrated both in sodium cooled to the temperature of liquid helium and in a semiconductor. This wave motion is therefore known to occur under the widely varying conditions represented by a metal, a semiconductor, and a gas plasma.

The body of literature on plasmas in solids is growing rapidly, and forms an important part of the broader field of work on the solid state.

1.4 FOUNDATIONS OF PLASMA DYNAMICS

There remains the final task of this introductory chapter—to present the structure of the book, expressing the reasons for taking up the particular topics covered, discussing the order in which they appear, and making clear what topics have had to be omitted.

The language of Cartesian tensors is used extensively throughout the book. One reason for this is that a plasma in a magnetic field is an anisotropic medium and its properties can be worked out with algebraic logic in this language. The justification for the procedure may be compared to the use of the Laplace transform in the solution of differential equations, where the problem is once again reduced to algebra and the student follows the steps with confidence. Chapter 2 on the Notation of Cartesian Tensors serves to teach the elements of this system. The newcomer to tensor manipulation will find that this language can be picked up with ease.

The next step is to develop the equations that apply to the plasma medium. They consist of the electrodynamic equations on the one hand (Chapter 3), and the kinetic equations on the other hand (Chapters 5 and 6). The electrodynamic equations are an integral part of electromagnetic theory, so, although they are presented in terms of the basic laws, the treatment is quite brief. In contrast, the kinetic equations comprise a major part of plasma theory and are therefore treated in depth. In fact we go back a step to the topic of particle interactions (Chapter 4) before beginning the kinetic treatment.

However it is possible to take up one form of plasma theory immediately. This is orbit theory, or collisionless plasma theory (Chapter 8), where the plasma is sufficiently tenuous that particle interactions may be neglected.

Particle interactions are discussed in portions of Chapters 9 and 15 as well as in Chapter 4. Taken together these sections form a major topic in plasma theory. In Chapter 4 we treat binary elastic collisions with examples and exercises pertaining to both electron-neutral and electron-ion collisions. These topics are fundamental to the development of the Boltzmann equation in the following chapter and the Fokker-Planck equation in Chapter 9, and we find repeated occasion to use the results obtained in Chapter 4.

The Boltzmann equation is the basis of the treatment of kinetic theory in this book. It is presented in Chapter 5 along with the elementary solution in the steady state case which results in the Maxwellian distribution of particle velocitie⌐. From the point of view of the development of plasma kinetic theory one can then proceed immediately to Chapter 10. However, we choose to continue with the development of the macroscopic equations in Chapter 6.

We wish to emphasize the importance of Chapter 6. After showing the procedure for obtaining the macroscopic equations from the Boltzmann equation, we present a discussion of the plasma as a conducting fluid in Section 6.3 and obtain the equations for the plasma fluid in Sections 6.4 and 6.5. The need for a careful and precise discussion at this point is simple. The plasma fluid consists of several constituents, and the relationship between the behavior of each constituent and the behavior of the fluid as a whole must be clearly shown. With the macroscopic equations properly formulated the foundations of magneto-fluid dynamics have been laid.

In Chapter 7 we begin to see some of the results of our formulation of equations in the earlier chapters. The diffusion, conductivity, and dielectric constant of a plasma are readily obtained. At this point we present the further insight into plasma behavior which is obtainable from orbit theory (Chapter 8). Having discussed the behavior of noninteracting charged particles we are led to the problem of Charged Particle Interactions (Chapter 9). In a sense we postponed this problem, which involves the treatment of multiple Coulomb collisions, as long as we could. For example, in Chapter 7, on weakly ionized plasmas, the assumption made about the particle interactions was that electron-neutral collisions predominate and Coulomb collisions could be neglected, while in Chapter 8 the assumption was that all particle interactions could be ignored. Thus Chapter 9 tackles one of the major problems of plasma theory. In the final section of this chapter a criterion for distinguishing when multiple Coulomb collisions are important is presented, and we see that they are frequently important. However the net effect of the multiple Coulomb collisions is presented in terms of an interaction (or relaxation) time or interaction frequency, which is analogous to the collision frequency which characterizes the electron-neutral collisions. This means that the procedures for calculating plasma properties that have been established for weakly ionized plasmas may be used for strongly ionized gases, with the multiple Coulomb interaction frequency replacing or combining with the electron-neutral collision frequency.

In Chapter 10 we return to the kinetic theory description of plasmas as contrasted with the macroscopic equation approach. We show that, if the Boltzmann equation is solved for the electron distribution function, then the transport coefficients may be calculated directly.

Next to the transport phenomena the wave behavior of plasmas is the most basic motion that can be studied. We take up this subject in depth in Chapters 11, 12, and 13. Chapter 11 presents an introductory discussion of the various ways in which the topic of waves can be approached. Chapters 12 and 13 expound further on two of these approaches.

In Chapter 14 we build upon the fluid equations developed in Chapter 6 to establish some of the initial concepts of magneto-fluid dynamics.

In the final chapter we return to the topic of particle interactions to discuss inelastic collisions and to take up the basic concepts of plasma generation. Fuller treatments of these subjects are given in the books on gaseous electronics and electrical discharges which are listed at the end of the chapter.

Plasma applications are discussed in more specialized works and although we describe the principles of a number of plasma measurements no attempt has been made to treat the field of plasma diagnostics.

Other topics which did not fall within the scope of the present work include plasma stability and radiation from plasmas.

A strong emphasis has been placed on the development of the kinetic theory. This is not at all to take away from the importance of the macroscopic equations in the solution of plasma problems, but rather to make sure that their origins in the kinetic equations are well understood. So far as the manner of presenting the material is concerned, we have felt it important to include the mathematical details quite comprehensively so that the student can follow the argument with only a modest amount of paperwork on the side. We will find that the use of the Cartesian tensor notation is very advantageous in this respect and we now turn to the development of this notation.

REFERENCES

Major sources of information relating to the classical work on electrical discharges in gases include

1   Townsend, J. S. *Electricity in Gases*. London: Oxford University Press, 1914.

2   Thomson, J. J., and G. P. Thomson. *Conduction of Electricity through Gases.* London: Cambridge University Press, 1933.

3   Loeb, L. B. *Fundamental Processes of Electrical Discharge in Gases.* New York: Wiley, 1939.

4   Suits, C. G. *The Collected Works of Irving Langmuir.* Vol. 4, *Electrical Discharge;* vol. 5, *Plasma and Oscillations.* New York: Pergamon, 1961.

Some of the charged particle aspects of kinetic theory referred to in the text are referenced in

5   Lorentz, H. A. *The Theory of Electrons.* New York: Dover, 1952.

6   Druyvesteyn, M. J., and F. M. Penning. "The Mechanism of Electrical Discharges in Gases of Low Pressure," *Rev. Mod. Phys.*, **12** (1940), pp. 87–174.

7   Chapman, S., and T. G. Cowling. *The Mathematical Theory of Non-Uniform Gases.* London: Cambridge University Press, 1960.

8   Allis, W. P. "Motions of Ions and Electrons," *Handbuch der Physik.* Springer-Verlag, vol. 21, 1956.

Discussions of concepts related to plasmas in the field of astronomy and reference to historical developments occur in

9   Kuiper, G. P. *The Sun.* Chicago: University of Chicago Press, 1953.

10   Ferraro, V. C. A., and C. Plumpton. *An Introduction to Magneto-Fluid Mechanics.* London: Oxford University Press, 1961.

11   Chandrasekhar, S. *Principles of Stellar Dynamics.* New York: Dover, 1960.

12   Aller, L. H. *Astrophysics: The Atmospheres of the Sun and Stars.* 2nd ed.; New York: Ronald, 1963.

Reference to early work on radio propagation in the ionosphere is made by

13   Ratcliffe, J. A. *The Magneto-Ionic Theory and its Applications to the Ionosphere.* London: Cambridge University Press, 1959.

14   Budden, K. G. *Radio Waves in the Ionosphere.* London: Cambridge University Press, 1961.

Major bibliographic lists in the plasma field include

15   *Research on Controlled Thermonuclear Fusion.* Bibliographical Series No. 7, International Atomic Energy Agency, 1962.

16   Napolitano, L. G., and G. Contursi. *Magneto-Fluid-Dynamics, Current Papers and Abstracts.* Agard Bibliography 1, Enlarged Edition. New York: Pergamon, 1962.

17   Manning, L. A. *Bibliography of the Ionosphere.* Stanford: Stanford University Press, 1962.

18   Aukland, M. F. *Plasma Physics and Magnetohydrodynamics, A Report Bibliography.* Defense Documentation Center AD 271 170, 1962, Supplement AD 405 732, 1963.

2

THE NOTATION
OF CARTESIAN TENSORS

Various types of quantities are encountered in the discussion of physical phenomena. Two familiar types are scalars—such as temperature and mass—and vectors—such as velocity and electric field strength. The scalar quantity is completely defined by its magnitude, while the definition of a vector quantity includes the stipulation of a direction as well as a magnitude. Some type of symbolic notation is used to distinguish between these two types of quantities. Thus we may write scalars in italics (T, m) but assign boldface type to vector quantities ($\mathbf{v}$, $\mathbf{E}$). The algebra of scalar quantities is ordinary algebra, while the algebra of vectors includes new multiplication symbols such as $\mathbf{v} \times \mathbf{B}$ and $\mathbf{E} \cdot \mathbf{B}$, where special rules must be learned before the symbols can be correctly used. However scalars and vectors are not the only types of quantities important to us. In particular, in the study of plasmas, we will often encounter quantities called "tensors."

The symbolic notation of vector algebra can be extended to include the use of tensors. However many new multiplication rules must be learned. It is also necessary to know many vector identities in order to carry through derivations

2 5

and analyses. Much of this difficulty can be avoided if, instead of a symbolic notation, one adopts an indicial notation. One then finds that it is unnecessary to remember vector identities and that manipulation of vector and tensor equations becomes a straightforward matter.

The general theory of tensor analysis deals with tensors referred to generalized curvilinear coordinates. Such a general theory is not needed in this book and will not be treated. We will instead deal with tensors referred to a right-handed Cartesian coordinate system. Such tensors are called *Cartesian tensors*.

The standard approach is to define vectors and tensors according to the manner in which their components, referred to one coordinate system, transform when referred to another coordinate system. This approach is treated briefly in Appendix B.

In this chapter we will adopt an alternative approach for introducing the indicial notation. We assume that the student is familiar with ordinary vector analysis using symbolic notation. We will, therefore, show how the indicial notation is related to the more familiar symbolic notation and how standard vector operations can be carried out in the indicial notation.

Section 2.1 introduces the indicial notation. The summation convention which applies to repeated indices is explained and the Kronecker delta δ_{ij}, which plays an important role in the algebraic manipulation of vector equations, is defined. These properties are then used to show how the scalar product of two vectors is written in indicial notation in a form equivalent to the symbolic vector notation for this quantity.

The notation of tensors and matrices is discussed in Section 2.2, where it is explained that tensors of the two lowest orders are in fact scalars and vectors. Multiplication involving tensors is discussed and the dyadic product is defined A brief mention is made of the operation of contracting a tensor by equating a pair of indices which are then summed out. The manipulation of matrices is shown in Section 2.22 in order to illustrate the procedure for calculating the inverse of a matrix. The alternating unit tensor ϵ_{ijk} is the second quantity that, together with the Kronecker delta δ_{ij}, plays an important role in the algebraic manipulation of vector equations. Its role in writing the vector product $\mathbf{A} \times \mathbf{B}$ in indicial notation is explained in Section 2.23, and an important relationship between δ_{ij} and ϵ_{ijk} is also discussed.

Our discussion of the indicial notation is completed in Section 2.3 with a treatment of the topic of tensor fields. Here we show the correspondence between the symbolic and indicial notations for differential operations which include the gradient, divergence, Laplacian, and curl for scalar and vector fields. The student is now equipped to perform vector manipulations and prove vector identities, and he should familiarize himself thoroughly with these operations by working the exercises.

2.1 VECTORS AND
THE INDICIAL NOTATION

In this section we will explain how the indicial representation of the vector **A**, that is A_i, is related to the symbolic notation in a right-handed Cartesian coordinate system. As a stepping stone we will use the *base vectors* in the coordinate directions. These will be designated $\mathbf{e}_{(i)}$. This symbol combines the boldface letter with a modified indicial notation. However the definition of the symbol is precise, and it is readily distinguished from the two standard forms.

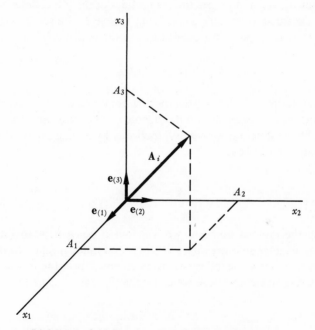

FIGURE 2.1   The Cartesian Coordinate System

Vector quantities are familiar in all branches of physical science. It was pointed out above that vectors can be defined according to the way their components transform under a change of coordinate system. However we saw that a vector has a more physical, geometrical meaning; namely, it is a quantity that has a magnitude and direction. Such a quantity is often represented as a directed line segment that is independent of any particular coordinate system. In fact, we are free to introduce any number of coordinate systems (for example, rectangular, cylindrical, spherical) in the course of discussing a problem and specify the vector **A** by giving the values of its components in the particular coordinate system useful at the moment.

Let us consider the vector **A** referred to the right-handed Cartesian co-ordinate system shown in Figure 2.1. The vectors $\mathbf{e}_{(1)}$, $\mathbf{e}_{(2)}$, and $\mathbf{e}_{(3)}$ are base vectors in the three orthogonal directions. That is, the components of the unit vectors can be written as

$$\mathbf{e}_{(1)} = (1, 0, 0)$$

$$\mathbf{e}_{(2)} = (0, 1, 0)$$

$$\mathbf{e}_{(3)} = (0, 0, 1)$$

where the three components of each vector are given in the brackets. The quantities A_1, A_2, and A_3 are the magnitudes of the projections of the vector **A** onto the three orthogonal axes. From Figure 2.1 we see that the vector **A** can be written as the vector sum of three other vectors. That is,

$$\mathbf{A} = A_1\mathbf{e}_{(1)} + A_2\mathbf{e}_{(2)} + A_3\mathbf{e}_{(3)} \qquad [2.1]$$

The subscripts on the A's denote the components of the vector **A**. The subscripts on the vectors $\mathbf{e}_{(i)}$ do not denote components but denote the entire vector. This distinction is made symbolically by adding the parentheses.

We can write [2.1] as

$$\mathbf{A} = \sum_{i=1}^{3} A_i\mathbf{e}_{(i)} \qquad [2.2]$$

In using the indicial notation we will find it convenient to introduce the following *summation convention*: Whenever an index is repeated in any term, it is understood that the indices are to be summed from 1 to 3 unless otherwise noted. Using this convention we can write [2.2] as

$$\mathbf{A} = A_i\mathbf{e}_{(i)} \qquad [2.3]$$

We see that A_i represents the three components of the vector **A** when we let the index take on the values 1, 2, and 3. It is, therefore, clear that we will know the vector **A** if we know its Cartesian components A_i. This simplification is the heart of the Cartesian tensor notation. We will often refer to A_i as a vector. The student always must bear in mind that A_i simply represents the three Cartesian components of the vector **A**.

In order to establish the correspondence between the indicial notation of Cartesian tensors and the symbolic vector notation, we use the bridge indicated by [2.3]. Note that this hybrid form involves the base vectors $\mathbf{e}_{(i)}$. We will see that in the final form of the indicial notation the base vectors do not appear since the indicial notation simply represents Cartesian components.

2.11 THE KRONECKER DELTA

The *Kronecker delta*, δ_{ij}, is defined by

$$\delta_{ij} = \begin{cases} 1 & \text{when } i = j \\ 0 & \text{when } i \neq j \end{cases} \qquad [2.4]$$

In the present context i and j may take on the values 1, 2, and 3 only.

The convention of summing repeated indices from 1 to 3 which was introduced in the previous section will be used in all indicial equations. Thus, for example,

$$A_i B_j C_j \equiv A_i B_1 C_1 + A_i B_2 C_2 + A_i B_3 C_3$$

and

$$M_{rs} C_s \equiv M_{r1} C_1 + M_{r2} C_2 + M_{r3} C_3$$

Notice that the repeated index gets "summed out" and is therefore called a *dummy* subscript. The subscripts i and r which are retained in these examples are called *floating* subscripts. It is improper to use the same index more than twice in any given term. Thus, $A_i B_i C_i$ and $M_{ii} C_i$ are meaningless terms.

An important property of the Kronecker delta can be shown by summing out the repeated index in the term $B_j \delta_{ij}$, thus:

$$B_j \delta_{ij} = B_1 \delta_{i1} + B_2 \delta_{i2} + B_3 \delta_{i3}$$

The components of this expression are found by letting i assume the values 1, 2, and 3 successively, thus:

$$x_1\text{-component} = B_1 \delta_{11} + B_2 \delta_{12} + B_3 \delta_{13} = B_1$$

$$x_2\text{-component} = B_1 \delta_{21} + B_2 \delta_{22} + B_3 \delta_{23} = B_2$$

$$x_3\text{-component} = B_1 \delta_{31} + B_2 \delta_{32} + B_3 \delta_{33} = B_3$$

Now the vector B_i has components B_1, B_2, B_3, so that

$$B_j \delta_{ij} = B_i \qquad [2.5]$$

In words we say that when the Kronecker delta appears in a term of an indicial equation in which one (or both) of its indices is repeated in other symbols of the same term, then the Kronecker delta can be removed if the repeated index on the other symbol is erased and replaced with the remaining index of the Kronecker delta.

2.12 SCALAR PRODUCT

The *scalar, or dot, product* of two vectors is equal to the product of the magnitudes of the two vectors multiplied by the cosine of the angle between them. Thus, adopting the usage shown by [2.3] we write

$$\mathbf{A} = A_i \mathbf{e}_{(i)}$$

and

$$\mathbf{B} = B_j \mathbf{e}_{(j)}$$

so that

$$\mathbf{A} \cdot \mathbf{B} = A_i \mathbf{e}_{(i)} \cdot B_j \mathbf{e}_{(j)}$$
$$= A_i B_j \mathbf{e}_{(i)} \cdot \mathbf{e}_{(j)} \qquad [2.6]$$

Note that we must use different subscripts in [2.6] to represent the vectors **A** and **B** since the same subscript can only appear twice in any given term.

Due to the orthogonality of the base vectors we have that

$$\mathbf{e}_{(i)} \cdot \mathbf{e}_{(j)} = \delta_{ij} \qquad [2.7]$$

Substituting [2.7] into [2.6] we obtain

$$\mathbf{A} \cdot \mathbf{B} = A_i B_j \delta_{ij} \qquad [2.8]$$

Both the i and the j on the right-hand side of [2.8] are repeated and therefore get summed out. Using the property of δ_{ij} described in the previous section we can write [2.8] as

$$\mathbf{A} \cdot \mathbf{B} = A_i B_i = A_j B_j$$
$$= A_1 B_1 + A_2 B_2 + A_3 B_3 \qquad [2.9]$$

We therefore see that the dot product is a scalar which is written in indicial notation as $A_i B_i$. Notice that since a dummy index is summed out any letter may be used for such an index.

It is important to distinguish between two operations performed on terms that are written in the indicial notation. If an index is repeated, it is *summed out* and the term becomes a sum of three terms. On the other hand, a vector consists of three Cartesian components which may be *listed* whenever it is desirable to do so. We will distinguish between the disappearance of a letter index by summing out and by listing out in the following example. Consider the term

$$A_i B_j C_j$$

Summing out the repeated index gives

$$A_i B_j C_j = A_i B_1 C_1 + A_i B_2 C_2 + A_i B_3 C_3 \qquad [2.10]$$

Listing out the three Cartesian components gives

$$x_1\text{-component} = A_1 B_1 C_1 + A_1 B_2 C_2 + A_1 B_3 C_3$$

$$x_2\text{-component} = A_2 B_1 C_1 + A_2 B_2 C_2 + A_2 B_3 C_3$$

$$x_3\text{-component} = A_3 B_1 C_1 + A_3 B_2 C_2 + A_3 B_3 C_3$$

It is clear that $A_i B_j C_j$ represents a vector which would be appropriately written

$$D_i = A_i B_j C_j \qquad [2.11]$$

where the vector A_i is simply changed in magnitude because it is multiplied by the scalar quantity $B_j C_j$.

2.2 CARTESIAN TENSORS AND MATRICES

In this section it is our purpose to explain how the notation of Cartesian tensors is used. All the quantities we are concerned with can be considered to be tensor quantities of one kind or another. The different kinds of tensors are classified according to their order. The *order* of a tensor can be determined by identifying the number of unsummed indices present in the term. If there are no unsummed indices, the quantity concerned is a tensor of order zero. Such is a scalar quantity. If only one index is unsummed, the quantity is a tensor of first order which is a vector quantity. If two indices are unsummed, the order is two, and so on.

A zero-order tensor represents just a number (which may be real or complex). A first-order Cartesian tensor represents three numbers which are the magnitudes of the Cartesian components of a vector quantity. We write this array of numbers as $A_i = (A_1, A_2, A_3)$. A second-order tensor represents an array of nine numbers because each of the two unsummed indices may take on the values 1, 2, or 3. A third-order tensor represents $(3)^3 = 27$ numbers, and so on.

We write the nine scalar quantities associated with a second-order tensor in a *matrix array* as follows

$$M_{ij} = \begin{bmatrix} M_{11} & M_{12} & M_{13} \\ M_{21} & M_{22} & M_{23} \\ M_{31} & M_{32} & M_{33} \end{bmatrix}$$

The *main diagonal* of the matrix is formed by the elements which have identical subscripts: M_{11}, M_{22}, M_{33}. The remaining elements are called *off-diagonal* elements.

Exercise 2.2.1   Show that the tensor M_{ij} multiplying the vector A_j results in a new vector D_i differing from A_j in both magnitude and direction.

2.21 DYADIC PRODUCT

We have already discussed the scalar product of two vectors, and we will take up the subject of the cross product in Section 2.31. It is convenient to identify a third way in which two vectors may be multiplied together. The *dyadic product* of two vectors is written as **AB** and the nine components of this dyadic product may be displayed in the matrix array

$$A_iB_j = \begin{bmatrix} A_1B_1 & A_1B_2 & A_1B_3 \\ A_2B_1 & A_2B_2 & A_2B_3 \\ A_3B_1 & A_3B_2 & A_3B_3 \end{bmatrix} \qquad [2.12]$$

Notice that we use different index letters for A_i and B_j, since to use the same subscript would yield a scalar product.

The dyadic product of the two second-order tensors A_{ij}, B_{rs} is written $A_{ij}B_{rs}$ and is a fourth-order tensor with 81 elements. Thus the dyadic product of two tensors gives a tensor of higher order.

Contraction of a Tensor   The operation that results in a tensor of lower order is called *contraction*. The contraction is performed by equating two subscripts, which then get summed out so that the tensor is lowered in order by 2. Thus equating j and r in the fourth-order tensor $A_{ij}B_{rs}$ gives $A_{ij}B_{js}$ which is a second-order tensor—that is, it has two unsummed indices. It can therefore be written

$$C_{is} = A_{ij}B_{js}$$

In matrix notation we find (Exercise 2.21.1) that this equation is written as,

$$
\begin{bmatrix} C_{11} & C_{12} & C_{13} \\ C_{21} & C_{22} & C_{23} \\ C_{31} & C_{32} & C_{33} \end{bmatrix} = \begin{bmatrix} A_{11} & A_{12} & A_{13} \\ A_{21} & A_{22} & A_{23} \\ A_{31} & A_{32} & A_{33} \end{bmatrix} \begin{bmatrix} B_{11} & B_{12} & B_{13} \\ B_{21} & B_{22} & B_{23} \\ B_{31} & B_{32} & B_{33} \end{bmatrix}
$$

$$
= \begin{bmatrix} A_{11}B_{11} + A_{12}B_{21} & A_{11}B_{12} + A_{12}B_{22} & A_{11}B_{13} + A_{12}B_{23} \\ \quad + A_{13}B_{31} & \quad + A_{13}B_{32} & \quad + A_{13}B_{33} \\ A_{21}B_{11} + A_{22}B_{21} & A_{21}B_{12} + A_{22}B_{22} & A_{21}B_{13} + A_{22}B_{23} \\ \quad + A_{23}B_{31} & \quad + A_{23}B_{32} & \quad + A_{23}B_{33} \\ A_{31}B_{11} + A_{32}B_{21} & A_{31}B_{12} + A_{32}B_{22} & A_{31}B_{13} + A_{32}B_{23} \\ \quad + A_{33}B_{31} & \quad + A_{33}B_{32} & \quad + A_{33}B_{33} \end{bmatrix}
$$

which reminds the student of the rule for multiplying matrices.

Exercise 2.21.1   Verify the matrix form of the equation $C_{ts} = A_{ij}B_{js}$. (Begin by summing out the repeated index.)

2.22 THE INVERSE OF A MATRIX

The *inverse of a matrix* M is written M^{-1} and is defined by the relation

$$ M^{-1}M = I \tag{2.13} $$

where I is the *unit matrix*

$$
\begin{bmatrix} 1 & & 0 \\ & \ddots & \\ 0 & & 1 \end{bmatrix}
$$

where all off-diagonal terms are zero. It can be shown that $MM^{-1} = I$ also holds.

Consider the following set of equations .

$$
\begin{aligned}
B_1 &= M_{11}A_1 + M_{12}A_2 + M_{13}A_3 \\
B_2 &= M_{21}A_1 + M_{22}A_2 + M_{23}A_3 \\
B_3 &= M_{31}A_1 + M_{32}A_2 + M_{33}A_3
\end{aligned} \tag{2.14}
$$

We can write these equations as a matrix equation

$$
\begin{bmatrix} B_1 \\ B_2 \\ B_3 \end{bmatrix} = \begin{bmatrix} M_{11} & M_{12} & M_{13} \\ M_{21} & M_{22} & M_{23} \\ M_{31} & M_{32} & M_{33} \end{bmatrix} \begin{bmatrix} A_1 \\ A_2 \\ A_3 \end{bmatrix}
$$

or

$$
\mathsf{B} = \mathsf{MA} \tag{2.15}
$$

Now suppose we want to solve for the A's. If we premultiply [2.15] by M^{-1}, we obtain

$$
\mathsf{M}^{-1}\mathsf{B} = \mathsf{M}^{-1}\mathsf{MA} = \mathsf{IA}
$$

and since $\mathsf{IA} = \mathsf{A}$ (the student should check this for himself)

$$
\mathsf{A} = \mathsf{M}^{-1}\mathsf{B} \tag{2.16}
$$

The problem is thus, given M find M^{-1}. We can find M^{-1} by solving [2.14] for A_1, A_2, and A_3. Thus

$$
A_1 = \frac{\begin{vmatrix} B_1 & M_{12} & M_{13} \\ B_2 & M_{22} & M_{23} \\ B_3 & M_{32} & M_{33} \end{vmatrix}}{\begin{vmatrix} M_{11} & M_{12} & M_{13} \\ M_{21} & M_{22} & M_{23} \\ M_{31} & M_{32} & M_{33} \end{vmatrix}} \tag{2.17}
$$

Expanding the *determinant* of the numerator by *minors* gives

$$
B_1 \begin{vmatrix} M_{22} & M_{23} \\ M_{32} & M_{33} \end{vmatrix} - B_2 \begin{vmatrix} M_{12} & M_{13} \\ M_{32} & M_{33} \end{vmatrix} + B_3 \begin{vmatrix} M_{12} & M_{13} \\ M_{22} & M_{23} \end{vmatrix}
$$

Let $\mu_{21} = $ minor of M_{21}. That is,

$$
\mu_{21} = \begin{vmatrix} M_{12} & M_{13} \\ M_{32} & M_{33} \end{vmatrix}
$$

Let μ_{11} = minor of M_{11}, and so forth. Then the numerator of [2.17] becomes

$$B_1\mu_{11} - B_2\mu_{21} + B_3\mu_{31}$$

so that [2.17] can be written as

$$A_1 = \frac{B_1\mu_{11} - B_2\mu_{21} + B_3\mu_{31}}{\Delta}$$

where Δ represents the determinant of M. Solving for A_2 and A_3 in a similar way gives for A_1, A_2, and A_3

$$A_1 = \frac{1}{\Delta}(B_1\mu_{11} - B_2\mu_{21} + B_3\mu_{31})$$

$$A_2 = \frac{1}{\Delta}(-B_1\mu_{12} + B_2\mu_{22} - B_3\mu_{32}) \qquad [2.18]$$

$$A_3 = \frac{1}{\Delta}(B_1\mu_{13} - B_2\mu_{23} + B_3\mu_{33})$$

In matrix form this becomes

$$\begin{bmatrix} A_1 \\ A_2 \\ A_3 \end{bmatrix} = \frac{1}{\Delta} \begin{bmatrix} \mu_{11} & -\mu_{21} & \mu_{31} \\ -\mu_{12} & \mu_{22} & -\mu_{32} \\ \mu_{13} & -\mu_{23} & \mu_{33} \end{bmatrix} \begin{bmatrix} B_1 \\ B_2 \\ B_3 \end{bmatrix}$$

or

$$\mathsf{A} = \mathsf{N}\mathsf{B} \qquad [2.19]$$

From [2.16] and [2.19] we see that

$$\mathsf{N} = \mathsf{M}^{-1}$$

so that

$$\mathsf{M}^{-1} = \frac{1}{\Delta} \begin{bmatrix} \mu_{11} & -\mu_{21} & \mu_{31} \\ -\mu_{12} & \mu_{22} & -\mu_{32} \\ \mu_{13} & -\mu_{23} & \mu_{33} \end{bmatrix} \qquad [2.20]$$

Thus we see that to take the inverse of a matrix M we perform the following operations:

1. For the various entries in M^{-1} insert the minors of the corresponding entries in the transpose of M. That is, for instance, μ_{21} is entered in the position of M_{12}; μ_{32} in the position of M_{23}, and so on.

2. Insert minus signs in a checkerboard array as shown in [2.20].

3. Form the determinant of M, Δ, and multiply the new matrix by $1/\Delta$ as shown in [2.20].

Exercise 2.22.1   Find the inverse of the matrix

$$\begin{bmatrix} 3 & 2 & 1 \\ 1 & 2 & 3 \\ 0 & 2 & 0 \end{bmatrix}.$$

2.23   THE ALTERNATING UNIT TENSOR

We now introduce the *alternating unit tensor*, ϵ_{ijk}, which enables us to express cross products in the indicial notation. It is defined as follows:

$$\epsilon_{ijk} = \begin{cases} +1, & \text{if } i,j,k \text{ are in cyclic order 123, 231, 312} \\ -1, & \text{if } i,j,k \text{ are in noncyclic order 321, 132, 213} \quad [2.21] \\ 0, & \text{if any two subscripts are repeated} \end{cases}$$

Note that interchanging two adjacent subscripts changes the sign of the alternating unit tensor. That is,

$$\epsilon_{ijk} = -\epsilon_{jik} = \epsilon_{jki} = -\epsilon_{kji} \qquad [2.22]$$

The properties of the alternating unit tensor will be shown by the following examples.

Example 1   Write the quantity $M_{ij} = \epsilon_{ijk}C_k$ as a three-by-three matrix. Let us first write out the expansion of the repeated index.

$$M_{ij} = \epsilon_{ijk}C_k = \epsilon_{ij1}C_1 + \epsilon_{ij2}C_2 + \epsilon_{ij3}C_3$$

Thus each of the nine terms of M_{ij} consists of the sum of three parts. The evaluation of each term is made by inserting the values of i and j according to the standard form. Thus applying the definition of ϵ_{ijk}, we obtain

$$M_{ij} = \epsilon_{ijk}C_k = \begin{bmatrix} 0 & C_3 & -C_2 \\ -C_3 & 0 & C_1 \\ C_2 & -C_1 & 0 \end{bmatrix}$$

Example 2   Evaluate the quantity $\epsilon_{ijk}A_iB_jC_k$. We note that all the indices get summed out. The result will, therefore, be a zero-order tensor—that is, a scalar. Since the subscripts i, j, and k get summed from 1 to 3 independently, the quantity $\epsilon_{ijk}A_iB_jC_k$ is the sum of 27 terms. However many of these terms are zero from the definition of ϵ_{ijk}. The only nonzero terms are the six terms that result when i, j, and k are in cyclic or noncyclic order according to [2.21]. That is, we obtain

$$\epsilon_{ijk}A_1B_jC_k = A_1B_2C_3 - A_1B_3C_2 - A_2B_1C_3 + A_2B_3C_1 + A_3B_1C_2 - A_3B_2C_1$$

However when a third-order determinant is expanded, we obtain

$$\begin{vmatrix} A_1 & A_2 & A_3 \\ B_1 & B_2 & B_3 \\ C_1 & C_2 & C_3 \end{vmatrix} = A_1B_2C_3 - A_1B_3C_2 - A_2B_1C_3 + A_2B_3C_1 + A_3B_1C_2 - A_3B_2C_1$$

so that

$$\epsilon_{ijk}A_iB_jC_k = \begin{vmatrix} A_1 & A_2 & A_3 \\ B_1 & B_2 & B_3 \\ C_1 & C_2 & C_3 \end{vmatrix}$$

This expression will be recognized to be identical to $\mathbf{A} \cdot \mathbf{B} \times \mathbf{C}$. We now proceed to discuss the cross product specifically.

The Vector or Cross Product   As a third example of the use of the alternating unit tensor, consider the quantity

$$D_i = \epsilon_{ijk}B_jC_k \tag{2.23}$$

Summing out the repeated indices and applying the definition of ϵ_{ijk}, we find that the components D_i are given by

$$\begin{aligned} D_1 &= B_2C_3 - B_3C_2 \\ D_2 &= B_3C_1 - B_1C_3 \\ D_3 &= B_1C_2 - B_2C_1 \end{aligned} \tag{2.24}$$

These may be recognized as the components of the cross product in the following way.

The cross product of two vectors $\mathbf{B}$ and $\mathbf{C}$ is defined as a new vector $\mathbf{D}$ whose magnitude is equal to the product of the magnitudes of $\mathbf{B}$ and $\mathbf{C}$ times the sine of the angle between them, and whose direction is normal to both $\mathbf{B}$ and $\mathbf{C}$ in a right-handed sense. Thus

$$\mathbf{D} = \mathbf{B} \times \mathbf{C} \tag{2.25}$$

points in the direction in which a right-handed screw would travel if $\mathbf{B}$ were rotated into $\mathbf{C}$.

Using the hybrid representation of [2.3] we can write [2.25] as

$$\mathbf{D} = D_i\mathbf{e}_{(i)} = B_i\mathbf{e}_{(i)} \times C_j\mathbf{e}_{(j)}$$

$$= B_iC_j\mathbf{e}_{(i)} \times \mathbf{e}_{(j)}$$

which, by applying the definition of the cross product to the base vectors, can be written as

$$\mathbf{D} = D_i\mathbf{e}_{(i)}$$
$$= (B_2C_3 - B_3C_2)\mathbf{e}_{(1)} + (B_3C_1 - B_1C_3)\mathbf{e}_{(2)} + (B_1C_2 - B_2C_1)\mathbf{e}_{(3)} \qquad [2.26]$$

We therefore see from [2.26] that the components D_i of the cross product **B** × **C** are given by the list [2.24] so that the representation of the cross product in indicial notation is given by [2.23], namely

$$D_i = \epsilon_{ijk}B_jC_k$$

Relationship Between the Alternating Unit Tensor and the Kronecker Delta   A particularly important relationship exists between the alternating unit tensor and the Kronecker delta which is very useful in manipulating vector equations. The relationship is the following:

$$\epsilon_{ijk}\epsilon_{irs} = \delta_{jr}\delta_{ks} - \delta_{js}\delta_{kr} \qquad [2.27]$$

Notice that there are four unrepeated, or floating, subscripts (j, k, r, s) in each term of [2.27]. Since each of these subscripts takes on the values 1, 2, and 3 independently, [2.27] represents 81 separate equations. The proof of [2.27] consists of showing that the identity holds for each of the 81 cases. (See Exercise 2.23.1.)

The particular subscripts used in [2.27] are, of course, immaterial. However one of the subscripts in each of the alternating unit tensors must be the same. The repeated index should be manipulated by means of [2.22] so that they both occur first in both alternating tensors. Once this is done, the subscripts on the four Kronecker deltas may be read directly from the subscripts of the two alternating unit tensors. They are, respectively:

1. both second subscripts
2. both third subscripts
3. one second and one third subscript
4. the other second and the other third subscript.

The power of the indicial notation lies in the facility with which complicated vector expressions can be simplified and the ability to manipulate vector equations involving tensor quantities of the second and higher order. In this section we will give preliminary examples of both these properties.

Example 3   Prove the vector identity

$$\mathbf{A} \times (\mathbf{B} \times \mathbf{C}) = (\mathbf{C} \cdot \mathbf{A})\mathbf{B} - (\mathbf{B} \cdot \mathbf{A})\mathbf{C}$$

PROOF: The quantity $\mathbf{A} \times (\mathbf{B} \times \mathbf{C})$ is written in indicial notation as

$$\epsilon_{rsi}A_s(\epsilon_{ijk}B_jC_k) = + \epsilon_{irs}\epsilon_{ijk}B_jC_kA_s$$
$$= (\delta_{rj}\delta_{sk} - \delta_{rk}\delta_{sj})B_jC_kA_s \qquad [2.28]$$

Eliminating the Kronecker deltas by replacing indices, we can write [2.28] as

$$\epsilon_{rsi}A_s(\epsilon_{ijk}B_jC_k) = B_rC_sA_s - B_sC_rA_s$$
$$= B_r(C_sA_s) - C_r(B_sA_s)$$

where we have grouped the scalar products together. Translating back into the symbolic notation

$$\mathbf{A} \times (\mathbf{B} \times \mathbf{C}) = \mathbf{B}(\mathbf{C} \cdot \mathbf{A}) - \mathbf{C}(\mathbf{B} \cdot \mathbf{A})$$

Exercise 2.23.1   Prove Equation [2.27]. HINT: Separate the 81 cases into groups: (a) $j = k$, 27 cases; (b) $r = s$, $j \neq k$, 18 cases; (c) $j = r$, $k = s$, 6 cases; (d) $j = s$, $r = k$, 6 cases; (e) $j \neq r$, $j \neq s$, 12 cases; (f) $r \neq k$, $s \neq k$, 12 cases.

Exercise 2.23.2   Write down the array of components represented by the expression $\epsilon_{stu}D_t$.

Exercise 2.23.3   List out the components of the expression $\epsilon_{prs}E_pH_s$. [It is good practice to first rewrite the expression so that the first index of the alternating unit tensor is the nonrepeated index. See [2.22].]

Exercise 2.23.4   Show that $\epsilon_{ijr}\epsilon_{ijs} = 2\delta_{rs}$.

Exercise 2.23.5   Show that $\epsilon_{ijk}\epsilon_{ijk} = 6$.

Exercise 2.23.6   Write the following expressions in indicial notation:

$$\mathbf{A}(\mathbf{B} \cdot \mathbf{C}), \quad (\mathbf{A} \times \mathbf{B}) \times \mathbf{C}$$

Exercise 2.23.7   Prove the vector identity

$$(\mathbf{A} \times \mathbf{B}) \times \mathbf{C} = \mathbf{B}(\mathbf{A} \cdot \mathbf{C}) - \mathbf{A}(\mathbf{B} \cdot \mathbf{C})$$

2.3 TENSOR FIELDS

When a tensor is defined as a function of position over a given region, it is often referred to as a tensor field. In this section we will discuss the standard operations of vector calculus, that is, the gradient, divergence, Laplacian and curl, showing the correspondence between the symbolic vector notation and the indicial notation.

Consider the tensor $M_{ij}(x_1, x_2, x_3)$ to be a function of the spatial coordinates x_1, x_2, and x_3. The derivative of M_{ij} with respect to x_k is written as

$$\frac{\partial M_{ij}}{\partial x_k}$$

In order to simplify the writing of equations we will designate partial derivatives with respect to spatial coordinates by means of a comma in the following manner

$$\frac{\partial}{\partial x_k} \equiv {}_{,k} \qquad\qquad [2.29]$$

Thus

$$\frac{\partial M_{ij}}{\partial x_k} \equiv M_{ij,k} \qquad\qquad [2.30]$$

The quantities in [2.30] are the components of a third-order tensor. Thus differentiation, in general, increases the order of a tensor. Tensors of lower order are obtained by contraction. Thus,

$$M_{ij,j}$$

form the components of a tensor of order one, or a vector, as the summation convention is not affected by the differentiation or comma.

In symbolic vector notation spatial differentiation is designated by the *"del" operator* ∇. This operator is defined as

$$\nabla = \mathbf{e}_{(i)} \frac{\partial}{\partial x_i} = \mathbf{e}_{(1)} \frac{\partial}{\partial x_1} + \mathbf{e}_{(2)} \frac{\partial}{\partial x_2} + \mathbf{e}_{(3)} \frac{\partial}{\partial x_3} \qquad [2.31]$$

The Gradient of a Scalar Field Consider a scalar function of position $\psi(x_1, x_2, x_3)$. The maximum rate of change of this function is given by the *gradient* of ψ. Thus

$$\operatorname{grad} \psi = \nabla\psi \qquad\qquad [2.32]$$

is a vector which is normal to the lines $\psi = \text{const.}$

Applying [2.31] to [2.32] gives

$$\operatorname{grad} \psi = \mathbf{e}_{(1)} \frac{\partial \psi}{\partial x_1} + \mathbf{e}_{(2)} \frac{\partial \psi}{\partial x_2} + \mathbf{e}_{(3)} \frac{\partial \psi}{\partial x_3}$$

We therefore see that the components of grad ψ can be written in indicial notation as

$$\frac{\partial \psi}{\partial x_i} \equiv \psi,_i \tag{2.33}$$

The components of the gradient are obtained by letting i take on the successive values 1, 2, and 3.

The Divergence of a Vector Field   The *divergence* of the vector **A** is given by

$$\text{div } \mathbf{A} = \boldsymbol{\nabla} \cdot \mathbf{A}$$

Using [2.31] and [2.3] this can be written as

$$\text{div } \mathbf{A} = \boldsymbol{\nabla} \cdot \mathbf{A} = \frac{\partial A_j}{\partial x_i} \mathbf{e}_{(i)} \cdot \mathbf{e}_{(j)}$$

or, by using [2.7]

$$\boldsymbol{\nabla} \cdot \mathbf{A} = \frac{\partial A_j}{\partial x_i} \delta_{ij} = \frac{\partial A_i}{\partial x_i} \tag{2.34}$$

Thus, the divergence of a vector **A** is written in indicial notation as

$$\frac{\partial A_i}{\partial x_i} \equiv A_{i,i} = A_{1,1} + A_{2,2} + A_{3,3} \tag{2.35}$$

The gradient of the vector **A** is given by the dyad

$$\boldsymbol{\nabla}\mathbf{A}$$

whose nine components are given in the indicial notation by

$$\frac{\partial A_i}{\partial x_j} \equiv A_{i,j} \tag{2.36}$$

Contraction of [2.36] yields the divergence as given by [2.35].

The Laplacian of Tensor Fields   Differentiation of the gradient given by [2.33] yields the second-order tensor

$$\psi,_{ij} = \frac{\partial^2 \psi}{\partial x_i \partial x_j} \tag{2.37}$$

Contraction of [2.37] gives the scalar

$$\psi_{,ii} = \frac{\partial^2 \psi}{\partial x_i \partial x_i} = \frac{\partial^2 \psi}{\partial x_1^2} + \frac{\partial^2 \psi}{\partial x_2^2} + \frac{\partial^2 \psi}{\partial x_3^2} \qquad [2.38]$$

which is called the *Laplacian* of the scalar field ψ.

Equation [2.38] expresses the divergence of the gradient of ψ and is written in symbolic vector notation as

$$\mathbf{\nabla} \cdot \mathbf{\nabla} \psi = \nabla^2 \psi = \Delta \psi \qquad [2.39]$$

If we differentiate [2.36] with respect to x_k, we obtain the third-order tensor

$$A_{i,jk} = \frac{\partial^2 A_i}{\partial x_j \partial x_k} \qquad [2.40]$$

Contraction of [2.40] yields the vector

$$A_{i,jj} = \frac{\partial^2 A_i}{\partial x_j \partial x_j} = \frac{\partial^2 A_i}{\partial x_1^2} + \frac{\partial^2 A_i}{\partial x_2^2} + \frac{\partial^2 A_i}{\partial x_3^2} \qquad [2.41]$$

which is called the Laplacian of the vector field A_i. In symbolic notation this would be written as

$$\mathbf{\nabla} \cdot \mathbf{\nabla} \mathbf{A} = \nabla^2 \mathbf{A} \qquad [2.42]$$

The Curl of a Vector Field   The *curl* of a vector $\mathbf{A}$ is given by

$$\text{curl } \mathbf{A} = \mathbf{\nabla} \times \mathbf{A} \qquad [2.43]$$

Using [2.31] and [2.3], we can write the curl as

$$\text{curl } \mathbf{A} = \frac{\partial A_j}{\partial x_i} \, \mathbf{e}_{(i)} \times \mathbf{e}_{(j)}$$

which, by evaluating the cross products of the base vectors, can be written as

$$\text{curl } \mathbf{A} = \left(\frac{\partial A_3}{\partial x_2} - \frac{\partial A_2}{\partial x_3} \right) \mathbf{e}_{(1)} + \left(\frac{\partial A_1}{\partial x_3} - \frac{\partial A_3}{\partial x_1} \right) \mathbf{e}_{(2)} + \left(\frac{\partial A_2}{\partial x_1} - \frac{\partial A_1}{\partial x_2} \right) \mathbf{e}_{(3)} \quad [2.44]$$

Now if we list the components of the vector $\epsilon_{ijk} A_{k,j}$ we find,

$$x_1\text{-component} = A_{3,2} - A_{2,3}$$
$$x_2\text{-component} = A_{1,3} - A_{3,1} \qquad [2.45]$$
$$x_3\text{-component} = A_{2,1} - A_{1,2}$$

which are the components of curl $\mathbf{A}$ in [2.44]. We therefore see that in the indicial notation the curl of a vector is written as $\epsilon_{ijk}A_{k,j}$.

Table 2.1 summarizes the common vector operations in their symbolic and indicial forms.

T A B L E 2.I   The Common Vector Operations in Symbolic Vector Notation and Cartesian Tensor Notation

QUANTITY	SYMBOLIC VECTOR NOTATION	CARTESIAN TENSOR NOTATION
Scalar	ψ	ψ
Vector	$\mathbf{A}$	A_i
Dyadic	$\mathbf{AB}$	A_iB_j
Scalar product	$\mathbf{A \cdot B}$	$A_iB_j\delta_{ij} = A_iB_i$
Cross product	$\mathbf{A \times B}$	$\epsilon_{ijk}B_jC_k$
Grad ψ	$\nabla\psi$	$\psi_{,i}$
Grad A	$\nabla\mathbf{A}$	$A_{i,j}$
Div A	$\nabla\cdot\mathbf{A}$	$A_{i,j}\delta_{ij} = A_{i,i}$
Laplacian of ψ	$\nabla\cdot\nabla\psi = \nabla^2\psi$	$\psi_{,ii}$
Vector Laplacian	$\nabla^2\mathbf{A}$	$A_{i,jj}$
Curl A	$\nabla \times \mathbf{A}$	$\epsilon_{ijk}A_{k,j}$
Grad Div A	$\nabla(\nabla\cdot\mathbf{A})$	$A_{i,ij}$

Exercise 2.3.1   Show that $\epsilon_{ijk}A_{k,j}$ represents the components of the curl of the vector A_k.

2.3I V E C T O R   I D E N T I T I E S

In this section we wish to prove two important vector identities. The procedure in proving all vector identities is to convert the symbolic notation to indicial notation and then to carry out the indicated operations.

Example 1   Prove that

$$\nabla \times \nabla\phi = 0 \qquad\qquad [2.46]$$

PROOF: In indicial notation [2.46] is written as $\epsilon_{ijk}\phi_{,kj}$. Since j and k are dummy indices, we can interchange the j's and the k's. Thus

$$\epsilon_{ijk}\phi_{,kj} = \epsilon_{ikj}\phi_{,jk} \qquad\qquad [2.47]$$

Since we can also interchange the order of differentiation, [2.47] can be written as

$$\epsilon_{ijk}\phi_{,kj} = \epsilon_{ikj}\phi_{,jk} = \epsilon_{ikj}\phi_{,kj} \qquad [2.48]$$

However, from [2.22] we see that

$$\epsilon_{ijk}\phi_{,kj} = -\epsilon_{ikj}\phi_{,kj} \qquad [2.49]$$

Equating [2.48] and [2.49] gives

$$\epsilon_{ikj}\phi_{,kj} = -\epsilon_{ikj}\phi_{,kj} = 0 \qquad [2.50]$$

which completes the proof.

Example 2   Prove the following identity:

$$\nabla \times \nabla \times \mathbf{A} = \nabla(\nabla \cdot \mathbf{A}) - \nabla^2 \mathbf{A}$$

Transforming to indicial notation we obtain

$$\epsilon_{rsi}\epsilon_{ijk}A_{k,js} = \epsilon_{irs}\epsilon_{ijk}A_{k,js}$$
$$= (\delta_{rj}\delta_{sk} - \delta_{rk}\delta_{sj})A_{k,js} = A_{s,rs} - A_{r,ss}$$
$$= A_{s,sr} - A_{r,ss}$$

or equivalently

$$\nabla \times \nabla \times \mathbf{A} = \nabla(\nabla \cdot \mathbf{A}) - \nabla^2 \mathbf{A}$$

which was to be proved.

Exercise 2.31.1   Write the following expressions in indicial notation:

(a) $\nabla \times \nabla\phi$
(b) $\nabla \cdot \nabla \times \mathbf{A}$
(c) $(\mathbf{B} \cdot \nabla)\mathbf{A}$
(d) $\nabla \cdot (\psi\mathbf{A})$
(e) $\nabla \times (\mathbf{A} + \mathbf{B})$
(f) $\nabla \times \nabla \times \mathbf{A}$

Exercise 2.31.2   Write the following expressions in vector notation:

(a) $\phi\chi_{,i}$
(b) $\epsilon_{rsi}\epsilon_{ijk}(A_jB_k)_{,s}$
(c) $A_iB_{j,j}$
(d) $A_jB_{i,j}$
(e) $\epsilon_{ijk}B_{k,j}A_i$
(f) $\psi A_{i,i}$
(g) $\epsilon_{ijk}(A_jB_k)_{,i}$

Exercise 2.31.3   Prove the following vector identities.

(a) $\nabla \cdot \nabla \times A = 0$

(b) $\nabla(\phi\chi) = \phi\nabla\chi + \chi\nabla\phi$

(c) $\nabla \cdot (\chi A) = A \cdot \nabla\chi + \chi\nabla \cdot A$

(d) $\nabla \cdot (A \times B) = B \cdot \nabla \times A - A \cdot \nabla \times B$

(e) $\nabla \times (\phi A) = \nabla\phi \times A + \phi\nabla \times A$

(f) $\nabla \times (A \times B) = A\nabla \cdot B - B\nabla \cdot A + (B \cdot \nabla)A - (A \cdot \nabla)B$

REFERENCES

Comprehensive treatments of Cartesian tensors can be found in the first chapters of

1   Aris, R. *Vectors, Tensors, and the Basic Equations of Fluid Mechanics.* Englewood Cliffs: Prentice-Hall, 1962.

2   Prager, W. *Introduction to Mechanics of Continua.* Boston: Ginn, 1961.

A more formal approach is given by

3   Jeffreys, H. *Cartesian Tensors.* London: Cambridge University Press, 1957.

More detailed information on matrices can be found in

4   Aitken, A. C. *Determinants and Matrices.* New York: Interscience, 1948.

3

THE ELECTRODYNAMIC EQUATIONS

Electromagnetic phenomena are dependent upon the existence of positively and negatively charged particles. The forces these charged particles exert upon each other and the resulting consequences form the subject matter of electromagnetic theory. The early experiments of Faraday laid the groundwork for the theory of electromagnetism. Using these experimental results, Maxwell formulated the mathematical theory of electricity and magnetism by introducing the concept that certain fields are produced by charged particles and that these fields, in turn, exert forces on other charged particles.

Since a plasma is composed of positively and negatively charged particles, it is apparent that electromagnetic theory must play a basic role in the theory of plasmas. The fields that exist within the plasma, and therefore the forces that act upon the particles of the plasma, are determined from the electrodynamic equations.

The purpose of the present chapter is twofold. First it is designed as a brief review of the equations of electromagnetic theory, with particular emphasis on those topics pertinent to plasma dynamics. Second it provides an opportunity for the student to use the indicial notation in dealing with somewhat familiar subject matter.

We begin this chapter with a brief discussion of the field vectors used to describe electromagnetic phenomena. The experimental laws of Faraday and Ampere are used to obtain Maxwell's equations. The last three sections of the chapter treat topics particularly pertinent to plasma media. In Section 3.3 we interpret Faraday's law for moving media and demonstrate the existence of an induced electric field in media moving across a magnetic field. We show in Section 3.4 that if the conductivity of the medium is infinite, the magnetic lines of force become "frozen" in the medium and move with it. Finally, in Section 3.5, we discuss electromagnetic stress and energy. We find that the forces acting on the charges and currents can be expressed in terms of the field vectors by introducing the Poynting vector and the electromagnetic stress tensor.

3.1   THE FIELD VECTORS AND THE PROPERTIES OF THE MEDIUM

The *electric field intensity* **E** and the *magnetic induction* **B** are defined in terms of the forces that act upon a charged particle. It is found experimentally that these forces are of two types: one that is independent of the velocity of the particle, and another that is a function of the particle velocity. The combination of these two forces, which can be written in terms of the electric and magnetic field vectors, is defined as the *Lorentz force*. If **R** represents this combination of forces in units of force per unit mass, then the Lorentz force is given by

$$m\mathbf{R} = q(\mathbf{E} + \mathbf{v} \times \mathbf{B}) \qquad [3.1]$$

where q is the electrical charge of the particle, **v** is the particle velocity, and m is the particle mass.

Equation [3.1] can be written in indicial notation as

$$mR_i = q(E_i + \epsilon_{ijk}v_jB_k) \qquad [3.2]$$

The dimensions of **E** and **B** in mks units are as follows:

$$\mathbf{E}: \quad \frac{\text{newtons}}{\text{coul}} \quad \text{or} \quad \frac{\text{kg-m}}{\text{coul-sec}^2} \quad \text{or} \quad \frac{\text{volts}}{\text{m}}$$

which defines a *volt*, and

$$\mathbf{B}: \quad \frac{\text{newton-sec}}{\text{coul-m}} \quad \text{or} \quad \frac{\text{kg}}{\text{coul-sec}} \quad \text{or} \quad \frac{\text{webers}}{\text{m}^2}$$

which defines a *weber*.

A plasma contains charged particles of different species. For example, a simple plasma may contain electrons and a single type of positive ion. Let $q^{(s)}$ be the charge of the sth type of particle and let $N^{(s)}$ be the number density of the sth species. Then the *space charge density*, or simply the charge density, η is defined as

$$\eta = \sum_s N^{(s)} q^{(s)} \qquad [3.3]$$

For a plasma containing only one type of singly ionized positive ion the charge of each ion is $(+e)$ while the charge of each electron is $(-e)$. For this case the charge density [3.3] becomes

$$\eta = e(N_+ - N_-) \qquad [3.4]$$

In this equation we have used the plus and minus signs to designate quantities referring to positive ions and electrons, respectively.

If there is a net motion of charge within a medium, then an electric current is said to flow. The *electric current density* J_i is defined as the net rate at which charge is transported across a unit area. Let $\langle v_i^{(s)} \rangle$ be the average or mean velocity of the sth species in a plasma. The current density J_i is then given by

$$J_i = \sum_s N^{(s)} q^{(s)} \langle v_i^{(s)} \rangle \qquad [3.5]$$

For the simple plasma described above the current density would then be

$$J_i = e(N_+ \langle v_i^+ \rangle - N_- \langle v_i^- \rangle) \qquad [3.6]$$

Notice that the plus and minus signs, which distinguish ion and electron quantities, appear in the subscript position when used with scalars ($N_\pm$) but must be kept in the superscript position when used with vectors ($v_i^\pm$). This procedure will be used throughout the book.

The charge density η and the current density J_i are related in the following way. The current leaving an arbitrary volume V bounded by the closed surface S must equal the rate at which the net charge is transported out of V. If n_i is a unit outward normal to the surface S, then we can write

$$\int_S J_i n_i \, dA = -\frac{d}{dt} \int_V \eta \, d\tau \qquad [3.7]$$

where dA and $d\tau$ are differential surface and volume elements, respectively. Applying the divergence theorem (Appendix C) to [3.7] we obtain

$$\int_V J_{i,i}\, d\tau = -\int_V \frac{\partial \eta}{\partial t}\, d\tau$$

or

$$\int_V \left(J_{i,i} + \frac{\partial \eta}{\partial t}\right) d\tau = 0 \qquad [3.8]$$

Since the volume V is arbitrary, the integrand in [3.8] must vanish, which leads to

$$\frac{\partial \eta}{\partial t} = -J_{i,i} \qquad [3.9]$$

which is the *equation of continuity of charge.*

The current density J_i can result from the application of an electric field E_i. However in a plasma a current density can also flow as the result of mass motion or density and thermal gradients. Let us consider a current density that results from the application of an electric field. We will assume that a linear relationship exists between the current density and the electric field intensity. Thus we can write

$$J_i = \sigma_{ij} E_j \qquad [3.10]$$

where σ_{ij} is called the *conductivity tensor.* If the plasma is isotropic then

$$\sigma_{ij} = \sigma \delta_{ij}$$

where σ is a *scalar conductivity.* For this case

$$J_i = \sigma E_i \qquad [3.11]$$

Equation [3.11] is a statement of *Ohm's law.* We will find in Section 6.51 that such a simple relation does not in general hold in a plasma, but that a generalization of this relation is necessary, and we will find in Section 10.4 that for sufficiently large field strengths the linear relationship between J_i and E_i expressed by [3.11] is not always valid. For this case, however, one can still define a conductivity σ by the relation [3.11] which will be a function of the electric field strength. Such a conductivity is said to be "nonlinear."

The electric field intensity E_i and the magnetic induction B_i were defined at the beginning of this section in terms of the forces acting on charged particles. There are other electromagnetic vector quantities of importance that depend upon the properties of the medium. We will review these ideas briefly by considering the dielectric and magnetic properties of a medium.

Dielectrics   Dielectrics are characterized by bound charges as contrasted with the free charges of conductors. When an electric field is applied to a dielectric, the centers of positive and negative charges of the atoms

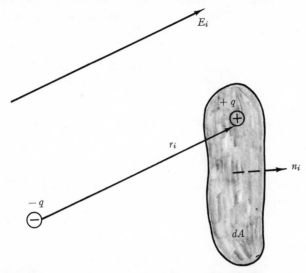

FIGURE 3.I   Dipole Moment Produced in a Dielectric Medium

become displaced by some distance, say r_i. Such a displacement creates a dipole moment equal to qr_i. The dipole moment per unit volume is given by Nqr_i. The amount of charge which will cross an area dA due to this displacement of charge will be (see Figure 3.1) $Nqr_i n_i\, dA$.

The net charge crossing a closed surface S enclosing a volume V will be

$$Q_N = \oint_S Nqr_i n_i\, dA \qquad [3.12]$$

Since the original net charge in V was zero, there will be a net charge left in V equal to $-Q_N$ and called the *polarization charge*

$$Q_P = -\oint_S Nqr_i n_i\, dA = -\oint_S P_i n_i\, dA \qquad [3.13]$$

where

$$P_i = Nqr_i \qquad [3.14]$$

is called the *polarization* and is equal to the dipole moment per unit volume. The dimensions of P_i are coul/m^2.

We assume that the polarization vector P_i is linearly related to the electric field E_j. That is

$$P_i = \epsilon_0 \alpha_{ij} E_j \qquad [3.15]$$

where α_{ij} is called the *electric susceptibility tensor*. It is taken to be dimensionless so that ϵ_0, called the *permittivity of free space*, is a constant which must have the dimensions

$$\epsilon_0 : \quad \frac{\text{coul}^2\text{-sec}^2}{\text{m}^3\text{-kg}} \quad \text{or} \quad \frac{\text{farads}}{\text{m}}$$

which defines a *farad*.

We define the *electric displacement* D_i by

$$D_i = \epsilon_0 E_i + P_i \qquad [3.16]$$

The dimensions of D_i are the same as P_i, namely coul/m^2. Substituting [3.15] into [3.16] gives

$$D_i = \epsilon_0 E_i + \epsilon_0 \alpha_{ij} E_j = \epsilon_0 (\delta_{ij} + \alpha_{ij}) E_j = \epsilon_0 \kappa_{ij} E_j \qquad [3.17]$$

where

$$\kappa_{ij} = (\delta_{ij} + \alpha_{ij}) \qquad [3.18]$$

is called the *dielectric tensor*.

If the dielectric is isotropic, then κ_{ij} reduces to a scalar dielectric constant κ. The quantity $\epsilon = \epsilon_0 \kappa$ is called the *permittivity* of the medium. In Section 7.2 we will see in what sense a plasma may be considered to have dielectric properties and be characterized by a dielectric constant.

The dimensions of the time derivative of D_i are those of a current density. The quantity $\dot{D}_i$ is called the *displacement current density*. The *total current density* is written as C_i so that

$$C_i = J_i + \dot{D}_i \qquad [3.19]$$

Magnetic Properties   The magnetic properties of matter may be described in a way analogous to the polarization properties of dielectrics. An orbiting electron produces a *magnetic dipole moment* equal to the circulating current I times the area of the loop. This orbital magnetic moment m_i is thus defined as

$$m_i = I n_i A \qquad [3.20]$$

where n_i is the unit normal to the area A. The direction of n_i is related to the direction of the circulating current in a right-handed sense. For a circular orbit or radius r the area A is πr^2 and the current is equal to the gyration frequency $\Omega/2\pi$ times the charge q. The orbital magnetic moment m_i can then be written as

$$m_i = \frac{q\Omega r^2}{2} n_i \qquad [3.21]$$

The *magnetization vector* M_i is defined as the magnetic moment per unit volume (analogous to P_i) and is given by

$$M_i = Nm_i \qquad [3.22]$$

Thus M_i has the units amperes/m or coul/m-sec. We define the *magnetic field intensity* H_i by

$$B_i = \mu_0(H_i + M_i) \qquad [3.23]$$

Thus H_i also has the units amperes/m or coul/m-sec. In [3.23] μ_0 is a constant called the *permeability of free space*; it must have the dimensions

$$\mu_0: \quad \frac{\text{kg-m}}{\text{coul}^2} \quad \text{or} \quad \frac{\text{henrys}}{\text{m}}$$

which defines a *henry*.

We assume a linear relationship between the magnetization vector and the magnetic field intensity. That is

$$M_i = \chi_{ij}H_j \qquad [3.24]$$

where χ_{ij} is called the *magnetic susceptibility tensor*.

Putting [3.24] in [3.23] we obtain

$$B_i = \mu_0(\delta_{ij} + \chi_{ij})H_j$$

or

$$B_i = \mu_{ij}H_j \qquad [3.25]$$

where

$$\mu_{ij} = \mu_0(\delta_{ij} + \chi_{ij}) \qquad [3.26]$$

is the *permeability tensor*.

The electromagnetic vectors introduced in this section are listed with their units in Table 3.1.

T A B L E 3.I List of Electromagnetic Vectors

SYMBOL	NAME	UNITS
E_i	Electric field intensity	$\dfrac{\text{volts}}{\text{m}} = \dfrac{\text{kg-m}}{\text{coul-sec}^2} = \dfrac{\text{newtons}}{\text{coul}}$
B_i	Magnetic induction	$\dfrac{\text{webers}}{\text{m}^2} = \dfrac{\text{kg}}{\text{coul-sec}} = \dfrac{\text{newton-sec}}{\text{coul-m}}$
J_i	Electric current density	$\dfrac{\text{amperes}}{\text{m}^2} = \dfrac{\text{coul}}{\text{m}^2\text{-sec}}$
P_i	Polarization	$\dfrac{\text{coul}}{\text{m}^2}$
D_i	Electric displacement	$\dfrac{\text{coul}}{\text{m}^2}$
H_i	Magnetic field intensity	$\dfrac{\text{amperes}}{\text{m}} = \dfrac{\text{coul}}{\text{m-sec}}$

3.2 M A X W E L L' S   E Q U A T I O N S

Electromagnetic theory is based upon experimental laws that relate four integral quantities. Consider a surface S bounded by a closed curve C as shown in Figure 3.2. The directions of ds_i and n_i form a right-handed system. We then define the following four integral quantities:

$$\text{Magnetic flux} \quad = \int_S B_i n_i \, dA \qquad [3.27]$$

$$\text{Electric current flux} \quad = \int_S C_i n_i \, dA \qquad [3.28]$$

$$\text{Magnetomotive force} = \oint_C H_i \, ds_i \qquad [3.29]$$

$$\text{Electromotive force} \quad = \oint_C E_i \, ds_i \qquad [3.30]$$

These four integral quantities are related by the experimental laws of Faraday and Ampere.

Faraday's Law: Every change in magnetic flux that traverses a given surface produces in its boundary an electromotive force numerically equal to the change in flux but opposite in sign. That is,

$$\frac{d}{dt} \int_S B_i n_i \, dA = -\oint_C E_i \, ds_i \qquad [3.31]$$

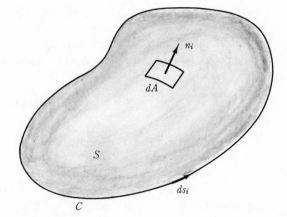

FIGURE 3.2 A Closed Curve C Bounding the Surface S

Ampere's Law: Electric current flux that traverses a surface is accompanied by a magnetomotive force equal in magnitude and direction to the electric current flux. That is,

$$\int_S C_i n_i \, dA = \oint_C H_i \, ds_i \qquad [3.32]$$

The differential form of Maxwell's equations is obtained by applying *Stokes' theorem* to the integral form of Faraday's and Ampere's laws. Thus applying Stokes' theorem (see Appendix C) to [3.31] we obtain

$$\frac{d}{dt} \int_S B_i n_i \, dA = -\int_S \epsilon_{ijk} E_{k,j} n_i \, dA$$

or

$$\int_S (\dot{B}_i + \epsilon_{ijk} E_{k,j}) n_i \, dA = 0 \qquad [3.33]$$

In [3.33] we have assumed that the only change in magnetic flux that traverses the surface is due to an explicit time dependence of B_i. For the case of moving media, additional terms must be included and we will consider this case separately in Section 3.3.

Since the surface S in [3.33] is arbitrary, we must have that

$$(\dot{B}_i + \epsilon_{ijk}E_{k,j})n_i = 0$$

Since we can also pick any orientation of the surface, n_i is also arbitrary so that we must have

$$\epsilon_{ijk}E_{k,j} = -\dot{B}_i \qquad\qquad [3.34]$$

which is the first of Maxwell's equations.

Applying Stokes' theorem to Ampere's law [3.32] we obtain

$$\int_S C_i n_i \, dA = \int_S \epsilon_{ijk}H_{k,j}n_i \, dA$$

Using the same arguments which led to [3.34], we see that we must have

$$\epsilon_{ijk}H_{k,j} = C_i$$

or, using [3.19]

$$\epsilon_{ijk}H_{k,j} = J_i + \dot{D}_i \qquad\qquad [3.35]$$

which is the second of Maxwell's equations.

It is often customary to state four Maxwell equations. However the last two can be deduced from [3.34] and [3.35] if we use [3.9].

Taking the divergence of [3.34] we obtain

$$\epsilon_{ijk}E_{k,ji} = -\dot{B}_{i,i} \equiv 0$$

where the divergence of the curl of a vector was shown to be zero in Exercise 2.31.3a. It follows that

$$B_{i,i} = \text{const} \qquad\qquad [3.36]$$

If the value of the magnetic field were ever zero, then the constant in [3.36] must be zero. Thus for magnetic fields of finite lifetime we have

$$B_{i,i} = 0 \qquad\qquad [3.37]$$

Taking the divergence of [3.35] we obtain

$$\epsilon_{ijk}H_{k,ji} = J_{i,i} + \dot{D}_{i,i} \equiv 0$$

from which, using [3.9] we obtain

$$\frac{\partial}{\partial t}(-\eta + D_{i,i}) = 0$$

which again, if the fields were ever zero, leads to

$$D_{i,i} = \eta \qquad \qquad [3.38]$$

If we substitute [3.23] into [3.35], we obtain

$$\epsilon_{ijk}B_{k,j} = \mu_0 J_i + \mu_0 \dot{D}_i + \mu_0 \epsilon_{ijk} M_{k,j}$$
$$= \mu_0(J_i + \dot{D}_i + J_i^M)$$

where

$$J_i^M = \epsilon_{ijk} M_{k,j} \qquad \qquad [3.39]$$

is called the *magnetization current*. Note from the definition of the magnetization vector given by [3.22] that if either the number density or the orbital magnetic moment of orbiting charged particles varies in space, then a magnetization current will flow according to [3.39].

   Scalar and Vector Potentials   It is possible (and often convenient) to formulate Maxwell's equations in terms of potential functions from which the field vectors are then obtained by differentiation.

   From [3.37] we see that there must exist a vector A_k such that

$$B_i = \epsilon_{ijk} A_{k,j} \qquad \qquad [3.40]$$

since $\epsilon_{ijk} A_{k,ji} \equiv 0$. Substituting [3.40] into [3.34], we obtain

$$\epsilon_{ijk} E_{k,j} = -\epsilon_{ijk} \dot{A}_{k,j} \quad \text{or} \quad \epsilon_{ijk}(E_k + \dot{A}_k)_{,j} = 0.$$

There thus exists a scalar ψ such that

$$E_k + \dot{A}_k = -\psi_{,k} \qquad \qquad [3.41]$$

since $\epsilon_{ijk}\psi_{,kj} \equiv 0$. Equation [3.41] can be written

$$E_i = -\psi_{,i} - \dot{A}_i \qquad \qquad [3.42]$$

   Equation [3.40] gives the magnetic induction B_i in terms of the *vector potential* A_k, while [3.42] gives the electric field intensity E_i in terms of the *scalar potential* ψ and the vector potential A_i.

In order to determine the equations satisfied by ψ and A_k we substitute [3.40] and [3.42] into Maxwell's equation [3.35]. Using $B_i = \mu H_i$ and $D_i = \epsilon E_i$, we then obtain

$$\epsilon_{ijk}\epsilon_{krs}A_{s,rj} = \mu J_i - \mu\epsilon\dot{\psi}_{,i} - \mu\epsilon\ddot{A}_i$$

from which

$$(\delta_{ir}\delta_{js} - \delta_{is}\delta_{jr})A_{s,rj} = \mu J_i - \mu\epsilon\dot{\psi}_{,i} - \mu\epsilon\ddot{A}_i$$

so that

$$A_{j,ij} - A_{i,jj} = \mu J_i - \mu\epsilon\dot{\psi}_{,i} - \mu\epsilon\ddot{A}_i \qquad [3.43]$$

Any continuous vector field A_i can be represented as the sum of two other vectors a_i and α_i where the curl of a_i vanishes and the divergence of α_i vanishes. That is, $A_i = a_i + \alpha_i$, where $\epsilon_{ijk}a_{k,j} = 0$ and $\alpha_{i,i} = 0$. This leads to the fact that we can separate the curl and divergence operations on the field A_i. Thus $\epsilon_{ijk}A_{k,j} = \epsilon_{ijk}\alpha_{k,j}$ and $A_{i,i} = a_{i,i}$. The quantity a_i is called the *lamellar* part of A_i, and α_i is called the *solenoidal* part of A_i.

For our case the solenoidal part of A_i is specified by [3.40]. We are still free to choose the lamellar part a_i anyway we wish, since $\epsilon_{ijk}a_{k,j} = 0$. We will therefore choose the lamellar part of A_i such that

$$A_{j,j} = -\mu\epsilon\dot{\psi} \qquad [3.44]$$

This equation is known as the *Lorentz condition* and relates the scalar potential ψ to the vector potential A_j. Using [3.44], we can write [3.43] as

$$A_{i,jj} - \mu\epsilon\ddot{A}_i = -\mu J_i \qquad [3.45]$$

Using [3.38], [3.42], and [3.44], we have that

$$E_{i,i} = \frac{\eta}{\epsilon} = -\psi_{,ii} - \dot{A}_{i,i} = -\psi_{,ii} + \mu\epsilon\ddot{\psi}$$

from which

$$\psi_{,ii} - \mu\epsilon\ddot{\psi} = -\frac{\eta}{\epsilon} \qquad [3.46]$$

The vector potential A_i is determined from [3.45] and the scalar potential ψ is determined from [3.46]. Note that these equations are of the same form. Once the potentials are known, the field vectors may be determined from [3.40] and [3.42].

A particularly important special case is that of electrostatic fields in which the field quantities do not vary with time. We then see from [3.42] that the electric field is given in terms of only a scalar potential by

$$E_i = -\psi_{,i} \tag{3.47}$$

where, from [3.46], ψ satisfies the equation

$$\psi_{,ii} = -\frac{\eta}{\epsilon} \tag{3.48}$$

which is known as *Poisson's equation*. If the charge density η is zero, then [3.48] reduces to the *Laplace equation*

$$\psi_{,ii} = 0 \tag{3.49}$$

3.3 FARADAY'S LAW FOR MOVING MEDIA[1]

Faraday's law as given by [3.31] also holds for moving media. However care must be taken in processing the left-hand side of this equation to include the total change in magnetic flux which traverses the surface. Thus the left-hand side of [3.31] is written

$$\frac{d}{dt} \int_S B_i n_i \, dA = \int_S \frac{dB_i}{dt} n_i \, dA \tag{3.50}$$

where dB_i/dt is no longer $\partial B_i/\partial t$ as it was in [3.33]. We now seek the expression for dB_i/dt when the surface S is moving.

Consider the surface S_1 to move to S_2 in the time dt, as shown in Figure 3.3. By the rules of differentiation we have

$$\frac{\Delta}{\Delta t} \int B_i n_i \, dA = \frac{1}{\Delta t} \int (B_i^{t+dt} n_i \, dA - B_i^t n_i \, dA) \tag{3.51}$$

In order to evaluate this, apply the divergence theorem to the volume shown in Figure 3.3. We thus have

$$\int_V B_{i,i} \, dV = \int_{S_2} B_i^t n_i \, dA - \int_{S_1} B_i^t n_i \, dA + \int_{S_3} B_i^t n_i^s \, dA_s \tag{3.52}$$

[1] May be omitted on a first reading and taken up later as appropriate.

Note that we must write B_i^t since the divergence theorem applies only to instantaneous values of B_i.

Now from Figure 3.3, $n_i^s \, dA_s = \epsilon_{ijk} \, ds_j v_k \, dt = -\epsilon_{ijk} v_j \, ds_k \, dt$, so that [3.52] becomes

$$\int_V B_{i,i} \, dV = \int_{S_2} B_i^t n_i \, dA - \int_{S_1} B_i^t n_i \, dA - \oint_C \epsilon_{ijk} B_i^t v_j \, ds_k \, dt \quad [3.53]$$

Now

$$B_i^{t+dt} = B_i^t + \frac{\partial B_i}{\partial t} \, dt + \cdots \quad [3.54]$$

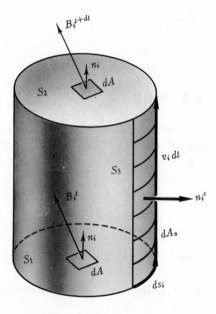

FIGURE 3.3 Change in Magnetic Flux which Traverses a Moving Surface

Putting [3.54] in [3.51], we obtain

$$\frac{d}{dt} \int B_i n_i \, dA = \frac{1}{dt} \left(\int_{S_2} B_i^t n_i \, dA - \int_{S_1} B_i^t n_i \, dA \right) + \int_{S_2} \frac{\partial B_i}{\partial t} n_i \, dA \quad [3.55]$$

Substituting [3.53] in [3.55], we obtain

$$\frac{d}{dt} \int B_i n_i \, dA = \int_V B_{i,i} \frac{dV}{dt} + \oint_C \epsilon_{ijk} B_i v_j \, ds_k + \int_{S_2} \frac{\partial B_i}{\partial t} n_i \, dA \quad [3.56]$$

Now, from Figure 3.3, $dV = n_i v_i \, dt \, dA$, and, applying Stokes' theorem to the second term on the right-hand side of [3.56], we obtain

$$\frac{d}{dt} \int B_i n_i \, dA = \int B_{j,j} n_i v_i \, dA + \int \epsilon_{rsk} \epsilon_{ijk} (B_i v_j)_{,s} n_r \, dA + \int \frac{\partial B_i}{\partial t} n_i \, dA$$

[3.57]

or

$$\int \frac{dB_i}{dt} n_i \, dA = \int \left[\frac{\partial B_i}{\partial t} + \epsilon_{isk} \epsilon_{rjk} (B_r v_j)_{,s} + B_{j,j} v_i \right] n_i \, dA$$

[3.58]

Since $B_{j,j} = 0$, we finally have from [3.58]

$$\frac{dB_i}{dt} = \frac{\partial B_i}{\partial t} + \epsilon_{isk} \epsilon_{krj} (B_r v_j)_{,s}$$

[3.59]

The first term on the right of [3.59] represents the change in flux due to the time variation of the vector field, while the second term represents the flux loss across the boundary of the moving surface.

Let E_i' be the electric field measured in the moving frame of reference; then Faraday's law [3.31] becomes

$$\oint_C E_i' \, ds_i = - \int_S \left[\frac{\partial B_i}{\partial t} + \epsilon_{isk} \epsilon_{krj} (B_r v_j)_{,s} \right] n_i \, dA$$

[3.60]

Applying Stokes' theorem to [3.60] we obtain

$$\int_S \epsilon_{isk} E_{k,s}' n_i \, dA = - \int_S \left[\frac{\partial B_i}{\partial t} + \epsilon_{isk} \epsilon_{krj} (B_r v_j)_{,s} \right] n_i \, dA$$

or

$$\int_S \left[\epsilon_{isk} (E_k' - \epsilon_{krj} v_r B_j)_{,s} + \frac{\partial B_i}{\partial t} \right] n_i \, dA = 0$$

from which, since the surface S is arbitrary,

$$\epsilon_{isk} (E_k' - \epsilon_{krj} v_r B_j)_{,s} = - \frac{\partial B_i}{\partial t}$$

[3.61]

In [3.61], $(E_k' - \epsilon_{krj} v_r B_j)$ actually represents the field measured in the stationary frame of reference. This is true since a moving charge q experiences a force

$$q(E_i + \epsilon_{ijk} v_j B_k)$$

[3.62]

In the frame of reference moving with the charge, the force on the charge is given by

$$qE_i' \qquad [3.63]$$

Equating [3.62] and [3.63], we see that

$$E_i = E_i' - \epsilon_{ijk}v_jB_k \qquad [3.64]$$

Therefore [3.61] becomes

$$\epsilon_{ijk}E_{k,j} = -\frac{\partial B_i}{\partial t} \qquad [3.65]$$

This is the same as Maxwell's equation [3.34] and shows that the differential formulation of Faraday's law is independent of the motion of the medium inside the field.

The electric field measured in the moving frame of reference is from [3.64]

$$E_i' = E_i + \epsilon_{ijk}v_jB_k \qquad [3.66]$$

so that the current density J_i in the moving frame can be written as

$$J_i = \sigma E_i'$$
$$= \sigma(E_i + \epsilon_{ijk}v_jB_k) \qquad [3.67]$$

3.4 FROZEN-IN FIELDS[2]

In this section we wish to show that for a medium of infinite conductivity the magnetic lines of force are "frozen" into the medium—that is, that they move with the velocity of the medium.

From [3.67] we see that for a finite current density J_i, if the conductivity of the medium is considered to be infinite, then we must have

$$E_i + \epsilon_{ijk}v_jB_k = 0 \qquad [3.68]$$

Maxwell's equation [3.34] is

$$\epsilon_{rsi}E_{i,s} = -\dot{B}_r \qquad [3.69]$$

and substituting [3.68] into [3.69] we obtain

$$\epsilon_{rsi}\epsilon_{ijk}(v_jB_k)_{,s} = \dot{B}_r \qquad [3.70]$$

Note that in this equation v_j is the velocity of the conducting medium.

---

[2] May be omitted on a first reading and taken up later as appropriate.

Now from [3.37] we see that the magnetic field B_k is divergence free. That is

$$B_{k,k} = 0 \qquad\qquad [3.71]$$

Since the divergence of the curl is identically zero, we can write B_k as the curl of an arbitrary vector. In particular, let this arbitrary vector be $\phi\psi_{,i}$. Then we can write

$$B_k = \epsilon_{krs}(\phi\psi_{,s})_{,r}$$

or

$$B_k = \epsilon_{krs}\phi_{,r}\psi_{,s} \qquad\qquad [3.72]$$

where we have made use of the fact that

$$\epsilon_{krs}\psi_{,sr} \equiv 0$$

Equation [3.72] tells us that the magnetic line of force B_k can be thought of as the intersection of a surface of constant ϕ and a surface of constant ψ as shown in Figure 3.4.

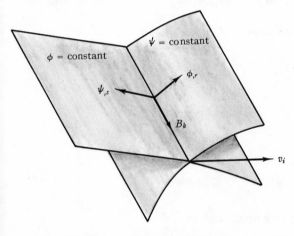

FIGURE 3.4 Surfaces of Constant ϕ and ψ

$$\mathbf{B} = (\nabla\phi)\times(\nabla\psi)$$

Now let the magnetic lines of force move with some velocity v_i. This is the same as moving both surfaces of constant ϕ and ψ with the velocity v_i. As we move with these surfaces, no change in ϕ or ψ will take place, so that

$$\frac{d\phi}{dt} = \dot{\phi} + v_m\phi_{,m} = 0 \qquad\qquad [3.73]$$

and

$$\frac{d\psi}{dt} = \dot{\psi} + v_m\psi_{,m} = 0 \qquad\qquad [3.74]$$

from which

$$v_m\phi_{,m} = -\dot{\phi} \qquad\qquad [3.75]$$

and

$$v_m\psi_{,m} = -\dot{\psi} \qquad\qquad [3.76]$$

Let us now form the cross product $\epsilon_{ijk}v_jB_k$, where v_j is the velocity with which the magnetic lines of force are moving. Using [3.72] we have

$$\epsilon_{ijk}v_jB_k = \epsilon_{ijk}\epsilon_{krs}v_j\phi_{,r}\psi_{,s} = (\delta_{ir}\delta_{js} - \delta_{is}\delta_{jr})v_j\phi_{,r}\psi_{,s}$$

and

$$\epsilon_{ijk}v_jB_k = v_s\phi_{,i}\psi_{,s} - v_r\phi_{,r}\psi_{,i} \qquad\qquad [3.77]$$

Substituting [3.75] and [3.76] into [3.77] we obtain

$$\epsilon_{ijk}v_jB_k = -\dot{\psi}\phi_{,i} + \dot{\phi}\psi_{,i} \qquad\qquad [3.78]$$

If we now take the curl of both sides of [3.78] we will obtain

$$\begin{aligned}
\epsilon_{rsi}\epsilon_{ijk}(v_jB_k)_{,s} &= \epsilon_{rsi}(\dot{\phi}\psi_{,i} - \dot{\psi}\phi_{,i})_{,s} \\
&= \epsilon_{rsi}(\dot{\phi}_{,s}\psi_{,i} - \dot{\psi}_{,s}\phi_{,i}) \\
&= \epsilon_{rsi}(\dot{\phi}_{,s}\psi_{,i} + \phi_{,s}\dot{\psi}_{,i})
\end{aligned}$$

whence

$$\epsilon_{rsi}\epsilon_{ijk}(v_jB_k)_{,s} = \frac{\partial}{\partial t}(\epsilon_{rsi}\phi_{,s}\psi_{,i}) \qquad\qquad [3.79]$$

Substituting [3.72] into [3.79] we finally obtain

$$\epsilon_{rsi}\epsilon_{ijk}(v_jB_k)_{,s} = \frac{\partial B_r}{\partial t} = \dot{B}_r \qquad\qquad [3.80]$$

which is identical with [3.70]. We have therefore demonstrated the following.

The magnetic field in an infinitely conducting medium moving with velocity v_i is described by [3.70]. The equation of a magnetic line of force which itself moves with a velocity v_i is given by [3.80]. Since these two equations are identical, we conclude that the magnetic lines of force move with the same velocity as the medium. The lines of force are thus said to be "frozen" into the conducting medium.

3.5 ELECTROMAGNETIC STRESS AND ENERGY[3]

In this section we wish to derive *Poynting's theorem* which is concerned with the rate at which electromagnetic energy in a given volume is lost. Maxwell's equations are, from [3.34] and [3.35],

$$\epsilon_{ijk}E_{k,j} = -\dot{B}_i \qquad [3.81]$$

and

$$\epsilon_{ijk}H_{k,j} = J_i + \dot{D}_i \qquad [3.82]$$

We note from Table 3.1 that terms with the dimensions of energy per unit volume per unit time can be obtained by multiplying [3.81] by H_i and [3.82] by E_i. These expressions then become

$$\epsilon_{ijk}E_{k,j}H_i = -\dot{B}_iH_i \qquad [3.83]$$

and

$$\epsilon_{ijk}H_{k,j}E_i = J_iE_i + \dot{D}_iE_i \qquad [3.84]$$

Subtracting [3.84] from [3.83] we obtain

$$\epsilon_{ijk}(E_{k,j}H_i - H_{k,j}E_i) = -J_iE_i - \dot{D}_iE_i - \dot{B}_iH_i$$

or

$$\epsilon_{ijk}[(E_kH_i)_{,j} - E_kH_{i,j} + H_{i,j}E_k] = -J_iE_i - \dot{D}_iE_i - \dot{B}_iH_i$$

or

$$\epsilon_{ijk}(E_jH_k)_{,i} + J_iE_i = -\dot{D}_iE_i - \dot{B}_iH_i \qquad [3.85]$$

Now each of the terms in [3.85] has the dimensions of energy per unit volume per unit time, or power per unit volume. If we integrate [3.85] over

---

[3] May be omitted on a first reading and taken up later as appropriate.

the volume V bounded by the closed surface S and apply Green's theorem to the first term, we obtain

$$\int_S \epsilon_{ijk} E_j H_k n_i \, dA + \int_V J_i E_i \, d\tau = -\int_V (\dot{D}_i E_i + \dot{B}_i H_i) \, d\tau \qquad [3.86]$$

The right-hand side of [3.86] is interpreted as the rate of decrease of stored electric and magnetic energy within the volume V. This energy loss contributes to the terms on the left-hand side of [3.86]. The second term on the left represents losses by Joule heating as well as possible gains by externally applied electromotive forces. The first term on the left, which represents the outward flow of energy across the bounding surface S, can be written as

$$\int_S G_i n_i \, dA = \int_S \epsilon_{ijk} E_j H_k n_i \, dA \qquad [3.87]$$

where

$$G_i = \epsilon_{ijk} E_j H_k \text{ watts/m}^2 \qquad [3.88]$$

is called the *Poynting vector*. Note that G_i is normal to both E_j and H_k and may be thought of as the energy per second which crosses a unit area or the intensity of energy flow at a point in the field.

Electromagnetic Stress Tensor   In the preceding discussion of energy flow we operated on Maxwell's equations to obtain terms with the dimensions of power per unit volume. We will now carry out a similar operation, but this time we wish to obtain terms with the dimensions of force per unit volume. We consider a region containing charges and currents but being free of neutral dielectric or magnetic materials.

In order to obtain terms with the dimensions of force per unit volume, we take the cross product of [3.81] with D_s and the cross product of [3.82] with B_s, and add the resulting equations to obtain

$$-\epsilon_{irs} \epsilon_{ijk} (E_{k,j} D_s + H_{k,j} B_s) = \epsilon_{ris} J_i B_s + \epsilon_{ris} \left(\frac{\partial D_i}{\partial t} B_s + \frac{\partial B_s}{\partial t} D_i \right)$$

which leads to

$$-(\delta_{rj}\delta_{sk} - \delta_{rk}\delta_{sj})(E_{k,j} D_s + H_{k,j} B_s) = \epsilon_{ris} J_i B_s + \epsilon_{ris} \left[\frac{\partial}{\partial t} (D_i B_s) \right]$$

so that

$$-E_{s,r} D_s + E_{r,s} D_s - H_{s,r} B_s + H_{r,s} B_s = \epsilon_{ris} J_i B_s + \frac{\partial}{\partial t} (\epsilon_{ris} D_i B_s) \qquad [3.89]$$

We now look at the first two terms of [3.89]. They are

$$E_{r,s}D_s - E_{s,r}D_s = E_{r,s}D_s - \epsilon_0 E_{s,r}E_s$$
$$= (E_r D_s)_{,s} - E_r D_{s,s} - \epsilon_0(\tfrac{1}{2}E_s E_s)_{,r}$$
$$= (E_r D_s)_{,s} - \eta E_r - (\tfrac{1}{2}E_j D_j \delta_{sr})_{,s}$$
$$= (E_r D_s - \tfrac{1}{2}E_j D_j \delta_{rs})_{,s} - \eta E_r \qquad [3.90]$$

where [3.38] was used in the third step. We can write [3.90] as

$$E_{r,s}D_s - E_{s,r}D_s = T^E_{rs,s} - \eta E_r \qquad [3.91]$$

where

$$T^E_{rs} = E_r D_s - \tfrac{1}{2}E_j D_j \delta_{rs} \qquad [3.92]$$

is called the *electric stress tensor*. The matrix of T^E_{rs} is thus

$$T^E_{rs} = \begin{bmatrix} E_1 D_1 - \tfrac{1}{2}E_j D_j & E_1 D_2 & E_1 D_3 \\ E_2 D_1 & E_2 D_2 - \tfrac{1}{2}E_j D_j & E_2 D_3 \\ E_3 D_1 & E_3 D_2 & E_3 D_3 - \tfrac{1}{2}E_j D_j \end{bmatrix} \qquad [3.93]$$

The third and fourth terms of [3.89] are

$$H_{r,s}B_s - H_{s,r}B_s = H_{r,s}B_s - \mu_0 H_{s,r}H_s$$
$$= (H_r B_s)_{,s} - H_r B_{s,s} - \mu_0(\tfrac{1}{2}H_s H_s)_{,r}$$
$$= (H_r B_s - \tfrac{1}{2}H_j B_j \delta_{rs})_{,s} \qquad [3.94]$$

where [3.37] was used in the last step. We can write [3.94] as

$$H_{r,s}B_s - H_{s,r}B_s = T^M_{rs,s} \qquad [3.95]$$

where

$$T^M_{rs} = H_r B_s - \tfrac{1}{2}H_j B_j \delta_{rs} \qquad [3.96]$$

is called the *magnetic stress tensor*.
    The matrix of T^M_{rs} is

$$T^M_{rs} = \begin{bmatrix} B_1 H_1 - \tfrac{1}{2}B_j H_j & B_1 H_2 & B_1 H_2 \\ B_2 H_1 & B_2 H_2 - \tfrac{1}{2}B_j H_j & B_2 H_3 \\ B_3 H_1 & B_3 H_2 & B_3 H_3 - \tfrac{1}{2}B_j H_j \end{bmatrix} \qquad [3.97]$$

The *total electromagnetic stress tensor* T_{rs} is defined as

$$T_{rs} = T_{rs}^E + T_{rs}^M \tag{3.98}$$

Substituting [3.91], [3.95], and [3.98] into [3.89], we obtain

$$T_{rs,s} - \eta E_r = \epsilon_{ris} J_i B_s + \frac{\partial}{\partial t}(\epsilon_{ris} D_i B_s)$$

or

$$\eta E_r + \epsilon_{ris} J_i B_s = T_{rs,s} - \frac{\partial}{\partial t}(\epsilon_{ris} D_i B_s) \tag{3.99}$$

Equation [3.99] gives the forces per unit volume on the charges and currents in terms of the field quantities alone. The last term in [3.99] can be written in terms of the Poynting vector [3.88] as

$$\frac{\partial}{\partial t}(\epsilon_{ris} D_i B_s) = \mu_0 \epsilon_0 \frac{\partial G_r}{\partial t} \tag{3.100}$$

If we substitute [3.100] into [3.99], integrate the equation over the volume V bounded by the closed surface S, and apply Green's theorem to the first term on the right, we obtain

$$\int_V \eta E_r \, d\tau + \int_V \epsilon_{ris} J_i B_s \, d\tau = \int_S T_{rs} n_s \, dA - \mu_0 \epsilon_0 \int_V \frac{\partial G_r}{\partial t} \, d\tau \tag{3.101}$$

The left-hand side of [3.101] represents the forces that act on the charges and currents contained in the volume V. If the fields do not vary with time, then the last term of [3.101] is zero, and we see that the forces acting on the charges and currents within the volume V can be expressed as the integral of the electromagnetic stress tensor over the surface enclosing the charges and currents.

Problems

3.1 (a) From Faraday's law show that the tangential component of E_i is continuous across a boundary.

 (b) From Ampere's law show that in the absence of surface current the tangential component of H_i is continuous across a boundary. What is the boundary condition on H_i when there is surface current on the boundary?

 (c) Show that the normal component of B_i is continuous across a boundary.

(d) Show that in the absence of surface charge the normal component of D_i is continuous across a boundary. What is the boundary condition on D_i when there is surface charge on the boundary?

3.2 Show that in a homogeneous, isotropic, conducting medium the space charge density is given by

$$\eta = \eta_0 e^{-(\sigma/\epsilon)t}$$

where σ is the conductivity and ϵ is the permittivity of the medium.

3.3 (a) What fields, if any, can exist in a perfect conductor?

(b) What are the boundary conditions on the surface of a perfect conductor?

3.4 (a) Show that in a source-free region where $\eta = 0$ and $J_i = 0$ one can define a *magnetic Hertzian potential* Π_i^M by the relation

$$E_i = -\mu\epsilon_{ijk}\dot{\Pi}_{k,j}^M$$

Show that Maxwell's equations require the existence of a scalar function ϕ such that $H_k + \mu\epsilon\ddot{\Pi}_k^M = \phi_{,k}$.

Picking the lamellar part of Π_k^M such that $\Pi_{j,j}^M = \phi$, show that Π_i^M satisfies the equation $\Pi_{i,jj}^M = \mu\epsilon\ddot{\Pi}_i^M$, and that the magnetic field is found from $H_i = -\mu\epsilon\ddot{\Pi}_i^M + \Pi_{j,ji}^M$.

(b) Starting with the fact that $H_{i,i} = 0$, show that an *electric Hertzian* potential Π_k^E can be defined by $H_i = \epsilon\epsilon_{ijk}\dot{\Pi}_{k,j}^E$ which satisfies the equation $\Pi_{i,jj}^E = \mu\epsilon\ddot{\Pi}_i^E$, and that the electric field is found from $E_i = -\mu\epsilon\ddot{\Pi}_i^E + \Pi_{j,ji}^E$.

REFERENCES

Several good texts on electromagnetic theory are available for reference. For example:

1   Fano, R., L. Chu, and R. Adler. *Electromagnetic Fields, Energy, and Forces*. New York: Wiley, 1960.

2   Moon, P., and D. Spencer. *Foundations of Electrodynamics*. Princeton: Van Nostrand, 1960.

3   Reitz, J. R., and F. J. Milford. *Foundations of Electromagnetic Theory*. Boston: Addison-Wesley, 1960.

More advanced graduate texts include

4   Panofsky, W., and M. Phillips. *Classical Electricity and Magnetism*. Boston: Addison-Wesley, 1955.

5   Stratton, J. *Electromagnetic Theory*. New York: McGraw-Hill, 1940.

6   Jackson, J. D. *Classical Electrodynamics*. New York: Wiley, 1962.

7   Collin, R. E. *Field Theory of Guided Waves*. New York: McGraw-Hill, 1960.

A discussion of frozen fields and the motion of magnetic fields can be found in

8   Dungey, J. W. *Cosmic Electrodynamics*. London: Cambridge University Press, 1958.

4

ELASTIC

COLLISION PROCESSES

The properties of matter in the plasma state depend upon the motions of the several types of particles that may be present in the plasma. These motions, in turn, depend upon the force fields that act upon the particles. Fields may be applied externally to a plasma—for example, the plasma may be immersed in a magnetic field—or they may exist internally due to the nature of the particles themselves. An electron surrounds itself by an electric field by virtue of the fact that it possesses an electrical charge. This electric field exerts a force on the other charged particles in the plasma. Even a neutral atom has a field associated with it and, if another particle approaches close enough to it, an interaction occurs between the particles, and their motions are changed.

In this chapter the words *collision* and *interaction* are used synonymously. At the atomic level the concept of physical contact between bodies loses the utility which it has normally, and a collision between particles must be thought of as an interaction—governed by the fields that act on each of the particles. This means that collisions involve the force fields within the plasma which are contributed by the plasma particles themselves.

Electrically charged particles interact with each other according to Coulomb's law. In this case the force between any two particles varies inversely with the square of the distance between them. The fields associated with electrically neutral particles are strong within the electronic shells of the particle but are weak outside the outermost, or valence, shell. These fields depend upon the particular atom or molecule being considered, and no simple inverse power dependence upon distance can be assigned. However the strength of the field falls off much more rapidly with the particle separation than in the case of the Coulomb field.

This distinction between the interactions of electrically charged particles and of neutral particles is of outstanding importance in the behavior of plasmas. The distinction is emphasized by calling the Coulomb interactions *long-range interactions*. Non-Coulomb interactions are called *short-range interactions*. In a plasma the long-range Coulomb field of one particle continuously interacts with a large number of other particles. In contrast, the short-range fields associated with a neutral particle only occasionally interact with another particle and very rarely interact with two other particles simultaneously.

A *binary collision* is a collision between two particles. The multiple-particle Coulomb interaction can be thought of as a number of simultaneous binary collisions. However the term *binary collision* is normally reserved for the situation in which a discrete change in the motions of two particles is due exclusively to the action of their own force fields. One method of dealing with multiple interactions is to assume that a series of consecutive binary collisions describes the situation. We will treat this case in Chapter 9 where we consider charged particle interactions.

The importance of multiple interactions in understanding the behavior of plasmas underlines the validity of describing plasma as the fourth state of matter. The status of a molecule in the progression solid, liquid, gas is one of increasing independence of motion. In fact in a gas the molecules describe rectilinear paths except for occasional collisions with other particles or the walls of the container. In contrast, particles in the plasma state are constrained by multiple interactions which result from the Coulomb force.

However binary collisions adequately describe plasma phenomena in the case of weakly ionized plasmas. In fact the term *weakly ionized plasma* will be taken to mean a plasma in which multiple interactions can be ignored. Binary collisions are also important in describing the transition of a material from the gas to the plasma state. This topic is treated in Chapter 15.

In the topics of plasma formation and weakly ionized plasmas the electrons tend to dominate the situation. Their low inertia results in a quick response to the influence of electric and magnetic fields. When we classify binary collisions into various types we find that we are mostly concerned with the phenomena caused by the versatile electron.

There are two broad classes of binary collisions—elastic, in which the laws of conservation of mass, momentum, and energy can be applied to the motions of the particles before and after collision, and inelastic, where the internal energy of one or both of the particles is changed by the collision. The inelastic collisions are of particular importance to the subject of plasma formation and are discussed in Chapter 15. The present chapter treats the subject of elastic binary collisions.

We begin by defining some terms used to describe the general features of a system of colliding particles. The fact that collisions occur is a consequence of the finite size of the particles, and this is expressed quantitatively by the magnitude of the *cross section* of the particle. Between collisions the particles are considered to move in free flight, and the distance traveled between collisions is called the *free path*. With an ensemble of particles present, the length of the free path varies in a statistical manner, and it is convenient to introduce the concept of a *mean free path*. The mean free path is known if the cross section and the number density of the particles is known. In addition it is important to know the rate at which collisions occur. The *collision frequency* depends upon the length of the mean free path and the velocity of the particles. Just as there is a distribution of the lengths of the free paths, so also is there a distribution in the velocities of the particles, but discussion of this topic must wait until the next chapter.

We next consider the case of a single binary collision and determine what information can be obtained by applying the laws of conservation of momentum and energy. At this stage the details of the collision (that is, the exact trajectories of the particles) are ignored and only the initial and final velocities of the particles are used.

The details of the collision are treated in Section 4.3. The general three-dimensional collision problem is shown to reduce to a simpler two-dimensional problem when referred to the center-of-mass coordinate system. The problem is then further reduced to that of a single particle moving in a spherically symmetric potential field. The distance of closest approach and the angle of deflection are calculated.

We return to the discussion of cross sections in Section 4.4. We are now able to calculate the magnitude of the cross section from a knowledge of the scattering caused by binary collisions. We consider the case of the hard sphere model of a particle and the important case of scattering in a Coulomb field. The cross section for momentum transfer is defined.

Exercise 4.0.1   Do some private reading and learn the significance of the terms *polar molecules*, *induced dipoles*, *van der Waals attraction of nonpolar molecules*, and *valence repulsion field*, in the description of interparticle forces.

4.I CROSS SECTION, MEAN FREE PATH, AND COLLISION FREQUENCY

The concept of a cross section enables us to describe and compare the various types of encounters between particles. In this chapter we are principally concerned with encounters in which particles are elastically scattered. However we will also need to describe encounters that lead to molecular excitation, ionization, recombination, and nuclear fusion, for example. With this in mind we may think of a molecule as representing a sphere of interaction. If another particle enters this sphere, the reaction which we are describing takes place. The cross section can then be interpreted as the cross-sectional area of the sphere of interaction for the encounter of interest. It must be borne in mind that the concept of cross section is used as a measure of the probability of a given type of interaction and that there is no fixed cross section for a molecule, which exists independently of interaction phenomena.

The cross section depends upon the type of impinging particle as well as the target particle. It is a function of the relative velocity of the particles and it varies over many orders of magnitude according to the specific interaction being considered.

If the molecules of a gas are considered to be hard spheres, then a collision is a precise event. In itself the collision takes up negligible time, and the molecules spend their time in free flight between collisions. The collision frequency ν, depends upon the relative speed of the two molecules g, the number density of the molecules N, and the molecular cross section Q.

Although in fact the molecules are not hard spheres, their behavior in elastic collisions approximates the behavior of hard spheres sufficiently closely for the kinetic theory to have had considerable success in predicting and describing gaseous phenomena. In discussing plasma problems, we will expect to be able to use these concepts with good success in the case of electron-neutral particle collisions. However we can expect difficulties to arise when particle interactions are governed by Coulomb forces. In this case a charged particle may never be in a state of free flight between collisions— other charged particles are always influencing its trajectory. The description of plasma phenomena based on a binary collision model of particle interactions will then need modification. We point out the problem when it arises in Sections 4.3 and 4.4 and indicate a solution insofar as the calculation of the cross section is concerned. Fuller discussion of charged particle interactions is given in Chapter 9.

The basic relationships between the cross section, mean free path, and collision frequency can be obtained from the following elementary arguments.

Consider a molecule moving with a speed g. If the cross section for interaction of this molecule with fixed scatterers is Q, then in a unit time the molecule can be thought of as sweeping through a volume gQ. If the number density of the scatterers within this volume of interaction is N, then the number of interactions which take place in a unit time is NgQ. This is just the collision frequency ν, so we can write

$$\nu = gQN \qquad [4.1]$$

Now the average length of the free path between collisions will equal the distance traveled per unit time g divided by the number of collisions which have occurred ν, so we have that the mean free path L is given by

$$L = \frac{g}{\nu} = \frac{1}{QN} \qquad [4.2]$$

Equations [4.1] and [4.2] relate the terms *cross section*, *mean free path*, and *collision frequency*. Because they depend upon the relative velocity of the particles which are in collision, they cannot properly be used to describe phenomena where there is a distribution of particle velocities, unless they are first used in an expression which is then integrated over the particle velocities.

4.11   THE DISTRIBUTION OF FREE PATHS

In the last section we defined the mean free path L as the average distance traveled between collisions. Now some free paths will be shorter than L, while others are longer. In this section we seek to determine the manner in which the free paths are distributed.

Let $p(l)$ be the probability that a molecule with a speed g shall describe a free path at least equal to l, so that $p(0) = 1$. Since ν/g is the number of collisions per unit time ν divided by the average distance traveled per unit time g, it is therefore equal to the number of collisions per unit distance that a molecule will experience, on the average. The probability of a collision occurring during the distance dl is then $\nu\, dl/g$ or, from [4.2], dl/L.

If dl/L is the probability of a collision occurring during dl, then the probability of a collision not occurring during dl is $1 - dl/L$. Now the probability that a molecule will describe a free path of at least $l + dl$ is equal to the probability that it will describe a free path of at least l times the probability that it will then travel a distance dl without a collision. That is,

$$p(l + dl) = p(l)\left(1 - \frac{dl}{L}\right) \qquad [4.3]$$

Expanding the left-hand side gives

$$p(l) + \frac{\partial p(l)}{\partial l}\, dl = p(l) - \frac{p(l)}{L}\, dl$$

from which

$$\frac{dp(l)}{p(l)} = -\frac{dl}{L}$$

whence

$$\ln p(l) = -\frac{l}{L} + \text{const}$$

The constant of integration is zero because $p(0) = 1$. Therefore

$$p(l) = e^{-l/L} \qquad\qquad [4.4]$$

Equation [4.4] gives the distribution of free paths. Thus, if M molecules start out from a collision, $Me^{-l/L}$ will survive a distance l without undergoing a collision. The quantity $p(l)$ is plotted in Figure 4.1.

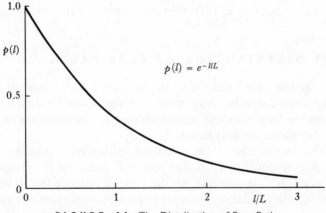

F I G U R E   4.1   The Distribution of Free Paths

Exercise 4.11.1   What proportion of the molecular population has a free path greater than $10L$?

Exercise 4.11.2   Let $p(t)$ be the probability that a molecule will travel for at least a time t without experiencing a collision. By arguments similar to those used in Section 4.11 to obtain equation [4.4] for $p(l)$, show that

$$p(t) = e^{-\nu t} = e^{-t/\tau}$$

where ν is the collision frequency and τ is the *mean time between collisions*.

4.2 BINARY COLLISIONS
AND THE CONSERVATION LAWS

In this section we consider two molecules A and B with masses m^A and m^B, respectively. If we let

$$m^0 = m^A + m^B, \quad M^A = \frac{m^A}{m^0}, \quad \text{and} \quad M^B = \frac{m^B}{m^0} \qquad [4.5]$$

then

$$M^A + M^B = 1 \qquad [4.6]$$

We will be concerned only with the initial and final velocities of the two colliding molecules. Let

v_i^A = velocity of molecule A before collision

v_i^B = velocity of molecule B before collision

$\tilde{v}_i^A$ = velocity of molecule A after collision

$\tilde{v}_i^B$ = velocity of molecule B after collision

g_i^{AB} = initial velocity of A relative to B

$\tilde{g}_i^{AB}$ = final velocity of A relative to B

g_i^{BA} = initial velocity of B relative to A

$\tilde{g}_i^{BA}$ = final velocity of B relative to A

that is

$$g_i^{AB} = v_i^A - v_i^B = -g_i^{BA}$$
$$\tilde{g}_i^{AB} = \tilde{v}_i^A - \tilde{v}_i^B = -\tilde{g}_i^{BA}$$

We will denote the magnitude of the relative velocities as

$$|g_i^{AB}| = |g_i^{BA}| = (g_i^{AB} g_i^{AB})^{1/2} = g$$

and

$$|\tilde{g}_i^{AB}| = |\tilde{g}_i^{BA}| = (\tilde{g}_i^{AB} \tilde{g}_i^{AB})^{1/2} = \tilde{g}$$

Now the conservation of energy and momentum may be expressed as follows:

$$\tfrac{1}{2}m^A v_i^A v_i^A + \tfrac{1}{2}m^B v_i^B v_i^B = \tfrac{1}{2}m^A \tilde{v}_i^A \tilde{v}_i^A + \tfrac{1}{2}m^B \tilde{v}_i^B \tilde{v}_i^B \qquad [4.7]$$

$$m^A v_i^A + m^B v_i^B = m^A \tilde{v}_i^A + m^B \tilde{v}_i^B \qquad [4.8]$$

The *center-of-mass* of the two molecules A and B is defined as that point about which the sum of the mass-moments of the two molecules is zero. Thus

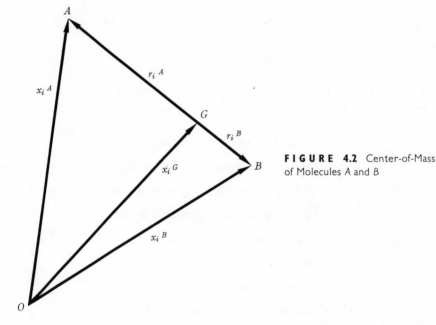

FIGURE 4.2 Center-of-Mass of Molecules A and B

if the center-of-mass G is located at the position x_i^G while molecules A and B are located at positions x_i^A and x_i^B, then we have, referring to Figure 4.2, that

$$m^A r_i^A + m^B r_i^B = 0$$

$$m^A(x_i^A - x_i^G) + m^B(x_i^B - x_i^G) = 0$$

$$m^A x_i^A + m^B x_i^B = m^0 x_i^G \qquad [4.9]$$

where we have used [4.5] in the last step. If we differentiate [4.9] with respect to time and denote the *velocity of the center-of-mass* by v_i^G, then we obtain

$$m^A v_i^A + m^B v_i^B = m^0 v_i^G \qquad [4.10]$$

The velocities of molecules A and B before and after a collision can be expressed in terms of their relative velocity and the velocity of the center-of-mass as follows. Since the total momentum of the two molecules is conserved, we see from [4.10] that the velocity of the center of mass v_i^G is a constant. Substituting $v_i^A - g_i^{AB}$ for v_i^B in [4.10], and using [4.5] gives

$$M^A v_i^A + M^B v_i^A - M^B g_i^{AB} = v_i^G$$

from which we obtain, using [4.6],

$$v_i^A = v_i^G + M^B g_i^{AB} \qquad [4.11]$$

Substituting $v_i^B - g_i^{BA}$ for v_i^A in [4.10], as before, gives

$$M^A v_i^B - M^A g_i^{BA} + M^B v_i^B = v_i^G$$

from which

$$v_i^B = v_i^G + M^A g_i^{BA} \qquad [4.12]$$

From the conservation of momentum [4.8] and [4.10] we see that

$$m^A \tilde{v}_i^A + m^B \tilde{v}_i^B = m^0 v_i^G \qquad [4.13]$$

and substituting for $\tilde{v}_i^A$ and $\tilde{v}_i^B$ in a similar manner to the above we find that

$$\tilde{v}_i^A = v_i^G + M^B \tilde{g}_i^{AB} \qquad [4.14]$$

and

$$\tilde{v}_i^B = v_i^G + M^A \tilde{g}_i^{BA} \qquad [4.15]$$

Equations [4.11], [4.12], [4.14], and [4.15] express the velocities of molecules A and B before and after a collision in terms of the velocity of the center-of-mass and the relative velocities of the two molecules.

If we substitute these equations into the expression for the conservation of energy [4.7], and if we write $v_i^G v_i^G$ as G^2, then the left-hand side of [4.7] will become

$$\tfrac{1}{2} m^A (v_i^G + M^B g_i^{AB})(v_i^G + M^B g_i^{AB}) + \tfrac{1}{2} m^B (v_i^G + M^A g_i^{BA})(v_i^G + M^A g_i^{BA})$$

$$= \tfrac{1}{2}(m^A G^2 + 2 m^A M^B g_i^{AB} v_i^G + m^A M^B M^B g^2 + m^B G^2 + 2 m^B M^A g_i^{BA} v_i^G$$
$$+ m^B M^A M^A g^2)$$

$$= \frac{1}{2}\left[(m^A + m^B)G^2 + \frac{m^A m^B}{(m^0)^2}(m^B + m^A)g^2\right] = \frac{1}{2} m^0 (G^2 + M^A M^B g^2)$$

Similarly the right-hand side of [4.7] becomes $\frac{1}{2}m^0(G^2 + M^A M^B \tilde{g}^2)$ so that $\frac{1}{2}m^0(G^2 + M^A M^B g^2) = \frac{1}{2}m^0(G^2 + M^A M^B \tilde{g}^2)$ from which

$$g = \tilde{g} \tag{4.16}$$

Thus the magnitude of the relative velocities is unchanged by an elastic collision.

4.21 REPRESENTATION
OF A COLLISION IN VELOCITY SPACE

Several important results can be readily obtained if we represent the collision by a diagram in what is called *velocity space*. This is simply a three-dimensional space in which v_i are the three components of velocity referred to a right-handed coordinate system.

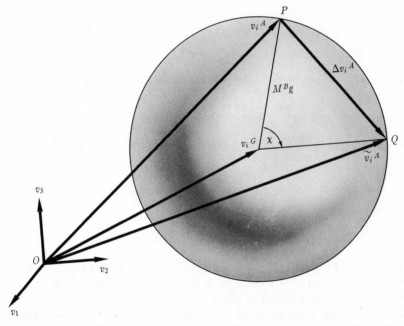

FIGURE 4.3 The Collision Sphere in Velocity Space

From [4.11], [4.12], [4.14], and [4.15] we see that the four velocity vectors v_i^A, v_i^B, $\tilde{v}_i^A$, $\tilde{v}_i^B$ are each the sum of two other vectors, and in each case one of these vectors is v_i^G, the constant velocity of the center-of-mass of the two colliding molecules. Now from [4.11] and [4.14] we see that a collision causes the velocity of molecule A to change from $v_i^G + M^B g_i^{AB}$ to $v_i^G + M^B \tilde{g}_i^{AB}$. Since, from [4.16], $g = \tilde{g}$, then the magnitude of $M^B g_i^{AB}$ is equal to the magnitude of $M^B \tilde{g}_i^{AB}$. We therefore conclude from [4.11] and [4.14] that v_i^A and $\tilde{v}_i^A$ lie on a sphere in velocity space which has its center at v_i^G and a radius equal to $|M^B g_i^{AB}| = |M^B \tilde{g}_i^{AB}| = M^B g$. Such a sphere is shown in Figure 4.3. In this figure χ is the angle between the initial and final velocity of molecule A relative to the center-of-mass and is thus the *deflection angle in the center-of-mass coordinate system*.

In a similar manner, from [4.12] and [4.15] we see that v_i^B and $\tilde{v}_i^B$ lie on a sphere in velocity space with center at v_i^G and with radius equal to $|M^A g_i^{BA}| = |M^A \tilde{g}_i^{BA}| = M^A g$. If the mass of molecule A is less than that of molecule B, then $M^A < M^B$, and the radius of the second sphere containing v_i^B and $\tilde{v}_i^B$ will be less than the radius of the sphere containing v_i^A and $\tilde{v}_i^A$. Using the facts that $g_i^{AB} = -g_i^{BA}$ and $\tilde{g}_i^{AB} = -\tilde{g}_i^{BA}$, we can draw both spheres in the same diagram as shown in Figure 4.4.

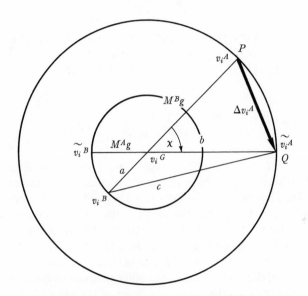

FIGURE 4.4 Geometry of a Binary Collision

Fractional Energy Loss of a Colliding Molecule   The energy lost by a molecule colliding with a second molecule initially at rest can readily be found from Figure 4.4. Referring to the triangle in the figure with sides a, b, and c, we may write the law of cosines as $c^2 = a^2 + b^2 - 2ab \cos(\pi - \chi)$ which becomes

$$(\tilde{v}_i^A - v_i^B)^2 = (M^A g)^2 + (M^B g)^2 + 2M^A M^B g^2 \cos \chi$$

Completing the square and using [4.6] we obtain

$$(\tilde{v}_i^A - v_i^B)^2 = g^2 - 2M^A M^B g^2 (1 - \cos \chi) \qquad [4.17]$$

If we assume that molecule B is initially at rest, then $v_i^B = 0$. That is, the origin is taken to be at v_i^B in Figure 4.4. For this case $v_i^A = g_i^{AB} = -g_i^{BA}$, or $v_i^A v_i^A = g^2$. Therefore, [4.17] becomes, for this case,

$$\tilde{v}_i^A \tilde{v}_i^A = v_i^A v_i^A - 2M^A M^B v_i^A v_i^A (1 - \cos \chi) \qquad [4.18]$$

The kinetic energy of molecule A before collision, K^A, is

$$K^A = \tfrac{1}{2} m^A v_i^A v_i^A \qquad [4.19]$$

while the kinetic energy of molecule A after collision, $\tilde{K}^A$ is

$$\tilde{K}^A = \tfrac{1}{2} m^A \tilde{v}_i^A \tilde{v}_i^A \qquad [4.20]$$

If we now multiply [4.18] by $m^A/2$ and use [4.19] and [4.20], we obtain $\tilde{K}^A = K^A - K^A 2M^A M^B (1 - \cos \chi)$ from which the fractional energy loss of molecule A is $\Delta K^A / K^A = (K^A - \tilde{K}^A)/K^A = 2M^A M^B (1 - \cos \chi)$ which is, using [4.5],

$$\frac{\Delta K^A}{K^A} = \frac{2m^A m^B}{(m^A + m^B)^2} (1 - \cos \chi) \qquad [4.21]$$

For the case of an electron (molecule A) colliding with a heavier neutral particle (molecule B) we have $m^A \ll m^B$, so that the fractional energy loss given by [4.21] is very much less than unity. The small amount of energy lost by the electron goes into the recoil of the heavier neutral particle.

If an electric field is applied to a plasma, the electrons will gain energy between collisions. Since they lose only a small fraction of this energy in collisions with heavier particles, we anticipate that the temperature of the electron gas will rise above that of the other plasma constituents. An example of this phenomenon is the positive column of the glow discharge where the temperature of the electron gas is typically 20,000 °K while the temperatures of the positive ion and neutral particle gases rise only a few hundred degrees above room temperature.

The fact that an electron loses only a small fraction of its energy in each collision with a neutral atom or molecule means that the electron gas of the plasma is loosely coupled to the neutral particle gas. In this context the phrase, loosely coupled, has a thermodynamic meaning. A difference in temperature between the electron gas and the neutral particle gas means that the average energy of the electrons is different from the average energy of the neutral particles. Equalization of the temperature or energy comes about solely through the agency of collisions. The small energy exchange per electron-neutral particle collision therefore means that temperature differences relax relatively slowly.

Example   Calculate the change in velocity Δv_i^A of molecule A due to a collision with molecule B. Write the components of Δv_i^A in a local center-of-mass coordinate system. Now $\Delta v_i^A = \tilde{v}_i^A - v_i^A$, as shown in Figure 4.3. Introduce a local Cartesian coordinate system, $v_i^G v_1' v_2' v_3'$ centered at v_i^G with the v_1'-axis oriented in the direction of the initial relative velocities of the two

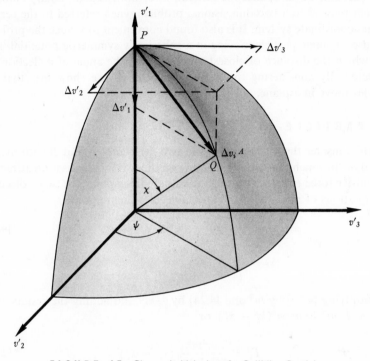

FIGURE 4.5   Change in Velocity of a Colliding Particle

molecules as shown in Figure 4.5. From this figure we can read off the three components of Δv_i in the center-of-mass coordinate system as

$$\Delta v_1' = M^B g(1 - \cos \chi) = 2 M^B g \sin^2 (\chi/2)$$
$$\Delta v_2' = M^B g \sin \chi \cos \psi \qquad\qquad [4.22]$$
$$\Delta v_3' = M^B g \sin \chi \sin \psi$$

Exercise 4.21.1   Consider a collision between molecules A and B in which molecule B is initially at rest. The deflection angle in the center-of-mass coordinate system is denoted by χ and is shown in Figure 4.3. In this figure, locate the *angle of deflection*, ξ, *in the laboratory coordinate system* (that is, the angle by which molecule A is deflected as measured by an observer at rest) and show that $\tan \xi = \sin \chi/(\cos \chi + m^A/m^B)$.

4.3 THE DYNAMICS
OF A BINARY COLLISION

In this section we show that the general, three-dimensional, binary collision problem reduces to a two-dimensional problem when referred to the center-of-mass coordinate system. It is also found convenient to reduce the problem to that of a single particle moving in a spherically symmetric potential field, from which the distance of closest approach and the angle of deflection are calculated. By considering the particle trajectories, we show first that the particles move in a plane.

4.31 PARTICLE TRAJECTORIES

We will consider the collision between two molecules A and B with masses m^A and m^B in which the only force acting on the two molecules is an attractive or repulsive force F_i directed along the straight line joining the two molecules. The equations of motion for the two molecules then become

$$F_i^A = m^A \ddot{x}_i^A \qquad [4.23]$$

and

$$F_i^B = -F_i^A = m^B \ddot{x}_i^B \qquad [4.24]$$

Multiplying [4.23] by m^B and [4.24] by $-m^A$ and adding the results gives $F_i^A m^B + F_i^A m^A = m^A m^B (\ddot{x}_i^A - \ddot{x}_i^B)$, or

$$F_i^A = \frac{m^A m^B}{m^A + m^B} (\ddot{x}_i^A - \ddot{x}_i^B) \qquad [4.25]$$

We define the *reduced mass m'* by

$$m' = \frac{m^A m^B}{m^A + m^B} \qquad [4.26]$$

and the relative displacement x_i^{AB} by

$$x_i^{AB} = x_i^A - x_i^B \qquad [4.27]$$

Note that

$$\frac{d}{dt}(x_i^{AB}) = \dot{x}_i^A - \dot{x}_i^B = g_i^{AB} \qquad [4.28]$$

Using [4.26] and [4.27] in [4.25] gives

$$F_i^A = m' \ddot{x}_i^{AB} = m' \frac{d}{dt} g_i^{AB} \qquad [4.29]$$

Thus the motion of the molecules is equivalent to the motion of a single mass m' moving with velocity g_i^{AB} under the same force F_i^A which was acting on molecule A. This equivalence will be demonstrated graphically in Section 4.33.

Let us form the vector or cross product of x_j^{AB} with F_k^A given by [4.29]. We obtain

$$\epsilon_{ijk}x_j^{AB}F_k^A = m'\epsilon_{ijk}x_j^{AB}\ddot{x}_k^{AB} = 0 \qquad [4.30]$$

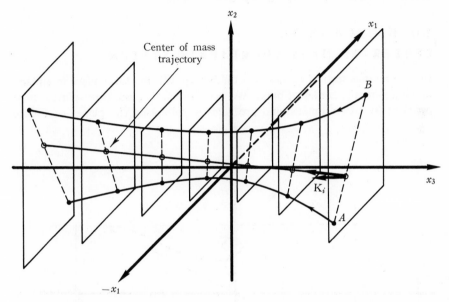

FIGURE 4.6   Particle Trajectories and the Plane of the Center-of-Mass

where the last equality applies because the force F_k^A is directed along the line of centers so that x_j^{AB} and F_k^A are in the same direction (that is $j = k$). Expanding [4.30] gives

$$m'\epsilon_{ijk}x_j^{AB}\ddot{x}_k^{AB} = m'\epsilon_{ijk}\left[\frac{d}{dt}(x_j^{AB}\dot{x}_k^{AB}) - \dot{x}_j^{AB}\dot{x}_k^{AB}\right] = 0 \qquad [4.31]$$

The second term in the brackets is identically zero since the j and k can be interchanged (this is the cross product of a vector with itself.) Since $\dot{x}_k^{AB} = g_k^{AB}$, [4.31] shows that

$$\epsilon_{ijk}\frac{d}{dt}(x_j^{AB}g_k^{AB}) = \frac{d}{dt}\epsilon_{ijk}x_j^{AB}g_k^{AB} = 0 \qquad [4.32]$$

Integrating [4.32] yields

$$\epsilon_{ijk}x_j^{AB}g_k^{AB} = K_i = \text{a constant vector} \tag{4.33}$$

Equation [4.33] states that the vector product of x_j^{AB} and g_k^{AB} is a constant. Thus the particles always lie in a plane perpendicular to K_i. The center-of-mass also lies in this plane and moves with the constant velocity v_i^G (see Section 4.2). Thus both particles can always be found in a plane normal to K_i which moves with the velocity v_i^G. This situation is depicted in Figure 4.6 where the vector K_i is directed along the negative x_3-axis.

4.32 MOTION IN THE CENTER-OF-MASS COORDINATE SYSTEM

In the previous section we saw that the binary collision takes place in a plane moving with the center-of-mass. We can thus reduce the three-dimensional problem to a two-dimensional problem by collapsing the planes of Figure

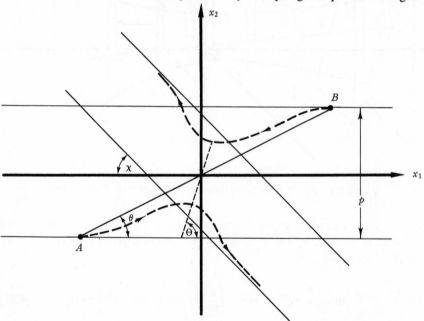

FIGURE 4.7   Particle Trajectories in the Center-of-Mass Coordinate System

4.6. We will collapse them along the line containing the center-of-mass. That is, the center-of-mass is at the origin in the x_1-x_2 plane and the trajectories of the particles will be as shown in Figure 4.7.

In this figure the collision is referred to the center-of-mass coordinate system. The angle χ is the deflection angle in this system and is the same as that in Figure 4.4. The *impact parameter p* shown in Figure 4.7 is defined as the minimum distance at which molecule A would pass by molecule B if the two molecules did not interact. Note that in the center-of-mass coordinate system the velocities of the two molecules are, at each instant, directed along antiparallel lines (see Exercise 4.32.1).

Now in Figure 4.7 the position of molecule A is given by x_i^A and the position of molecule B is given by x_i^B. Since the center-of-mass is located at the origin, we have, from [4.9], $m^A x_i^A + m^B x_i^B = 0$ so that $x_i^B = -(m^A/m^B)x_i^A$ and $x_i^A = -(m^B/m^A)x_i^B$. Using these values for x_i^B and x_i^A successively in [4.27] we obtain

$$x_i^A = \frac{m'}{m^A} x_i^{AB} \quad \text{and} \quad x_i^B = -\frac{m'}{m^B} x_i^{AB} \qquad [4.34]$$

Let us now calculate the total kinetic energy K of the two-particle system shown in Figure 4.7. We thus have

$$K = \tfrac{1}{2} m^A \dot{x}_i^A \dot{x}_i^A + \tfrac{1}{2} m^B \dot{x}_i^B \dot{x}_i^B \qquad [4.35]$$

Differentiating [4.34] and substituting into [4.35] gives

$$K = \tfrac{1}{2} m' \dot{x}_i^{AB} \dot{x}_i^{AB} \left(\frac{m'}{m^A} + \frac{m'}{m^B} \right) = \tfrac{1}{2} m' \dot{x}_i^{AB} \dot{x}_i^{AB} \qquad [4.36]$$

From [4.36] it is clear that the kinetic energy of the two-particle system is the same as the kinetic energy of a single particle of mass m' whose position about a fixed center is given by the relative displacement x_i^{AB}. A similar equivalence between the angular momentum of a two-particle and a one-particle system can be shown to exist (see Exercise 4.32.2). This dynamical equivalence between a two-particle system and a one-particle system will be used in the following section where the binary collision will be treated in terms of the equivalent one-body problem.

Exercise 4.32.1 Using the results of Section 4.2, show that the velocities of molecules A and B are always directed along antiparallel lines in the center-of-mass coordinate system. Calculate the momenta of the two molecules in this coordinate system.

Exercise 4.32.2 Show that the total angular momentum of the two-particle system shown in Figure 4.7 can be written as $\gamma_3 = m'(x_1^{AB} \dot{x}_2^{AB} - x_2^{AB} \dot{x}_1^{AB})$. NOTE: The angular momentum is defined as $\gamma_i = m\epsilon_{ijk} x_j v_k$.

4.33 MOTION IN A
SPHERICALLY SYMMETRIC POTENTIAL FIELD

In the previous section we determined that the binary collision is dynamically equivalent to the motion of a single particle of reduced mass m' moving about a fixed center of force. Its distance from this center can be written as

$$r = (x_i^{AB} x_i^{AB})^{1/2} \qquad [4.37]$$

It is convenient to write the equations describing the motion of this particle in terms of the polar coordinates r and θ shown in Figure 4.8, where

$$x_1^{AB} = r \cos \theta \quad \text{and} \quad x_2^{AB} = r \sin \theta \qquad [4.38]$$

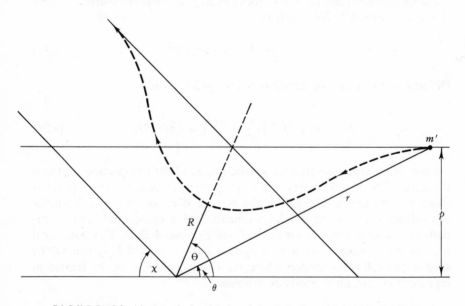

FIGURE 4.8 Motion of a Particle in a Spherically Symmetric Potential Field

The kinetic energy of this particle is, from [4.36], in the center-of-mass coordinate system,

$$K = \tfrac{1}{2}m' \dot{x}_i^{AB} \dot{x}_i^{AB} = \tfrac{1}{2}m'[(\dot{x}_1^{AB})^2 + (\dot{x}_2^{AB})^2] \qquad [4.39]$$

Differentiating [4.38] and substituting into [4.39] gives

$$K = \tfrac{1}{2}m'(\dot{r}^2 + r^2 \dot{\theta}^2) \qquad [4.40]$$

Similarly, if we substitute [4.38] into the result of Exercise 4.32.2, we obtain for the angular momentum,

$$\gamma_3 = m'r^2\dot{\theta} \qquad [4.41]$$

The next step is to use the conservation laws of energy and angular momentum. These laws can be deduced from Newton's laws of motion (see Exercise 4.33.1). They state that the energy and angular momentum are conserved—that is, that they remain constant throughout the motion of the particles.

The total energy of the particle is the sum of the kinetic energy given by [4.40] and the *potential energy of interaction* $\Phi(r)$ which results from the force of interaction $F(r)$ between the two molecules. The potential energy function and the force function are related by $\Phi(r) = \int_r^\infty F(r)\,dr$ and $F(r) = -d\Phi/dr$, where Φ is in units of energy (eV, for example).

A sufficiently long time before the collision the interaction potential will be zero and the total energy will be the relative kinetic energy given by $\frac{1}{2}m'g^2$, where g is the initial relative velocity. Since the total energy is conserved, we equate this to the total energy during the collision and obtain

$$\tfrac{1}{2}m'g^2 = \tfrac{1}{2}m'(\dot{r}^2 + r^2\dot{\theta}^2) + \Phi(r) \qquad [4.42]$$

Similarly a sufficiently long time before the collision the angular momentum is given by

$$\gamma_3 = m'pg \qquad [4.43]$$

where p is the impact parameter. Since the angular momentum is conserved, we equate [4.41] and [4.43] and obtain

$$m'r^2\dot{\theta} = m'pg \qquad [4.44]$$

We can eliminate θ in [4.42] by using [4.44]. This gives

$$\tfrac{1}{2}m'g^2 = \tfrac{1}{2}m'\dot{r}^2 + \tfrac{1}{2}m'g^2\left(\frac{p^2}{r^2}\right) + \Phi(r) \qquad [4.45]$$

From [4.45] we see that our original three-dimensional binary collision problem has been reduced to a one-dimensional problem of a single particle of mass m' with total energy $\frac{1}{2}m'g^2$ moving in an effective potential energy field given by

$$\Phi_{\text{eff}}(r) = \Phi(r) + \tfrac{1}{2}m'g^2\left(\frac{p^2}{r^2}\right) \qquad [4.46]$$

The last term of [4.46] is called the *centrifugal potential*.

Distance of Closest Approach   When the particle of mass m' approaches closest to the center of force in Figure 4.8 the values of r and θ are denoted by R and Θ. The condition for closest approach is $dr/d\theta = 0$. Since $dr/d\theta = \dot{r}/\dot{\theta}$ and since $\dot{\theta}$ cannot be infinite, we can also write the condition for closest approach as $\dot{r} = 0$. Using this condition, [4.45] shows that the point of closest approach corresponds to the turning point in the one-dimensional model, occurring when the effective potential energy is equal to the total energy, and is found from the equation

$$1 = \frac{p^2}{R^2} + \frac{\Phi(R)}{\frac{1}{2}m'g^2} \qquad [4.47]$$

For any given potential function $\Phi(r)$, [4.47] can be used to find the distance of closest approach R.

Exercise 4.33.1

(a) Show that the radial and transverse components of acceleration of the particle in Figure 4.8 are given respectively by

$$a_r = \ddot{r} - r\dot{\theta}^2 \quad \text{and} \quad a_\theta = 2\dot{r}\dot{\theta} + r\ddot{\theta}$$

(b) Since the particle is under the influence of a central force $F(r)$, the equations of motion can be written $m'a_r = F(r)$ and $m'a_\theta = 0$. Differentiate [4.41] with respect to time and show that $\dot{\gamma}_3 = 0$. This result shows that the angular momentum remains unchanged throughout the motion.

(c) Show that the equation $m'a_r = F(r)$ obtained in part (b) above, can be written $m'\ddot{r} = -d\Phi_{\text{eff}}/dr$.

(d) Obtain the energy conservation law [4.42] by multiplying the equation obtained in part (c) by $\dot{r}$ and integrating with respect to time.

Exercise 4.33.2

(a) Sketch plots of Φ_{eff} for the case when, (i) $\Phi(r) = A/r$ (repulsive force), (ii) $\Phi(r) = -A/r$ (attractive force).

(b) How does the kinetic energy of the particle with reduced mass m' vary as a function of r for each of the above cases?

Exercise 4.33.3   Find the distance of closest approach for a Coulomb potential function $\Phi(r) = q^A q^B/(4\pi\epsilon_0 r)$. Show that if the impact parameter is zero, the distance of closest approach R_0 is given by $R_0 = 2p_c$, where $p_c = q^A q^B/(4\pi\epsilon_0 m'g^2)$. Find the distance of closest approach when the impact parameter is equal to p_c.

4.34 THE ANGLE OF DEFLECTION

From Figure 4.8 the angle of deflection χ is given by $\chi = \pi - 2\Theta$, where Θ is the value of θ when $r = R$. We wish to express χ in terms of the impact parameter p and the initial relative velocity g. From [4.45] we have

$$\dot{r} = \pm g \left(1 - \frac{p^2}{r^2} - \frac{\Phi(r)}{\frac{1}{2}m'g^2}\right)^{1/2}$$ [4.48]

and from [4.44]

$$\dot{\theta} = \frac{pg}{r^2}$$ [4.49]

Substituting [4.48] and [4.49] into the equation $dr/d\theta = \dot{r}/\dot{\theta}$, we obtain

$$\frac{dr}{d\theta} = -\frac{r^2}{p}\left(1 - \frac{p^2}{r^2} - \frac{\Phi(r)}{\frac{1}{2}m'g^2}\right)^{1/2}$$ [4.50]

where the negative sign was chosen since r decreases as θ increases for an incoming trajectory. Solving [4.50] for $d\theta$ gives

$$d\theta = -\frac{(p/r^2)\,dr}{\left(1 - \frac{p^2}{r^2} - \frac{\Phi(r)}{\frac{1}{2}m'g^2}\right)^{1/2}}$$

from which

$$\Theta = \int_0^{\Theta} d\theta = -\int_{\infty}^{R} \frac{(p/r^2)\,dr}{\left(1 - \frac{p^2}{r^2} - \frac{\Phi(r)}{\frac{1}{2}m'g^2}\right)^{1/2}}$$

so that the angle of deflection is given by

$$\chi(p, g) = \pi - 2p \int_{R}^{\infty} \frac{dr/r^2}{\left(1 - \frac{p^2}{r^2} - \frac{\Phi(r)}{\frac{1}{2}m'g^2}\right)^{1/2}}$$ [4.51]

where R is determined from [4.47].

The Angle of Deflection in a Coulomb Potential Field As an example of the use of [4.51] in determining the deflection angle in terms of the impact parameter and the initial relative velocity, we consider the important case of the Coulomb potential function $\Phi(r) = q^A q^B/(4\pi\epsilon_0 r)$. Substituting in [4.51], the deflection angle is given by

$$\chi(p, g) = \pi - 2p \int_{R}^{\infty} \frac{dr/r^2}{\left(1 - \frac{p^2}{r^2} - \frac{2q^A q^B}{m'g^2 r 4\pi\epsilon_0}\right)^{1/2}}$$

Making the change of variables $u = 1/r$ and inserting the value for p_c given in Exercise 4.33.3, we obtain

$$\chi(p, g) = \pi - 2p \int_0^U \frac{du}{(1 - 2p_c u - p^2 u^2)^{1/2}} \qquad [4.52]$$

where U is the value of u which makes the denominator in the integrand zero (see Equation [4.47]). Setting this denominator equal to zero, we can readily show that U must satisfy the equation

$$p^2 U + p_c = (p_c + p^2)^{1/2} \qquad [4.53]$$

(see Exercise 4.34.2).

Now the integral in [4.52] is of the standard form

$$\int \frac{dx}{(\alpha + \beta x + \gamma x^2)^{1/2}} = \frac{1}{\sqrt{-\gamma}} \sin^{-1} \frac{(-2\gamma x - \beta)}{(\beta^2 - 4\alpha\gamma)^{1/2}}$$

where in our case $\alpha = 1$, $\beta = -2p_c$, and $\gamma = -p^2$. Therefore

$$\int \frac{du}{(1 - 2p_c u - p^2 u^2)^{1/2}} = \frac{1}{p} \sin^{-1} \frac{p^2 u + p_c}{(p_c^2 + p^2)^{1/2}} \qquad [4.54]$$

Applying the limits 0 and U to [4.54] we have, using [4.53],

$$\int_0^U \frac{du}{(1 - 2p_c u - p^2 u^2)^{1/2}} = \frac{1}{p} \left[\frac{\pi}{2} - \sin^{-1} \frac{p_c}{(p_c^2 + p^2)^{1/2}} \right] \qquad [4.55]$$

Substituting [4.55] into [4.52], we find for the deflection angle

$$\chi(p, g) = 2 \sin^{-1} \frac{p_c}{(p_c^2 + p^2)^{1/2}} \qquad [4.56]$$

where $p_c = q^A q^B / (4\pi\epsilon_0 m' g^2)$.

From [4.56] we note the important result that

$$\tan \frac{\chi}{2} = \frac{p_c}{p} \qquad [4.57]$$

We will use this result in deriving the differential cross section for Coulomb scattering in Section 4.4.

Note that p_c is the *value of the impact parameter which will yield a deflection angle of 90°*. It is one half the value of R_0 defined in Exercise 4.33.3. If the signs of the two charged particles are the same, then p_c (and χ) will be positive.

On the other hand, if the charged particles are of opposite sign, then p_c (and χ) will be negative. The situation is shown in Figure 4.9.

Exercise 4.34.1 Obtain an integral expression for the deflection angle $\chi(p, g)$ for the case of a screened Coulomb potential

$$\Phi(r) = \frac{q^A q^B}{4\pi\epsilon_0 r} e^{-r/h} \qquad\qquad [4.58]$$

Exercise 4.34.2 Show that U is given by Equation [4.53].

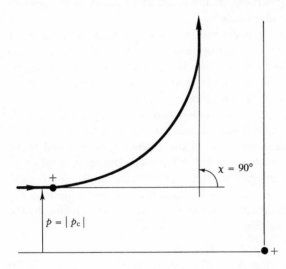

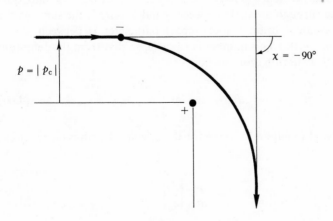

FIGURE 4.9 Deflection Angle for a Coulomb Potential Field

4.4 THE DIFFERENTIAL CROSS SECTION AND THE SCATTERING CROSS SECTION

Cross sections, in general, are related to the probabilities that certain types of collisions will occur. In particular the differential cross section is concerned with the probability that a particle, as the result of an elastic collision, will be scattered by some particular angle.

The differential cross section is defined in terms of a beam of particles of intensity I incident upon a fixed scattering center. As described in the previous sections, the angle of deflection will then be the deflection angle χ in the center-of-mass coordinate system. The intensity I is the number of particles crossing a unit area normally, per unit time.

We define the *differential elastic scattering cross section dQ* as the number of particles scattered into the differential element of solid angle $d\omega$ per unit time, divided by the incident intensity. If the scattering is assumed to be symmetrical about the beam axis, then the differential element of solid angle $d\omega = \sin \chi \, d\chi \, d\psi$ may be integrated over the azimuth angle ψ to yield $d\omega = 2\pi \sin \chi \, d\chi$. The number of particles scattered per unit time into the solid angle between the cones with polar angle χ and $\chi + d\chi$, divided by the unit intensity can then be written

$$dQ = S(\chi) \, d\omega = S(\chi) \, 2\pi \sin \chi \, d\chi \qquad [4.59]$$

where $S(\chi)$ is the *angular distribution function* (it is often referred to in the literature as the *differential scattering cross section*).

Now for a given incident velocity the number of particles per unit time that get scattered through an angle between χ and $\chi + d\chi$ is the same as the number in the incident beam whose impact parameter is between p and $p - dp$. (See Figure 4.10.) This number is $I 2\pi p \, dp$, so that from the definition of the differential scattering cross section,

$$dQ = 2\pi p \, dp \qquad [4.60]$$

Equating [4.59] and [4.60] and solving for the angular distribution function, we obtain

$$S(\chi) = \frac{p}{\sin \chi} \left| \frac{dp}{d\chi} \right| \qquad [4.61]$$

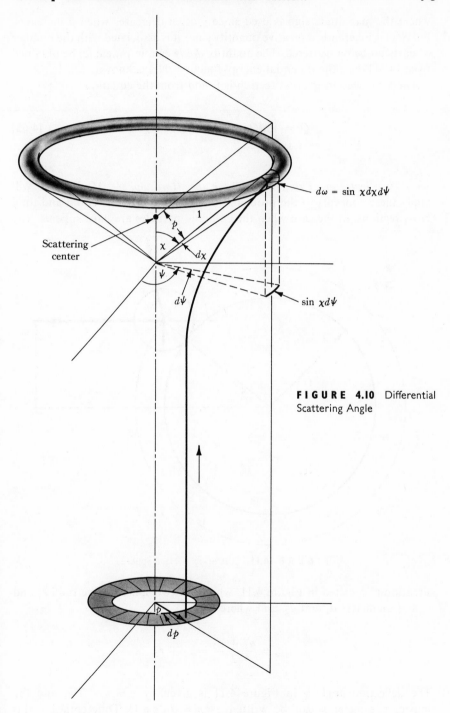

$d\omega = \sin \chi \, d\chi \, d\psi$

Scattering
center

$\sin \chi \, d\psi$

FIGURE 4.10 Differential Scattering Angle

where the magnitude sign is used since χ often decreases when p increases, but $S(\chi)$ is inherently a positive quantity since it is associated with the number of particles being scattered. The quantity $dp/d\chi$ can, in principle, be obtained from [4.51] once the potential energy function $\Phi(r)$ is known.

The total scattering cross section is found from the equation,

$$Q = \int_{\substack{\text{solid angle} \\ \text{of } 4\pi}} dQ = 2\pi \int_0^\pi S(\chi) \sin \chi \, d\chi \qquad [4.62]$$

The Scattering Cross Section for the Hard Sphere Model We will apply these concepts to the problem of calculating the differential and total cross sections, in the case when the colliding particles are hard spheres. The

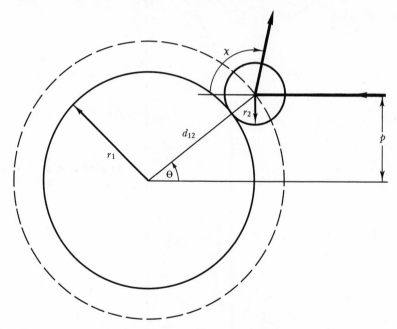

FIGURE 4.11 Scattering of Hard Spheres

situation is depicted in Figure 4.11, where the two spheres have radii r_1 and r_2 and diameters d_1 and d_2, and where

$$d_{12} = \frac{d_1 + d_2}{2} = r_1 + r_2$$

The deflection angle χ in Figure 4.11 is given by $\chi = \pi - 2\Theta$, and the impact parameter p can be written as $p = d_{12} \sin \Theta$. Differentiating this equation, we obtain $dp = d_{12} \cos \Theta \, d\Theta$, so that the product $p \, dp$ can be written

$$p \, dp = d_{12}^2 \sin \Theta \cos \Theta \, d\Theta = \tfrac{1}{2} d_{12}^2 \sin 2\Theta \, d\Theta$$

or

$$p \, dp = -\tfrac{1}{4} d_{12}^2 \sin \chi \, d\chi \qquad [4.63]$$

Substituting the value of $dp/d\chi$ obtained from [4.63] in [4.61], we obtain for the angular distribution function, $S(\chi) = \tfrac{1}{4} d_{12}^2$. Substituting this value into [4.62], we obtain

$$Q = \frac{\pi}{2} \int_0^\pi d_{12}^2 \sin \chi \, d\chi = \pi d_{12}^2$$

Two special cases are of interest. For the case of an electron colliding with a molecule, we can take $d_{12} = r_1 = r$, the radius of the molecule. For this case we obtain $S(\chi) = \tfrac{1}{4} r^2$ and $Q = \pi r^2$.

The second case of interest is that of molecules colliding with themselves. For this case $d_{12} = d_1 = d_2 = D$, the diameter of the colliding molecules. We then obtain $S(\chi) = \tfrac{1}{4} D^2$ and $Q = \pi D^2$.

The Scattering Cross Section in a Coulomb Potential Field   Let us now consider the Coulomb potential function treated in Section 4.34. The deflection angle is related to the impact parameter by [4.57] and is written as

$$\tan \frac{\chi}{2} = \frac{p_c}{p}, \qquad \text{where } p_c = \frac{q^A q^B}{4\pi\epsilon_0 m' g^2}$$

Differentiating yields

$$\frac{d\chi}{2\cos^2(\chi/2)} = -\frac{p_c}{p^2} \, dp$$

from which

$$\left| \frac{dp}{d\chi} \right| = \frac{p^2}{2 p_c \cos^2(\chi/2)}$$

Substituting this value for $dp/d\chi$ in [4.61] gives, for the angular distribution function,

$$S(\chi) = \frac{p^3}{2 p_c \sin \chi \cos^2(\chi/2)} \qquad [4.64]$$

Now we can rewrite the equation $p_c/p = \tan(\chi/2)$ in the form

$$p = p_c \cos(\chi/2)/\sin(\chi/2).$$

Using this in [4.64] together with the fact that $\sin\chi = 2\sin(\chi/2)\cos(\chi/2)$ gives

$$S(\chi) = \frac{p_c^2}{4\sin^4(\chi/2)} \qquad [4.65]$$

Equation [4.65] is the Rutherford scattering formula which, since $\sin^2\chi/2 = \frac{1}{2}(1 - \cos\chi)$, can also be written as

$$S(\chi) = \frac{p_c^2}{(1 - \cos\chi)^2} \qquad [4.66]$$

The total cross section can be found by substituting [4.66] into [4.62] to yield

$$Q = 2\pi p_c^2 \int_0^\pi \frac{\sin\chi\, d\chi}{(1 - \cos\chi)^2}$$

which becomes infinite at the lower limit as can be seen by making the substitution $u = 1 - \cos\chi$. The fact that the total scattering cross section is infinite is due to the long-range effect of the Coulomb potential.

The screened Coulomb potential described in Exercise 4.34.1 eliminates this difficulty. However the differential cross section for this potential function must be calculated numerically.[1]

Exercise 4.4.1   In the previous section $S(\chi)$ was the angular distribution function in the center-of-mass coordinate system. Let $S'(\xi)$ be the angular distribution function in the laboratory coordinate system such that $dQ = S'(\xi)\,2\pi\sin\xi\,d\xi$, where ξ is the deflection angle in the laboratory system. Write $S'(\xi)$ in terms of $S(\chi)$. What does your result reduce to if the masses of the colliding particles are equal? For this case find $S'(\xi)$ when the particles are hard spheres. What is the total cross section in the laboratory system for this case? (HINT: Use the result of Exercise 4.21.1.)

4.41   THE CROSS SECTION
FOR MOMENTUM TRANSFER

The transfer of momentum during a collision will be seen to be the basic microscopic event in the transport phenomena of diffusion and mobility.

[1] E. Everhart, G. Stone, and R. J. Carbone, "Classical Calculation of Differential Cross Section for Scattering from a Coulomb Potential with Exponential Screening," *Physical Review*, **99** (1955), 1287.

For the case of an electron colliding with a molecule, the transfer of momentum is nearly complete. In this section we will indicate in what sense this is true.

In Section 4.21 we showed (Equation [4.21]) that the fractional energy of molecule A colliding with molecule B is

$$\frac{\Delta K^A}{K^A} = \frac{2m^A m^B}{(m^A + m^B)^2} (1 - \cos \chi) \qquad [4.67]$$

If we let molecule A be an electron of mass m_- and molecule B be a neutral molecule of mass m_N, then the fractional energy loss of the electron will be

$$\frac{\Delta K}{K} = \frac{2m_-}{m_N} (1 - \cos \chi) \qquad [4.68]$$

since $m_- \ll m_N$.

Let $F(\chi)$ be some function of the scattering angle χ and let $\langle F(\chi) \rangle$ be the mean value of $F(\chi)$ averaged over all values of χ. Since $F(\chi) S(\chi) d\omega$ is the contribution to the total value of $F(\chi)$ resulting from the particles scattered into $d\omega$ and since the total number of particles scattered is $\int S(\chi) d\omega$, then it follows that

$$\langle F(\chi) \rangle \int S(\chi) d\omega = \int F(\chi) S(\chi) d\omega$$

or

$$\langle F(\chi) \rangle = \frac{\int F(\chi) S(\chi) d\omega}{\int S(\chi) d\omega} \qquad [4.69]$$

Using [4.67] and [4.69], we can write the mean fractional energy loss of molecule A colliding with molecule B as

$$\left\langle \frac{\Delta K^A}{K^A} \right\rangle = \frac{2m^A m^B}{(m^A + m^B)^2} \frac{\int (1 - \cos \chi) S(\chi) d\omega}{\int S(\chi) d\omega} \qquad [4.70]$$

If we now assume that an electron is colliding with a molecule and both are considered to be hard spheres so that $S(\chi) = \frac{1}{4} r^2$, we can write [4.70] as

$$\left\langle \frac{\Delta K}{K} \right\rangle = \frac{2m_-}{m_N} \frac{\int_0^\pi (1 - \cos \chi) \sin \chi \, d\chi}{\int_0^\pi \sin \chi \, d\chi} \qquad [4.71]$$

from which

$$\left\langle \frac{\Delta K}{K} \right\rangle = \frac{2m_-}{m_N}$$

[4.72]

Thus an electron on the average loses very little energy in a collision with a molecule. If we assume therefore that the speed of the electron remains constant to a first approximation (that is, assuming that the molecule has an infinite mass) and denote this speed by g, then the change in momentum of the electron along the initial direction will be $mg(1 - \cos \chi)$. The mean value of this quantity is $mg\langle 1 - \cos \chi \rangle$ which, for the case of hard spheres, can be seen from [4.71] to be equal to mg, indicating a complete transfer of momentum.

More generally, for any potential function the mean value of $(1 - \cos \chi)$ is, from [4.69], given by

$$\langle 1 - \cos \chi \rangle = \frac{\int (1 - \cos \chi) S(\chi)\, d\omega}{\int S(\chi)\, d\omega}$$

[4.73]

The total cross section is, by definition (see [4.62]), $Q = \int S(\chi)\, d\omega$, and we now define a *cross section for momentum transfer* Q_M by the equation

$$Q_M = \int (1 - \cos \chi) S(\chi)\, d\omega$$

or

$$Q_M = 2\pi \int_0^\pi (1 - \cos \chi) S(\chi) \sin \chi\, d\chi$$

[4.74]

so that [4.73] can be written

$$\langle 1 - \cos \chi \rangle = \frac{Q_M}{Q}$$

from which

$$Q_M = Q \langle 1 - \cos \chi \rangle$$

We have shown above that for the hard sphere model $\langle 1 - \cos \chi \rangle = 1$ so that for this case $Q_M = Q$. However for other forms of the potential energy function the mean value of $(1 - \cos \chi)$ will, in general, be less than unity so that Q_M will be less than Q. It is possible for Q_M to be finite in cases where Q is infinite. From [4.74] we see that the cross section for momentum transfer is a weighted cross section in which deflection angles of zero degrees do not count at all, deflections of $90°$ count one, and deflections of $180°$ count two. This weighting is seen to be proportional to the amount of momentum transferred as a result of the collision.

Problem

4–1 Show that if the potential energy function varies as $1/r^4$, then the cross section for momentum transfer varies as $1/g$ and the collision frequency for momentum transfer is independent of the particle energy. Molecules that satisfy this potential energy function are called *Maxwellian molecules*. This concept is not related to the Maxwellian distribution of molecules.

REFERENCES

The geometry of a binary collision based on the conservation of energy and momentum is discussed in

1   Chapman, S., and T. G. Cowling. *The Mathematical Theory of Non-Uniform Gases*. London: Cambridge University Press, 1960.

General treatments of the dynamics of binary collisions and differential scattering cross sections are discussed in

2   Hirschfelder, J. O., C. F. Curtiss, and R. B. Bird. *Molecular Theory of Gases and Liquids*. New York: J. Wiley, 1954.

3   Delcroix, J. L. *Introduction to the Theory of Ionized Gases*. New York: Interscience, 1960, Chaps. 1 and 2.

4   Present, R. D. *Kinetic Theory of Gases*. New York: McGraw-Hill, 1958.

5

PLASMA KINETIC THEORY: THE BOLTZMANN EQUATION

Kinetic theory attempts to explain the macroscopically observed phenomena of gases by considering the forces of interaction between the molecules of the gas. If at some instant of time we knew the position and velocity of each molecule of the gas and the forces that acted on each molecule, then we could, in principle, determine the subsequent motion of all molecules by classical mechanics. We do not, of course, have such detailed information about the molecules. Even if we did, the problem would be too difficult and time-consuming to solve and would, in fact, give us more information than we really need.

An alternative approach to the problem is through the methods of statistical mechanics. Let us consider a box of gas containing n molecules at some instant of time. The three components of momentum and the three components of position of each molecule are given by a list of $6n$ numbers. These $6n$ numbers can be thought of as representing a point in a $6n$-dimensional space. Thus the entire gas at that instant of time is represented by a single point in the $6n$-dimensional space. Such a space is called a *gas phase space*, or Γ-space.

Let us again consider a box of gas that contains n molecules which may be the same box as we considered previously, but at some later instant of time. As before we can represent this box of gas as another point in Γ-space. We continue this process until we have considered all possible states that the molecules can assume. The total number of points in Γ-space will be the number of different dynamical states of the particular system. These points are said to form an ensemble of points in Γ-space.

Statistical mechanics deals with the probability of finding one system of the ensemble, chosen at random, in a particular region of Γ-space. The assumption of statistical mechanics is that the macroscopically observed variables of the gas correspond to those dynamical states that are most probable. The fundamental theorem of statistical mechanics is Liouville's which states that the volume occupied by a given set of points in Γ-space is constant throughout the motion of these points. This is stated mathematically by the *Liouville equation*. Statistical mechanics is well suited for the study of equilibrium states. However for nonequilibrium states, which are of interest in plasma phenomena, serious difficulties arise.

Solution of the Liouville equation will give the probability of finding a point at a given place in Γ-space. That is, we would know the probability that each molecule has a specified position and momentum. It is often unnecessary to have such a complete description of the gas, and it would be sufficient to know only the probability that any single molecule has a given position and momentum. This part of statistical mechanics dealing with one-particle distribution functions forms the framework of kinetic theory. For this theory it is not necessary to consider a $6n$-dimensional Γ-space, but rather we need only deal with a *six-dimensional molecular phase space* called μ-space.

We first define the distribution function of molecular velocities as the density of points in μ-space, or, simply, phase space. This is a one-particle distribution function because the position and velocity of any given particle is not correlated with the position and velocity of any other particle or particles. If the distribution function of molecular velocities is known, then we show how the various molecular properties involving the pressure and energy of the gas can be obtained by integrating the quantity of interest times the distribution function over all velocity space (Section 5.1). Some properties of the pressure of a gas are described in Section 5.2. In general the pressure varies with the direction and is appropriately described by a second-order tensor, but in an isotropic medium this can be simplified to the form of the hydrostatic pressure. After the kinetic theory definition of temperature has been given, the equation of state for an ideal gas is written in terms of the hydrostatic pressure, the number density of the molecules, and the temperature.

The *Boltzmann equation*, which describes the time variation of the distribution function, is derived in Section 5.3. The derivation is in two steps, with the collisionless Boltzmann equation derived first. The derivation of the term that must be added when binary collisions occur completes the Boltzmann equation. The equilibrium solution of this equation describes the state of the gas when the distribution function remains constant. The velocities of individual particles continue to suffer the abrupt changes characteristic of collisions, but the same number of particles enter a given volume of phase space as leave it, so that the distribution function is unchanged. This collisional equilibrium distribution is known as the *Maxwellian distribution*. In Section 5.5 we consider the factor that modifies the particle density in the presence of a potential field. The gravitational and electrostatic potentials are examples of this case which produces a *Boltzmann distribution* in the density of the particles.

Finally, in Section 5.6, we return to a more detailed discussion of statistical mechanics and its relation to kinetic theory. The so-called *BBGKY* hierarchy of equations for the higher order distribution functions is derived and the lowest order equation is shown to reduce to the Boltzmann equation under certain conditions.

5.1 THE DISTRIBUTION
OF MOLECULAR VELOCITIES

Let us consider a certain volume of gas and represent the location of each molecule by its position in a Cartesian coordinate system. This three-dimensional space is our ordinary everday space, and we will call it *configuration space*. It is shown in Figure 5.1. In this figure dr ($= dx_1\, dx_2\, dx_3$) is a small, but finite, volume element which is assumed to be large enough to contain a great number of molecules but which is, nevertheless, small compared to the lengths involved in spatial variations of the macroscopic parameters of the gas. Thus dr is large enough for an individual particle to be lost in the crowd within dr. At the same time there is no incremental change in the temperature, for example, within the element dr.

If $N(x_i, t)$ is the number density of molecules in configuration space, then the number of molecules in dr is $N\, dr$. Note that $N(x_i, t)$ can be a function of position and also of time. We speak of molecules as being in dr. By this it is meant that the molecule is located at a position with its x_1-component between x_1 and $x_1 + dx_1$, its x_2-component between x_2 and $x_2 + dx_2$, and its x_3-component between x_3 and $x_3 + dx_3$. We will often refer to such a molecule as being at x_i in dr, or simply as being in dr. All the molecules in dr have the same value of x_i as far as macroscopic variations of the gas are concerned.

Now the $N\, dr$ molecules in dr have a wide range of different velocities. To represent all these different velocities we plot, for each of the $N\, dr$ molecules in *dr*, its three components of linear velocity in a Cartesian coordinate system with axes v_1, v_2, v_3. This three-dimensional space we call *velocity space*, and it is shown in Figure 5.2. There are $N\,dr$ points plotted, one for each of the $N\,dr$ molecules in *dr*.

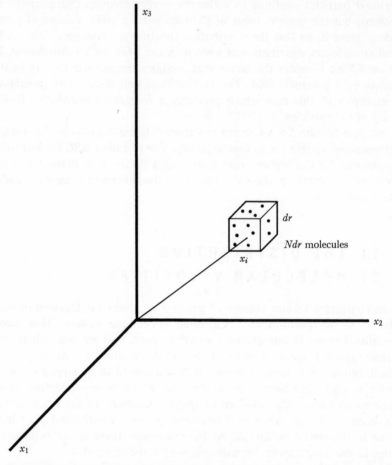

FIGURE 5.1 Configuration Space. Element *dr* contains the molecules which have the velocities shown in Figure 5.2

The density of molecules in configuration space was given by $N(x_i, t)$. We now define the density of the $N\,dr$ points in velocity space shown in Figure 5.2 to be $f(v_i, x_i, t)\,dr$, where f is called the *velocity distribution function*. If $dc\,(= dv_1\,dv_2\,dv_3)$ is a differential volume element in velocity space, then $f\,dr\,dc$ is the number of points in the volume element dc. It will be convenient to refer to a molecule as having a velocity v_i in dc. What is meant by this is that the molecule has a velocity with components between v_1 and $v_1 + dv_1$, v_2 and $v_2 + dv_2$, and v_3 and $v_3 + dv_3$.

Now, if $f\,dr\,dc$ is the number of molecules in dr whose velocities are in dc, we see that f is the density of points in the six-dimensional phase space made up of the three components of position and the three components of velocity. Dividing $f\,dr\,dc$ by the volume dr we note that $f\,dc$ is the number of molecules per unit volume with velocities v_i in dc. If we integrate the expression $f\,dr\,dc$

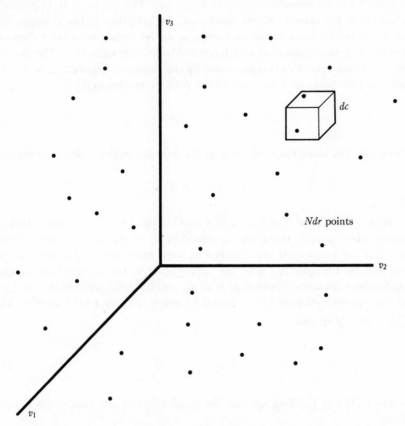

FIGURE 5.2   Velocity Space. Showing the velocities of molecules located in volume element dr in configuration space

over all velocity space, we will obtain the total number of points in Figure 5.2. This number is $N\,dr$. Thus $N\,dr = dr \int f\,dc$ and

$$N = \int f\,dc \qquad\qquad [5.1]$$

Note that the single integral sign is really a triple integral extending over all of velocity space. For convenience, we will, in the future, use only a single integral sign, and its range of integration will be understood to be over all velocity space.

5.11 MEAN VALUES OF MOLECULAR PROPERTIES

Suppose that we associate with each of the $N dr$ molecules in dr shown in Figure 5.1 some *molecular property* $\phi(v_i, x_i, t)$. This property is, in general, a function of the velocity v_i, the position x_i, and the time t. The x_i dependence of ϕ will be the same for all molecules in dr. At some time t the values of ϕ for the $N dr$ molecules in dr will depend only on their velocity v_i. The distribution of these velocities is represented by the points in Figure 5.2. Now let us add up the values of ϕ for each of the $N dr$ molecules in dr,

$$\phi^{(1)} + \phi^{(2)} + \cdots \phi^{(N\ dr)} = \sum \phi$$

We define the mean value $\langle \phi \rangle$ of ϕ for the $N dr$ molecules in dr by the equation

$$\sum \phi = \langle \phi \rangle N\ dr$$

Now some of the $N dr$ values of ϕ making up $\sum \phi$ will have essentially the same value: namely those whose velocities lie in the same velocity element dc. But we know that the number of such molecules is $f\ dr\ dc$ and each contributes the quantity ϕ to the sum $\sum \phi$. Thus the contribution of these molecules with velocities in dc is $\phi f\ dr\ dc$, and the total contribution to $\sum \phi$ of molecules with all velocities is found by integrating over all velocities. Thus $\sum \phi = dr \int \phi f\ dc$ and

$$N\langle \phi \rangle = \int \phi f\ dc \qquad\qquad [5.2]$$

From [5.1] and [5.2] we see that the mean value of any function ϕ is found from

$$\langle \phi \rangle = \frac{\int \phi f\ dc}{N} = \frac{\int \phi f\ dc}{\int f\ dc} \qquad\qquad [5.3]$$

Mean Velocity and Peculiar Velocity   To find the mean velocity $\langle v_i \rangle$, let $\phi = v_i$ in [5.3]. Then

$$\langle v_i \rangle = \frac{1}{N(x_i, t)} \int v_i f(v_i, x_i, t)\ dc \qquad\qquad [5.4]$$

We note that whereas v_i, x_i, and t are independent variables and are thus independent of each other, $\langle v_i \rangle$ is a function of the position x_i and the time t.

We define the *peculiar velocity* V_i as the velocity of a molecule relative to the mean velocity. That is

$$V_i = v_i - \langle v_i \rangle \qquad [5.5]$$

Since v_i is a function of x_i and t, then V_i is also a function of x_i and t. From [5.5] we see that the mean value of the peculiar velocity is zero since

$$\langle V_i \rangle = \langle v_i - \langle v_i \rangle \rangle = \langle v_i \rangle - \langle v_i \rangle = 0 \qquad [5.6]$$

Exercise 5.11.1 In Figure 5.2 the velocities of the molecules are referred to the coordinate axes v_1, v_2, v_3. We could also refer them to the coordinate axes of the peculiar velocities V_1, V_2, V_3. For this case a volume element would be given by $dC = dV_1\,dV_2\,dV_3$.

(a) What is the relationship between these two sets of coordinate axes?

(b) How many molecules per unit volume are there with peculiar velocities V_i in dC?

(c) Write an expression for the mean value of any function $\phi(V_i)$, which depends on the peculiar velocities V_i.

5.2 THE PRESSURE
AND TEMPERATURE OF A GAS

The state of an ideal gas is determined by the values of the state variables—pressure, temperature, density, and volume. In kinetic theory we are concerned with the concepts of pressure and temperature as they are related to the motions of the molecules.

The pressure of a gas is often defined as the force per unit area exerted on the walls of the containing vessel. This force results from molecular impacts and is equal to the rate at which momentum is imparted to the wall. However it is desirable to have a more general definition which will enable us to define pressure without involving boundaries. We will then define the pressure at any point within a gas in terms of a surface element dS which moves with the mean velocity of the gas $\langle v_i \rangle$. The *pressure* P_j across any surface element dS, moving with the mean velocity of the gas $\langle v_i \rangle$, with positive unit normal n_i, is defined as the rate at which molecular momentum mv_i is transported across dS, per unit area, in the positive direction.

5.21 THE PRESSURE TENSOR
AND HYDROSTATIC PRESSURE

In order to calculate the pressure P_j across a surface element dS (Figure 5.3), we must calculate the rate at which molecular momentum mv_i crosses dS, per unit area, in the positive direction. Since dS moves with the mean molecular velocity $\langle v_i \rangle$, a molecule with peculiar velocity V_i will only cross dS in the time interval dt if it lies in the cylinder shown in Figure 5.3.

The number of molecules in this cylinder that have velocities V_i in dC is (see Exercise 5.11.1) $f(V_i)\, dC\, dr$, where dr is the volume of the cylinder and

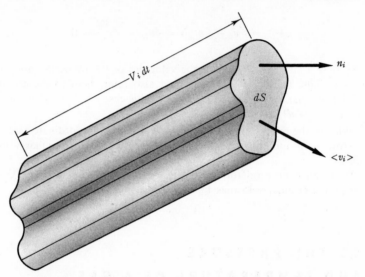

FIGURE 5.3 Pertaining to the Calculation of the Pressure Tensor

is given by $dr = V_i n_i\, dt\, dS$. Thus the number of molecules with velocities V_i in dC which cross dS in dt is $f(V_i)V_i n_i\, dC\, dt\, dS$. Each of these molecules carries with it an amount of molecular momentum mv_i. Therefore the total amount of momentum crossing dS in dt due to molecules with peculiar velocities V_i is $mv_j f(V_i)V_i n_i\, dC\, dt\, dS$.

The total amount of momentum crossing dS in dt due to molecules with all velocities is found by integrating this expression with respect to dC and is $dt\, dS \int mv_j f(V_i)V_i n_i\, dC$. This integration corresponds to rotating the line segments $V_i\, dt$ in Figure 5.3 in all possible directions about dS. We thus pick up the contributions from all molecules crossing dS in either direction.

By definition the pressure P_j is equal to the total momentum crossing dS divided by $dt\, dS$. Thus

$$P_j = \int mv_j f(V_i)V_i n_i\, dC \qquad [5.7]$$

From [5.5] we can substitute $V_j + \langle v_j \rangle$ for v_j in [5.7] so that

$$P_j = \int mn_i V_i (V_j + \langle v_j \rangle) f \, dC,$$

from which, using the results of Exercise 5.11.1c, we have

$$P_j = Nm \langle n_i V_i (V_j + \langle v_j \rangle) \rangle = Nmn_i (\langle V_i V_j \rangle + \langle V_i \rangle \langle v_j \rangle)$$

Therefore

$$P_j = Nmn_i \langle V_i V_j \rangle = \rho n_i \langle V_i V_j \rangle \qquad [5.8]$$

where [5.6] has been used and $\rho = Nm$ is the *mass density*. Alternatively we can write [5.8] as

$$P_j = n_i \Psi_{ij} \qquad [5.9]$$

where Ψ_{ij} is called the *pressure tensor* and is given by

$$\Psi_{ij} = \rho \langle V_i V_j \rangle \qquad [5.10]$$

Hydrostatic Pressure   In order to understand the significance of the components of the pressure tensor, let us consider the pressure across three orthogonal planes at some point P in the gas as shown in Figure 5.4. Now we had from [5.9] that the pressure is given by $P_j = n_i \Psi_{ij}$. Let us see what this gives for the pressure on each of the three surfaces. First sum the repeated index i to obtain $P_j = n_1 \Psi_{1j} + n_2 \Psi_{2j} + n_3 \Psi_{3j}$. Now consider the pressure on surface 1. For this surface $n_1 = 1$, $n_2 = n_3 = 0$. It follows that

$$P_1 = \Psi_{11}, \quad P_2 = \Psi_{12}, \quad P_3 = \Psi_{13}$$

Similarly on surface 2,

$$P_1 = \Psi_{21}, \quad P_2 = \Psi_{22}, \quad P_3 = \Psi_{23}$$

and, on surface 3,

$$P_1 = \Psi_{31}, \quad P_2 = \Psi_{32}, \quad P_3 = \Psi_{33}$$

The sum of the normal pressures across the three planes is

$$\Psi_{11} + \Psi_{22} + \Psi_{33} = \Psi_{ij} \delta_{ij} = \Psi_{ii}.$$

Let us now define the *mean hydrostatic pressure*, or the pressure P, to be given by

$$P = \tfrac{1}{3}\Psi_{ij}\delta_{ij} = \tfrac{1}{3}\Psi_{ii} = \tfrac{1}{3}(\Psi_{11} + \Psi_{22} + \Psi_{33}) \qquad [5.11]$$

If $\Psi_{11} = \Psi_{22} = \Psi_{33} = P$ and if the off-diagonal elements of Ψ_{ij} are zero, then $\Psi_{ij} = P\delta_{ij}$ and [5.9] becomes

$$P_j = n_i\Psi_{ij} = n_iP\delta_{ij} = Pn_j$$

For this case the pressure on any surface element is normal to the surface. The magnitude of the pressure is equal to the hydrostatic pressure P, and is independent of the orientation of the surface.

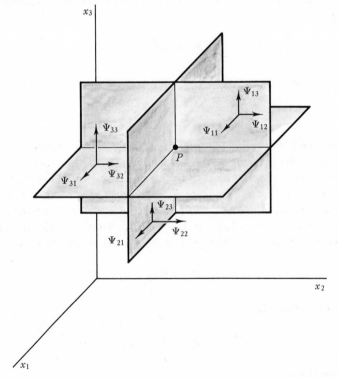

F I G U R E 5.4 Components of the Pressure Tensor

Exercise 5.21.1 Let dS be a surface element of a wall. Assume that the number of molecules impinging on dS is equal to the number of molecules rebounding. Then show that the normal component of the mean velocity relative to the wall is zero. This is a justification of the hydrodynamic assumption that the normal component of the fluid velocity is zero at a boundary.

5.22 HEAT AND TEMPERATURE

The concept of heat in a gas can be discussed by considering the translatory kinetic energy possessed by the molecules of the gas. Now the number of molecules in the volume element dr that have velocities v_i (that is, have velocities in dc) is $f\,dr\,dc$. Each of these $f\,dr\,dc$ molecules has a kinetic energy $mv_iv_i/2$. Thus the total amount of translatory kinetic energy possessed by all of the molecules in dr is found by integrating $\frac{1}{2}mv_iv_if\,dr\,dc$ over all velocities, and is

$$dr \int \tfrac{1}{2}mv_iv_if\,dc = N\,dr\,\tfrac{1}{2}m\langle v_iv_i\rangle$$

where we have used [5.2]. In terms of the peculiar velocity we obtain

$$N\,dr\tfrac{1}{2}m\left\langle (V_i + \langle v_i\rangle)(V_i + \langle v_i\rangle)\right\rangle$$
$$= N\,dr\tfrac{1}{2}m(\langle V_iV_i\rangle + 2\langle V_i\rangle\langle v_i\rangle + \langle v_i\rangle\langle v_i\rangle)$$
$$= \tfrac{1}{2}\rho\,dr\langle v_i\rangle\langle v_i\rangle + N\,dr\tfrac{1}{2}m\langle V_iV_i\rangle \qquad [5.12]$$

where [5.6] was used in the last step.

The first term of [5.12] represents the kinetic energy of the mass motion of the gas, since $\rho\,dr$ is the mass of the gas in dr. The second term of [5.12] represents the kinetic energy of the peculiar motion. This hidden invisible molecular energy is defined as the *heat energy* of the gas. The heat density or heat energy per unit volume is then given by

$$\tfrac{1}{2}Nm\langle V_iV_i\rangle = \tfrac{1}{2}\rho\langle V_iV_i\rangle \qquad [5.13]$$

This equation gives the total hidden kinetic energy per unit volume. Each of the N molecules per unit volume then has, on the average, an amount of hidden kinetic energy given by $\tfrac{1}{2}m\langle V_iV_i\rangle$. We define the *temperature* T of the gas to be proportional to this hidden kinetic energy and to be defined by the relation

$$\tfrac{1}{2}m\langle V_iV_i\rangle = \tfrac{3}{2}kT \qquad [5.14]$$

The constant k, known as Boltzmann's constant, is the same for all gases, and has a value of $k = 1.38 \times 10^{-16}$ ergs/°K.

The hydrostatic pressure P can be written as

$$P = \tfrac{1}{3}\Psi_{ii} = \tfrac{1}{3}Nm\langle V_iV_i\rangle \qquad [5.15]$$

Using the definition of temperature given by [5.14] we obtain

$$P = NkT \qquad\qquad [5.16]$$

Equation [5.16] is the equation of state of an ideal gas and can be rewritten as $PV = RT$, where V is the gas volume and R is the universal gas constant.

   Exercise 5.22.1

   (a)   Plot the number density N in cm^{-3} as a function of pressure in mm Hg for an ideal gas at room temperature ($T = 3 \times 10^2 \,^\circ K$). Plot pressures from 10^{-5} to 10^3 mm Hg (Torr).

   (b)   What is the approximate number density at atmospheric pressure?

   (c)   The best vacuums attainable at the present time are vacuums of about 10^{-14} mm Hg. What is the number density at this pressure?

   (d)   "Fusion plasmas" have a temperature of about $3 \times 10^8 \,^\circ K$. Plot the number density vs. pressure on the same graph as in part (a) for this temperature.

5.3   THE   BOLTZMANN   EQUATION

We have seen that the macroscopic properties, or the mean value of molecular properties, of a gas can be determined from a knowledge of the velocity distribution function f. Since we will be interested in the time variation of these macroscopic properties, it is important to obtain an equation describing the time variation of the velocity distribution function. The equation that describes this time variation is the Boltzmann equation.

We will derive the Boltzmann equation in two parts, considering first the form which it takes in the absence of collisions, and then deriving the collision term. The collision term of the Boltzmann equation takes account of binary collisions, typified by the electron-neutral particle collision. In plasma theory these collisions are not the only ones of importance. Multiple Coulomb collisions must always be considered and may be of more importance than binary collisions. This problem is discussed in Chapter 9, Charged Particle Interactions, where a modification of the Boltzmann equation is introduced.

5.31   THE   COLLISIONLESS
BOLTZMANN   EQUATION

Let R_i be the force per unit mass on a particle in the gas. In most cases the force will not be a function of velocity. However in the case of a plasma a force that is a function of velocity does exist. This is the force on a charged particle moving in a magnetic field given by $q\mathbf{v} \times \mathbf{B}$, where q is the electrical charge on the particle. This force can be written in terms of the alternating unit tensor ϵ_{ijk} as $q\epsilon_{ijk}v_jB_k$. We will, therefore, write the force per unit mass R_i as the sum of two terms: R_i' which is independent of velocity, and the velocity dependent term $q\epsilon_{ijk}v_jB_k$. That is,

$$R_i = R_i' + \frac{q}{m}\,\epsilon_{ijk}v_jB_k \qquad\qquad [5.17]$$

and from Newton's second law we have that $R_i = \dot{v}_i$.

At time t the number of molecules in the volume element $dr^{(t)}$ at x_i with velocities in the velocity element $dc^{(t)}$ at v_i is $f(v_i, x_i, t)\,dc^{(t)}\,dr^{(t)}$. In the time interval dt the location of a molecule will change by an amount $\dot{x}_i\,dt = v_i\,dt$, while its velocity will change by an amount $\dot{v}_i\,dt = R_i\,dt$. Thus at the time $t + dt$, in the absence of any collisions, the number of molecules in the volume element $dr^{(t+dt)}$ at $x_i + v_i\,dt$ with velocities in the velocity element $dc^{(t+dt)}$ at $v_i + R_i\,dt$ is $f(v_i + R_i\,dt, x_i + v_i\,dt, t + dt)\,dc^{(t+dt)}\,dr^{(t+dt)}$. However these are exactly the same molecules as considered at time t, so that we can equate the two expressions and obtain

$$f(v_i, x_i, t)\,dc^{(t)}\,dr^{(t)} = f(v_i + R_i\,dt, x_i + v_i\,dt, t + dt)\,dc^{(t+dt)}\,dr^{(t+dt)} \quad [5.18]$$

The fact that we are considering the same molecules at both instants of time can be pictured as follows: Suppose that at time t we paint red all of the molecules in $dr^{(t)}$ whose velocities lie in the velocity element $dc^{(t)}$. We then let an interval of time dt elapse during which it is assumed that no collisions occur. The molecules will move to new positions and their velocities will change. We then draw a volume element $dr^{(t+dt)}$ around all of the red molecules. Similarly in velocity space we draw a velocity element $dc^{(t+dt)}$ around all of the points representing velocities of the red molecules. We are then obviously considering the same molecules at both instants of time. It remains to determine the relationship between $dc^{(t)}\,dr^{(t)}$ and $dc^{(t+dt)}\,dr^{(t+dt)}$.

The changes in the volume elements $dc^{(t)}$ and $dr^{(t)}$ are given by the *Jacobian transformations* (see Appendix D)

$$dr^{(t+dt)} = J^{(r)}\,dr^{(t)} = \frac{\partial(x_i + v_i\,dt)}{\partial(x_j)}\,dr^{(t)} \qquad\qquad [5.19]$$

and

$$dc^{(t+dt)} = J^{(c)}\,dc^{(t)} = \frac{\partial[v_i + R_i'\,dt + (q/m)\epsilon_{ijk}v_jB_k\,dt]}{\partial(v_s)}\,dc^{(t)} \qquad [5.20]$$

Since v_i and x_j are independent variables, we note that in [5.19]

$$J^{(r)} = \frac{\partial(x_i + v_j\,dt)}{\partial(x_j)} = \det \delta_{ij} = 1$$

where det stands for determinant, so that

$$dr^{(t+dt)} = dr^{(t)} \tag{5.21}$$

The situation is not so simple in [5.20] since the force term involving the magnetic field is velocity-dependent. Expanding the Jacobian in [5.20] by noting that

$$\frac{\partial[(q/m)\epsilon_{ijk}v_j B_k \, dt]}{\partial(v_s)} = \frac{q}{m}\,\epsilon_{ijk}\delta_{js}B_k \, dt = \frac{q}{m}\,\epsilon_{isk}B_k \, dt$$

we obtain

$$J^{(c)} = \begin{vmatrix} 1 & \dfrac{q}{m}\,B_3\,dt & -\dfrac{q}{m}\,B_2\,dt \\[2mm] -\dfrac{q}{m}\,B_3\,dt & 1 & \dfrac{q}{m}\,B_1\,dt \\[2mm] \dfrac{q}{m}\,B_2\,dt & -\dfrac{q}{m}\,B_1\,dt & 1 \end{vmatrix} = 1$$

if we neglect terms of order $(dt)^2$. Thus [5.20] can be written

$$dc^{(t+dt)} = dc^{(t)} \tag{5.22}$$

Using [5.21] and [5.22] we can write [5.18] as

$$f(v_i, x_i, t) = f(v_i + R_i\,dt, x_i + v_i\,dt, t + dt) \tag{5.23}$$

Expanding the right-hand side of [5.23] in a *Taylor series* about $dt = 0$ (see Appendix E), we obtain

$$f(v_i, x_i, t) = f(v_i, x_i, t) + \left[\frac{\partial f}{\partial v_i}\,R_i\,dt + \frac{\partial f}{\partial x_i}\,v_i\,dt + \frac{\partial f}{\partial t}\,dt\right]$$
$$+ \text{ terms of order } (dt)^2$$

Neglecting terms of order $(dt)^2$ and higher we have

$$\frac{\partial f}{\partial t} + v_i\frac{\partial f}{\partial x_i} + R_i\frac{\partial f}{\partial v_i} = 0 \tag{5.24}$$

This is the collisionless Boltzmann equation expressing the time dependence of the velocity distribution function. The first term, $\partial f/\partial t$, is the local variation of the distribution function. The term $v_i\partial f/\partial x_i$ is the variation of the distribution function resulting from molecules streaming in and out of a given volume element. We will see that this term relates to the description of diffusion. The term $R_i\,\partial f/\partial v_i$ is the variation of the distribution function resulting from the external forces acting on the molecules.

The distribution function will also vary as the result of collisions between the molecules of the gas. We can include this variation by writing a collision term on the right-hand side of [5.24] thus:

$$\frac{\partial f}{\partial t} + v_i \frac{\partial f}{\partial x_i} + R_i \frac{\partial f}{\partial v_i} = \left(\frac{\partial f}{\partial t}\right)_{\text{coll}} \qquad [5.25]$$

The form of this collision term has to be determined. For the case of a gas of low density, where binary collisions only need to be considered, this collision term can be written as an integral known as the collision integral. This integral will be discussed in the following section.

Exercise 5.31.1   Since the mean velocity $\langle v_i \rangle(x_i, t)$ is a function of x_i and t, the peculiar velocity $V_i = v_i - \langle v_i \rangle(x_i, t)$ is also a function of x_i and t. Show that the Boltzmann equation satisfied by the distribution function $f(V_i, x_i, t)$ expressed in terms of the peculiar velocities is

$$\frac{Df}{Dt} + V_i \frac{\partial f}{\partial x_i} + \left(R_i - \frac{D\langle v_i \rangle}{Dt}\right) \frac{\partial f}{\partial V_i} - V_i \frac{\partial f}{\partial V_j} \frac{\partial \langle v_j \rangle}{\partial x_i} = \left(\frac{\partial f}{\partial t}\right)_{\text{coll}}$$

where

$$\frac{D}{Dt} = \frac{\partial}{\partial t} + \langle v_i \rangle \frac{\partial}{\partial x_i}$$

HINT: The term $\partial f(v_i)/\partial t$ in the original Boltzmann equation represented only the explicit time dependence of f. Now, however, $f(V_i(t), x_i, t)$ has a time dependence due to V_i as well as an explicit time dependence. The first term of the "revised" Boltzmann equation thus becomes

$$\frac{\partial f}{\partial t} + \frac{\partial f}{\partial V_j} \frac{\partial V_j}{\partial t} \quad \text{or} \quad \frac{\partial f}{\partial t} - \frac{\partial f}{\partial V_j} \frac{\partial \langle v_j \rangle}{\partial t}$$

and so forth. What does this equation reduce to if $\langle v_i \rangle = 0$? If $\langle v_i \rangle = $ constant?

5.32   THE COLLISION INTEGRAL

The term $(\partial f/\partial t)_{\text{coll}}$ which appears in the Boltzmann equation represents the time rate of change of f due to collisions of the molecules with one another. We seek an explicit expression for this term in this section by considering the statistical nature of binary collisions.

For a given distribution f at a specific time t there will be a certain number of molecules with velocities in particular regions of velocity space. That is, there will be, for example, a certain number of molecules per unit volume with velocities v_i^A in dc^A as shown in Figure 5.5. This number is $f(v_i^A)\, dc^A$ which we will write as $f^A\, dc^A$. If as a result of a collision the velocity of a molecule changes from v_i^A to $\tilde{v}_i^A$, then we will say that the molecule has been knocked from the velocity element dc^A into the velocity element $d\tilde{c}^A$.

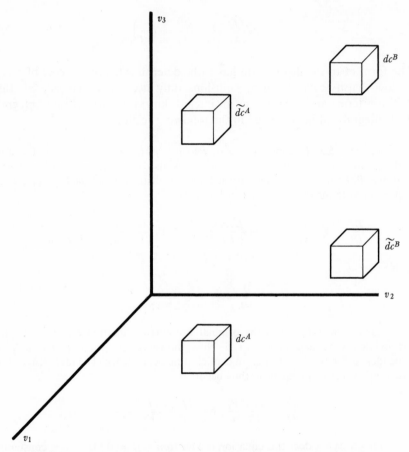

FIGURE 5.5   Scattering of Points in Velocity Space due to Binary Collisions

Let us say that the molecule that collided with the molecule described above had an initial velocity v_i^B and a final velocity $\tilde{v}_i^B$. That is to say, this molecule was knocked from the velocity element dc^B into the velocity element $d\tilde{c}^B$.

Now in order to calculate $(\partial f/\partial t)_{\text{coll}}$ we need to determine the net gain of molecules with velocities in a certain velocity element due to collisions with molecules of all other velocities. We will take as our typical molecules those with velocities v_i^A—that is, with velocities lying in dc^A.

We then proceed by defining:

A molecule of Class A: a molecule with velocity components in dc^A.

A molecule of Class B: a molecule with velocity components in dc^B.

A collision of Type α: a collision in which a molecule leaves dc^A. Before collision, one molecule is of Class A and the other is of Class B.

A collision of Type β: a collision in which a molecule enters dc^A. After collision, one molecule is of Class A and the other is of Class B.

Type α Collisions We consider first collisions of Type α in which molecules are knocked out of the velocity element dc^A. The collision occurs between molecule A with velocity in dc^A and molecule B with velocity in dc^B. The number of molecules per unit volume with velocities in dc^B is $f(v_i^B)\, dc^B$ or $f^B\, dc^B$. Consider now a collision between molecule A and molecule B as shown in Figure 5.6. The relative speed between the two molecules is g.

We wish to determine the frequency of collisions between molecules of Class B and a single molecule of Class A such that the projected initial path of molecule B intersects the plane containing the differential area $p\, dp\, d\psi$. In general, molecule B will not pass through this area since it will be deflected away from molecule A.

Let T be the number of such collisions occurring in the time interval dt. This will be equal to the number of molecules of Class B which at a certain instant lie in the volume element $p\, dp\, d\psi\, g\, dt$. Since the number of molecules per unit volume of Class B is $f^B\, dc^B$, it follows that $T = f^B\, dc^B\, p\, dp\, d\psi\, g\, dt$. This is the number of collisions occurring in the time dt between molecules of Class B and a single molecule of Class A. Since the number of molecules of Class A per unit volume is $f^A\, dc^A$ and each one makes T collisions with Class B molecules in the time dt, then the total number of such collisions between Class A and Class B molecules is

$$f^A\, dc^A\, T = f^A f^B\, dc^A\, dc^B\, gp\, dp\, d\psi\, dt \qquad [5.26]$$

Now we are taking molecule A as our typical molecule. Thus to find the total number of molecules of Class A that enter into collisions with molecules of all velocities in the time dt, we must integrate [5.26] with respect to dc^B, dp, and $d\psi$. Denoting this quantity by "Out" (these molecules are knocked out of dc^A) we have, from [5.26],

$$\text{"Out"} = dc^A\, dt \int f^A f^B gp\, dp\, d\psi\, dc^B \qquad [5.27]$$

where again the multiple integral is represented by a single integral sign.

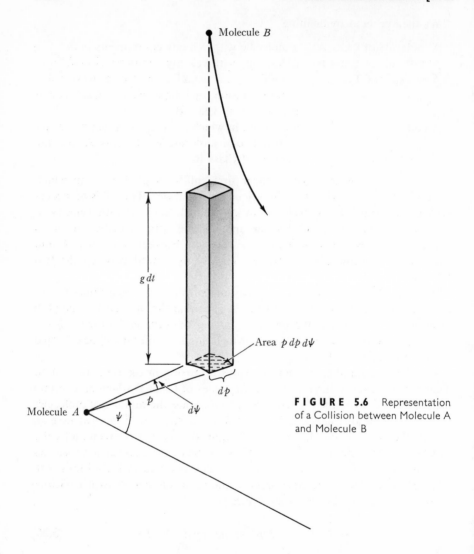

FIGURE 5.6 Representation of a Collision between Molecule A and Molecule B

Type β Collisions   In Figure 5.5 the velocity element $d\tilde{c}^A$ is the element into which a molecule originally in dc^A gets knocked due to a collision with a molecule originally in dc^B. This molecule in dc^B gets knocked into $d\tilde{c}^B$. Now for each of these so-called direct encounters in which molecules get knocked from dc^A and dc^B into $d\tilde{c}^A$ and $d\tilde{c}^B$ there is an inverse encounter in which molecules get knocked from $d\tilde{c}^A$ and $d\tilde{c}^B$ into dc^A and dc^B. This relationship is shown in Figure 5.7. Thus for an inverse encounter we can consider $\tilde{v}_i^A$ to be the pre-collision velocity of a molecule which, after collision, has its velocity in dc^A. We then calculate, as before, the number of collisions $\tilde{T}$ of the type depicted in Figure 5.6, but this time between molecules with velocities in

$d\tilde{c}^A$ and $d\tilde{c}^B$, so that the relative speed is $\tilde{g}$. The result, analogous to our expression for T above, is $\tilde{T} = \tilde{f}^B \, d\tilde{c}^B p \, dp \, d\psi \tilde{g} \, dt$.

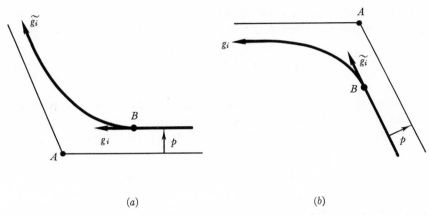

(a)   (b)

FIGURE 5.7   Direct (a) and Inverse (b) Encounters

Since each of the $\tilde{f}^A \, d\tilde{c}^A$ molecules per unit volume in $d\tilde{c}^A$ makes $\tilde{T}$ collisions with molecules in $d\tilde{c}^B$ in the time dt, the total number of these collisions between molecules in $d\tilde{c}^A$ and molecules in $d\tilde{c}^B$ is, analogously to [5.26],

$$\tilde{f}^A \, d\tilde{c}^A \, \tilde{T} = \tilde{f}^A \tilde{f}^B \, d\tilde{c}^A \, d\tilde{c}^B \, \tilde{g} p \, dp \, d\psi \, dt \qquad [5.28]$$

Thus the total number of molecules of Class A that emerge from a collision is found by integrating [5.28] with respect to $d\tilde{c}^B$, dp, $d\psi$. Denoting this quantity by "In" (these molecules get knocked into dc^A) we have

$$\text{"In"} = d\tilde{c}^A \, dt \int \tilde{f}^A \tilde{f}^B \, \tilde{g} p \, dp \, d\psi \, d\tilde{c}^B \qquad [5.29]$$

The net gain of molecules of Class A is the difference between [5.29] and [5.27]. We have already seen that $g = \tilde{g}$ (Equation [4.16]). It can also be shown that $dc^A \, dc^B = d\tilde{c}^A \, d\tilde{c}^B$ (see Exercise 5.32.1). Using these results, the net gain of molecules to Class A is

$$\text{"In"} - \text{"Out"} = dc^A \, dt \int (\tilde{f}^A \tilde{f}^B - f^A f^B) \, gp \, dp \, d\psi \, dc^B \qquad [5.30]$$

Now $(\partial f^A/\partial t)_{\text{coll}}$ is the rate of change of f^A due to collisions. The number of molecules per unit volume of Class A at the beginning of dt is $f^A dc^A$. The number of molecules per unit volume of Class A at the end of dt is

$$[f^A + (\partial f^A/\partial t)_{\text{coll}} \, dt] \, dc^A.$$

Thus the net gain of molecules to Class A is $(\partial f^A/\partial t)_{\text{coll}} \, dt \, dc^A$. But the net gain of molecules to Class A is also given by [5.30], so that we can write

$$\left(\frac{\partial f^A}{\partial t}\right)_{\text{coll}} = \int (\tilde{f}^A \tilde{f}^B - f^A f^B) g p \, dp \, d\psi \, dc^B \qquad [5.31]$$

In deriving this equation we have considered v_i^A to be the velocity of our typical molecule. We might just as well have chosen any velocity v_i. In this case $f(v_i^A) = f^A$ would become $f(v_i) = f$ and [5.31] would be written

$$\left(\frac{\partial f}{\partial t}\right)_{\text{coll}} = \int (\tilde{f}\tilde{f}^B - ff^B) g p \, dp \, d\psi \, dc^B \qquad [5.32]$$

Note that we retain the identity of the Class B molecules since we integrate these over all velocities.

Using [5.32] we can write the Boltzmann equation [5.25] as

$$\frac{\partial f}{\partial t} + v_i \frac{\partial f}{\partial x_i} + R_i \frac{\partial f}{\partial v_i} = \int (\tilde{f}\tilde{f}^B - ff^B) g p \, dp \, d\psi \, dc^B \qquad [5.33]$$

We can also write the collision integral in terms of the differential cross section. Using [4.59] and [4.61], we can write [5.32] as

$$\left(\frac{\partial f}{\partial t}\right)_{\text{coll}} = \int (\tilde{f}\tilde{f}^B - ff^B) g \, dQ \, dc^B$$

$$= \int (\tilde{f}\tilde{f}^B - ff^B) g S(\chi) \, d\omega \, dc^B$$

or, if the distribution function is independent of the azimuthal angle ψ,

$$\left(\frac{\partial f}{\partial t}\right)_{\text{coll}} = 2\pi \int (\tilde{f}\tilde{f}^B - ff^B) g S(\chi) \sin \chi \, d\chi \, dc^B \qquad [5.34]$$

Exercise 5.32.1   Show that $dc^A \, dc^B = d\tilde{c}^A \, d\tilde{c}^B$. HINT: The relationship between $dc^A \, dc^B$ and $d\tilde{c}^A \, d\tilde{c}^B$ is given by the Jacobian transformations $dc^A \, dc^B = |J| \, d\tilde{c}^A \, d\tilde{c}^B$, where

$$J = \frac{\partial(v_i^A, v_i^B)}{\partial(\tilde{v}_i^A, \tilde{v}_i^B)} = \begin{vmatrix} \dfrac{\partial v_i^A}{\partial \tilde{v}_i^A} & \dfrac{\partial v_i^A}{\partial \tilde{v}_i^B} \\[2mm] \dfrac{\partial v_i^B}{\partial \tilde{v}_i^A} & \dfrac{\partial v_i^B}{\partial \tilde{v}_i^B} \end{vmatrix}$$

and

$$d\tilde{c}^A \, d\tilde{c}^B = |J'| \, dc^A \, dc^B$$

where

$$J' = \frac{\partial(\tilde{v}_i^A, \tilde{v}_i^B)}{\partial(v_i^A, v_i^B)} = \begin{vmatrix} \dfrac{\partial \tilde{v}_i^A}{\partial v_i^A} & \dfrac{\partial \tilde{v}_i^A}{\partial v_i^B} \\[2mm] \dfrac{\partial \tilde{v}_i^B}{\partial v_i^A} & \dfrac{\partial \tilde{v}_i^B}{\partial v_i^B} \end{vmatrix}$$

Now a general property of Jacobians is that

$$JJ' = \frac{\partial(v_i^A, v_i^B)}{\partial(\tilde{v}_i^A, \tilde{v}_i^B)} \cdot \frac{\partial(\tilde{v}_i^A, \tilde{v}_i^B)}{\partial(v_i^A, v_i^B)} = 1$$

If we can show that for our case $J = J'$ then $J = \pm 1$ and $dc^A \, dc^B = d\tilde{c}^A \, d\tilde{c}^B$. In order to show that $J = J'$ use can be made of the relations [4.11], [4.12], [4.14], and [4.15].

5.4 THE EQUILIBRIUM SOLUTION OF THE BOLTZMANN EQUATION

We will use the term *equilibrium solution of the Boltzmann equation* to mean that expression for the velocity distribution function f that satisfies the equation when there are no external forces and when interparticle collisions no longer cause any change in the distribution.

It will be convenient to begin with a discussion of functions called *summational invariants*. Consider a collision between two molecules A and B. If a function ϕ of the molecular velocities is associated with each molecule, and if the sum of the ϕ's for the two molecules is conserved during a collision, then ϕ is called a summational invariant. Thus ϕ has the property that

$$\phi^A + \phi^B = \tilde{\phi}^A + \tilde{\phi}^B \qquad [5.35]$$

If we consider a collision between any arbitrary molecule with a second molecule B, we can write this as

$$\phi + \phi^B = \tilde{\phi} + \tilde{\phi}^B \qquad [5.36]$$

We know certain quantities that are conserved during a collision—for example, the total energy and the components of linear momentum. That is,

$$\tfrac{1}{2} m v_i v_i + \tfrac{1}{2} m^B v_i^B v_i^B = \tfrac{1}{2} m \tilde{v}_i \tilde{v}_i + \tfrac{1}{2} m^B \tilde{v}_i^B \tilde{v}_i^B \qquad [5.37]$$

and

$$mv_i + m^B v_i^B = m\tilde{v}_i + m^B \tilde{v}_i^B \qquad [5.38]$$

Thus, $mv_i v_i/2$ and mv_i are summational invariants. A numerical constant is another summational invariant.

Equations [5.37] and [5.38] are four equations giving the six quantities $\tilde{v}_1$, $\tilde{v}_2$, $\tilde{v}_3$, $\tilde{v}_1^B$, $\tilde{v}_2^B$, $\tilde{v}_3^B$ in terms of v_1, v_2, v_3, v_1^B, v_2^B, v_3^B. Thus solving these four equations in six unknowns leaves two unknowns to be determined. However there are two geometrical unknowns required to specify the collisions completely—p and ψ in Figure 5.6. Knowing these, the problem is determined by [5.37] and [5.38]. Thus any other summational invariant cannot be independent and must be a linear combination of

$$\phi^{(1)} = 1, \quad \phi_i^{(2)} = mv_i, \quad \phi^{(3)} = \tfrac{1}{2}mv_j v_j \qquad [5.39]$$

Now the Boltzmann equation is written from [5.33], as

$$\frac{\partial f}{\partial t} + v_i \frac{\partial f}{\partial x_i} + R_i \frac{\partial f}{\partial v_i} = \int (\tilde{f}\tilde{f}^B - ff^B)gp\, dp\, d\psi\, dc^B \qquad [5.40]$$

We wish to determine the form of the distribution function f for the case of a uniform gas ($\partial f/\partial x_i = 0$) on which no external forces are acting ($R_i = 0$). For this case [5.40] becomes

$$\frac{\partial f}{\partial t} = \int (\tilde{f}\tilde{f}^B - ff^B)gp\, dp\, d\psi\, dc^B \qquad [5.41]$$

Now we are looking for an equilibrium, or steady-state solution—that is, a solution for which $\partial f/\partial t = 0$. From [5.41] this requires that the integral on the right-hand side vanish. Clearly this integral will vanish if

$$\tilde{f}\tilde{f}^B - ff^B = 0 \qquad [5.42]$$

Equation [5.42] is therefore a sufficient condition for [5.41] to be zero, but is it also necessary? For instance, it might be possible for the integral to be positive in some parts of velocity space and negative in other parts so that integrating over all velocity space causes the integral to vanish.

The answer is that [5.42] is also necessary for a steady-state solution, and the proof of this fact is given by Boltzmann's H-theorem. We defer this proof for the time being and first look for the form of f which satisfies [5.42]. We will then show that this is the only solution for the equilibrium case by proving Boltzmann's H-theorem.

Taking the natural logarithm of [5.42], we obtain

$$\ln \tilde{f} + \ln \tilde{f}^B = \ln f + \ln f^B \qquad [5.43]$$

Comparing [5.43] with [5.36] we see that $\ln f$ must be a summational invariant. Thus, as we have seen, it must be a linear combination of $\phi^{(1)}$, $\phi_i^{(2)}$, and $\phi^{(3)}$ given in [5.39]. That is,

$$\begin{aligned}
\ln f &= \sum_{n=1}^{3} \alpha^{(n)} \phi^{(n)} \\
&= \alpha^{(1)} \phi^{(1)} + \alpha_i^{(2)} \phi_i^{(2)} - \alpha^{(3)} \phi^{(3)} \\
&= \alpha^{(1)} + \alpha_i^{(2)} m v_i - \alpha^{(3)} \tfrac{1}{2} m v_j v_j
\end{aligned}$$

Note that $\alpha_i^{(2)}$ is a vector having three components. The sign of the constant $\alpha^{(3)}$ is taken negative for later convenience. Summing over repeated indices gives

$$\ln f = \alpha^{(1)} + m(\alpha_1^{(2)} v_1 + \alpha_2^{(2)} v_2 + \alpha_3^{(2)} v_3) - \tfrac{1}{2}\alpha^{(3)} m (v_1^2 + v_2^2 + v_3^2)$$

$$= \ln \alpha^{(0)} - \alpha^{(3)} \tfrac{1}{2} m \left[\left(v_1 - \frac{\alpha_1^{(2)}}{\alpha^{(3)}} \right)^2 + \left(v_2 - \frac{\alpha_2^{(2)}}{\alpha^{(3)}} \right)^2 + \left(v_3 - \frac{\alpha_3^{(2)}}{\alpha^{(3)}} \right)^2 \right]$$

If we write $\dfrac{\alpha_i^{(2)}}{\alpha^{(3)}} = \beta_i$, we obtain

$$\ln f = \ln \alpha^{(0)} - \alpha^{(3)} \tfrac{1}{2} m [(v_1 - \beta_1)^2 + (v_2 - \beta_2)^2 + (v_3 - \beta_3)^2]$$

or

$$f = \alpha^{(0)} e^{-\alpha^{(3)}(1/2)m[(v_1 - \beta_1)^2 + (v_2 - \beta_2)^2 + (v_3 - \beta_3)^2]} \qquad [5.44]$$

The form of f given by [5.44] is known as the Maxwellian distribution. There are five arbitrary constants, $\alpha^{(0)}$, $\alpha^{(3)}$, β_1, β_2, β_3, which we must determine. We will determine these in Section 5.42. However, before doing this, we will show that [5.44] is the only equilibrium solution by proving the Boltzmann H-theorem.

5.41   THE BOLTZMANN H-THEOREM

In deriving the collision integral we calculated the net gain of molecules into a velocity element dc^A. It was simply for mathematical convenience that we talked about elements dc^A, dc^B, $d\tilde{c}^A$, and $d\tilde{c}^B$. In fact we later deleted the A from our notation and obtained

$$\left(\frac{\partial f}{\partial t}\right)_{\text{coll}} = \int (\tilde{f}\tilde{f}^B - ff^B)\, gp\, dp\, d\psi\, dc^B \tag{5.45}$$

and we can clearly replace B in [5.45] by any other symbol since it is only a variable of integration and gets "integrated out."

For the present, again for convenience, let us retain the distinction between dc^A, dc^B, $d\tilde{c}^A$, and $d\tilde{c}^B$. Equation [5.41] would become, considering dc^A as our typical element,

$$\frac{\partial f^A}{\partial t} = \int (\tilde{f}^A\tilde{f}^B - f^Af^B)\, gp\, dp\, d\psi\, dc^B \tag{5.46}$$

with the sufficient condition that

$$\tilde{f}^A\tilde{f}^B - f^Af^B = 0 \tag{5.47}$$

for an equilibrium solution.

We have seen that [5.47] leads to the Maxwellian distribution. To show that [5.47] is also a necessary condition we must show, for instance, that the integrand of [5.46] is always of the same sign and thus can never be made to "integrate out" to zero. However [5.46] is a too restricted case, since it considers dc^A as our "typical" element, and we clearly could have picked dc^B, $d\tilde{c}^A$, or $d\tilde{c}^B$ as our typical element.

Boltzmann now introduced the H-function, defined as

$$H = \int f \ln f\, dc \tag{5.48}$$

where the reason for considering this general form is that H is then independent of whatever we choose as our typical element. Thus

$$H = \int f^A \ln(f^A)\, dc^A = \int f^B \ln(f^B)\, dc^B = \int \tilde{f}^A \ln(\tilde{f}^A)\, d\tilde{c}^A = \int \tilde{f}^B \ln(\tilde{f}^B)\, d\tilde{c}^B \tag{5.49}$$

Now H is a number, independent of v_i, but which can be a function of t. Clearly it depends only on the form of f. Thus a necessary condition for the steady state is that $\partial H/\partial t = 0$. Considering dc^A as our typical element, we have from [5.49],

$$\frac{\partial H}{\partial t} = \int \frac{\partial}{\partial t}(f^A \ln f^A)\, dc^A = \int \left[\frac{\partial f^A}{\partial t}\ln f^A + \frac{f^A}{f^A}\frac{\partial f^A}{\partial t}\right] dc^A$$

$$= \int (1 + \ln f^A)\frac{\partial f^A}{\partial t}\, dc^A \tag{5.50}$$

Substituting [5.46] into [5.50], we obtain

$$\frac{\partial H}{\partial t} = \int (1 + \ln f^A)(\tilde{f}^A \tilde{f}^B - f^A f^B)\, gp\, dp\, d\psi\, dc^B\, dc^A \qquad [5.51]$$

If we had considered dc^B as our typical element, then we could form $\partial H/\partial t$ in a similar way, and $\partial f^B/\partial t$ would be given by [5.46] except that the A's and B's would be interchanged. Thus $\partial H/\partial t$ would be given by [5.51] with the A's and B's interchanged—that is, by

$$\frac{\partial H}{\partial t} = \int (1 + \ln f^B)(\tilde{f}^B \tilde{f}^A - f^B f^A)\, gp\, dp\, d\psi\, dc^A\, dc^B \qquad [5.52]$$

Adding [5.51] and [5.52] and dividing by 2, we obtain

$$\frac{\partial H}{\partial t} = \frac{1}{2} \int [2 + \ln (f^A f^B)](\tilde{f}^A \tilde{f}^B - f^A f^B)\, gp\, dp\, d\psi\, dc^A\, dc^B \qquad [5.53]$$

Now we could equally well repeat this calculation using $d\tilde{c}^A$ and $d\tilde{c}^B$ as our typical elements. In this case we would obtain an equation analogous to [5.53], that is,

$$\frac{\partial H}{\partial t} = \frac{1}{2} \int (2 + \ln \tilde{f}^A \tilde{f}^B)(f^A f^B - \tilde{f}^A \tilde{f}^B)\, gp\, dp\, d\psi\, d\tilde{c}^A\, d\tilde{c}^B \qquad [5.54]$$

Adding [5.53] and [5.54], and remembering that $dc^A\, dc^B = d\tilde{c}^A\, d\tilde{c}^B$ (see Exercise 5.32.1), we obtain

$$\frac{\partial H}{\partial t} = \frac{1}{4} \int \left(\ln \frac{f^A f^B}{\tilde{f}^A \tilde{f}^B} \right)(\tilde{f}^A \tilde{f}^B - f^A f^B)\, gp\, dp\, d\psi\, dc^A\, dc^B \qquad [5.55]$$

Now when $\ln (f^A f^B/\tilde{f}^A \tilde{f}^B)$ is negative, $(\tilde{f}^A \tilde{f}^B - f^A f^B)$ is positive, and vice versa. Thus the integrand of [5.55] is either negative or zero, so that the integral will only be zero if the integrand is zero. However it is only zero when $\tilde{f}^A \tilde{f}^B - f^A f^B$ is zero, so that this condition is necessary for $\partial H/\partial t$ to be equal to zero, and thus it is a necessary condition for the equilibrium case. This is the same as the sufficient condition given by [5.47] which yielded the Maxwellian distribution. Thus the Maxwellian distribution is the only equilibrium distribution that can exist in a uniform gas with no external forces.

5.42   THE MAXWELLIAN DISTRIBUTION

The *Maxwellian distribution* of particle velocities given by [5.44] is the most important of the several velocity distributions discussed in Chapter 10,

Plasma Kinetic Theory. It is the distribution of a set of particles in collisional equilibrium with themselves. Under this condition a temperature may properly be assigned to the gas and the various thermodynamic properties of the gas may be discussed. When this condition is not fulfilled, that is to say, when the external forces are too strong to be masked by collisions, then thermodynamic properties cannot properly be applied to the gas. In such a case it may be a very difficult problem to solve the Boltzmann equation for the distribution function. If the distribution function is unknown then the rigorous calculation of transport coefficients, as discussed in Chapter 10, cannot be made. It is therefore important in plasma problems to know when the particles possess a Maxwellian velocity distribution or when such a distribution may be a good assumption.

In discussing this distribution we must first evaluate the constants contained in [5.44].

Physical Interpretation of Arbitrary Constants The Maxwellian distribution, given by [5.44] is

$$f = \alpha^{(0)} e^{-\alpha^{(3)}(1/2)m[(v_1 - \beta_1)^2 + (v_2 - \beta_2)^2 + (v_3 - \beta_3)^2]} \qquad [5.56]$$

We wish to determine the physical meaning of the five constants $\alpha^{(0)}$, $\alpha^{(3)}$, β_1, β_2, β_3. Let us make the following changes of variables: $U_1 = v_1 - \beta_1$, $U_2 = v_2 - \beta_2$, $U_3 = v_3 - \beta_3$. Then [5.56] becomes

$$f = \alpha^{(0)} e^{-\alpha^{(3)}(1/2)m[U_1^2 + U_2^2 + U_3^2]} \qquad [5.57]$$

The mean value of any function ϕ was given as

$$N\langle \phi \rangle = \int \phi f \, dc = \int \phi f \, dv_1 \, dv_2 \, dv_3$$

so that

$$N\langle \phi \rangle = \int \phi \alpha^{(0)} e^{-\alpha^{(3)}(1/2)m[U_1^2 + U_2^2 + U_3^2]} \, dU_1 \, dU_2 \, dU_3 \qquad [5.58]$$

Let $\phi = U_1$ in [5.58]. Then

$$N\langle U_1 \rangle = \alpha^{(0)} \int_{-\infty}^{\infty} U_1 e^{-\alpha^{(3)}(1/2)m U_1^2} \, dU_1 \int_{-\infty}^{\infty} e^{-\alpha^{(3)}(1/2)m U_2^2} \, dU_2$$

$$\int_{-\infty}^{\infty} e^{-\alpha^{(3)}(1/2)m U_3^2} \, dU_3 = 0 \qquad [5.59]$$

since the first integral is the integral from $-\infty$ to ∞ of an odd function of U_1. Thus, from the definition of U_1, $\langle U_1 \rangle = \langle v_1 - \beta_1 \rangle = \langle v_1 \rangle - \beta_1 = 0$, and therefore $\beta_1 = \langle v_1 \rangle$ is the x_1-component of the mean velocity of the gas.

In a similar manner we can show that $\beta_2 = \langle v_2 \rangle$ and $\beta_3 = \langle v_3 \rangle$, so that we can write

$$U_1 = v_1 - \langle v_1 \rangle = V_1$$
$$U_2 = v_2 - \langle v_2 \rangle = V_2$$
$$U_3 = v_3 - \langle v_3 \rangle = V_3$$

where V_1, V_2, and V_3 are the components of the peculiar velocity V_i. The Maxwellian distribution can thus be written as

$$f = \alpha^{(0)} e^{-\alpha^{(3)}(1/2)m[V_1^2 + V_2^2 + V_3^2]} \qquad [5.60]$$

It is shown in Exercise 5.42.1 that if [5.60] is used in the expression

$$N\langle \phi \rangle = \int \phi f \, dC$$

and is transformed to spherical coordinates, where $V_i V_i = W^2$, then by letting $\phi = 1$ and $\phi = mV_i V_i/2$ respectively, we can determine $\alpha^{(0)}$ and $\alpha^{(3)}$. The result is that [5.60] can be written as

$$f = N\left(\frac{m}{2\pi kT}\right)^{3/2} e^{-(mW^2/2kT)} \qquad [5.61]$$

Thus we see that for a given number density N, mean velocity $\langle v_i \rangle$, and temperature T there is only one possible equilibrium distribution of molecular velocities and that any different distribution will tend to approach this distribution in the absence of external forces.

The Distribution of Peculiar Velocities The number of molecules per unit volume with velocities v_i is $f\,dc$ and is, if f is the Maxwellian distribution,

$$f \, dc = N\left(\frac{m}{2\pi kT}\right)^{3/2} e^{-m(v_1 - \langle v_1 \rangle)^2/2kT} \, dv_1 e^{-m(v_2 - \langle v_2 \rangle)^2/2kT} \, dv_2 e^{-m(v_3 - \langle v_3 \rangle)^2/2kT} \, dv_3$$

We therefore see that each velocity component is distributed independently about its mean value $\langle v_i \rangle$. A typical Maxwellian distribution of points in velocity space is shown in Figure 5.8. For most cases of interest the mean velocity $\langle v_i \rangle$ is much less than the mean thermal speed represented by the spread of the points in Figure 5.8.

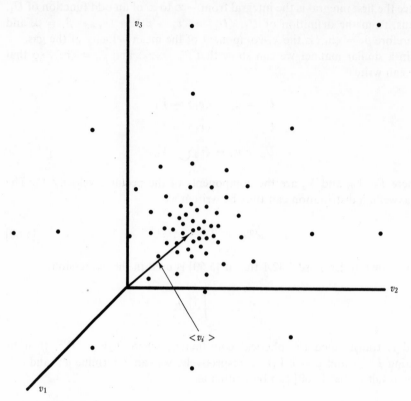

FIGURE 5.8 A Maxwellian Distribution of Points in Velocity Space

The Maxwellian distribution f is plotted for a given number density N as a function of the peculiar velocity component V_1 for three different temperatures in Figure 5.9. Each component of V_i is distributed proportionately to $\exp(-mV_i^2/2kT)$.

The Distribution of Peculiar Speeds   The number of molecules per unit volume with peculiar velocities V_i in dC is

$$f\,dC = fW^2 \sin\theta\,d\theta\,d\varphi\,dW \qquad [5.62]$$

(see Figure 5.10). We find the number of molecules per unit volume with peculiar speeds between W and $W + dW$ by integrating [5.62] with respect to θ and φ. This gives

$$4\pi f W^2\,dW = 4\pi N\left(\frac{m}{2\pi kT}\right)^{3/2} W^2 e^{-(mW^2/2kT)}\,dW$$

$$= \left(\frac{2}{\pi}\right)^{1/2} N\left(\frac{m}{kT}\right)^{3/2} W^2 e^{-(mW^2/2kT)}\,dW$$

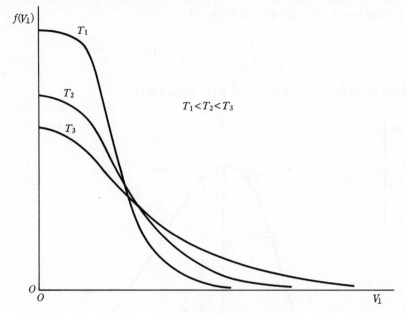

FIGURE 5.9 Maxwellian Distribution of Peculiar Velocities at Different Temperatures

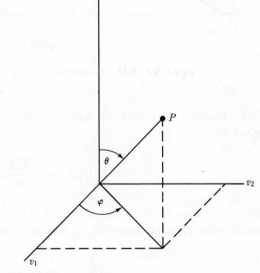

FIGURE 5.10 Spherical Coordinate System

Thus the probability density or probability of finding a molecule with peculiar speed between W and $W + dW$ is

$$4\pi f W^2 = \left(\frac{2}{\pi}\right)^{1/2} N\left(\frac{m}{kT}\right)^{3/2} W^2 e^{-(mW^2/2kT)}$$

which is plotted as a function of W in Figure 5.11.

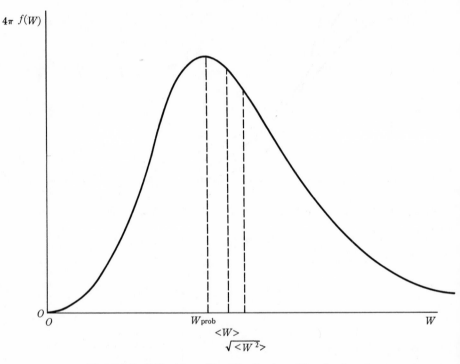

FIGURE 5.11   Maxwellian Distribution of Peculiar Speeds

By maximizing $4\pi f W^2$ we find that the most probable speed W_{prob} is given by

$$W_{\text{prob}} = \sqrt{\frac{2kT}{m}} \tag{5.63}$$

Since the curve $4\pi f W^2$ is asymmetrical, the average speed will not be equal to the most probable speed W_{prob}. It is given by

$$\langle W \rangle = \frac{1}{N} \int W f \, dC$$

or

$$\langle W \rangle = \sqrt{\frac{8kT}{\pi m}} = \frac{2}{\sqrt{\pi}} W_{\text{prob}} = 1.128 W_{\text{prob}} \qquad [5.64]$$

The definition of temperature was given by $\frac{1}{2}m\langle V_i V_i \rangle = \frac{3}{2}kT$ so that $\langle V_i V_i \rangle = \langle (V_1^2 + V_2^2 + V_3^2) \rangle = \langle W^2 \rangle = 3kT/m$ from which

$$\sqrt{\langle W^2 \rangle} = \sqrt{3kT/m} = \sqrt{\frac{3}{2}} W_{\text{prob}}$$

or

$$\sqrt{\langle W^2 \rangle} = 1.224 W_{\text{prob}} \qquad [5.65]$$

Thus we see that three quantities must be distinguished in describing molecular speeds:

1. the most probable speed W_{prob}
2. the average speed $\langle W \rangle = 1.128 W_{\text{prob}}$
3. the square root of the mean square speed $\sqrt{\langle W^2 \rangle} = 1.224 W_{\text{prob}}$

It is sometimes convenient in calculating orders of magnitude of certain properties of the gas to consider all molecules of the gas to have the same velocity. In order to be consistent with our definition of temperature and pressure we must take for this velocity $\sqrt{\langle W^2 \rangle}$ given by [5.65].

Exercise 5.42.1

(a) Given $f = \alpha^{(0)} e^{-\alpha^{(3)}(1/2)m[V_1^2 + V_2^2 + V_3^2]}$, change $N\langle \phi \rangle = \int \phi f \, dV_1 \, dV_2 \, dV_3$ to spherical coordinates (see Appendix D) and show that

$$N\langle \phi \rangle = 4\pi\alpha^{(0)} \int_0^\infty \phi W^2 e^{-\alpha^{(3)}(1/2)mW^2} \, dW \qquad [5.66]$$

(b) Let $\phi = 1$ in [5.66] and show that $\alpha^{(0)} = N(m\alpha^{(3)}/2\pi)^{3/2}$ (see Appendix F).
(c) Let $\phi = mV_i V_i/2 = mW^2/2$ in [5.66]. Use the definition of temperature: $m\langle V_i V_i \rangle/2 = 3kT/2$ and show that $\alpha^{(3)} = 1/kT$.

Exercise 5.42.2 Verify equations [5.63] and [5.64].

Exercise 5.42.3 Consider a plasma made up of an equal number of electrons and positive ions. Assume that the electrons and the ions each have a separate Maxwellian distribution as the result of collisions between like particles. Plot the two distribution functions $f_\pm$ vs. V_i on the same scale for the case when (a) $T_- = T_+$ and (b) $T_- > T_+$.

5.5 THE BOLTZMANN FACTOR

In the previous sections we have shown that in equilibrium when no external forces act on the gas the steady-state velocity distribution function is Maxwellian. In Chapter 10 we will consider the problem of determining the velocity distribution function when external forces or density gradients produce drifts in a plasma. We will, in this section, consider the special case of a conservative force field acting on a gas in which the mean velocity of the molecules is zero. That is, we wish to determine how the molecules become distributed in response to the conservative force field.

The Boltzmann equation is

$$\frac{\partial f}{\partial t} + v_i \frac{\partial f}{\partial x_i} + R_i \frac{\partial f}{\partial v_i} = \left(\frac{\partial f}{\partial t}\right)_{\text{coll}} \qquad [5.67]$$

where R_i is assumed to be a conservative force per unit mass such that

$$mR_i = -\Phi_{,i} \qquad [5.68]$$

where Φ is the potential energy. Let us assume that for this case the steady-state solution of [5.67] is of the form

$$f = f_0 e^{-(\Phi/kT)} \qquad [5.69]$$

where f_0 is the Maxwellian distribution given by

$$f_0 = N_0 \left(\frac{m}{2\pi kT}\right)^{3/2} e^{-(mv_iv_i/2kT)} \qquad [5.70]$$

for the case when $\langle v_i \rangle = 0$.

Since the factor $e^{-\Phi/kT}$ is independent of velocity, then substitution of [5.69] in the collision integral [5.32] leads to $(\partial f/\partial t)_{\text{coll}} = 0$ since the collision integral vanishes for a Maxwellian distribution. Therefore, the right-hand side of [5.67] is zero so that in the steady state it is only necessary to show that [5.69] satisfies the equation

$$v_i \frac{\partial f}{\partial x_i} + R_i \frac{\partial f}{\partial v_i} = 0 \qquad [5.71]$$

This is readily verified (see Exercise 5.5.1) so that from [5.69] and [5.70] we can write the velocity distribution function as

$$f = f_0 e^{-\Phi/kT}$$

$$= N(x_i)\left(\frac{m}{2\pi kT}\right)^{3/2} e^{-(mv_iv_i/2kT)} \qquad [5.72]$$

where

$$N(x_i) = N_0 e^{-(\Phi(x_i)/kT)} \qquad [5.73]$$

The factor $e^{-\Phi/kT}$ is called the *Boltzmann factor*.

If the force is due to an electrostatic field $E_i = -\psi_{,i}$, then the potential energy $\Phi = q\psi$. This form of the Boltzmann factor will be used in Chapter 9 in the discussion of electrostatic shielding in plasmas.

Exercise 5.5.1 Show that [5.71] is satisfied by [5.69].

5.6 STATISTICAL MECHANICS AND PLASMA KINETIC THEORY*

In this chapter we have discussed the basic concepts of classical kinetic theory. The derivation of the Boltzmann equation given in Section 5.3 was based on physical arguments. Our purpose in this section is to discuss the relationship of the Boltzmann equation and kinetic theory to the more general concepts of statistical mechanics.

The variables which we need to describe molecular behavior are of three types. First, we distinguish quantities pertaining to the molecules themselves, like mass and electrical charge. Second, there are external parameters which determine boundary conditions and external forces. Third are the variables which describe the molecular motion such as position, velocity, momentum, and energy. These we call *dynamical variables* and a particular set of these variables will define the *dynamical state* of the molecule. We choose to identify the dynamical state (**s**) of a molecule by the six variables of position and velocity, thus,

$$\mathbf{s} = (\mathbf{x}, \mathbf{v}) = (x_1, x_2, x_3, v_1, v_2, v_3)$$

These variables are independent and they determine the remaining dynamical variables of a given molecule. Thus, the dynamical state of a molecule corresponds to a point in the six-dimensional space of **s**. This space is called the *one-particle phase space*, although this term is sometimes reserved for the space of vectors similar to **s** in which the velocity is replaced by momentum.

The dynamical state of a collection of n molecules can be described by

$$\mathbf{S} = (\mathbf{s}^{(1)}, \mathbf{s}^{(2)}, \cdots, \mathbf{s}^{(k)}, \cdots, \mathbf{s}^{(n)})$$

* In collaboration with Dr. H. B. Hollinger, Chemistry Department, Rensselaer Polytechnic Institute.

where $s^{(k)}$ is the *state vector* for the molecule k. This specification of the dynamical state of n particles may be interpreted as either one point in $6n$-dimensional phase space (i.e., *n-particle phase space*) or as a cloud of n points in one-particle phase space. The problem of mechanics is that of predicting the state S at a given time from a knowledge of the initial state and the forces acting on the molecules. The force acting on molecule k is a known function of S which may be denoted by $F^{(k)}$ and written as

$$F^{(k)} = F_{INT}^{(k)} + F_{EXT}^{(k)}$$

The internal part of the force arises from the interactions between the molecules and the external part is due to the presence of external fields. We proceed by considering a way of describing the probability of various possible states S.

Let us divide n-particle phase space into cells of "volume" dS, where

$$dS = ds^{(1)} ds^{(2)} \cdots ds^{(n)}$$

and

$$ds^{(1)} = dx_1^{(1)} dx_2^{(1)} dx_3^{(1)} dv_1^{(1)} dv_2^{(1)} dv_3^{(1)}, \text{ etc.}$$

If we can assign to each cell a probability that the system is in a state S which is represented by a point in that cell, then the value of any macroscopic property can be determined from a certain averaging procedure.

We have selected the cells in the n-particle phase space as the elementary events in a probabilistic sense, since they are not correlated and it is possible to assign probabilities on well-established intuitive grounds. This procedure is the approach adopted in *statistical mechanics*. On the other hand, if the elementary events are taken to be the cells in the one-particle phase space, then probabilities can only be assigned by introducing assumptions concerning the *correlations* of the states of different particles. This is the approach adopted in *kinetic theory*.

In the application of statistical mechanics to the description of systems at equilibrium, microscopic states are eliminated if they have properties, such as total energy, which are not compatible with macroscopic properties. The remaining microscopic states are assumed to be equally probable. From this hypothesis it is possible to calculate new macroscopic properties. The purpose of macroscopic theory, to find relationships between macroscopic variables, is thereby fulfilled. A rigorous development of this program has been carried to a useful stage for gases consisting of molecules with short-range interactions.

Returning to the non-equilibrium problem we introduce the probability density $P^{(n)}$ defined as follows. The probability that a system of n molecules is within a cell of volume dS in n-particle phase space is $P(S)\, dS$. Since the system must occupy some cell in n-particle phase space we have the normalization condition

$$\int P^{(n)}(S)\, dS = 1 \qquad\qquad [5.74]$$

We will interpret the meaning of $P^{(n)}(S)$ in the following way. Consider an infinity of systems each one of which is described by one point in n-particle phase space. These points can be viewed as forming, as it were, a continuous fluid in this space. Then $P^{(n)}(S)$ represents the density of this fluid. Thus, the time variation of $P^{(n)}$ can be interpreted as the variation in the density of the fluid as the points which represent the systems move along their trajectories, which are determined by mechanics. If $P^{(n)}(S)$ is specified everywhere at an initial time, then its value is determined at later times by the motions of this fluid.

Now the rate of change of $P^{(n)}$ along the trajectory followed by an element of this fluid can be expressed in terms of the partial derivatives of $P^{(n)}$ as follows:

$$\frac{d}{dt} P^{(n)}(S, t) = \mathbf{W} \cdot \frac{\partial}{\partial S} P^{(n)} + \frac{\partial P^{(n)}}{\partial t}$$

where the dot product has the same meaning as it has in ordinary vectors, and $\mathbf{W}$ is the velocity of the fluid given by

$$\mathbf{W} = (\mathbf{w}^{(1)}, \mathbf{w}^{(2)}, \cdots, \mathbf{w}^{(k)}, \cdots, \mathbf{w}^{(n)})$$

$$\mathbf{w}^{(k)} = (\dot{x}_i^{(k)}, \dot{v}_i^{(k)})$$

$$= \left(v_i^{(k)}, \frac{1}{m^{(k)}} F_i^{(k)}\right)$$

where the rate of change of velocity is expressed in terms of the force $F_i^{(k)}$ on molecule k and the mass $m^{(k)}$ of molecule k according to Newton's law.

It is a property of this fluid in $6n$-dimensional phase space that the cell volume of the fluid element remains constant along a trajectory and the amount of fluid contained in the cell is constant. It follows that the density of the fluid as seen by an observer moving with the fluid is constant. This property is expressed by a theorem which is called Liouville's theorem. The operator $\mathbf{W} \cdot \partial/\partial S$ is known as the Liouville operator L and the equation expressing the constancy of the density is known as the Liouville equation,

$$\frac{\partial P^{(n)}}{\partial t} + LP^{(n)} = 0 \qquad\qquad [5.75]$$

where $L = \mathbf{W} \cdot \partial/\partial \mathbf{S}$. This equation expresses the fact that the fluid is a simple incompressible fluid.

Let us now consider a group of the first q molecules from the original set of n molecules. The dynamical state of these q molecules can be represented as a point in q-particle phase space (a $6q$-dimensional space). The probability that the system of q molecules is in a cell of volume $ds^{(1)} ds^{(2)}, \cdots, ds^{(q)}$ may be written as $P^{(q)} ds^{(1)} ds^{(2)}, \cdots, ds^{(q)}$. This represents the probability that the first q molecules are located in the phase space elements $ds^{(1)}, \cdots, ds^{(q)}$ while the remaining $n - q$ molecules may be anywhere. Thus, the lower order probability density function $P^{(q)}$ is obtained by integrating $P^{(n)}$ over the phase space of these remaining $n - q$ molecules. That is,

$$P^{(q)} = \int P^{(n)} ds^{(q+1)} ds^{(q+2)}, \cdots, ds^{(n)} \qquad [5.76]$$

We now focus our attention on a particular distribution of molecules in one-particle phase space. This particular distribution is then represented by a single point in n-particle phase space. However, if the molecules are indistinguishable we can interchange any or all of them and still maintain the same distribution in one-particle phase space. Each change of molecules will, of course, lead to a different point in n-particle phase space. Since the n molecules in one-particle phase space can be arranged in $n!$ ways, then $n!$ points in n-particle phase space represent the same situation in one-particle phase space. It is therefore convenient to introduce the *n-particle distribution function* $f^{(n)}$ which we define by the equation

$$f^{(n)} = n! P^{(n)} \qquad [5.77]$$

It is then clear that $f^{(n)}$ is the probability density of a particular distribution of n molecules into one-particle states without regard for which molecule is in which state.

Now $P^{(q)}$ is the probability density in q-particle phase space. Since in one-particle phase space we can choose q molecules from the original n molecules in $n!/(n - q)!$ ways, then we can write the q-particle distribution function $f^{(q)}$ as

$$f^{(q)} = \frac{n!}{(n - q)!} P^{(q)} \qquad [5.78]$$

or, using [5.76] and [5.77],

$$f^{(q)} = \frac{n!}{(n - q)!} \int P^{(n)} ds^{(q+1)} ds^{(q+2)}, \cdots, ds^{(n)}$$

$$= \frac{1}{(n - q)!} \int f^{(n)} ds^{(q+1)} ds^{(q+2)}, \cdots, ds^{(n)} \qquad [5.79]$$

From [5.79] we can write

$$f^{(q+1)} = \frac{1}{(n-q-1)!} \int f^{(n)} \, ds^{(q+2)} \, ds^{(q+3)}, \cdots, ds^{(n)} \qquad [5.80]$$

so that

$$\int f^{(q+1)} \, ds^{(q+1)} = \frac{1}{(n-q-1)!} \int f^{(n)} \, ds^{(q+1)} \, ds^{(q+2)}, \cdots, ds^{(n)}$$

$$= (n-q) f^{(q)}$$

or

$$f^{(q)} = \frac{1}{n-q} \int f^{(q+1)} \, ds^{(q+1)} \qquad [5.81]$$

In particular, we see from [5.81] and [5.79] that we can write the one-particle distribution function $f^{(1)}$ as

$$f^{(1)} = \frac{1}{(n-1)} \int f^{(2)} \, ds^{(2)} = \frac{1}{(n-1)!} \int f^{(n)} \, ds^{(2)} \, ds^{(3)}, \cdots, ds^{(n)} \quad [5.82]$$

Using [5.79] and [5.74], we have from [5.82] that

$$\int f^{(1)} \, ds^{(1)} = \int f^{(1)} \, dr^{(1)} \, dc^{(1)}$$

$$= \frac{n!}{(n-1)!} \int P^{(n)} \, dS^{(n)}$$

$$= n$$

$$= \int N^{(1)} \, dr^{(1)} \qquad [5.83]$$

where $N^{(1)}$ is the one-particle density and is given by

$$N^{(1)} = \int f^{(1)} \, dc^{(1)} \qquad [5.84]$$

as was found earlier in the chapter from the kinetic theory point of view.

5.61   THE BBGKY HIERARCHY

If the Liouville equation is integrated over the phase space of one or more molecules, then new equations are obtained which involve the lower order distribution functions. This hierarchy of equations is known as the BBGKY hierarchy after Bogoliubov, Born and Green, Kirkwood, and Yvon, who independently recognized these equations between 1939 and 1946. We can obtain this hierarchy of equations in the following manner.

The Liouville equation [5.75] may be written in expanded form as

$$\frac{\partial P^{(n)}}{\partial t} + \sum_{k=1}^{n} \mathbf{v}^{(k)} \cdot \frac{\partial P^{(n)}}{\partial \mathbf{x}^{(k)}} + \frac{1}{m} \sum_{k=1}^{n} \mathbf{F}^{(k)} \cdot \frac{\partial P^{(n)}}{\partial \mathbf{v}^{(k)}} = 0 \qquad [5.85]$$

where the summation is over the n identical molecules each of mass m. The force $\mathbf{F}^{(k)}$ which appears in [5.85] may be divided into an external force $\mathbf{F}_{\text{EXT}}^{(k)}$ and an internal force $\mathbf{F}_{\text{INT}}^{(k)}$ which is due to the interactions of molecule k with all the other molecules. If the potential energy of interaction between molecule k and molecule j is written as

$$\Phi(|\mathbf{x}^{(k)} - \mathbf{x}^{(j)}|) = \Phi^{(k, j)} \qquad [5.86]$$

then the force on molecule k due to molecule j is

$$\mathbf{F}_{\text{INT}}^{(k, j)} = -\frac{\partial \Phi^{(k, j)}}{\partial \mathbf{x}^{(k)}}$$

and the total internal force on molecule k due to interactions with all the other molecules is

$$\mathbf{F}_{\text{INT}}^{(k)} = -\sum_{\substack{j=1 \\ j \neq k}}^{n} \frac{\partial \Phi^{(k, j)}}{\partial \mathbf{x}^{(k)}} \qquad [5.87]$$

Substituting [5.87] into [5.85] we obtain

$$\frac{\partial P^{(n)}}{\partial t} + \sum_{k=1}^{n} \mathbf{v}^{(k)} \cdot \frac{\partial P^{(n)}}{\partial \mathbf{x}^{(k)}} + \frac{1}{m} \sum_{k=1}^{n} \mathbf{F}_{\text{EXT}}^{(k)} \cdot \frac{\partial P^{(n)}}{\partial \mathbf{v}^{(k)}}$$

$$- \frac{1}{m} \sum_{\substack{k=1 \\ k \neq j}}^{n} \sum_{j=1}^{n} \frac{\partial \Phi^{(k, j)}}{\partial \mathbf{x}^{(k)}} \cdot \frac{\partial P^{(n)}}{\partial \mathbf{v}^{(k)}} = 0 \quad [5.88]$$

Let us now multiply [5.88] by $n!/(n - q)!$ and integrate over $ds^{(q+1)} \, ds^{(q+2)}$, $\cdots, ds^{(n)}$. The first term then becomes, using [5.79],

$$\frac{n!}{(n - q)!} \int \frac{\partial P^{(n)}}{\partial t} \, ds^{(q+1)} \, ds^{(q+2)}, \cdots, ds^{(n)} = \frac{\partial f^{(q)}}{\partial t} \qquad [5.89]$$

The second term in [5.88] will contain a sum over the n molecules. However, if $P^{(n)}$ vanishes at $\mathbf{x}^{(k)} = \pm\infty$ (that is, if there are no molecules at infinite distances away) then for example

$$\int \frac{\partial P^{(n)}}{\partial x_1^{(k)}} \, ds^{(k)} = \int P^{(n)} \Big]_{x_1^{(k)} = -\infty}^{x_1^{(k)} = \infty} dx_2^{(k)} \, dx_3^{(k)} \, dc^{(k)} = 0 \qquad [5.90]$$

so that the second term becomes

$$\frac{n!}{(n-q)!} \sum_{k=1}^{n} \int \mathbf{v}^{(k)} \cdot \frac{\partial P^{(n)}}{\partial \mathbf{x}^{(k)}} \, ds^{(q+1)} \, ds^{(q+2)}, \cdots, ds^{(n)} = \sum_{k=1}^{q} \mathbf{v}^{(k)} \cdot \frac{\partial f^{(q)}}{\partial \mathbf{x}^{(k)}} \qquad [5.91]$$

That is, the terms occurring when $k \geq q + 1$ vanish due to [5.90].
Similarly, the third term in [5.88] becomes

$$\frac{n!}{(n-q)!} \frac{1}{m} \sum_{k=1}^{n} \mathbf{F}_{\text{EXT}}^{(k)} \cdot \frac{\partial P^{(n)}}{\partial \mathbf{v}^{(k)}} \, ds^{(q+1)} \, ds^{(q+2)}, \cdots, ds^{(n)} = \frac{1}{m} \sum_{k=1}^{q} \mathbf{F}_{\text{EXT}}^{(k)} \cdot \frac{\partial f^{(q)}}{\partial \mathbf{v}^{(k)}}$$

$$[5.92]$$

since, for example,

$$\int \frac{\partial P^{(n)}}{\partial v_1^{(k)}} \, ds^{(k)} = \int P^{(n)} \Bigg]_{v_1^{(k)} = -\infty}^{v_1^{(k)} = \infty} dv_2^{(k)} \, dv_3^{(k)} \, dr^{(k)} = 0 \qquad [5.93]$$

if no molecules have infinite velocities.
Finally, the fourth term in [5.88] contains a double sum which may be broken up as follows

$$\sum_{\substack{k=1 \\ k \neq j}}^{n} \sum_{j=1}^{n} = \sum_{\substack{k=1 \\ k \neq j}}^{q} \sum_{j=1}^{q} + \sum_{k=1}^{q} \sum_{j=q+1}^{n} + \sum_{k=q+1}^{n} \sum_{\substack{j=1 \\ k \neq j}}^{n} \qquad [5.94]$$

When integrated over $ds^{(q+1)} \, ds^{(q+2)}, \cdots, ds^{(n)}$ the term involving the last sum in [5.94] will vanish due to [5.93] since $k \geq q + 1$. The remaining two terms are then

Fourth term of [5.88] =

$$-\frac{n!}{(n-q)!} \frac{1}{m} \sum_{\substack{k=1 \\ k \neq j}}^{q} \sum_{j=1}^{q} \int \frac{\partial \Phi^{(k,j)}}{\partial \mathbf{x}^{(k)}} \cdot \frac{\partial P^{(n)}}{\partial \mathbf{v}^{(k)}} \, ds^{(q+1)} \, ds^{(q+2)}, \cdots, ds^{(n)}$$

$$-\frac{n!}{(n-q)!} \frac{1}{m} \sum_{k=1}^{q} \sum_{j=q+1}^{n} \int \frac{\partial \Phi^{(k,j)}}{\partial \mathbf{x}^{(k)}} \cdot \frac{\partial P^{(n)}}{\partial \mathbf{v}^{(k)}} \, ds^{(q+1)} \, ds^{(q+2)}, \cdots, ds^{(n)}$$

$$= -\frac{1}{m} \sum_{\substack{k=1 \\ k \neq j}}^{q} \sum_{j=1}^{q} \frac{\partial \Phi^{(k,j)}}{\partial \mathbf{x}^{(k)}} \cdot \frac{\partial f^{(q)}}{\partial \mathbf{v}^{(k)}}$$

$$-\frac{n!(n-q)}{(n-q)!} \frac{1}{m} \sum_{k=1}^{q} \int \frac{\partial \Phi^{(k,q+1)}}{\partial \mathbf{x}^{(k)}} \cdot \frac{\partial P^{(n)}}{\partial \mathbf{v}^{(k)}} \, ds^{(q+1)} \, ds^{(q+2)}, \cdots, ds^{(n)} \qquad [5.95]$$

where [5.79] was used directly in the first term since the internal force only involves interactions among the first q molecules. On the other hand, the second term in [5.95] involves interactions between the first q molecules and the remaining $(n - q)$ molecules. Since these $(n - q)$ molecules are identical and we integrate over the phase space of these $(n - q)$ molecules, then we can sum over these $(n - q)$ molecules as indicated in [5.95]. The last term in [5.95] now involves the force between molecule $k(1 \leq k \leq q)$ and molecule $(q + 1)$. If we therefore integrate over $ds^{(q+2)} ds^{(q+3)}, \cdots, ds^{(n)}$ and use [5.80], we may write [5.95] as

Fourth term in [5.88]

$$-\frac{1}{m} \sum_{\substack{k=1 \\ k \neq 1}}^{q} \sum_{j=1}^{q} \frac{\partial \Phi^{(k,j)}}{\partial \mathbf{x}^{(k)}} \cdot \frac{\partial f^{(q)}}{\partial \mathbf{v}^{(k)}}$$

$$-\frac{1}{m} \sum_{k=1}^{q} \int \frac{\partial \Phi^{(k,q+1)}}{\partial \mathbf{x}^{(k)}} \cdot \frac{\partial f^{(q+1)}}{\partial \mathbf{v}^{(k)}} ds^{(q+1)}$$

[5.96]

If we now combine [5.89], [5.91], [5.92], and [5.96] we obtain the BBGKY hierarchy

$$\frac{\partial f^{(q)}}{\partial t} + \sum_{k=1}^{q} \mathbf{v}^{(k)} \cdot \frac{\partial f^{(q)}}{\partial \mathbf{x}^{(k)}} + \frac{1}{m} \sum_{k=1}^{q} \mathbf{F}_{EXT}^{(k)} \cdot \frac{\partial f^{(q)}}{\partial \mathbf{v}^{(k)}}$$

$$-\frac{1}{m} \sum_{\substack{k=1 \\ k \neq j}}^{q} \sum_{j=1}^{q} \frac{\partial \Phi^{(k,j)}}{\partial \mathbf{x}^{(k)}} \cdot \frac{\partial f^{(q)}}{\partial \mathbf{v}^{(k)}}$$

$$= \frac{1}{m} \sum_{k=1}^{q} \int \frac{\partial \Phi^{(k,q+1)}}{\partial \mathbf{x}^{(k)}} \cdot \frac{\partial f^{(q+1)}}{\partial \mathbf{v}^{(k)}} ds^{(q+1)} \quad [5.97]$$

The lowest order equation, found by setting $q = 1$, is then

$$\frac{\partial f^{(1)}}{\partial t} + \mathbf{v}^{(1)} \cdot \frac{\partial f^{(1)}}{\partial \mathbf{x}^{(1)}} + \frac{1}{m} \mathbf{F}_{EXT}^{(1)} \cdot \frac{\partial f^{(1)}}{\partial \mathbf{v}^{(1)}} = \frac{1}{m} \int \frac{\partial \Phi^{(1,2)}}{\partial \mathbf{x}^{(1)}} \cdot \frac{\partial f^{(2)}}{\partial \mathbf{v}^{(1)}} ds^{(2)} \quad [5.98]$$

This equation resembles the Boltzmann equation. It may appear that the Boltzmann equation has been derived from statistical mechanics. Such is not the case, however, for [5.98] involves $f^{(2)}$ in the integral on the right-hand side. Furthermore, each of the higher equations in the BBGKY hierarchy also relates one of the distribution functions to the next higher distribution function. Thus the entire set of equations must be solved to find $f^{(1)}$. This is equivalent to solving the Liouville equation so that it is not clear that we have advanced in any way toward the goal of finding a path that connects molecular dynamics to kinetic theory and thence to observable plasma

behavior by means of statistical mechanics. On the other hand, this development does focus the problem more sharply. What is now required is a way
of expressing $f^{(2)}$ in terms of $f^{(1)}$ so that [5.98] can be transformed into an
equation for $f^{(1)}$ only.

The equation for $f^{(1)}$ is called the "kinetic equation." Various forms of the
kinetic equation, including the Boltzmann form, have been used successfully
in applications to plasmas.

The limitation of each form and the relationships between the different
forms, are clarified by considering the various assumptions made about $f^{(2)}$
in the derivation from [5.98]. A unified view of the development of new
kinetic equations is obtained by considering their relation to the BBGKY
equations.

5.62 THE KINETIC EQUATION

The kinetic equation is an equation for the one-particle distribution function
$f^{(1)}$, which will be denoted in this section by f. Earlier in this chapter we have
considered the Boltzmann equation which is one form of the kinetic equation.
In the previous section we have discussed the derivation of the kinetic
equation from the Liouville equation of statistical mechanics. In order to be
able to derive the kinetic equation and avoid solving all the other equations
in the BBGKY hierarchy we must find a way of expressing $f^{(2)}$ in terms of f.
This problem is the subject of this section.

Recall that $f^{(1)}(s^{(1)}, t)$, or simply f, is the one-particle probability density
in one-particle phase space. That is, it is the number of the n particles which
are found in a given state $s^{(1)} = (x^{(1)}, v^{(1)})$ at a particular time t.   Similarly,
$f^{(2)}(s^{(1)}, s^{(2)}, t)$ is the two-particle probability density and represents the
probability of finding one molecule in the state $s^{(1)} = (x^{(1)}, v^{(1)})$ while a
second molecule is simultaneously in the state $s^{(2)} = (x^{(2)}, v^{(2)})$.

Perhaps the simplest assumption that can be made about $f^{(2)}$ is that it
factors into a product $f(s^{(1)}) f(s^{(2)})$ of one-particle distribution functions.
This expresses the idea that the particles are not correlated; that is, that the
probability of finding one particle in a particular state does not depend on the
state of the other particle. This makes sense if the particles do not interact
at all and if they are not correlated initially, but if they interact, then correlations will develop.   For example, repulsive interactions will lead to a
situation in which one particle has a low probability of being located where
there is another particle. To deny such correlations is to interfere with the
molecular dynamics; i.e., to alter Newton's law in an unknown way. Nevertheless, there are interesting cases in which this assumption about $f^{(2)}$ is successful. In plasmas, for example, where the forces are long range, each charged
particle is influenced by so many other particles that its correlations with
one other particle are partially drowned out and the assumption of no

correlations turns out to be adequate for some purposes. If we use this assumption in [5.98] we obtain, as the kinetic equation,

$$\frac{\partial f(\mathbf{s}^{(1)})}{\partial t} + \mathbf{v}^{(1)} \cdot \frac{\partial f(\mathbf{s}^{(1)})}{\partial \mathbf{x}^{(1)}} + \frac{1}{m} \mathbf{F}_{\text{EXT}}^{(1)} \cdot \frac{\partial f(\mathbf{s}^{(1)})}{\partial \mathbf{v}^{(1)}}$$

$$= \frac{1}{m} \int \frac{\partial \Phi^{(1, 2)}}{\partial \mathbf{x}^{(1)}} f(\mathbf{s}^{(2)}) \, ds^{(2)} \cdot \frac{\partial}{\partial \mathbf{v}^{(1)}} f(\mathbf{s}^{(1)})$$

$$= \frac{1}{m} \frac{\partial}{\partial \mathbf{x}^{(1)}} \langle \Phi^{(1)} \rangle \cdot \frac{\partial f(\mathbf{s}^{(1)})}{\partial \mathbf{v}^{(1)}} \qquad\qquad [5.99]$$

where

$$\langle \Phi^{(1)} \rangle = \int \Phi^{(1, 2)} f(\mathbf{s}^{(2)}) \, ds^{(2)} \qquad\qquad [5.100]$$

is the average potential at $\mathbf{x}^{(1)}$ due to all of the particles at other positions. This is the "correlationless" BBGKY equation, which is sometimes called the "collisionless Boltzmann equation" (a misnomer) or the *Vlasov equation*. We shall use a form of this equation in Chapter 11 to describe wave phenomena in plasmas.

The Boltzmann Equation   In the remainder of this section we will relax the assumption about $f^{(2)}$ by assuming that it will factor only on that part of two-particle phase space where velocities are pre-collision velocities. However we will not make this assumption about that part of $f^{(2)}$ where the velocities are post-collision velocities. We will see that this reduced assumption enables us to derive the collision term of the Boltzmann equation. In fact, a careful review of Section 5.32 will show that the collision integral was calculated there on the basis of the pre-collision velocities only.

If we consider $f^{(2)}$ at a point $(\mathbf{s}^{(1)}, \mathbf{s}^{(2)})$ where the velocities direct the particles into a future collision, then these particles have a long history of independent existence and it makes sense to assume that they are not correlated. On the other hand, if $f^{(2)}$ is evaluated at a point where particles have just emerged from a collision, then the probability that one particle is at $\mathbf{s}^{(1)}$ may depend strongly on the condition that another particle, now at $\mathbf{s}^{(2)}$, deflected it from a trajectory that would have led it to a different state. In order to use this assumption it is necessary to modify the integral on the right side of [5.98] so that $f^{(2)}$ is always evaluated at pre-collision velocities. This can be done in the following way.

First we consider the case of molecules with short range interactions. In fact, we assume that the molecules are rigid spheres of diameter d.   Consider the value of $f^{(2)}$ at a point where $\mathbf{x}^{(1)}$ and $\mathbf{x}^{(2)}$ are separated by a distance d and the velocities $\tilde{\mathbf{v}}^{(1)}$ and $\tilde{\mathbf{v}}^{(2)}$ are post-collision velocities. That is, if spheres are placed at $\mathbf{x}^{(1)}$ and $\mathbf{x}^{(2)}$ with these velocities, then they are touching, having just collided, and are moving apart. Since these post-collision velocities are strongly correlated we do not want to factor the corresponding $f^{(2)}$. This statement may be expressed by writing

$$f^{(2)}(\mathbf{x}^{(1)}, \mathbf{x}^{(2)}, \tilde{\mathbf{v}}^{(1)}, \tilde{\mathbf{v}}^{(2)}, t) \neq f(\mathbf{x}^{(1)}, \tilde{\mathbf{v}}^{(1)}, t)f(\mathbf{x}^{(2)}, \tilde{\mathbf{v}}^{(2)}, t) \qquad [5.101]$$

Now a collision between rigid spheres takes zero time. The probability that two rigid spheres are about to collide must therefore be the same as the probability that they have just collided. This can be expressed by writing

$$f^{(2)}\big|_{t=t_{\text{coll}}^-} = f^{(2)}\big|_{t=t_{\text{coll}}^+}$$

Writing pre-collision velocities as $\mathbf{v}^{(1)\prime}$, $\mathbf{v}^{(2)\prime}$ we therefore have that

$$f^{(2)}(\mathbf{x}^{(1)}, \mathbf{x}^{(2)}, \tilde{\mathbf{v}}^{(1)}, \tilde{\mathbf{v}}^{(2)}, t) = f^{(2)}(\mathbf{x}^{(1)}, \mathbf{x}^{(2)}, \mathbf{v}^{(1)\prime}, \mathbf{v}^{(2)\prime}, t) \qquad [5.102]$$

Since we are assuming that $f^{(2)}$ evaluated at pre-collision velocities can be factored

$$f^{(2)}(\mathbf{x}^{(1)}, \mathbf{x}^{(2)}, \mathbf{v}^{(1)\prime}, \mathbf{v}^{(2)\prime}, t) = f(\mathbf{x}^{(1)}, \mathbf{v}^{(1)\prime}, t) f(\mathbf{x}^{(2)}, \mathbf{v}^{(2)\prime}, t) \qquad [5.103]$$

from which, using [5.102],

$$f^{(2)}(\mathbf{x}^{(1)}, \mathbf{x}^{(2)}, \tilde{\mathbf{v}}^{(1)}, \tilde{\mathbf{v}}^{(2)}, t) = f(\mathbf{x}^{(1)}, \mathbf{v}^{(1)\prime}, t) f(\mathbf{x}^{(2)}, \mathbf{v}^{(2)\prime}, t) \qquad [5.104]$$

The integral on the right-hand side of [5.98] is

$$J = J(\mathbf{x}^{(1)}, \mathbf{v}^{(1)}, t) = \int dc^{(2)} \int dr^{(2)} A f^{(2)} \qquad [5.105]$$

where

$$A = \frac{1}{m} \frac{\partial \Phi^{(1,2)}}{\partial \mathbf{x}^{(1)}} \cdot \frac{\partial}{\partial \mathbf{v}^{(1)}} \qquad [5.106]$$

It is helpful to recall that $A f^{(2)}$ is the rate of change of $f^{(2)}$ due to the variation of $\mathbf{v}^{(1)}$ along the two-particle trajectory. Since $\mathbf{v}^{(1)}$ can be written in terms of the relative velocity $\mathbf{g}^{(1,2)}$ and the constant velocity of the center-of-mass $\mathbf{v}^G$ (see Section 4.2), then $A f^{(2)}$ is also the rate of change of $f^{(2)}$ due to the variation of $\mathbf{g}^{(1,2)}$ along the two-particle trajectory. If two rigid spheres are colliding, then $\mathbf{g}^{(1,2)}$ is constant before and after the collision and merely changes direction abruptly at the time of impact. Thus, $A f^{(2)}$ is zero except at the instant when the two colliding rigid spheres touch.

To make this definition of $Af^{(2)}$ more precise, let τ be a small advance in time. If $\mathbf{g}^{(1,\,2)}$ is the relative velocity at time t, let $\bar{\mathbf{g}}^{(1,\,2)}$ be the relative velocity at time $t + \tau$. Similarly, let $\bar{f}^{(2)}$ be the value of $f^{(2)}$ evaluated at the displaced velocity $\bar{\mathbf{g}}^{(1,\,2)}$. Then we can define $Af^{(2)}$ by the relation

$$Af^{(2)} = \lim_{\tau \to 0} \frac{\partial \bar{f}^{(2)}}{\partial \tau} \qquad [5.107]$$

For the integration over $dr^{(2)}$ in [5.105] let us choose cylindrical coordinates (p, ψ, z) with the origin at $\mathbf{x}^{(1)}$ and the z-axis in the direction of the relative velocity; that is, the coordinates of $\mathbf{x}^{(2)} - \mathbf{x}^{(1)}$ are $(p \cos \psi, p \sin \psi, z)$. (See, for example, Figure 5.6.) We may then write [5.105] in the form

$$J = \int dc^{(2)} \int_0^{2\pi} d\psi \int_0^d p \, dp \int_{-\infty}^{\infty} dz \lim_{\tau \to 0} \frac{\partial \bar{f}^{(2)}}{\partial \tau} \qquad [5.108]$$

where the upper limit for the integration over p is taken as d since the integrand is zero if the particles do not interact.

Let us now consider the z integration. The integrand is zero except at the two points $z = \pm z_0 = \pm \sqrt{d^2 - p^2}$ corresponding to where the two spheres touch (Figure 5.12). In order to determine the contribution to the integral at the point $z = -z_0$, let us keep τ finite and consider the integral

$$B = \int_{-\infty}^{-z_0} dz \frac{\partial \bar{f}^{(2)}}{\partial \tau} \qquad [5.109]$$

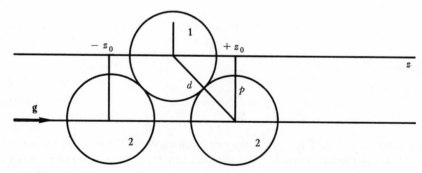

FIGURE 5.12 Collision between particle 1 moving with z-directed velocity **g** and particle 2 which is stationary

For τ small enough we can assume that

$$\bar{f}^{(2)} = f^{(2)}(z, \bar{\mathbf{g}}^{(1,\,2)}) = f^{(2)}(z - g\tau, \mathbf{g}^{(1,\,2)}) \qquad [5.110]$$

so that

$$B = \int_{-\infty}^{-z_0} dz \, \frac{\partial}{\partial \tau} f^{(2)}(z - g\tau) = -\int_{-\infty}^{-z_0} dz \, g \, \frac{\partial}{\partial z} f^{(2)}(z - g\tau)$$
$$= -g f^{(2)}(-z_0 - g\tau) \quad [5.111]$$

in which the dependence of $f^{(2)}$ on variables other than z has been suppressed from the notation. If we were careful enough to follow the dependence on $\mathbf{v}^{(1)}$ and $\mathbf{v}^{(2)}$ we would find that B is evaluated at pre-collision velocities, but that does not matter; in the limit of small τ, B has the same value at pre- and post-collision velocities. A similar argument can be used to show that the contribution from the other point at $z = z_0$ is $gf^{(2)}$ evaluated at z_0 and pre- or post-collision velocities. Thus, we obtain the lowest BBGKY equation for rigid spheres in the form of [5.98] with the integral on the right-hand side replaced by

$$J = \int dc^{(2)} \int_0^{2\pi} d\psi \int_0^d p \, dp \, g[f^{(2)}(z_0) - f^{(2)}(-z_0)] \qquad [5.112]$$

Since $f^{(2)}(z_0)$ and $f^{(2)}(-z_0)$ may both be evaluated at pre-collision velocities we may factor these two-particle distribution functions. After the factorization it is possible to neglect the difference between $+z_0$ and $-z_0$ and simply evaluate both one-particle distribution functions at the point $\mathbf{x}^{(1)}$. We may then write [5.112] as

$$J = \int dc^{(2)} \int_0^{2\pi} d\psi \int_0^d p \, dp \, g[f(\mathbf{x}^{(1)}, \mathbf{v}_+^{(1)}, t) f(\mathbf{x}^{(1)}, \mathbf{v}_+^{(2)}, t)$$
$$- f(\mathbf{x}^{(1)}, \mathbf{v}_-^{(1)}, t) \, f(\mathbf{x}^{(1)}, \mathbf{v}_-^{(2)}, t)] \quad [5.113]$$

This introduces a restriction to gases in which f does not vary appreciably over distances comparable to d.

If we compare [5.113] with the collision integral [5.32] we see that they will be identical if the pre-collision velocities $\mathbf{v}_+^{(1)}$ and $\mathbf{v}_+^{(2)}$ are the same as the post-collision velocities $\tilde{\mathbf{v}}^{(1)}$ and $\tilde{\mathbf{v}}^{(2)}$. That is to say that they will be identical if the collision which occurs at $+z_0$ is the inverse to the collision which occurs at $-z_0$. This will only be the case for zero impact parameter. However, the discrepancy is only apparent, since in each case we integrate over $dc^{(2)}$, $d\psi$, and dp and thus pick up all direct and inverse collisions. The value of J given by [5.113] is therefore equal to the value of the collision integral [5.32]. In making use of the collision integral the form given by [5.32] is usually the most convenient.

The assumption that $f^{(2)}$ factors on the part of phase space where velocities are pre-collision velocities is called the "molecular chaos assumption." We have seen that this assumption is a sufficient basis for the kinetic equation of rigid spheres. In the case of particles with an interaction potential Φ that varies continuously with position, the molecular chaos assumption can be used in a similar way to derive the kinetic equation. In fact, the kinetic equation generally used with such particles is the rigid-sphere Boltzmann equation with the modification that the velocities $v^{(i)\prime}$ are calculated from the non-rigid dynamics, as in Chapter 4, and the upper limit for the P integration is changed to infinity. Thus the displacement of positions to pre-collision positions is ignored, which introduces serious restrictions.

In the first place, since the displacement of positions in the non-rigid case is appreciable, it is important to recognize the variation of f with position and it is important to recognize a time displacement so that the functions f in the integral J are evaluated at earlier times. Since the effects of these displacements are generally ignored, the Boltzmann equation for non-rigid particles is restricted to systems near equilibrium. Secondly, the displacements required for the molecular chaos assumption, whether or not they are recognized, introduce an error in the neglect of interactions involving more than two particles. Thus the equation is restricted to dilute gases where two-body interactions predominate over more complex interactions. On the contrary the Boltzmann equation for rigid spheres is not restricted to dilute gases or to gases near equilibrium.

REFERENCES

Detailed treatments of kinetic theory can be found in the classic works of

1   Chapman, S., and T. G. Cowling. *The Mathematical Theory of Non-Uniform Gases.* London: Cambridge University Press, 1939.

2   Jeans, J. *The Dynamical Theory of Gases.* 4th ed.; London: Cambridge University Press, 1954.

A good description of the relationship between the Boltzmann equation and the Liouville equation is given by

3   Hirschfelder, J. O., C. F. Curtiss, and R. B. Bird. *Molecular Theory of Gases and Liquids.* New York: Wiley, 1954.

A book which includes chapters on kinetic theory, thermodynamics, and statistical mechanics is

4   Huang, K. *Statistical Mechanics.* New York: Wiley, 1963.

A more extended discussion of the relation of the BBGKY equations to plasma theory is given by

5   Montgomery, C. G., and D. A. Tidman. *Plasma Kinetic Theory.* New York: McGraw-Hill, 1964.

The application of statistical mechanics to plasmas near equilibrium is discussed by

6   Balescu, R. *The Statistical Mechanics of Charged Particles.* New York: Interscience, 1964.

6

THE MACROSCOPIC
EQUATIONS

In the previous chapter we introduced certain elements of kinetic theory. We now wish to apply these results to obtain equations which describe macroscopically observable phenomena.

We pointed out in Chapter 5 that the most complete description of a gas is given by statistical mechanics and the Liouville equation. However by being content with less information it was possible under the assumptions of molecular chaos and binary collisions to derive the Boltzmann equation describing the time variation of the velocity distribution function either from physical arguments or from the Liouville equation.

Once the velocity distribution function is known, the mean value of any molecular property can be calculated. These mean values, known as *state variables*, include such quantities as the density, pressure, mean velocity, and temperature of the gas. We will see in this chapter that it is possible to derive from the Boltzmann equation expressions that give the time variation of these state variables directly. However we will see again that this is not possible without a loss of information and that additional assumptions must be imposed in order to obtain a determined set of equations.

In Section 6.1 we obtain an equation of change of molecular properties by taking moments of the Boltzmann equation. The macroscopic equations of the gas can then be obtained from this equation of change.

When the gas contains more than a single species of particles, as in the case of a plasma, then two categories of macroscopic equations can be distinguished. The first is a set of macroscopic equations for each species in which the equations are referred to the mean velocity of each species. These equations are useful in describing transport properties and other phenomena that depend explicitly on the relative motions of the various constituents. They are called the *single-species equations* and are derived in Section 6.2. They are used to discuss transport processes in Chapter 7 and for the treatment of plasma oscillations in Chapter 12.

The second category of macroscopic equations are referred to the mean mass-velocity of the gas. This is a velocity weighted according to the mass density of the various constituents. It is defined in Section 6.3, where the plasma is considered to be a conducting fluid. If the macroscopic equations for each species are referred to the mean mass-velocity and then summed over all species, one obtains macroscopic equations for the entire gas. At this level all information about the individual constituents is lost, and in the case of a plasma one has the equations for a conducting fluid. These equations are discussed in Sections 6.4 and 6.5 and form the basis for the discussion of magneto-fluid dynamics in Chapter 14.

6.1 THE EQUATION OF CHANGE OF MOLECULAR PROPERTIES

The Boltzmann equation [5.25] describes the time variation of the velocity distribution function f. We wish to derive an equation that will describe the average time variation of any function $\phi(v_i, x_i, t)$ which is a function of the molecular velocities, their positions, and time. Since the average value of ϕ is obtained by multiplying the distribution function by ϕ and integrating over velocity space, we suspect that the time variation of the average of ϕ can be obtained by multiplying the Boltzmann equation by ϕ and integrating over velocity space. Thus, if we multiply [5.25] by ϕ and integrate over velocity space, we obtain

$$\int \phi \left(\frac{\partial f}{\partial t} + v_i \frac{\partial f}{\partial x_i} + R_i \frac{\partial f}{\partial v_i} \right) dc = \int \phi \left(\frac{\partial f}{\partial t} \right)_{\text{coll}} dc \qquad [6.1]$$

We will evaluate each term of [6.1] separately: The first term is

$$\int \phi \frac{\partial f}{\partial t} dc = \int \frac{\partial (f\phi)}{\partial t} dc - \int f \frac{\partial \phi}{\partial t} dc$$

$$= \frac{\partial}{\partial t} \int f\phi \, dc - \int f \frac{\partial \phi}{\partial t} dc$$

or

$$\int \phi \frac{\partial f}{\partial t} dc = \frac{\partial}{\partial t} (N\langle\phi\rangle) - N\left\langle\frac{\partial\phi}{\partial t}\right\rangle \tag{6.2}$$

where [5.3] was used in the last step.

In a similar manner the second term of [6.1] can be written

$$\int \phi v_i \frac{\partial f}{\partial x_i} dc = \int v_i \frac{\partial}{\partial x_i} (\phi f) dc - \int v_i \frac{\partial\phi}{\partial x_i} f dc$$

$$= \frac{\partial}{\partial x_i} \int v_i \phi f dc - \int v_i \frac{\partial\phi}{\partial x_i} f dc \tag{6.3}$$

$$= \frac{\partial}{\partial x_i} (N\langle v_i\phi\rangle) - N\left\langle v_i \frac{\partial\phi}{\partial x_i}\right\rangle$$

In the second step of [6.3] $\partial/\partial x_i$ could be taken outside the integral since v_i and x_i are independent variables.

The third term of [6.1] can be written as

$$\int \phi R_i \frac{\partial f}{\partial v_i} dc = \int R_i \frac{\partial}{\partial v_i} (\phi f) dc - \int R_i \frac{\partial\phi}{\partial v_i} f dc$$

$$= \int \frac{\partial}{\partial v_i} (R_i\phi f) dc - \int \frac{\partial R_i}{\partial v_i} \phi f dc - \int R_i \frac{\partial\phi}{\partial v_i} f dc \tag{6.4}$$

Now the first term on the right of [6.4] is the sum of three terms; it can be written as

$$\int \frac{\partial}{\partial v_i} (R_i\phi f) dc = \int\int\int \frac{\partial}{\partial v_1} (R_1\phi f) dv_1 dv_2 dv_3 + \int\int\int \frac{\partial}{\partial v_2} (R_2\phi f) dv_1 dv_2 dv_3$$

$$+ \int\int\int \frac{\partial}{\partial v_3} (R_3\phi f) dv_1 dv_2 dv_3$$

or

$$\int \frac{\partial}{\partial v_i} (R_i\phi f) dc = R_1\phi f\Big]_{-\infty}^{+\infty} \left(\int\int dv_2 dv_3\right) + R_2\phi f\Big]_{-\infty}^{+\infty} \left(\int\int dv_1 dv_3\right)$$

$$+ R_3\phi f\Big]_{-\infty}^{+\infty} \left(\int\int dv_1 dv_2\right) \tag{6.5}$$

Since f is assumed to go to zero at $\pm\infty$ (that is, it is assumed that no molecules have an infinite velocity), then each of the three terms on the right of [6.5] vanishes, so that

$$\int \frac{\partial}{\partial v_i} (R_i\phi f) dc = 0 \tag{6.6}$$

Now in the second term on the right of [6.4] there appears the factor $\partial R_i/\partial v_i$. Using [5.17] we can write this as

$$\frac{\partial R_i}{\partial v_i} = \frac{\partial R_i'}{\partial v_i} + \frac{q}{m} \frac{\partial}{\partial v_i} (\epsilon_{ijk} v_j B_k)$$

Since R_i' is, by definition, independent of velocity and $\partial v_j/\partial v_i = \delta_{ji}$ we find that

$$\frac{\partial R_i}{\partial v_i} = \frac{q}{m} \epsilon_{ijk} \delta_{ji} B_k = \frac{q}{m} \epsilon_{iik} B_k = 0$$

so that

$$\int \frac{\partial R_i}{\partial v_i} \phi f\, dc = 0 \qquad [6.7]$$

Thus, using [6.6] and [6.7], we can write [6.4] as

$$\int \phi R_i \frac{\partial f}{\partial v_i}\, dc = -\int R_i \frac{\partial \phi}{\partial v_i} f\, dc = -N \left\langle R_i \frac{\partial \phi}{\partial v_i} \right\rangle \qquad [6.8]$$

If we substitute [6.2], [6.3], and [6.8] into [6.1], we obtain

$$\frac{\partial}{\partial t}(N\langle\phi\rangle) - N\left\langle\frac{\partial\phi}{\partial t}\right\rangle + \frac{\partial}{\partial x_i}(N\langle v_i\phi\rangle) - N\left\langle v_i\frac{\partial\phi}{\partial x_i}\right\rangle - N\left\langle R_i\frac{\partial\phi}{\partial v_i}\right\rangle$$
$$= \int \phi\left(\frac{\partial f}{\partial t}\right)_{coll} dc \qquad [6.9]$$

This is the desired equation of change describing the average time variation of ϕ. For a multiconstituent gas there exists a Boltzmann equation for each species. There thus exists an equation of change for each species s of the gas which we can write from [6.9] in the form

$$\frac{\partial(N^{(s)}\langle\phi^{(s)}\rangle)}{\partial t} + \frac{\partial(N^{(s)}\langle v_i^{(s)}\phi^{(s)}\rangle)}{\partial x_i}$$
$$- N^{(s)}\left[\left\langle\frac{\partial\phi^{(s)}}{\partial t}\right\rangle + \left\langle v_i^{(s)}\frac{\partial\phi^{(s)}}{\partial x_i}\right\rangle + \left\langle R_i^{(s)}\frac{\partial\phi^{(s)}}{\partial v_i^{(s)}}\right\rangle\right] \qquad [6.10]$$
$$= \int \phi^{(s)}\left(\frac{\partial f^{(s)}}{\partial t}\right)_{coll} dc^{(s)}$$

In this equation of change for the sth species the first term represents the local time variation of the mean value of $\phi^{(s)}$. The remaining terms contribute in some way to this variation. The second term represents the rate of change of $\langle\phi^{(s)}\rangle$ due to molecules streaming in and out of a volume element. The three terms in the bracket represent the rate of change of $\langle \phi^{(s)} \rangle$ due respectively to the dependence of $\phi^{(s)}$ on the time, the position of the particles, and the external forces. The right-hand side of [6.10] represents the rate of change of $\langle \phi^{(s)} \rangle$ due to collisions. The form of this collision term will be investigated in the following section.

6.11 THE COLLISION TERM

In determining the collision term in the equation of change [6.10], it is necessary to determine an expression for the quantity $(\partial f / \partial t)_{\text{coll}}$. In Chapter 5 we found that for the case of binary collisions we could write this quantity in the form of a collision integral. We would expect this expression to be valid in a rarefied plasma for collisions between charged and neutral particles— that is, for electron-neutral or ion-neutral collisions. From [5.34] we can therefore write the collision integral for the sth charged species as

$$\left(\frac{\partial f^{(s)}}{\partial t} \right)_{\text{coll}} = \int \int (\tilde{f}^{(s)} \tilde{f}^N - f^{(s)} f^N) g S(\chi) \, d\omega \, dc^N \qquad [6.11]$$

where the superscript N refers to the neutral scattering particles.

If we form the right-hand side of [6.10] using [6.11] we obtain

$$\int \phi^{(s)} \left(\frac{\partial f^{(s)}}{\partial t} \right)_{\text{coll}} dc^{(s)} = \int \int \int \phi^{(s)} (\tilde{f}^{(s)} \tilde{f}^N - f^{(s)} f^N) g S(\chi) \, d\omega \, dc^N \, dc^{(s)}$$

$$= \int \int \int \phi^{(s)} \tilde{f}^{(s)} \tilde{f}^N g S(\chi) \, d\omega \, dc^N \, dc^{(s)} - \int \int \int \phi^{(s)} f^{(s)} f^N g S(\chi) \, d\omega \, dc^N \, dc^{(s)} \qquad [6.12]$$

Recall from Figure 5.7 that for every direct encounter there is a corresponding inverse encounter. Therefore the first term on the right-hand side of [6.12] can be written as

$$\int \int \int \phi^{(s)} \tilde{f}^{(s)} \tilde{f}^N g S(\chi) \, d\omega \, dc^N \, dc^{(s)} = \int \int \int \tilde{\phi}^{(s)} f^{(s)} f^N \tilde{g} S(\chi) \, d\omega \, d\tilde{c}^N \, d\tilde{c}^{(s)} \qquad [6.13]$$

since the integration is over all velocities.

Substituting [6.13] into [6.12] and recalling from [4.16] and Exercise 5.32.1 that $g = \tilde{g}$ and $dc^N \, dc^{(s)} = d\tilde{c}^N \, d\tilde{c}^{(s)}$ we obtain

$$\int \phi^{(s)} \left(\frac{\partial f^{(s)}}{\partial t} \right)_{\text{coll}} dc^{(s)} = \int \int \int (\tilde{\phi}^{(s)} - \phi^{(s)}) f^{(s)} f^N g S(\chi) \, d\omega \, dc^N \, dc^{(s)} \qquad [6.14]$$

which is a form for the collision term in the equation of change [6.10].

In the following sections we will let $\phi^{(s)}$ assume various values in [6.10] in order to obtain the macroscopic equations for each species of the gas.

6.2 THE MOMENT
EQUATIONS FOR EACH SPECIES

Equation [6.10] is a general equation of change involving the arbitrary function $\phi^{(s)}$. The so-called *moment equations* are obtained by letting $\phi^{(s)}$ take on values which are proportional to increasing powers of the velocity $v_i^{(s)}$. We will see that setting $\phi^{(s)} = 1$, corresponding to the zeroth moment, leads to the *continuity equation*; the first moment, obtained by setting $\phi^{(s)} = m^{(s)}v_j^{(s)}$, leads to the *momentum equation*; while setting $\phi^{(s)} = \frac{1}{2}m^{(s)}v_j^{(s)}v_j^{(s)}$ (the second moment) leads to the *energy equation*. It is possible to continue taking higher moments but this is not often done for the reason we will now explain.

The moment equations are never complete because one always has more unknowns than equations. We will see that the continuity equation involves the quantities $N^{(s)}$ and $\langle v_i^{(s)} \rangle$. The momentum equation contains these unknowns plus the pressure tensor $\Psi_{ij}^{(s)}$. The energy equation provides a third equation but introduces a fourth unknown, the *heat flux vector* $Q_i^{(s)}$. Each successive moment equation will introduce an additional unknown, so that it is always necessary to truncate the set of equations at some point by making assumptions about some of the unknown quantities. It is usually most convenient to truncate the set at the energy equation. It should be noted that if the Boltzmann equation could be solved for the distribution function f, then all of the unknown quantities that appear in the moment equations could be calculated exactly. Some information has therefore been lost in the process of integrating the Boltzmann equation to obtain the moment equations.

Now the moment equations for each species involve terms containing the mean velocity of each species $\langle v_i^{(s)} \rangle$. This means that the equations describe the average motion of the individual constituents of the plasma. Quantities such as the pressure tensor $\Psi_{ij}^{(s)}$ are then defined relative to surfaces moving with the mean velocities $\langle v_i^{(s)} \rangle$. We will see later in this chapter that in order to describe the motion of the plasma as a whole it is necessary to write the equations in terms of the weighted mean mass-velocity and to define quantities such as the pressure tensor relative to a surface moving with this mean mass-velocity.

These ideas will be discussed further in Section 6.3. We proceed now to obtain the moment equations for each species.

6.21 THE CONTINUITY EQUATION

If we let $\phi^{(s)} = 1$ in [6.10], we obtain the continuity equation for each species

$$\frac{\partial N^{(s)}}{\partial t} + \frac{\partial}{\partial x_i}(N^{(s)}\langle v_i^{(s)} \rangle) = S_{\text{coll}}^{(s)} \qquad [6.15]$$

which expresses the conservation of the number of particles of type s. The collision term $S_{\text{coll}}^{(s)}$ on the right-hand side of [6.15] represents the rate at which particles of type s are gained (or lost) due to collisions. Contributions to this term could therefore arise from such gain and loss processes as ionization, attachment, and recombination. In the absence of such collision processes, the continuity equation [6.15] reduces to

$$\frac{\partial N^{(s)}}{\partial t} + \frac{\partial}{\partial x_i}(N^{(s)}\langle v_i^{(s)}\rangle) = 0 \qquad [6.16]$$

Now $\partial N^{(s)}/\partial t$ is the local time variation of the number density. That is, it is the rate at which the number density $N^{(s)}$ changes at a fixed point in the plasma. Suppose that we were to follow a small-volume element dr as it moved through the plasma with the mean velocity $\langle v_i^{(s)}\rangle$. How would the number density $N^{(s)}$ in this small-volume element change with time as we moved along? During the time interval δt we would have traveled a distance

$$\delta x_i = \langle v_i^{(s)}\rangle \delta t \qquad [6.17]$$

Since $N^{(s)}$ is a function of x_i and t, then in the time interval δt the change in $N^{(s)}$ will be given by

$$\delta N^{(s)} = \frac{\partial N^{(s)}}{\partial x_i}\,\delta x_i + \frac{\partial N^{(s)}}{\partial t}\,\delta t$$

or, using [6.17],

$$\delta N^{(s)} = \left(\frac{\partial N^{(s)}}{\partial x_i}\,\langle v_i^{(s)}\rangle + \frac{\partial N^{(s)}}{\partial t}\right)\delta t$$

We therefore see that the total rate at which the number density $N^{(s)}$ changes as we move along with the velocity $\langle v_i^{(s)}\rangle$ is given by

$$\frac{\delta N^{(s)}}{\delta t} = \frac{dN^{(s)}}{dt} = \frac{\partial N^{(s)}}{\partial t} + \langle v_i^{(s)}\rangle \frac{\partial N^{(s)}}{\partial x_i} \qquad [6.18]$$

By differentiating the second term of [6.16], we can rewrite the continuity equation as

$$\frac{\partial N^{(s)}}{\partial t} + \langle v_i^{(s)}\rangle \frac{\partial N^{(s)}}{\partial x_i} + N^{(s)}\frac{\partial \langle v_i^{(s)}\rangle}{\partial x_i} = 0$$

or, using [6.18],

$$\frac{dN^{(s)}}{dt} + N^{(s)} \frac{\partial \langle v_i^{(s)} \rangle}{\partial x_i} = 0 \qquad [6.19]$$

Let us now consider the form of the collision term in [6.15] for various gain and loss mechanisms which are important in plasmas.

Ionization   The collision term [6.14] was derived for elastic scattering and is therefore not directly applicable to inelastic collision processes such as ionization. However we can include the effect of ionization in the continuity equation by defining the *ionization rate* v_I such that the number of electrons produced per second is $N_- v_I$. The continuity equation for electrons can then be written as

$$\frac{\partial N_-}{\partial t} + \frac{\partial}{\partial x_i} (N_- \langle v_i^- \rangle) = N_- v_I$$

Electron-Ion Recombination   A possible method by which electrons can be lost from a plasma is by electron-ion recombination. The rate at which electrons are lost by recombination will be proportional to both the number of electrons and the number of ions present. If only one species of positive ion is present so that $N_- = N_+$, then the rate of recombination will be proportional to N_-^2 and the collision term in the continuity equation for electrons can be written as

$$S_{coll}^- = -\alpha N_-^2$$

where α is the *recombination coefficient* which may be measured experimentally.

Electron Attachment   An alternative mechanism of electron loss in a plasma occurs when an electron becomes attached to a neutral particle to form a negative ion. The rate at which electrons will be lost by attachment will be proportional to the number densities of both the electrons and the neutral particles. In a weakly ionized gas the neutral particle density can be considered to be constant so that the rate of electron loss by attachment is proportional only to the electron density. The corresponding collision term in the continuity equation for electrons is then

$$S_{coll}^- = -v_A N_-$$

where v_A is the *frequency of attaching collisions* and is measured experimentally.

These inelastic collisions processes will be discussed in more detail in Chapter 15.

6.22 THE MOMENTUM EQUATION

The momentum equation for each species can be obtained by letting $\phi^{(s)} = m^{(s)}v_j^{(s)}$ in [6.10]. Since $v_j^{(s)}$, x_i, and t are the independent variables, then $\partial\phi^{(s)}/\partial t$ and $\partial\phi^{(s)}/\partial x_i$ are both zero in [6.10]. The term $\langle R_i^{(s)}\partial\phi^{(s)}/\partial v_i^{(s)}\rangle$ becomes

$$\left\langle R_i^{(s)}\frac{\partial}{\partial v_i^{(s)}}(m^{(s)}v_j^{(s)})\right\rangle = \langle m^{(s)}R_i^{(s)}\delta_{ji}\rangle = m^{(s)}\langle R_j^{(s)}\rangle$$

If the external forces consist of an electric field and a magnetic field then this term becomes

$$m^{(s)}\langle R_j^{(s)}\rangle = q^{(s)}(E_j + \epsilon_{jmn}\langle v_m^{(s)}\rangle B_n) \qquad [6.20]$$

Using these results, we can write [6.10] as

$$\frac{\partial(N^{(s)}m^{(s)}\langle v_j^{(s)}\rangle)}{\partial t} + \frac{\partial(N^{(s)}m^{(s)}\langle v_i^{(s)}v_j^{(s)}\rangle)}{\partial x_i}$$
$$- N^{(s)}q^{(s)}(E_j + \epsilon_{jmn}\langle v_m^{(s)}\rangle B_n) = (A_j^{(s)})_{\text{coll}} \qquad [6.21]$$

where the collision term

$$(A_j^{(s)})_{\text{coll}} = \int m^{(s)}v_j^{(s)}\left(\frac{\partial f^{(s)}}{\partial t}\right)_{\text{coll}} dc^{(s)} \qquad [6.22]$$

represents the rate of change of momentum due to collisions. Since the total momentum is conserved during a collision, the momentum lost by one of the colliding molecules must equal the momentum gained by the other molecule. Thus for collisions involving molecules of the same species the collision term will be zero. However in general the collision term is not zero for collisions between molecules of different species. For example, collisions between electrons and neutral particles result in a net transfer of momentum from the electron gas to the neutral gas. Thus a collision term $(P_j^-)_{\text{coll}}$ due to these collisions will appear in the momentum equation for the electrons. The form of this collision term will be discussed later in this section.

Let us first consider the second term in the momentum equation [6.21]. In Section 5.21 we found that if we defined pressure as the rate at which momentum is transferred across a surface moving with the mean velocity of the gas, then the pressure tensor Ψ_{ij} was given by

$$\Psi_{ij} = Nm\langle V_iV_j\rangle$$

In an analogous way we will define the pressure tensor $\Psi_{ij}^{(s)}$ for the sth species of the gas by

$$\Psi_{ij}^{(s)} = N^{(s)}m^{(s)}\langle V_i^{(s)}V_j^{(s)}\rangle \qquad [6.23]$$

where

$$V_i^{(s)} = v_i^{(s)} - \langle v_i^{(s)} \rangle \qquad [6.24]$$

is the random or peculiar velocity of the sth species relative to its own mean velocity. Note that $\Psi_{ij}^{(s)}$ describes a pressure relative to a surface moving with the mean velocity $\langle v_i^{(s)} \rangle$.

The expression $\langle v_i^{(s)} v_j^{(s)} \rangle$ in the second term of the momentum equation [6.21] can be written, using [6.24], as

$$\langle v_i^{(s)} v_j^{(s)} \rangle = \langle V_i^{(s)} V_j^{(s)} \rangle + \langle v_i^{(s)} \rangle \langle v_j^{(s)} \rangle \qquad [6.25]$$

where we have used the fact that $\langle V_i^{(s)} \rangle = 0$. Substituting [6.25] into the momentum equation [6.21] and using [6.23], we obtain

$$\frac{\partial(N^{(s)} m^{(s)} \langle v_i^{(s)} \rangle)}{\partial t} + \frac{\partial(N^{(s)} m^{(s)} \langle v_i^{(s)} \rangle \langle v_j^{(s)} \rangle)}{\partial x_j} + \frac{\partial \Psi_{ij}^{(s)}}{\partial x_j}$$
$$- N^{(s)} q^{(s)} (E_i + \epsilon_{ijk} \langle v_j^{(s)} \rangle B_k) = (A_i^{(s)})_{\text{coll}} \qquad [6.26]$$

The momentum equation [6.26] can be written in an alternative form as follows: The first two terms in [6.26] are

$$\frac{\partial(N^{(s)} m^{(s)} \langle v_i^{(s)} \rangle)}{\partial t} + \frac{\partial(N^{(s)} m^{(s)} \langle v_i^{(s)} \rangle \langle v_j^{(s)} \rangle)}{\partial x_j}$$

$$= N^{(s)} m^{(s)} \frac{\partial \langle v_i^{(s)} \rangle}{\partial t} + \langle v_i^{(s)} \rangle \frac{\partial(N^{(s)} m^{(s)})}{\partial t} + \langle v_i^{(s)} \rangle \frac{\partial(N^{(s)} m^{(s)} \langle v_j^{(s)} \rangle)}{\partial x_j}$$
$$+ N^{(s)} m^{(s)} \langle v_j^{(s)} \rangle \frac{\partial \langle v_i^{(s)} \rangle}{\partial x_j}$$

$$= N^{(s)} m^{(s)} \left(\frac{\partial \langle v_i^{(s)} \rangle}{\partial t} + \langle v_j^{(s)} \rangle \frac{\partial \langle v_i^{(s)} \rangle}{\partial x_j} \right) + m^{(s)} \langle v_i^{(s)} \rangle S_{\text{coll}}^{(s)} \qquad [6.27]$$

where the continuity equation [6.15] was used in the last step. Substituting [6.27] into [6.26] we obtain for the momentum equation

$$N^{(s)} m^{(s)} \left(\frac{\partial \langle v_i^{(s)} \rangle}{\partial t} + \langle v_j^{(s)} \rangle \frac{\partial \langle v_i^{(s)} \rangle}{\partial x_j} \right) + \frac{\partial \Psi_{ij}^{(s)}}{\partial x_j}$$
$$- N^{(s)} q^{(s)} (E_i + \epsilon_{ijk} \langle v_j^{(s)} \rangle B_k) = (A_i^{(s)})_{\text{coll}} - m^{(s)} \langle v_i^{(s)} \rangle S_{\text{coll}}^{(s)} \qquad [6.28]$$

We now wish to consider the collision term $(A_i^{(s)})_{\text{coll}}$. Let us specifically consider collisions between charged particles of species s and neutral particles. Then from [6.22] and [6.14] we can write the collision term as

$$(A_i^{(s)})_{\text{coll}} = \int m^{(s)} v_i^{(s)} \left(\frac{\partial f^{(s)}}{\partial t} \right)_{\text{coll}} dc^{(s)}$$

$$= \iiint m^{(s)} (\tilde{v}_i^{(s)} - v_i^{(s)}) f^{(s)} f^N g S(\chi) \, d\omega \, dc^N dc^{(s)} \qquad [6.29]$$

In this equation we can write the solid angle $d\omega = \sin \chi \, d\chi \, d\psi$. When we integrate over the azimuthal scattering angle ψ, the only component of $(\bar{v}_i^{(s)} - v_i^{(s)})$ that is nonzero is the component in the direction of the initial relative velocities which is given by $M^N(v_i^N - v_i^{(s)})(1 - \cos \chi)$ (see the example in Section 4.21 and Exercise 6.22.1), where, in this case, $M^N = m^N/(m^N + m^{(s)})$. The collision term [6.29] can then be written as

$$\int m^{(s)}v_i^{(s)}\left(\frac{\partial f^{(s)}}{\partial t}\right)_{\text{coll}} dc^{(s)} = 2\pi \int_{-\infty}^{\infty} \int_{-\infty}^{\infty} \int_0^{\pi} m^{(s)}M^N(v_i^N - v_i^{(s)}) \times$$
$$(1 - \cos \chi)f^{(s)}f^N g S(\chi) \sin \chi \, d\chi \, dc^N \, dc^{(s)} \quad [6.30]$$

We define the frequency of collisions between charged particles of species s and neutral particles as

$$\nu_{\text{SN}}^G = 2\pi \int_0^{\pi} N^N g(1 - \cos \chi)S(\chi) \sin \chi \, d\chi \quad [6.31]$$

Note that this is a collision frequency for momentum transfer in the center-of-mass coordinate system (see Section 4.41). The effective collision frequency in the laboratory system will be written as

$$\nu_{\text{SN}} = M^N \nu_{\text{SN}}^G \quad [6.32]$$

Since $M^N = m^N/(m^N + m^{(s)})$, we see that for electron-neutral collisions $M^N \approx 1$, so that

$$\nu_{\text{EN}} = \nu_{\text{EN}}^G \quad [6.33]$$

Using [6.31] and [6.32] we can write [6.30] as

$$\int m^{(s)}v_i^{(s)}\left(\frac{\partial f^{(s)}}{\partial t}\right)_{\text{coll}} dc^{(s)} = m^{(s)} \int_{-\infty}^{\infty} \int_{-\infty}^{\infty} (v_i^N - v_i^{(s)})\frac{\nu_{\text{SN}}}{N^N} f^{(s)}f^N \, dc^N \, dc^{(s)} \quad [6.34]$$

If we assume that the collision frequency ν_{SN} is independent of the relative velocity, this corresponds to a cross section which varies as $1/g$ (see Problem 4.1); then we can take ν_{SN} outside the integral in [6.34] and proceed to integrate without knowing the actual forms of the distribution functions. We obtain

$$(A_i^{(s)})_{\text{coll}} = \int m^{(s)}v_i^{(s)}\left(\frac{\partial f^{(s)}}{\partial t}\right)_{\text{coll}} dc^{(s)} = m^{(s)}N^{(s)}\nu_{\text{SN}}(\langle v_i^N \rangle - \langle v_i^{(s)} \rangle) \quad [6.35]$$

Using [6.35], we can write the momentum equation for the sth charged species from [6.26] and [6.28] in the alternative forms

$$\frac{\partial(N^{(s)}m^{(s)}\langle v_i^{(s)}\rangle)}{\partial t} + \frac{\partial(N^{(s)}m^{(s)}\langle v_i^{(s)}\rangle\langle v_j^{(s)}\rangle)}{\partial x_j} + \frac{\partial\Psi_{ij}^{(s)}}{\partial x_j}$$
$$- N^{(s)}q^{(s)}(E_i + \epsilon_{ijk}\langle v_j^{(s)}\rangle B_k) = m^{(s)}N^{(s)}\nu_{SN}(\langle v_i^N\rangle - \langle v_i^{(s)}\rangle) \quad [6.36]$$

or

$$\frac{\partial\langle v_i^{(s)}\rangle}{\partial t} + \langle v_j^{(s)}\rangle\frac{\partial\langle v_i^{(s)}\rangle}{\partial x_j} + \frac{1}{N^{(s)}m^{(s)}}\frac{\partial\Psi_{ij}^{(s)}}{\partial x_j} - \frac{q^{(s)}}{m^{(s)}}(E_i + \epsilon_{ijk}\langle v_j^{(s)}\rangle B_k)$$
$$= \nu_{SN}(\langle v_i^N\rangle - \langle v_i^{(s)}\rangle) - \frac{\langle v_i^{(s)}\rangle}{N^{(s)}}S_{coll}^{(s)} \quad [6.37]$$

The collision frequency which appears on the right-hand side of [6.36] and [6.37] represents either electron-neutral or ion-neutral collisions. The determination of ν_{SN} requires a knowledge of the cross section for momentum transfer which must, in general, be found experimentally.

The question now arises as to how collisions between two charged particles will affect the momentum equations. Suppose we are considering the momentum equation for the electrons. Since the total momentum of two colliding electrons is conserved, then the total momentum of the electrons in the plasma cannot be changed as the result of electron-electron collisions. However electron-electron collisions can influence the manner in which this momentum is distributed among the electrons.

On the other hand collisions between electrons and ions will change the total momentum of the electrons and will thus contribute a term to the right-hand side of [6.36] and [6.37]. The expression for the electron-ion collision frequency will be discussed in Chapter 9.

Exercise 6.22.1   Write the components of $\tilde{v}_i^{(s)} - v_i^{(s)}$ in the center-of-mass coordinate system and show that the component in the direction of the initial relative velocities is $M^N(v_i^N - v_i^{(s)})(1 - \cos\chi)$.

6.23 THE ENERGY EQUATION

If we let $\phi^{(s)} = \frac{1}{2}m^{(s)}v_j^{(s)}v_j^{(s)}$ then $\partial\phi^{(s)}/\partial t$ and $\partial\phi^{(s)}/\partial x_i$ are zero and

$$\left\langle R_i^{(s)}\frac{\partial\phi^{(s)}}{\partial v_i^{(s)}}\right\rangle = \left\langle R_i^{(s)}\frac{1}{2}m^{(s)}\frac{\partial(v_j^{(s)}v_j^{(s)})}{\partial v_i^{(s)}}\right\rangle$$
$$= \langle R_i^{(s)}m^{(s)}v_j^{(s)}\delta_{ji}\rangle$$
$$= \langle m^{(s)}R_i^{(s)}v_i^{(s)}\rangle$$

so that the equation of change [6.10] becomes

$$\frac{\partial(\frac{1}{2}N^{(s)}m^{(s)}\langle v_j^{(s)}v_j^{(s)}\rangle)}{\partial t} + \frac{\partial(\frac{1}{2}N^{(s)}m^{(s)}\langle v_i^{(s)}v_j^{(s)}v_j^{(s)}\rangle)}{\partial x_i}$$
$$- N^{(s)}\langle m^{(s)}R_i^{(s)}v_i^{(s)}\rangle = M_{\text{coll}}^{(s)} \qquad [6.38]$$

where

$$M_{\text{coll}}^{(s)} = \int \frac{1}{2}m^{(s)}v_j^{(s)}v_j^{(s)}\left(\frac{\partial f^{(s)}}{\partial t}\right)_{\text{coll}} dc^{(s)} \qquad [6.39]$$

represents the rate of change of kinetic energy of the sth species due to collisions. This collision term is clearly zero for collisions between like particles. Equation [6.14] can be used to determine the form of this collision term for collisions between charged particles of species s and neutral molecules (see Exercise 6.23.1).

Now [6.38] is a general form of an energy equation that describes the time variation of the total kinetic energy of the sth species. It would be convenient if we could characterize this energy by a certain temperature of the sth species. However the temperature of the various species in a multicomponent plasma is not a very well-defined concept. This is due to the fact that for temperature to have a significant meaning the system must be in equilibrium. However in most plasma problems of interest the various plasma species are not in equilibrium with each other. Nevertheless it is still desirable to ascribe a temperature to the various components of the plasma.

We found in Chapter 5 that in equilibrium a gas has a Maxwellian velocity distribution and may be assigned a certain temperature. The temperature is related to the spread in the velocity distribution. We could imagine, for example, a plasma in which the electrons and ions each had Maxwellian distributions at different temperatures. The Maxwellian distribution of electrons could be maintained by electron-electron collisions. Since the electron and ion gases are coupled the electron temperature might relax to the ion temperature. This relaxation time must be longer than the electron-electron collision time required to maintain the Maxwellian distribution of electrons if we are to be able to speak of a relaxation of the temperature of the electron gas.

Let us therefore note from [5.11] and [6.23] that a scalar pressure of the sth species $P^{(s)}$ can be defined relative to a surface moving with the velocity $\langle v_i^{(s)}\rangle$ by

$$P^{(s)} = \frac{1}{3}N^{(s)}m^{(s)}\langle V_j^{(s)}V_j^{(s)}\rangle \qquad [6.40]$$

When the sth species is in quasi-equilibrium (that is, has a Maxwellian distribution) then we can associate a temperature $T^{(s)}$ with the sth species where

$$\frac{1}{2}m^{(s)}\langle V_j^{(s)}V_j^{(s)}\rangle = \frac{3}{2}kT^{(s)} \qquad [6.41]$$

or, from [6.40]

$$P^{(s)} = N^{(s)}kT^{(s)} \qquad [6.42]$$

We can write the energy equation [6.38] in an alternate form. In the first term of [6.38] we have the quantity $\langle v_j^{(s)} v_j^{(s)} \rangle$ which can be written, using [6.24], as

$$\langle v_j^{(s)} v_j^{(s)} \rangle = \langle V_j^{(s)} V_j^{(s)} \rangle + \langle v_j^{(s)} \rangle \langle v_j^{(s)} \rangle \qquad [6.43]$$

where we have noted that $\langle V_j^{(s)} \rangle = 0$. Similarly in the second term of [6.38] the quantity $\langle v_i^{(s)} v_j^{(s)} v_j^{(s)} \rangle$ can be written as

$$
\begin{aligned}
\langle v_i^{(s)} v_j^{(s)} v_j^{(s)} \rangle &= \big\langle (V_i^{(s)} + \langle v_i^{(s)} \rangle)(V_j^{(s)} + \langle v_j^{(s)} \rangle)(V_j^{(s)} + \langle v_j^{(s)} \rangle) \big\rangle \\
&= \langle V_i^{(s)} V_j^{(s)} V_j^{(s)} \rangle + 2 \langle V_i^{(s)} V_j^{(s)} \rangle \langle v_j^{(s)} \rangle \\
&\quad + \langle V_i^{(s)} \rangle \langle v_j^{(s)} \rangle \langle v_j^{(s)} \rangle + \langle v_i^{(s)} \rangle \langle V_j^{(s)} V_j^{(s)} \rangle \\
&\quad + 2 \langle v_i^{(s)} \rangle \langle v_j^{(s)} \rangle \langle V_j^{(s)} \rangle + \langle v_i^{(s)} \rangle \langle v_j^{(s)} \rangle \langle v_j^{(s)} \rangle
\end{aligned} \qquad [6.44]
$$

The third and fifth terms on the right-hand side of [6.44] are zero since $\langle V_i^{(s)} \rangle = 0$. The first term $\langle V_i^{(s)} V_j^{(s)} V_j^{(s)} \rangle$ is also zero when the average is taken over an isotropic distribution function (see Exercise 6.23.2). For anisotropic distribution functions this term may not be zero and is used to define the *heat flux vector* $Q_i^{(s)}$ for the sth species as

$$Q_i^{(s)} = \tfrac{1}{2} N^{(s)} m^{(s)} \langle V_i^{(s)} V_j^{(s)} V_j^{(s)} \rangle \qquad [6.45]$$

If we substitute [6.45] and the remaining terms of [6.44] together with [6.43] into the energy equation [6.38], we obtain

$$
\frac{\partial (\tfrac{1}{2} N^{(s)} m^{(s)} \langle V_j^{(s)} V_j^{(s)} \rangle)}{\partial t} + \frac{\partial (\tfrac{1}{2} N^{(s)} m^{(s)} \langle V_j^{(s)} V_j^{(s)} \rangle \langle v_i^{(s)} \rangle)}{\partial x_i}
$$

$$
+ \frac{\partial (N^{(s)} m^{(s)} \langle V_i^{(s)} V_j^{(s)} \rangle \langle v_j^{(s)} \rangle)}{\partial x_i} + \frac{\partial (\tfrac{1}{2} N^{(s)} m^{(s)} \langle v_j^{(s)} \rangle \langle v_j^{(s)} \rangle)}{\partial t}
$$

$$
+ \frac{\partial (\tfrac{1}{2} N^{(s)} m^{(s)} \langle v_j^{(s)} \rangle \langle v_j^{(s)} \rangle \langle v_i^{(s)} \rangle)}{\partial x_i} + \frac{\partial Q_i^{(s)}}{\partial x_i} - N^{(s)} m^{(s)} \langle R_i^{(s)} v_i^{(s)} \rangle = M_{\text{coll}}^{(s)} \qquad [6.46]
$$

The fourth and fifth term in [6.46] can be written as

$$
\frac{\partial (\tfrac{1}{2} N^{(s)} m^{(s)} \langle v_j^{(s)} \rangle \langle v_j^{(s)} \rangle)}{\partial t} + \frac{\partial (\tfrac{1}{2} N^{(s)} m^{(s)} \langle v_j^{(s)} \rangle \langle v_j^{(s)} \rangle \langle v_i^{(s)} \rangle)}{\partial x_i}
$$

$$
= \tfrac{1}{2} m^{(s)} \langle v_j^{(s)} \rangle \langle v_j^{(s)} \rangle \left(\frac{\partial N^{(s)}}{\partial t} + \frac{\partial N^{(s)} \langle v_i^{(s)} \rangle}{\partial x_i} \right)
$$

$$
+ m^{(s)} N^{(s)} \langle v_j^{(s)} \rangle \left(\frac{\partial \langle v_j^{(s)} \rangle}{\partial t} + \langle v_i^{(s)} \rangle \frac{\partial \langle v_j^{(s)} \rangle}{\partial x_i} \right)
$$

$$
= \tfrac{1}{2} m^{(s)} \langle v_j^{(s)} \rangle \langle v_j^{(s)} \rangle S_{\text{coll}}^{(s)} - \langle v_j^{(s)} \rangle \frac{\partial \Psi_{ij}^{(s)}}{\partial x_i} + N^{(s)} m^{(s)} \langle R_j^{(s)} \rangle \langle v_j^{(s)} \rangle
$$

$$
+ (A_j^{(s)})_{\text{coll}} \langle v_j^{(s)} \rangle - m^{(s)} \langle v_j^{(s)} \rangle \langle v_j^{(s)} \rangle S_{\text{coll}}^{(s)} \qquad [6.47]
$$

where the continuity equation [6.15] and the momentum equation [6.28] were used in the last step. If we substitute [6.47] into the energy equation [6.46] and use the scalar pressure [6.40] and the pressure tensor [6.23], we obtain

$$\frac{\partial \frac{3}{2} P^{(s)}}{\partial t} + \frac{\partial \frac{3}{2} P^{(s)} \langle v_i^{(s)} \rangle}{\partial x_i} + \frac{\partial \Psi_{ij}^{(s)} \langle v_j^{(s)} \rangle}{\partial x_i} - \langle v_j^{(s)} \rangle \frac{\partial \Psi_{ij}^{(s)}}{\partial x_i} + \frac{\partial Q_i^{(s)}}{\partial x_i}$$

$$+ N^{(s)} m^{(s)} (\langle R_j^{(s)} \rangle \langle v_j^{(s)} \rangle - \langle R_j^{(s)} v_j^{(s)} \rangle)$$

$$= M_{\text{coll}}^{(s)} - (A_j^{(s)})_{\text{coll}} \langle v_j^{(s)} \rangle + \tfrac{1}{2} m^{(s)} \langle v_j^{(s)} \rangle \langle v_j^{(s)} \rangle S_{\text{coll}}^{(s)} \quad [6.48]$$

Combining the third and fourth term in [6.48] and noting that the sixth term vanishes for electric and magnetic fields (see Exercise 6.23.3), we obtain

$$\frac{3}{2} \frac{\partial P^{(s)}}{\partial t} + \frac{3}{2} \frac{\partial P^{(s)} \langle v_i^{(s)} \rangle}{\partial x_i} + \Psi_{ij}^{(s)} \frac{\partial \langle v_j^{(s)} \rangle}{\partial x_i} + \frac{\partial Q_i^{(s)}}{\partial x_i}$$

$$= M_{\text{coll}}^{(s)} - (A_j^{(s)})_{\text{coll}} \langle v_j^{(s)} \rangle + \tfrac{1}{2} m^{(s)} \langle v_j^{(s)} \rangle \langle v_j^{(s)} \rangle S_{\text{coll}}^{(s)} \quad [6.49]$$

Let us assume that collisions do not alter the number of particles of species s, their total momentum, or their total energy. Then the right-hand side of [6.49] is zero. As we have pointed out, this will always be the case if only one species is present. Let us also assume that the heat flux vector $Q_i^{(s)}$ can be neglected. If we finally assume that the pressure tensor $\Psi_{ij}^{(s)}$ can be written as a scalar pressure $P^{(s)} \delta_{ij}$, then by differentiating the second term of [6.49], we obtain for the simplified energy equation

$$\frac{3}{2} \left(\frac{\partial P^{(s)}}{\partial t} + \langle v_i^{(s)} \rangle \frac{\partial P^{(s)}}{\partial x_i} \right) + \frac{3}{2} P^{(s)} \frac{\partial \langle v_i^{(s)} \rangle}{\partial x_i} + P^{(s)} \frac{\partial \langle v_i^{(s)} \rangle}{\partial x_i} = 0 \quad [6.50]$$

The first term in this equation is the total time derivative of $P^{(s)}$ (see Equation [6.18]). If we add the last two terms in [6.50] and use the continuity equation [6.19], we then obtain

$$\frac{3}{2} \frac{dP^{(s)}}{dt} - \frac{5}{2} \frac{P^{(s)}}{N^{(s)}} \frac{dN^{(s)}}{dt} = 0$$

from which

$$\frac{dP^{(s)}}{P^{(s)}} = \frac{5}{3} \frac{dN^{(s)}}{N^{(s)}} \quad [6.51]$$

Integrating [6.51] we obtain

$$\frac{P^{(s)}}{P_0} = \left(\frac{N^{(s)}}{N_0} \right)^{5/3} \quad [6.52]$$

where P_0 and N_0 are constants.

Equation [6.52] is the adiabatic law relating $P^{(s)}$ and $N^{(s)}$ for an ideal gas. More generally one can write [6.52] as

$$\frac{P^{(s)}}{P_0} = \left(\frac{N^{(s)}}{N_0}\right)^{\gamma}$$

[6.53]

where the adiabatic exponent γ is the *ratio of the specific heat at constant pressure to the specific heat at constant volume.*

Notice that to assume the validity of the adiabatic law is one method of truncating the moment equations, since together with the continuity equation and the momentum equation, we can now solve for $N^{(s)}$, $P^{(s)}$, and $\langle v_i^{(s)} \rangle$.

Thus far in this chapter we have considered the moment equations for each species of the plasma. The remainder of the chapter is devoted to obtaining macroscopic equations which describe the behavior of the plasma as a whole.

Exercise 6.23.1   By using equation [6.14] show that for a gas at rest the collision term $M_{\text{coll}}^{(s)}$ given by [6.39] can be written as

$$M_{\text{coll}}^{(s)} = \frac{2m^{(s)}N^{(s)}}{m^{(s)} + m^N}\, v_{\text{SN}}(\tfrac{1}{2}m^{(s)}\langle v_i^{(s)}v_i^{(s)}\rangle - \tfrac{1}{2}m^N\langle v_i^N v_i^N\rangle)$$

Exercise 6.23.2   Show that if the distribution function is isotropic (that is, an even function with respect to V_i), then the average quantity $\langle V_i^{(s)}V_j^{(s)}V_j^{(s)}\rangle$ is zero. Give an anisotropic distribution function for which this average is not zero. What is the physical meaning of the heat flux vector $Q_i^{(s)}$?

Exercise 6.23.3   Show that for electric and magnetic fields

$$\langle R_i^{(s)}\rangle\langle v_i^{(s)}\rangle - \langle R_i^{(s)}v_i^{(s)}\rangle = 0$$

Relate this result to the symmetry property of the pressure tensor.

6.3 THE PLASMA
AS A CONDUCTING FLUID

The macroscopic equations we have derived so far in this chapter describe the behavior of an individual species of the plasma. We now wish to determine what set of equations will describe the behavior of the plasma as a whole. That is, we want to think of the plasma as a conducting fluid in which we no longer consider the individual species directly. Historically this was the first approach to a macroscopic description of a plasma since the hydrodynamic equations for a nonconducting fluid were well known. One then simply added appropriate terms to the equation of motion of a fluid in order to include the electromagnetic forces that act on a conducting fluid.

In this chapter we have obtained macroscopic equations by taking moments of the Boltzmann equation. The equations of fluid dynamics are not usually derived in this way. Rather one considers a fluid element of mass density ρ where

$$\rho = \sum_s N^{(s)} m^{(s)} \qquad [6.54]$$

If the velocity of this fluid element is denoted by v_i^*, then the fluid dynamic equations are obtained by applying the conservation laws of mass, momentum and energy.

A plasma fluid element of mass density ρ moving with the velocity v_i^* is shown in Figure 6.1. Each species of the plasma has its own mean velocity as is also shown in the figure. The question arises as to how the fluid velocity v_i^*

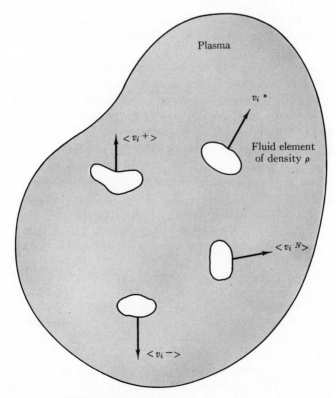

FIGURE 6.1 Mean Velocities in a Plasma Fluid

is related to the mean velocity of the individual species $\langle v_i^{(s)} \rangle$. This question does not arise in ordinary fluid dynamics where only the motion of a fluid element of mass density ρ is considered. However, as we have seen, the relative motion of the individual species within a plasma is of the utmost importance. We will answer this question of the relation between v_i^* and $\langle v_i^{(s)} \rangle$ by deriving the equations for a conducting fluid from the moment equations for each species. We will therefore bridge the gap not only between the Boltzmann equation and the fluid equations but also between the moment equations for each species and the moment equations for a conducting fluid.

The fluid velocity v_i^* should be defined so that the momentum of the gas per unit volume is the same as if each molecule moved with the velocity v_i^*. This suggests defining v_i^* by the relation

$$\rho v_i^* = \sum_s N^{(s)} m^{(s)} \langle v_i^{(s)} \rangle \qquad [6.55]$$

Defined in this way v_i^*, known as the *mean mass-velocity*, is a weighted mean velocity where each molecule is weighted in proportion to its mass. That this is the proper definition of v_i^* will be demonstrated in Section 6.4, where we will show that by writing the moment equations for each species in terms of v_i^* and then summing over all species, we obtain the moment equation for a conducting fluid.

One point, however, must be stressed. Whereas in the single species moment equations quantities such as the pressure and heat flow were referred to the mean velocity of each species, in the moment equations for a conducting fluid these quantities must be referred to the mean mass-velocity v_i^*. This idea will be discussed further in the following section.

6.31 PLASMA PRESSURE

The pressure tensor $\Psi_{ij}^{(s)}$ for each species in the plasma is given by [6.23] as

$$\Psi_{ij}^{(s)} = N^{(s)} m^{(s)} \langle V_i^{(s)} V_j^{(s)} \rangle \qquad [6.56]$$

where

$$V_i^{(s)} = v_i^{(s)} - \langle v_i^{(s)} \rangle \qquad [6.57]$$

Recall from Section 5.21 that $n_i \Psi_{ij}^{(s)}$ is the rate at which molecular momentum from species s is transported across a surface element with normal n_i which is moving with the velocity $\langle v_i^{(s)} \rangle$.

When writing the equations for a conducting fluid that moves with a velocity v_i^*, one should calculate the pressure relative to v_i^*. That is, the pressure is defined as the rate at which molecular momentum from all species of the plasma is transported across a surface element that moves with the mean mass-velocity v_i^*.

It is therefore necessary to define the random or *peculiar velocity*, $U_i^{(s)}$, *of the sth species relative to the mean mass-velocity v_i^** by the relation

$$U_i^{(s)} = v_i^{(s)} - v_i^* \tag{6.58}$$

Compare this velocity with $V_i^{(s)}$ given by [6.57]. Note that whereas $\langle V_i^{(s)} \rangle$ is equal to zero, $\langle U_i^{(s)} \rangle$ is not equal to zero. However we see from [6.58], [6.54], and [6.55] that

$$\sum_s N^{(s)} m^{(s)} \langle U_i^{(s)} \rangle = \sum_s N^{(s)} m^{(s)} \langle v_i^{(s)} \rangle - \sum_s N^{(s)} m^{(s)} v_i^*$$

$$= \rho v_i^* - \rho v_i^*$$

or

$$\sum_s N^{(s)} m^{(s)} \langle U_i^{(s)} \rangle = 0 \tag{6.59}$$

It is now readily shown (see Exercise 6.31.1) that the *total pressure tensor* Ψ_{ij}^* for the plasma as a whole is given by

$$\Psi_{ij}^* = \sum_s N^{(s)} m^{(s)} \langle U_i^{(s)} U_j^{(s)} \rangle \tag{6.60}$$

That is, $n_i \Psi_{ij}^*$ is the rate at which molecular momentum from all species of the plasma is transported across a surface element with unit normal n_i that moves with the velocity v_i^*.

The velocities $U_i^{(s)}$ and $V_i^{(s)}$ are related (see Exercise 6.31.2) according to

$$\langle U_i^{(s)} U_j^{(s)} \rangle = \langle V_i^{(s)} V_j^{(s)} \rangle + \langle U_i^{(s)} \rangle \langle U_j^{(s)} \rangle \tag{6.61}$$

Using [6.61] and [6.56] we can therefore write [6.60] as

$$\Psi_{ij}^* = \sum_s \Psi_{ij}^{(s)} + \sum_s N^{(s)} m^{(s)} \langle U_i^{(s)} \rangle \langle U_j^{(s)} \rangle \tag{6.62}$$

Bear in mind that Ψ_{ij}^* is measured relative to v_i^*, while $\Psi_{ij}^{(s)}$ is measured relative to $\langle v_i^{(s)} \rangle$.

If the pressure tensor Ψ_{ij}^* is isotropic, then the hydrostatic pressure P^* is defined by

$$\Psi_{ij}^* = P^* \delta_{ij} \tag{6.63}$$

Since

$$\Psi^*_{ii} = 3P^*$$

then using [6.60], we have that

$$P^* = \tfrac{1}{3}\sum_s N^{(s)}m^{(s)}\langle U^{(s)}_i U^{(s)}_i \rangle \qquad\qquad [6.64]$$

Exercise 6.31.1 Show that the rate at which molecular momentum from all species of the plasma is transported across a surface element dS with unit normal n_i that is moving with the velocity v^*_i is given by $n_i\Psi^*_{ij}$ where

$$\Psi^*_{ij} = \sum_s N^{(s)}m^{(s)}\langle U^{(s)}_i U^{(s)}_j \rangle$$

Exercise 6.32.2 Show that

$$\langle v^{(s)}_i v^{(s)}_j \rangle = \langle V^{(s)}_i V^{(s)}_j \rangle + \langle v^{(s)}_i \rangle\langle v^{(s)}_j \rangle$$
$$= \langle U^{(s)}_i U^{(s)}_j \rangle - \langle U^{(s)}_i \rangle\langle U^{(s)}_j \rangle + \langle v^{(s)}_i \rangle\langle v^{(s)}_j \rangle$$

and thus verify [6.61].

6.4 THE MOMENT EQUATIONS
FOR A CONDUCTING FLUID

We now wish to obtain the moment equations for a conducting fluid by first writing the moment equations for each species referred to the mean mass-velocity v^*_i and then summing over all species. In order to write the single species moment equations in terms of v^*_i, it is convenient to transform the equation of change [6.10] into an equation satisfied by a function $\phi^{(s)}(U^{(s)}_k)$ which depends only on the peculiar velocity $U^{(s)}_k$ relative to v^*_i.

The equation of change of any molecular property is given by [6.10] as

$$\frac{\partial(N^{(s)}\langle\phi^{(s)}\rangle)}{\partial t} + \frac{\partial(N^{(s)}\langle v^{(s)}_i\phi^{(s)}\rangle)}{\partial x_i}$$

$$- N^{(s)}\left(\left\langle\frac{\partial\phi^{(s)}}{\partial t}\right\rangle + \left\langle v^{(s)}_i\frac{\partial\phi^{(s)}}{\partial x_i}\right\rangle + \left\langle R^{(s)}_i\frac{\partial\phi^{(s)}}{\partial v^{(s)}_i}\right\rangle\right) \qquad [6.65]$$

$$= \int \phi^{(s)}\left(\frac{\partial f^{(s)}}{\partial t}\right)_{\text{coll}} dc^{(s)}$$

We wish to determine the corresponding equation of change of $\phi^{(s)} = \phi^{(s)}(U^{(s)}_k)$ when $\phi^{(s)}$ is given in terms of the velocity $U^{(s)}_k$ where, from [6.58]

$$U^{(s)}_k = v^{(s)}_k - v^*_k(x_i, t) \qquad\qquad [6.66]$$

In this case, $\phi^{(s)}$ will have a time and position dependence due to $U_k^{(s)}$ as well as, in general, an explicit time and position dependence. Thus in transforming [6.65] we have to replace

$$\frac{\partial}{\partial t} \quad \text{by} \quad \frac{\partial}{\partial t} + \frac{\partial U_j^{(s)}}{\partial t}\frac{\partial}{\partial U_j^{(s)}} = \frac{\partial}{\partial t} - \frac{\partial v_j^*}{\partial t}\frac{\partial}{\partial U_j^{(s)}} \qquad [6.67]$$

$$\frac{\partial}{\partial x_i^{(s)}} \quad \text{by} \quad \frac{\partial}{\partial x_i} + \frac{\partial U_j^{(s)}}{\partial x_i}\frac{\partial}{\partial U_j^{(s)}} = \frac{\partial}{\partial x_i} - \frac{\partial v_j^*}{\partial x_i}\frac{\partial}{\partial U_j^{(s)}} \qquad [6.68]$$

and

$$\frac{\partial}{\partial v_i^{(s)}} \quad \text{by} \quad \frac{\partial U_j^{(s)}}{\partial v_i^{(s)}}\frac{\partial}{\partial U_j^{(s)}} = \delta_{ji}\frac{\partial}{\partial U_j^{(s)}} = \frac{\partial}{\partial U_i^{(s)}} \qquad [6.69]$$

The mean values are not affected by the change of variables, since

$$N^{(s)}\langle\phi^{(s)}\rangle = \int \phi^{(s)}(v_i^{(s)})f^{(s)}(v_i^{(s)})\,dc^{(s)} = \int \phi^{(s)}(U_i^{(s)})f^{(s)}(U_i^{(s)})\,dC^{(s)}$$

and is no longer a function of velocity. Thus the first two terms in [6.65] are unaffected by the change of variables.

We will now assume that $\phi^{(s)}(U_k^{(s)})$ does not depend explicitly on x_i or t. That is,

$$\frac{\partial}{\partial t} = 0 \quad \text{and} \quad \frac{\partial}{\partial x_i} = 0$$

Then, using [6.67] to [6.69], we have from [6.65] the transformed equation

$$\frac{\partial(N^{(s)}\langle\phi^{(s)}\rangle)}{\partial t} + \frac{\partial(N^{(s)}\langle v_i^{(s)}\phi^{(s)}\rangle)}{\partial x_i} - N^{(s)}\left(-\left\langle\frac{\partial v_j^*}{\partial t}\frac{\partial\phi^{(s)}}{\partial U_j^{(s)}}\right\rangle - \left\langle v_i^{(s)}\frac{\partial v_j^*}{\partial x_i}\frac{\partial\phi^{(s)}}{\partial U_j^{(s)}}\right\rangle\right)$$

$$- N^{(s)}\left\langle R_i^{(s)}\frac{\partial\phi^{(s)}}{\partial U_i^{(s)}}\right\rangle = \int \phi^{(s)}\left(\frac{\partial f^{(s)}}{\partial t}\right)_{\text{coll}}\,dc^{(s)} \qquad [6.70]$$

Substituting $v_i^* + U_i^{(s)}$ for $v_i^{(s)}$ in [6.70], we obtain

$$\frac{\partial(N^{(s)}\langle\phi^{(s)}\rangle)}{\partial t} + \frac{\partial(N^{(s)}v_i^*\langle\phi^{(s)}\rangle)}{\partial x_i} + \frac{\partial(N^{(s)}\langle U_i^{(s)}\phi^{(s)}\rangle)}{\partial x_i}$$

$$+ N^{(s)}\left(\frac{\partial v_j^*}{\partial t}\left\langle\frac{\partial\phi^{(s)}}{\partial U_j^{(s)}}\right\rangle + v_i^*\frac{\partial v_j^*}{\partial x_i}\left\langle\frac{\partial\phi^{(s)}}{\partial U_j^{(s)}}\right\rangle + \left\langle U_i^{(s)}\frac{\partial v_j^*}{\partial x_i}\frac{\partial\phi^{(s)}}{\partial U_j^{(s)}}\right\rangle\right)$$

$$- N^{(s)}\left\langle R_i^{(s)}\frac{\partial\phi^{(s)}}{\partial U_i^{(s)}}\right\rangle = \int \phi^{(s)}\left(\frac{\partial f^{(s)}}{\partial t}\right)_{\text{coll}}\,dc^{(s)} \qquad [6.71]$$

This is the equation of change of a molecular property $\phi^{(s)}(U_k^{(s)})$ which is explicitly only a function of the peculiar velocity $U_k^{(s)}$. We will now consider the particular values $\phi^{(s)} = 1$, $\phi^{(s)} = m^{(s)} U_k^{(s)}$ and $\phi^{(s)} = \frac{1}{2} m^{(s)} U_k^{(s)} U_k^{(s)}$ in order to obtain the moment equations for each species, and then sum over all species to obtain the moment equations for a conducting fluid.

6.41 THE CONTINUITY EQUATION

By letting $\phi^{(s)} = 1$ in [6.71], we obtain

$$\frac{\partial N^{(s)}}{\partial t} + \frac{\partial N^{(s)} v_i^*}{\partial x_i} + \frac{\partial N^{(s)} \langle U_i^{(s)} \rangle}{\partial x_i} = S_{\text{coll}}^{(s)} \qquad [6.72]$$

If we multiply [6.72] through by $m^{(s)}$ and sum over all species, then, by using [6.54] and [6.59], we obtain

$$\frac{\partial \rho}{\partial t} + \frac{\partial \rho v_i^*}{\partial x_i} = 0 \qquad [6.73]$$

which is the continuity equation for a conducting fluid. Note that the collision term, which represents the rate at which particles of species s are gained or lost by collisions, must vanish when summed over all species.

We can differentiate the second term in [6.73] to obtain

$$\frac{\partial \rho}{\partial t} + v_i^* \frac{\partial \rho}{\partial x_i} + \rho \frac{\partial v_i^*}{\partial x_i} = 0 \qquad [6.74]$$

As was discussed in Section 6.21 for the single species continuity equation, the first two terms in [6.74] represent the total time derivative of ρ in a fluid element moving with the velocity v_i^*. In fluid dynamics it is customary to call this total time derivative the *substantial* or *convective time derivative*, and it is often given the special symbol

$$\frac{D}{Dt} = \frac{\partial}{\partial t} + v_i^* \frac{\partial}{\partial x_i} \qquad [6.75]$$

We can then write the continuity equation [6.74] as

$$\frac{D\rho}{Dt} + \rho \frac{\partial v_i^*}{\partial x_i} = 0 \qquad [6.76]$$

6.42 THE MOMENTUM EQUATION

The momentum equation for each species referred to the mean mass-velocity of the plasma is found by letting $\phi^{(s)} = m^{(s)} U_k^{(s)}$ in [6.71]. For this case note that

$$\frac{\partial \phi^{(s)}}{\partial U_j^{(s)}} = m^{(s)} \frac{\partial U_k^{(s)}}{\partial U_j^{(s)}} = m^{(s)} \delta_{kj}$$

so that [6.71] becomes

$$\frac{\partial(N^{(s)}m^{(s)}\langle U_k^{(s)}\rangle)}{\partial t} + \frac{\partial(N^{(s)}m^{(s)}v_i^*\langle U_k^{(s)}\rangle)}{\partial x_i} + \frac{\partial(N^{(s)}m^{(s)}\langle U_i^{(s)}U_k^{(s)}\rangle)}{\partial x_i}$$

$$+ N^{(s)}m^{(s)}\left(\frac{\partial v_k^*}{\partial t} + v_i^*\frac{\partial v_k^*}{\partial x_i} + \langle U_i^{(s)}\rangle\frac{\partial v_k^*}{\partial x_i} - \langle R_k^{(s)}\rangle\right) = (A_k^{(s)})_{\text{coll}} \quad [6.77]$$

By summing [6.77] over all species and using [6.59], [6.60], and [6.54], we obtain

$$\rho\left(\frac{\partial v_k^*}{\partial t} + v_i^*\frac{\partial v_k^*}{\partial x_i}\right) + \frac{\partial \Psi_{ik}^*}{\partial x_i} - \sum_s N^{(s)}m^{(s)}\langle R_k^{(s)}\rangle = 0 \quad [6.78]$$

Note that since the total momentum of the plasma particles is conserved the collision term vanishes when summed over all species.

If the external forces acting on the plasma are electric and magnetic fields so that

$$m^{(s)}\langle R_i^{(s)}\rangle = q^{(s)}(E_i + \epsilon_{ijk}\langle v_j^{(s)}\rangle B_k)$$

then, using [3.3] and [3.5], we have that

$$\sum_s N^{(s)}m^{(s)}\langle R_i^{(s)}\rangle = \eta E_i + \epsilon_{ijk}J_jB_k \quad [6.79]$$

Using [6.79], we can write [6.78] as

$$\rho\left(\frac{\partial v_i^*}{\partial t} + v_j^*\frac{\partial v_i^*}{\partial x_j}\right) + \frac{\partial \Psi_{ij}^*}{\partial x_j} - \eta E_i - \epsilon_{ijk}J_jB_k = 0 \quad [6.80]$$

which is the momentum equation for a conducting fluid. We can write this equation in terms of the convective derivative [6.75] as

$$\rho\frac{Dv_i^*}{Dt} = \eta E_i + \epsilon_{ijk}J_jB_k - \frac{\partial \Psi_{ij}^*}{\partial x_j} \quad [6.81]$$

which will be recognized as an equation of motion expressing Newton's second law.

Finally one should note that the current density J_i can consist of two parts. From [3.3], [3.5], and [6.58] we have that

$$J_i = \sum_s N^{(s)}q^{(s)}\langle v_i^{(s)}\rangle$$

$$= \sum_s N^{(s)}q^{(s)}v_i^* + \sum_s N^{(s)}q^{(s)}\langle U_i^{(s)}\rangle$$

$$= \eta v_i^* + J_i' \quad [6.82]$$

Thus J_i is the sum of a convection current density and a conduction current density. The *convection current density* ηv_i^* represents the transport of space charge with velocity v_i^*. The *conduction current density* J_i' is the current density measured in a frame of reference moving with the velocity v_i^*. That is,

$$J_i' = J_i - \eta v_i^* = \sum_s N^{(s)} q^{(s)} \langle U_i^{(s)} \rangle \tag{6.83}$$

Exercise 6.42.1   From the results of Section 3.5 show that the momentum equation [6.81] can be written as

$$\rho \frac{Dv_i^*}{Dt} + \mu_0 \epsilon_0 \frac{\partial G_i}{\partial t} = \frac{\partial}{\partial x_j} (T_{ij} - \Psi_{ij}^*)$$

where T_{ij} is the electromagnetic stress tensor and G_i is the Poynting vector. What physical interpretation can you give to this form of the momentum equation?

6.43 THE ENERGY EQUATION

We now let $\phi^{(s)} = \frac{1}{2} m^{(s)} U_k^{(s)} U_k^{(s)}$ in [6.71] in order to obtain the energy equation for each species of the gas. Note that in this case

$$\frac{\partial \phi^{(s)}}{\partial U_j^{(s)}} = \frac{\partial (\frac{1}{2} m^{(s)} U_k^{(s)} U_k^{(s)})}{\partial U_j^{(s)}} = m^{(s)} U_k^{(s)} \frac{\partial U_k^{(s)}}{\partial U_j^{(s)}} = m^{(s)} U_k^{(s)} \delta_{kj} = m^{(s)} U_j^{(s)}$$

so that [6.71] becomes

$$\frac{\partial}{\partial t} \left(\frac{1}{2} N^{(s)} m^{(s)} \langle U_k^{(s)} U_k^{(s)} \rangle \right) + \frac{\partial}{\partial x_i} \left(v_i^* \frac{1}{2} N^{(s)} m^{(s)} \langle U_k^{(s)} U_k^{(s)} \rangle \right)$$

$$+ \frac{\partial}{\partial x_i} \left(\frac{1}{2} N^{(s)} m^{(s)} \langle U_i^{(s)} U_k^{(s)} U_k^{(s)} \rangle \right) + m^{(s)} N^{(s)} \langle U_j^{(s)} \rangle \left(\frac{\partial v_j^*}{\partial t} + v_i^* \frac{\partial v_j^*}{\partial x_i} \right)$$

$$+ N^{(s)} m^{(s)} \langle U_i^{(s)} U_j^{(s)} \rangle \frac{\partial v_j^*}{\partial x_i} - N^{(s)} m^{(s)} \langle R_i^{(s)} U_i^{(s)} \rangle = M_{\text{coll}}^{(s)} \tag{6.84}$$

The *thermal energy density* of the plasma $\mathscr{E}^*$ is defined as

$$\mathscr{E}^* = \sum_s \frac{1}{2} N^{(s)} m^{(s)} \langle U_k^{(s)} U_k^{(s)} \rangle \tag{6.85}$$

(see Exercise 6.43.1), and the heat flux vector Q_i^* relative to the mean mass-velocity v_i^* is defined as

$$Q_i^* = \sum_s \frac{1}{2} N^{(s)} m^{(s)} \langle U_i^{(s)} U_k^{(s)} U_k^{(s)} \rangle \tag{6.86}$$

If we now sum [6.84] over all species and use [6.85] and [6.86] together with [6.59] and [6.60], we obtain

$$\frac{\partial \mathscr{E}^*}{\partial t} + \frac{\partial v_i^* \mathscr{E}^*}{\partial x_i} + \frac{\partial Q_i^*}{\partial x_i} + \Psi_{ij}^* \frac{\partial v_j^*}{\partial x_i} = \sum_s N^{(s)} m^{(s)} \langle R_i^{(s)} U_i^{(s)} \rangle \qquad [6.87]$$

Note again that the collision term $M_{\text{coll}}^{(s)}$ vanishes when summed over all species.

If the external forces acting on the plasma are electric and magnetic fields, then the right-hand side of [6.87] can be written as

$$\sum_s N^{(s)} m^{(s)} \langle R_i^{(s)} U_i^{(s)} \rangle = \sum_s N^{(s)} q^{(s)} (E_i \langle U_i^{(s)} \rangle + \epsilon_{ijk} \langle v_j^{(s)} U_i^{(s)} \rangle B_k) \qquad [6.88]$$

Substituting $U_j^{(s)} + v_j^*$ for $v_j^{(s)}$ in [6.88] and noting that $\epsilon_{ijk} \langle U_j^{(s)} U_i^{(s)} \rangle$ is identically zero since $\langle U_j^{(s)} U_i^{(s)} \rangle$ is symmetric while ϵ_{ijk} is antisymmetric, then we obtain by using [6.83]

$$\sum_s N^{(s)} m^{(s)} \langle R_i^{(s)} U_i^{(s)} \rangle = J_i' (E_i + \epsilon_{ijk} v_j^* B_k)$$

$$= J_i' E_i' \qquad [6.89]$$

where we have noted from [3.66] that

$$E_i' = E_i + \epsilon_{ijk} v_j^* B_k \qquad [6.90]$$

is the electric field measured in the frame of reference moving with the velocity v_i^*.

If we now differentiate the second term of [6.87] and use the convective derivative [6.75] together with [6.89] we can write the energy equation for a conducting fluid in the form

$$\frac{D\mathscr{E}^*}{Dt} + \mathscr{E}^* \frac{\partial v_i^*}{\partial x_i} + \frac{\partial Q_i^*}{\partial x_i} + \Psi_{ij}^* \frac{\partial v_j^*}{\partial x_i} = J_i' E_i' \qquad [6.91]$$

The first term in this equation represents the total rate of change of the thermal energy of the gas in a volume element moving with the mean mass-velocity. The remaining terms contribute in some way to this change. The second term represents energy carried into the moving volume element by the net flow of molecules, while the third term represents a change due to heat flow. The fourth term represents work done on the moving element by the pressures on its surface. The term on the right-hand side of [6.91] represents Joule heating.

One can show (see Exercise 6.43.2) that if the heat flux vector Q_i^* is zero, if the pressure tensor is isotropic and given by $P^* \delta_{ij}$, and if there is no Joule heating, then the energy equation [6.91] reduces to the adiabatic law

$$\frac{P^*}{P_0} = \left(\frac{\rho}{\rho_0}\right)^{5/3} \tag{6.92}$$

This represents a possible method of truncating the moment equations. Note, however, that the set of equations is still not complete since the moment equations for a conducting fluid contain not only the fluid dynamic variables ρ, v_i^*, and P^* but also the electrodynamic variables E_i, B_i, J_i, and η. The electrodynamic equations needed to complete the set will be discussed in the following section.

Exercise 6.43.1   Calculate the total kinetic energy per unit volume of all species in a gas in terms of the mean mass-velocity v_i^*. Show that it can be written as the sum of the kinetic energy of the mass motion plus a thermal energy density $\mathscr{E}^*$ given by

$$\mathscr{E}^* = \sum_s \tfrac{1}{2} N^{(s)} m^{(s)} \langle U_i^{(s)} U_i^{(s)} \rangle$$

Exercise 6.43.2   Show that when $Q_i^* = 0$, $\Psi_{ij}^* = P^* \delta_{ij}$, and there is no Joule heating, the energy equation [6.91] reduces to the adiabatic law [6.92].

6.5   THE ELECTRODYNAMIC EQUATIONS FOR A CONDUCTING FLUID

We have found that the moment equations for a conducting fluid describe the time variation of the various fluid dynamic variables. Thus the time variation of the density ρ is given by the continuity equation, while the momentum equation gives the time variation of v_i^*. The energy equation can be thought of as giving the time variation of the pressure P^*. More generally one could obtain an equation giving the time variation of the pressure tensor Ψ_{ij}^* by letting $\phi^{(s)} = N^{(s)} m^{(s)} \langle U_i^{(s)} U_j^{(s)} \rangle$ in the equation of change [6.71] and then summing over all species. One could continue taking higher moments in order to obtain equations giving the time variation of, say, the heat flux vector. However, as we have pointed out, one must always eventually truncate the set of equations at some point.

Even after the truncation procedure though, the moment equations contain the electrodynamic variables E_i, B_i, J_i, and η. We must therefore have, in addition to the moment equations, ten electrodynamic equations which give the time variation of E_i, B_i, J_i, and η. Some of these equations we already know.

Maxwell's curl equations

$$\epsilon_{ijk}E_{k,j} = -\dot{B}_i \qquad [6.93]$$

and

$$\epsilon_{ijk}B_{k,j} = \mu_0 J_i + \mu_0\epsilon_0\dot{E}_i \qquad [6.94]$$

can be thought of as giving the time variations of B_i and E_i, respectively.

The time variation of η is given by the equation of continuity of charge [3.9]. It is instructive to rederive this equation from the continuity equation for each species. If we multiply the continuity equation [6.72] by $q^{(s)}$ and sum over all species, we obtain by using [3.3] and [6.82]

$$\frac{\partial \eta}{\partial t} + \frac{\partial J_i}{\partial x_i} = 0 \qquad [6.95]$$

which is the equation of continuity of charge giving the time variation of η.

The only equation we don't have yet is one giving the time variation of the current density J_i. However the way to obtain such an equation is suggested by the method used to obtain [6.95]. We should clearly multiply the momentum equations for each species by $q^{(s)}$ and sum over all species. This procedure is carried out in the following section, and the resulting equation is known as the *generalized Ohm's law*.

6.51 THE GENERALIZED OHM'S LAW

In order to obtain an equation for the time variation of J_i, let us multiply the momentum equation [6.77] by $q^{(s)}/m^{(s)}$ and sum over all species. By using [6.83] and [3.3], we then obtain

$$\frac{\partial J_k'}{\partial t} + \frac{\partial v_i^* J_k'}{\partial x_i} + \frac{\partial L_{ik}^*}{\partial x_i} + \eta\left(\frac{\partial v_k^*}{\partial t} + v_i^*\frac{\partial v_k^*}{\partial x_i}\right)$$
$$+ J_i'\frac{\partial v_k^*}{\partial x_i} - \sum_s N^{(s)}q^{(s)}\langle R_k^{(s)}\rangle = \sum_s \frac{q^{(s)}}{m^{(s)}}(A_k^{(s)})_{\text{coll}} \qquad [6.96]$$

where

$$L_{ik}^* = \sum_s q^{(s)}N^{(s)}\langle U_i^{(s)}U_k^{(s)}\rangle \qquad [6.97]$$

is referred to as the *electrokinetic stress tensor* (see Exercise 6.51.1).

The fourth and fifth terms in [6.96] can be written with the help of [6.95] and [6.82] as

$$\eta\left(\frac{\partial v_k^*}{\partial t} + v_i^* \frac{\partial v_k^*}{\partial x_i}\right) + J_i' \frac{\partial v_k^*}{\partial x_i} = \frac{\partial \eta v_k^*}{\partial t} - v_k^* \frac{\partial \eta}{\partial t} + \eta v_i^* \frac{\partial v_k^*}{\partial x_i} + J_i' \frac{\partial v_k^*}{\partial x_i}$$

$$= \frac{\partial \eta v_k^*}{\partial t} + v_k^* \frac{\partial J_i}{\partial x_i} + J_i \frac{\partial v_k^*}{\partial x_i}$$

$$= \frac{\partial \eta v_k^*}{\partial t} + \frac{\partial v_k^* J_i}{\partial x_i} \qquad [6.98]$$

Substituting [6.98] into [6.96] and again using [6.82] we obtain

$$\frac{\partial J_k}{\partial t} + \frac{\partial}{\partial x_i}(v_i^* J_k' + v_k^* J_i) + \frac{\partial L_{ik}^*}{\partial x_i} - \sum_s N^{(s)} q^{(s)} \langle R_k^{(s)} \rangle = \sum_s \frac{q^{(s)}}{m^{(s)}} (A_k^{(s)})_{\text{coll}} \qquad [6.99]$$

This is an equation for the time variation of J_k. However in its present form it is too general to be of practical use. In order to put [6.99] into a more useful form we will consider the case in which the plasma consists only of electrons and positive ions of one kind. We assume charge neutrality so that

$$\eta = e(N_+ - N_-) = 0$$

and

$$N_+ = N_- = N \qquad [6.100]$$

The current density is then given by

$$J_i = J_i' = Ne(\langle v_i^+ \rangle - \langle v_i^- \rangle) \qquad [6.101]$$

For this case let us now consider the various terms in [6.99]. The electrokinetic stress tensor becomes

$$L_{ij}^* = eN(\langle U_i^+ U_j^+ \rangle - \langle U_i^- U_j^- \rangle) \qquad [6.102]$$

If we assume that the mean velocity $\langle U_i^\pm \rangle$ of the electrons and ions relative to the mean mass-velocity v_i^* is small compared with the thermal velocities, then from [6.61] and [6.56] we can write [6.102] as

$$L_{ij}^* = -\frac{e}{m_-}\left(\Psi_{ij}^- - \frac{m_-}{m_+}\Psi_{ij}^+\right) \qquad [6.103]$$

For electric and magnetic fields the force term in [6.99] becomes

$$\sum_s N^{(s)}q^{(s)}\langle R_i^{(s)}\rangle = \frac{Ne^2}{m_-}\left[\left(1 + \frac{m_-}{m_+}\right)E_i + \epsilon_{ijk}\left(\langle v_j^-\rangle + \frac{m_-}{m_+}\langle v_j^+\rangle\right)B_k\right] \qquad [6.104]$$

From [6.55] we see that for our case the mean mass-velocity v_i^* is given by

$$(m_+ + m_-)v_i^* = m_+\langle v_i^+\rangle + m_-\langle v_i^-\rangle \qquad [6.105]$$

Using [6.105] and [6.101], we can write $\langle v_i^+\rangle$ and $\langle v_i^-\rangle$ in terms of J_i and v_i^* (see Exercise 6.51.2). We obtain

$$\langle v_i^+\rangle = v_i^* + \left(\frac{m_-}{m_- + m_+}\right)\frac{J_i}{Ne} \approx v_i^* + \frac{m_-}{m_+}\frac{J_i}{Ne} \qquad [6.106]$$

$$\langle v_i^-\rangle = v_i^* - \left(\frac{m_+}{m_- + m_+}\right)\frac{J_i}{Ne} \approx v_i^* - \frac{J_i}{Ne} \qquad [6.107]$$

If we substitute [6.106] and [6.107] into [6.104] and neglect m_-/m_+ compared with unity we obtain

$$\sum_s N^{(s)}q^{(s)}\langle R_i^{(s)}\rangle = \frac{Ne^2}{m_-}\left[E_i + \epsilon_{ijk}\left(v_j^* - \frac{J_j}{Ne}\right)B_k\right] \qquad [6.108]$$

The collision term in [6.99] is

$$\sum_s \frac{q^{(s)}}{m^{(s)}}(A_k^{(s)})_{\text{coll}} = \frac{e}{m_+}(A_k^+)_{\text{coll}} - \frac{e}{m_-}(A_k^-)_{\text{coll}} \qquad [6.109]$$

Now $(A_k^-)_{\text{coll}}$ represents the rate at which the momentum of the electrons is altered due to collisions with the ions. Similarly $(A_k^+)_{\text{coll}}$ represents the rate at which the momentum of the ions is altered due to collisions with the electrons. Since the total momentum of the colliding particles must be conserved, we have that

$$(A_k^+)_{\text{coll}} = -(A_k^-)_{\text{coll}} \qquad [6.110]$$

We can infer the form of $(A_k^-)_{\text{coll}}$ from [6.35] which is given for electron-neutral collisions. Thus we can write

$$(A_k^-)_{\text{coll}} = Nm_-\nu_{\text{EI}}(\langle v_i^+\rangle - \langle v_i^-\rangle) \qquad [6.111]$$

where ν_{EI} is a constant *effective collision frequency for electron-ion collisions.* If we use [6.110] and [6.111] in [6.109] and neglect m_-/m_+ compared with unity, we obtain

$$\sum_s \frac{q^{(s)}}{m^{(s)}} (A_k^{(s)})_{coll} = -eN\nu_{EI}(\langle v_i^+ \rangle - \langle v_i^- \rangle)$$

$$= -\nu_{EI} J_i \qquad [6.112]$$

where [6.101] has been used.

Finally we will assume that J_i and v_i^* can be treated as small perturbations so that the second term in [6.99] involving their product can be neglected. If we now collect our results by substituting [6.103], [6.108], and [6.112] into [6.99], we obtain

$$\frac{\partial J_i}{\partial t} - \frac{e}{m_-}\frac{\partial}{\partial x_j}\left(\Psi_{ij}^- - \frac{m_-}{m_+}\Psi_{ij}^+\right) - \frac{Ne^2}{m_-}\left[E_i + \epsilon_{ijk}\left(v_j^* - \frac{J_j}{Ne}\right)B_k\right] = -\nu_{EI} J_i$$

which can be written as

$$\frac{m_-}{Ne^2}\frac{\partial J_i}{\partial t} = E_i + \epsilon_{ijk}v_j^* B_k - \frac{1}{Ne}\epsilon_{ijk}J_j B_k + \frac{1}{Ne}\frac{\partial}{\partial x_j}\left(\Psi_{ij}^- - \frac{m_-}{m_+}\Psi_{ij}^+\right) - \frac{1}{\sigma'}J_i$$

$$[6.113]$$

where

$$\sigma' = \frac{Ne^2}{m_-\nu_{EI}} \qquad [6.114]$$

Equation [6.113] is known as the generalized Ohm's law.

Notice that σ' has the dimensions of conductivity so that $1/\sigma'$ is a resistivity. However σ' is not the constant of proportionality between J_i and E_i and is therefore not the conductivity σ defined in Chapter 3. If we consider a (quasi-) steady state so that $\partial J_i/\partial t$ is equal to zero, and neglect the pressure terms, then [6.113] can be written as

$$J_i + \frac{1}{\nu_{EI}}\epsilon_{ijk}J_j\Omega_k^- = \sigma'(E_i + \epsilon_{ijk}v_j^* B_k) \qquad [6.115]$$

where

$$\Omega_k^- = \frac{eB_k}{m_-}$$

is the electron cyclotron frequency (see Chapter 8).

From [6.115] we see that E_i and J_i are, in general, not in the same direction. The current represented by the second term in [6.115] is known as the *Hall current*. This current will be small if $|\Omega_k^-| \ll \nu_{EI}$. If this term can be neglected, then [6.115] becomes

$$J_i = \sigma'(E_i + \epsilon_{ijk}v_j^* B_k)$$

$$= \sigma' E_i' \qquad\qquad [6.116]$$

where E_i' is the electric field in the moving frame of reference (see Equation [3.66]). In the absence of a magnetic field [6.115] reduces to

$$J_i = \sigma' E_i \qquad\qquad [6.117]$$

which is the usual form of Ohm's law.

Exercise 6.51.1   Show that $n_i L_{ij}^*$ is the rate at which current flows across a surface element with normal n_i that is moving with the velocity v_i^*, where L_{ij}^* is the electrokinetic stress tensor given by [6.97].

Exercise 6.51.2   Verify equations [6.106] and [6.107].

REFERENCES

Discussions of the macroscopic plasma equations and their relation to the Boltzmann equation can be found in

1   Allis, W. P. "Motions of Ions and Electrons," *Handbuch der Physik*, vol. 21, Springer-Verlag, 1956.

2   Chapman, S., and T. G. Cowling. *The Mathematical Theory of Non-Uniform Gases*. London: Cambridge University Press, 1960.

3   Delcroix, J. L. *Introduction to the Theory of Ionized Gases*. New York: Interscience (Wiley), 1960.

4   Gartenhaus, S. *Elements of Plasma Physics*. New York: Holt, Rinehart and Winston, 1964.

5   Pai, Shih-I. *Magnetogasdynamics and Plasma Dynamics*. New York: Prentice-Hall, 1962.

6   Rose, D. J., and M. Clark. *Plasmas and Controlled Fusion.* Cambridge, Mass., and New York: Massachusetts Institute of Technology Press and Wiley, 1961.

7   Spitzer, L. *Physics of Fully Ionized Gases.* 2nd ed.; New York: Interscience (Wiley), 1962.

7

BASIC
PLASMA PHENOMENA

In the previous chapters we have laid the foundations of kinetic theory and electromagnetic theory we need in order to describe plasma phenomena. In Chapter 6 we saw that the macroscopic plasma equations consist of the continuity, momentum, and energy equations and that these enable us to describe the basic flow phenomena that arise in a plasma. These phenomena are called the *transport processes*.

The diffusion coefficient relates the flux of particles to the density gradient. The electrical conductivity relates the electric current density to the electric field. The thermal conductivity relates the heat flux to the temperature gradient. Diffusion involves the transport of momentum in the plasma, and thermal conduction involves the transport of kinetic energy in the plasma. In the present chapter we discuss diffusion and electrical conductivity in particular. The electrical nature of plasmas means that the plasma medium interacts with electromagnetic fields. In presenting the electrodynamic equations in Chapter 3, we saw that the relevant properties of the medium are its conductivity and dielectric constant. In the present chapter we are able to obtain expressions for both of these quantities, although we will see that they represent alternative models of the plasma medium.

Section 7.1 is concerned with diffusion and mobility—which is closely related to conductivity. First we simplify the momentum equation to obtain expressions for free electron diffusion and electron mobility (Section 7.11). Under conditions of somewhat higher plasma density we find that the electron flow is also influenced by the positive ions and ambipolar diffusion results (Section 7.12). The effect of an applied magnetic field is discussed in Section 7.13.

In Section 7.2 we give a unified treatment of the conductivity coefficient and dielectric constant of a plasma. These quantities are discussed in relationship to their use in the electrodynamic equations. We find that in the presence of an applied magnetic field these quantities become second-order tensors.

7.I DIFFUSION

When a gradient in the number density of a charged particle species exists, the charged particles will tend to move, as a result of collisions with the neutral particles, toward the region of lower density. This process of diffusion can be analyzed by considering the momentum equation given by [6.36] as

$$
\frac{\partial}{\partial t}(N^{(s)}m^{(s)}\langle v_i^{(s)}\rangle) + \frac{\partial}{\partial x_j}(N^{(s)}m^{(s)}\langle v_i^{(s)}\rangle\langle v_j^{(s)}\rangle) + \frac{\partial\Psi_{ij}^{(s)}}{\partial x_j}
$$
$$
- N^{(s)}q^{(s)}(E_i + \epsilon_{ijk}\langle v_j^{(s)}\rangle B_k) = -m^{(s)}N^{(s)}\nu_{\mathrm{SN}}\langle v_i^{(s)}\rangle \quad [7.1]
$$

where the neutral particles are assumed to have no mean velocity. The collision frequency ν_{SN} is the effective collision frequency for momentum transfer for a charged particle of species s interacting with the neutral particles. The pressure tensor $\Psi_{ij}^{(s)}$ which appears in the third term is given by [6.23] as $\Psi_{ij}^{(s)} = N^{(s)}m^{(s)}\langle V_i^{(s)}V_j^{(s)}\rangle$. We will assume that the pressure is hydrostatic so that we can write

$$
\Psi_{ij}^{(s)} = P^{(s)}\delta_{ij} = N^{(s)}kT^{(s)}\delta_{ij} \qquad [7.2]
$$

where the final equality assumes a Maxwellian velocity distribution of the s particles.

If the mean thermal velocity of the sth charged species is much greater than the drift velocity $\langle v_i^{(s)}\rangle$, then the second term in [7.1] can be neglected compared with the third term. For example, from the relation $\langle W^2\rangle = 3kT/m$ we find that the mean thermal velocity of an electron at room temperature is about 1.2×10^5 m/sec. We will assume that the drift velocity of the electrons is always much less than this value and therefore neglect the second term in

[7.1]. This assumption means that we are considering the transport phenomena of interest to comprise a minor perturbation of the over-all motion of the s-type particles.

We can now write [7.1] as

$$\frac{\partial}{\partial t}(N^{(s)}m^{(s)}\langle v_i^{(s)}\rangle) + \frac{\partial}{\partial x_i}(N^{(s)}kT^{(s)}) - N^{(s)}q^{(s)}(E_i + \epsilon_{ijk}\langle v_j^{(s)}\rangle B_k)$$
$$= -m^{(s)}N^{(s)}\nu_{SN}\langle v_i^{(s)}\rangle \quad [7.3]$$

We will use this equation in the following section to describe electron diffusion and mobility. For this treatment the effect of the positive ions is ignored. We will consider the role the positive ions play in the following section on ambipolar diffusion.

7.11 ELECTRON DIFFUSION AND MOBILITY

Let us consider an electron gas interacting with a neutral background gas. Neglecting an external magnetic field for the time being, we can write the momentum equation [7.3] for electrons in the form

$$\frac{\partial}{\partial t}(N_-m_-\langle v_i^-\rangle) + \frac{\partial}{\partial x_i}(N_-kT_-) - N_-q_-E_i = -\nu_{EN}m_-N_-\langle v_i^-\rangle \quad [7.4]$$

where ν_{EN} denotes the effective collision frequency for electron-neutral collisions. We now assume that the electron temperature is independent of position and write the *electron flux density* Γ_i^- as $\Gamma_i^- = N_-\langle v_i^-\rangle$ to obtain

$$\frac{1}{\nu_{EN}}\frac{\partial \Gamma_i^-}{\partial t} + \frac{kT_-}{m_-\nu_{EN}}\frac{\partial N_-}{\partial x_i} - \frac{N_-q_-}{m_-\nu_{EN}}E_i = -\Gamma_i^- \quad [7.5]$$

Now the flux of particles due to the transport phenomena of diffusion and mobility is normally discussed in terms of steady state conditions. The flux of particles due to diffusion is expressed as the density gradient multiplied by the diffusion coefficient, thus defining the diffusion coefficient. Similarly the flux of particles due to the electric field is given by the electric field times the number density of drifting particles, multiplied by the mobility, thus defining the mobility.

For the moment we therefore drop the first term of [7.5] and write

$$\Gamma_i^- = -D_-\frac{\partial N_-}{\partial x_i} + N_-\mu_-E_i \quad [7.6]$$

where the *free diffusion coefficient of electrons* D_- is given by

$$D_- = \frac{kT_-}{m_-\nu_{EN}} \quad [7.7]$$

and the *electron mobility* μ_- is given by

$$\mu_- = \frac{q_-}{m_- \nu_{\text{EN}}}$$ [7.8]

Notice that

$$\frac{D_-}{\mu_-} = \frac{kT_-}{q_-}$$ [7.9]

which is known as the *Einstein relation* and holds for a Maxwellian distribution of particle velocities.

In order to express the time rate of change of the electron density $\partial N_-/\partial t$ in terms of the diffusion coefficient, we return to [7.5] and write this equation without the electric field term as

$$-\Gamma_i^- = D_- \frac{\partial N_-}{\partial x_i} + \frac{1}{\nu_{\text{EN}}} \frac{\partial \Gamma_i^-}{\partial t}$$ [7.10]

From the continuity equation [6.16], we may write

$$\frac{\partial N_-}{\partial t} + \frac{\partial \Gamma_i^-}{\partial x_i} = 0$$ [7.11]

Let us take the time derivative of [7.11] to obtain $\partial^2 N_-/\partial t^2 = -\partial^2 \Gamma_i^-/\partial x_i \partial t$ and the spatial derivative of [7.10] to obtain

$$-\frac{\partial \Gamma_i^-}{\partial x_i} = D_- \frac{\partial^2 N_-}{\partial x_i \partial x_i} + \frac{1}{\nu_{\text{EN}}} \frac{\partial^2 \Gamma_i^-}{\partial x_i \partial t}$$

Finally, substituting for $\partial \Gamma_i^-/\partial x_i$ from [7.11] and for $\partial^2 \Gamma_i^-/\partial x_i \partial t$ from the time derivative of [7.11] we obtain

$$\frac{\partial N_-}{\partial t} = D_- \frac{\partial^2 N_-}{\partial x_i \partial x_i} - \frac{1}{\nu_{\text{EN}}} \frac{\partial^2 N_-}{\partial t^2}$$ [7.12]

which is a form of the *Telegrapher's equation*. If the characteristic time for density changes (the diffusion time) is long compared with the time between collisions $(1/\nu_{\text{EN}})$ then the last term in [7.12] may be neglected compared with the term on the left-hand side (see Exercise 7.11.1). This condition is normally well satisfied for cases of collisional diffusion. The diffusion equation then assumes the form

$$\frac{\partial N_-}{\partial t} = D_- \frac{\partial^2 N_-}{\partial x_i \partial x_i}$$ [7.13]

Exercise 7.11.1   Assume that $N_-(t) = N^0 \exp(-t/\tau_{\text{diff}})$ in [7.12] and show that [7.12] then reduces to [7.13] provided that $\tau_{\text{coll}} \ll \tau_{\text{diff}}$. Note that this equation may be written as $\partial N_-/\partial t = D_- \nabla^2 N_-$.

7.12 AMBIPOLAR DIFFUSION

In the previous section we considered only the diffusion of the electrons. However in plasmas the diffusion of the positive ions must also be considered. Due to their lighter mass the electrons will tend to diffuse out of the plasma at a faster rate than the positive ions. The charge separation that results will set up an electric field which will retard the electron diffusion and at the same time enhance the diffusion of the positive ions. The net result is that the electrons and positive ions will tend to diffuse together at an intermediate rate. This is called *ambipolar diffusion*.

In the steady state the electron flux density Γ_i^- can be written from [7.6] as

$$\Gamma_i^- = -D_- \frac{\partial N_-}{\partial x_i} + N_- \mu_- E_i \qquad [7.14]$$

Similarly for the positive ions we can write

$$\Gamma_i^+ = -D_+ \frac{\partial N_+}{\partial x_i} + N_+ \mu_+ E_i \qquad [7.15]$$

where the positive ion diffusion coefficient D_+ and mobility μ_+ are given by [7.7] and [7.8] if we change the minus signs to plus signs.

If the rate of electron production is equal to the rate of positive ion production, then in the steady state the continuity equations for electrons and ions can be written from [6.15] as

$$\Gamma_{i,i}^- = \Gamma_{i,i}^+ = \nu_I N_- \qquad [7.16]$$

where ν_I is the ionization rate. The electric field in [7.14] and [7.15] satisfies Poisson's equation

$$E_{i,i} = \frac{e}{\epsilon_0}(N_+ - N_-) \qquad [7.17]$$

The set of coupled equations [7.14] to [7.17] is nonlinear due to the presence of the terms $N_- E_i$ and $N_+ E_i$. In order to proceed we make the following assumptions. We assume that the density of charged particles is sufficiently high that we can take $N_+ = N_- = N$ (although we retain the weakly ionized condition that $N \ll N_N$, where N_N is the density of neutral particles). This condition assumes that the diffusion takes place over distances large compared with the Debye length (see Chapter 9). We will also assume that $\Gamma_i^+ = \Gamma_i^- = \Gamma_i$, which is suggested by both the physics of the problem and by [7.16].

Equations [7.14], [7.15] can now be written

$$\Gamma_i = -D_- \frac{\partial N}{\partial x_i} + N\mu_- E_i \qquad [7.18]$$

and

$$\Gamma_i = -D_+ \frac{\partial N}{\partial x_i} + N\mu_+ E_i \qquad [7.19]$$

If we multiply [7.18] by μ_+ and [7.19] by $-\mu_-$ and add the resulting equations, we obtain

$$(\mu_+ - \mu_-)\Gamma_i = -(\mu_+ D_- - \mu_- D_+)\frac{\partial N}{\partial x_i}$$

or

$$\Gamma_i = -D_A \frac{\partial N}{\partial x_i} \qquad [7.20]$$

where

$$D_A = \frac{\mu_+ D_- - \mu_- D_+}{\mu_+ - \mu_-} \qquad [7.21]$$

and D_A is called the *ambipolar diffusion coefficient*.

Since $|\mu_-| \gg |\mu_+|$, we can approximate [7.21] as

$$D_A \approx \left(1 - \frac{D_-\mu_+}{\mu_- D_+}\right)D_+ \qquad [7.22]$$

Using the Einstein relation [7.9] and the corresponding relation for the positive ions, we can write [7.22] as

$$D_A \approx \left(1 + \frac{T_-}{T_+}\right)D_+ \qquad [7.23]$$

In the positive column $T_- \gg T_+$, while in isothermal afterglow plasmas $T_- = T_+$. For this latter case [7.23] reduces to

$$D_A \approx 2D_+ \qquad [7.24]$$

so that the ambipolar diffusion coefficient is approximately twice the free diffusion coefficient of the positive ions.

7.13 DIFFUSION IN A MAGNETIC FIELD

We now wish to investigate the problem of electron diffusion in a magnetic field. If we assume that no electric field is present and that the electron temperature is independent of position, then from [7.3] we can write the momentum equation for the electrons in the form

$$\frac{\partial}{\partial t}(N_- m_- \langle v_i^- \rangle) + kT_- \frac{\partial N_-}{\partial x_i} - N_- q_- \epsilon_{ijk} \langle v_j^- \rangle B_k = -\nu_{EN} m_- N_- \langle v_i^- \rangle$$

[7.25]

Using [7.7], we can write [7.25] for the steady-state case as

$$D_- \frac{\partial N_-}{\partial x_i} + \epsilon_{ijk} \Gamma_j^- \frac{\Omega_k^-}{\nu_{EN}} = -\Gamma_i^-$$

[7.26]

where

$$\Omega_k^- = -\frac{q_- B_k}{m_-}$$

[7.27]

is the electron cyclotron frequency (see Chapter 8).

Since $\tau_{coll} = 1/\nu_{EN}$ we can write [7.26] in the form

$$(\delta_{ij} + \epsilon_{ijk} \Omega_k^- \tau_{coll}) \Gamma_j^- = -D_- \frac{\partial N_-}{\partial x_i}$$

[7.28]

If we assume that the magnetic field is in the x_3-direction—that is, $\Omega_k^- = (0, 0, \Omega_-)$, then we can write [7.28] in matrix form as

$$\begin{bmatrix} 1 & \Omega_- \tau_{coll} & 0 \\ -\Omega_- \tau_{coll} & 1 & 0 \\ 0 & 0 & 1 \end{bmatrix} \begin{bmatrix} \Gamma_1^- \\ \Gamma_2^- \\ \Gamma_3^- \end{bmatrix} = -D_- \begin{bmatrix} \dfrac{\partial N_-}{\partial x_1} \\ \dfrac{\partial N_-}{\partial x_2} \\ \dfrac{\partial N_-}{\partial x_3} \end{bmatrix}$$

[7.29]

Solving for Γ_j^-, this matrix equation becomes

$$\begin{bmatrix} \Gamma_1^- \\ \Gamma_2^- \\ \Gamma_3^- \end{bmatrix} = \frac{-D_-}{1 + \Omega_-^2 \tau_{coll}^2} \begin{bmatrix} 1 & -\Omega_- \tau_{coll} & 0 \\ \Omega_- \tau_{coll} & 1 & 0 \\ 0 & 0 & 1 + \Omega_-^2 \tau_{coll}^2 \end{bmatrix} \begin{bmatrix} \dfrac{\partial N_-}{\partial x_1} \\ \dfrac{\partial N_-}{\partial x_2} \\ \dfrac{\partial N_-}{\partial x_3} \end{bmatrix}$$

[7.30]

where we have taken the inverse of the 3 × 3 matrix in [7.29].

Let us define the diffusion coefficient $D_{\bar{\perp}}$ as

$$D_{\bar{\perp}} = \frac{D_-}{1 + (\Omega_- \tau_{\text{coll}})^2} \quad [7.31]$$

Then from [7.30] we can write the three component equations

$$\Gamma_{\bar{1}} = -D_{\bar{\perp}} \frac{\partial N_-}{\partial x_1} + \Omega_- \tau_{\text{coll}} D_{\bar{\perp}} \frac{\partial N_-}{\partial x_2} \quad [7.32]$$

$$\Gamma_{\bar{2}} = -D_{\bar{\perp}} \frac{\partial N_-}{\partial x_2} - \Omega_- \tau_{\text{coll}} D_{\bar{\perp}} \frac{\partial N_-}{\partial x_1} \quad [7.33]$$

$$\Gamma_{\bar{3}} = -D_- \frac{\partial N_-}{\partial x_3} \quad [7.34]$$

From these equations we see that the electron flux density in the direction of the magnetic field lines is unaffected by the presence of the magnetic field. In the steady state the continuity equation for electrons can be written as

$$\Gamma_{\bar{i,i}} = \Gamma_{\bar{1,1}} + \Gamma_{\bar{2,2}} + \Gamma_{\bar{3,3}} = \nu_I N_- \quad [7.35]$$

Substituting [7.32], [7.33] and [7.34] into [7.35], we note that the coupling terms cancel, and we obtain

$$D_{\bar{\perp}} \left(\frac{\partial^2 N_-}{\partial x_1^2} + \frac{\partial^2 N_-}{\partial x_2^2} \right) + D_- \frac{\partial^2 N_-}{\partial x_3^2} + \nu_I N_- = 0 \quad [7.36]$$

We therefore see that although diffusion along the magnetic field is not changed, the diffusion across the magnetic field lines is inhibited since $D_{\bar{\perp}} < D_-$. From [7.31] we see that for large magnetic fields the diffusion is proportional to $1/B^2$.

Many experiments have been performed, however, in which the diffusion of electrons across the magnetic field lines has been found to be more nearly proportional to $1/B$. Explanations for this so-called anomalous diffusion usually involve the idea that microelectric fields are set up in the plasma due to density fluctuations. These electric fields then give rise to drifts across the magnetic field which results in a "diffusion" proportional to $1/B$.

If the diffusion in the absence of a magnetic field is ambipolar rather than pure electron diffusion, it can be shown (Exercise 7.13.1) that the diffusion across the magnetic field lines is given by

$$D_A^{\perp} = \frac{D_A}{1 + \Omega_- \Omega_+ \tau_{\text{coll}}^- \tau_{\text{coll}}^+} \quad [7.37]$$

Exercise 7.13.1   By including the space charge electric field in [7.25] and by writing a similar equation for the ions verify [7.37].

7.2 CONDUCTIVITY
AND DIELECTRIC CONSTANT

In adopting a model for a plasma it has proved convenient to describe a plasma by analogy with two common types of materials—dielectrics and electrical conductors. In the *dielectric analogy* electrons are treated as bound charges, each being associated with a positive ion to form an electric dipole. In the *electrical conductor analogy* the electrons are treated as free charges whose response to applied fields is impeded by interactions with the other particles.

The fact that a plasma may be looked at in these two ways demonstrates its diverse behavior. As a conductor we find that the plasma conductivity has both real and imaginary parts indicating both resistive and reactive current components. As a dielectric we find that the plasma dielectric constant is also complex, resulting in a medium called a *lossy dielectric*.

We emphasize that these are alternative models. It invites a confusion of physical concepts to adopt a model for the plasma that assigns both a conductivity and a dielectric constant and requires that the plasma be thought of as a conductor and a dielectric at the same time. The use of these alternative models in Maxwell's equations will be illustrated in Section 11.2.

7.2I THE LANGEVIN EQUATION

The Langevin equation is a simple form of the equation of motion, or momentum equation, for the electrons of a weakly ionized gas. It is derived independently of the Boltzmann equation, but its assumptions and limitations are most clearly seen by comparing it to the momentum equation derived from the Boltzmann equation.

We continue to concern ourselves with a plasma in which the number densities of electrons and positive ions is considerably less than the number density of the neutral particles. Only the electron gas component of the mixture participates in the phenomena of interest. The electronic motion is modified by collisions with the neutral particles which are assumed to have an infinite mass. Interactions with the positive ions are unimportant, as are electron-electron interactions. These conditions describe the plasma model known as the *Lorentz gas*. For this model of the plasma we wish to determine how the equation of motion for a single electron in applied electric and magnetic fields

$$m_- \dot{v}_i^- = q_-(E_i + \epsilon_{ijk} v_j^- B_k) \qquad [7.38]$$

can be modified so as to include the effect of collisions on the motion of an average electron.

The left-hand side of [7.38] represents the rate of change of momentum of the electron and is equal to the total force acting on the electron, which is given by the right-hand side of the equation. A collision between an electron and a heavy neutral particle will change the momentum of the electron in the direction of its initial velocity, as described in Chapter 4. Thus, if the neutral particle is assumed to be infinitely massive, then the change in momentum in the forward direction is

$$\Delta(m_-v_i^-) = m_-v_i^-(1 - \cos\chi) \qquad [7.39]$$

If we average [7.39] over all scattering angles according to [4.73] using the angular distribution function for hard spheres given in Section 4.4, we find that

$$\langle\Delta(m_-v_i^-)\rangle = m_-v_i^-\langle1 - \cos\chi\rangle = m_-v_i^- \qquad [7.40]$$

Therefore, on the average, each collision results in a change in momentum equal to the initial momentum. Since the average rate at which collisions occur is simply the collision frequency ν, then the average rate of change of momentum is given by $m_-v_i^-\nu$. This term must be added to the left-hand side of [7.38]. To generalize beyond the hard sphere model, we write the added term as $m_-v_i^-\nu_{EN}$, where ν_{EN} is the effective collision frequency for momentum transfer between electrons and neutral particles. We therefore obtain an equation of motion for an average electron of the form

$$m_-\dot{v}_i^- + m_-\nu_{EN}v_i^- = q_-(E_i + \epsilon_{ijk}v_j^-B_k) \qquad [7.41]$$

Equation [7.41] is known as the *Langevin equation* and is very often used in conjunction with Maxwell's equations to describe the dynamics of plasmas. One must bear in mind, however, its inherent assumptions and remember that the results obtained will not be generally valid. We will take a closer look at the role collisions play in the dynamics of plasmas in Chapters 9 and 10.

The Langevin equation has the advantage that it is simple to use. As an example of its use we will derive, in the following section, an expression for the conductivity of a weakly ionized gas under the influence of an electromagnetic wave.

Exercise 7.21.1   Derive the Langevin equation [7.41] from the momentum equation [7.1], and list the assumptions and simplifications implicit in the Langevin equation.

7.22 CONDUCTIVITY AND DIELECTRIC CONSTANT OF ISOTROPIC PLASMAS

Let us consider a plasma for which the Lorentz model is applicable, when it is subjected to the passage of an electromagnetic wave, but in the absence of an applied magnetic field. Then in the Langevin equation the electric field E_i is the alternating field vector of the electromagnetic wave.

Now the electromagnetic wave is made up of an electric field E_i and a magnetic field H_i. Consider the magnitude of the forces exerted on an electron by these fields. For the electric field the force is $F_{elec} = -eE$, and for the magnetic field the maximum force is $F_{mag} = -ew\mu_o H$, where w is the speed of the electron. It is shown in Section 11.1 that the magnitude of H_i is related to the magnitude of E_i by the relation $H = (\epsilon_o/\mu_o)^{1/2}E$ so that

$$\frac{F_{mag}}{F_{elec}} = \frac{ew(\mu_o\epsilon_o)^{1/2}E}{-eE} = \frac{w}{c} \qquad [7.42]$$

where $c = (\mu_o\epsilon_o)^{-1/2}$ is the speed of light. Thus, if the speed of the electrons is much less than the speed of light, the magnetic field of an electromagnetic wave will have a small effect compared with the electric field on the motion of the electron. We therefore neglect the magnetic field of the electromagnetic wave.

The Langevin equation then becomes

$$m_-\dot{v}_i^- + m_-\nu_{EN}v_i^- = -eE_i \qquad [7.43]$$

Now if E_i varies with time as $e^{-i\omega t}$ where ω is the angular frequency of the electromagnetic wave, the electron velocity will have the same form of time-dependence with a time derivative $\partial/\partial t = -i\omega$. Therefore [7.43] can be written as $-i\omega v_i^- + \nu_{EN}v_i^- = -(e/m_-)E_i$, or

$$v_i^- = -\frac{e}{m_-}\frac{1}{(\nu_{EN} - i\omega)}E_i \qquad [7.44]$$

The velocity of an electron is related to the electric field by the electron mobility μ_-—that is, $v_i^- = \mu_-E_i$. From [7.44] we therefore see that

$$\mu_- = -\frac{e}{m_-}\frac{1}{(\nu_{EN} - i\omega)} \qquad [7.45]$$

The electron current density J_i is given by $J_i = -N_-ev_i^-$, where N_- is the electron density and the electron current density is related to the electric field by the equation that defines the *conductivity*, σ (taken to be a scalar in this case),

$$J_i = \sigma E_i = -N_- e v_i^- \qquad [7.46]$$

from which we see that $\sigma = -N_- e \mu_-$ or, from [7.45],

$$\sigma = \frac{N_- e^2}{m_-} \frac{1}{(\nu_{EN} - i\omega)}$$

which can be written as

$$\sigma = \frac{N_- e^2}{m_-} \frac{\nu_{EN}}{(\nu_{EN}^2 + \omega^2)} + i \frac{N_- e^2}{m_-} \frac{\omega}{(\nu_{EN}^2 + \omega^2)} \qquad [7.47]$$

We notice that the conductivity has a real and an imaginary part indicating that the electromagnetic wave is attenuated and shifted in phase as it propagates through the plasma.

When $\omega = 0$ the scalar conductivity reduces to the d-c value

$$\sigma_{\text{d.c.}} = \frac{N_- e^2}{m_- \nu_{EN}} \qquad [7.48]$$

The expressions for the conductivity derived in this section are in terms of the constant collision frequency ν_{EN}. When the collision frequency is a function of velocity (as it is in most gases), it is necessary, in calculating the conductivity, to integrate over the distribution of electron velocities. This procedure is discussed in Chapter 10.

The Dielectric Properties of an Isotropic Plasma   We now wish to show that the motion of the electrons under the influence of the same alternating electric field can, alternatively, be thought of as giving rise to a polarization current rather than a conduction current. Consider an electron situated at point A as shown in Figure 7.1a. As the result of an impressed electric field the electron moves a distance x_i to the point B as in Figure 7.1b. The resulting charge distribution is exactly the same as if the electron had remained at rest and a dipole moment equal to $-ex_i$ were added to the plasma as shown in Figure 7.1c. It is in this way that the motion of the electrons can be considered to give rise to a polarization vector P_i, which is the dipole moment per unit volume (see Section 3.1) given by

$$P_i = -N_- e x_i = \epsilon_0 \alpha E_i \qquad [7.49]$$

where α is the *electric susceptibility* of the plasma.

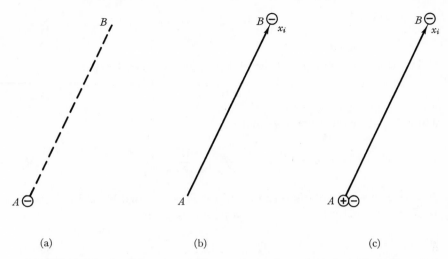

(a)   (b)   (c)

FIGURE 7.I   Representation of Electron Motion by an Equivalent Dipole Moment

Let us consider a Lorentz gas, as was done in discussing the conductivity. Then, assuming there is no external magnetic field, we can write the Langevin equation from [7.41] as

$$m_-\ddot{x}_i + m_-\nu_{EN}\dot{x}_i = -eE_i \tag{7.50}$$

Assuming time variations of the form $e^{-i\omega t}$ we can write [7.50] as

$$-\omega^2 x_i - i\omega\nu_{EN}x_i = -\frac{e}{m_-}E_i$$

from which

$$x_i = \frac{eE_i}{m_-\omega(\omega + i\nu_{EN})} \tag{7.51}$$

Substituting [7.51] into [7.49] we find that

$$\alpha = -\frac{N_-e^2}{m_-\epsilon_0\omega(\omega + i\nu_{EN})} \tag{7.52}$$

The *plasma frequency* Π, which is discussed in Chapter 9, is defined by

$$\Pi^2 = \frac{N_-e^2}{m_-\epsilon_0} \tag{7.53}$$

We can then write [7.52] as

$$\alpha = -\frac{\Pi^2}{\omega^2 + \nu_{EN}^2} + i\frac{\Pi^2\nu_{EN}/\omega}{\omega^2 + \nu_{EN}^2} \tag{7.54}$$

The *dielectric constant* κ of the plasma is given by (see Chapter 3)

$$\kappa = 1 + \alpha \tag{7.55}$$

Using [7.54] we therefore have that

$$\kappa = 1 - \frac{\Pi^2}{\omega^2 + \nu_{EN}^2} + i\frac{\Pi^2\nu_{EN}/\omega}{\omega^2 + \nu_{EN}^2} \tag{7.56}$$

For cases in which collisions can be neglected, we see that by setting $\nu_{EN} = 0$ in [7.56], the dielectric constant for a plasma is given by

$$\kappa = 1 - \frac{\Pi^2}{\omega^2} \tag{7.57}$$

Notice that the preceding description of a plasma in terms of dielectric properties is exactly equivalent to the description in terms of conducting properties. Both descriptions consider only the motion of the electrons under the influence of an alternating electric field. We can therefore think of a simple plasma as having either conducting properties or dielectric properties. This equivalence will be further demonstrated in the following section.

7.23 RELATIONSHIP BETWEEN THE CONDUCTIVITY AND THE DIELECTRIC CONSTANT

When the motion of the electrons in a plasma is described in terms of a current density J_i, then Maxwell's equation [3.35] is written as

$$\epsilon_{ijk}H_{k,j} = J_i + \epsilon_o\dot{E}_i \tag{7.58}$$

where the displacement current is that of free space. Setting $J_i = \sigma E_i$ and assuming a time variation of E_i in the form $e^{-i\omega t}$, we can write [7.58] as

$$\epsilon_{ijk}H_{k,j} = (\sigma - i\omega\epsilon_o)E_i \tag{7.59}$$

Now if we adopt the dielectric picture of a plasma which was described in the previous section, then we must set the current density J_i equal to zero. Maxwell's equation [3.35] can then be written in terms of a dielectric constant κ by using [3.17] as

$$\epsilon_{ijk}H_{k,j} = \dot{D}_i = \epsilon_o\kappa\dot{E}_i = -i\omega\epsilon_o\kappa E_i \tag{7.60}$$

Since [7.59] and [7.60] describe the same plasma, the right-hand sides of these two equations must be equal. Equating these, we find that the dielectric constant and the conductivity of a plasma are related by the following expression

$$\kappa = 1 + \frac{i}{\omega \epsilon_0} \sigma \qquad [7.61]$$

By substituting the expression for σ given by [7.47] into [7.61] and using [7.53] we obtain

$$\kappa = 1 - \frac{\Pi^2}{\omega^2 + \nu_{EN}^2} + i\frac{\Pi^2 \nu_{EN}/\omega}{\omega^2 + \nu_{EN}^2} \qquad [7.62]$$

which is identical with [7.56].

As a final indication of this equivalence between the two plasma descriptions, note that the total current density on the right-hand side of [7.60] is given by $\dot{D}_i$ which from [3.16] can be written as

$$\dot{D}_i = \dot{P}_i + \epsilon_0 \dot{E}_i \qquad [7.63]$$

However from [7.49] and the equation, $J_i = -N_- e v_i^-$, we see that,

$$\dot{P}_i = -N_- e\dot{x}_i = J_i \qquad [7.64]$$

so that [7.63] is also the right-hand side of [7.58].

We therefore see that we can consider an isotropic plasma to have either a conductivity σ or a dielectric constant κ. The choice will be one of convenience depending upon the particular problem being considered. In the following section we will extend these results by including the effect of an externally applied magnetic field.

7.24 THE CONDUCTIVITY AND DIELECTRIC TENSORS

In this section we will extend the treatment of the conductivity of a Lorentz gas given in Section 7.22 to include the case when the plasma is located in a static magnetic field. The Langevin equation for this case can then be written from [7.41] as

$$m_- \dot{v}_i^- + m_- \nu_{EN} v_i^- = -eE_i - e\epsilon_{ijk} v_j^- B_k \qquad [7.65]$$

Since we are only interested in the velocity component which varies at the signal frequency ω, we can write [7.65] as

$$-i\omega v_i^- + \nu_{EN} v_i^- = -\frac{e}{m_-} E_i - \epsilon_{ijk} v_j^- \Omega_k^- \qquad [7.66]$$

where

$$\Omega_k^- = \frac{eB_k}{m_-} \qquad [7.67]$$

is the *electron cyclotron frequency*.

Equation [7.66] can be rewritten as

$$(U\delta_{ij} + i\epsilon_{ijk}Y_k^-)v_j^- = -i\frac{e}{m_-\omega}E_i \qquad [7.68]$$

where we have introduced the quantities

$$U = 1 + iZ, \quad Z = \nu_{\mathrm{EN}}/\omega, \quad Y_k^- = \frac{\Omega_k^-}{\omega} \qquad [7.69]$$

If we assume that the magnetic field is directed along the x_3-axis so that $Y_k^- = (0, 0, Y_-)$, then [7.68] can be written in matrix form as

$$\begin{bmatrix} U & iY_- & 0 \\ -iY_- & U & 0 \\ 0 & 0 & U \end{bmatrix} \begin{bmatrix} v_1^- \\ v_2^- \\ v_3^- \end{bmatrix} = -i\frac{e}{m_-\omega} \begin{bmatrix} E_1 \\ E_2 \\ E_3 \end{bmatrix} \qquad [7.70]$$

which can be abbreviated as

$$\mathbf{Y_-v_-} = -i\frac{e}{m_-\omega}\mathbf{E} \qquad [7.71]$$

From [7.71] the velocity of the electron is given by

$$\mathbf{v_-} = -i\frac{e}{m_-\omega}\mathbf{Y_-^{-1}E} \qquad [7.72]$$

where $\mathbf{Y_-^{-1}}$ can be written from [7.70] as (see Exercise 7.24.1)

$$\mathbf{Y_-^{-1}} = \frac{1}{U(U^2 - Y_-^2)} \begin{bmatrix} U^2 & -iUY_- & 0 \\ iUY_- & U^2 & 0 \\ 0 & 0 & U^2 - Y_-^2 \end{bmatrix} \qquad [7.73]$$

The conductivity tensor σ_{ij} is defined in terms of the current density J_i, by

$$J_i = \sigma_{ij}E_j = -N_-ev_i^- \qquad [7.74]$$

Using this equation together with [7.72] and [7.73], we obtain the matrix form of the conductivity tensor

$$\sigma_{ij} = i \frac{N_- e^2}{m_- \omega U(U^2 - Y_-^2)} \begin{bmatrix} U^2 & -iUY_- & 0 \\ iUY_- & U^2 & 0 \\ 0 & 0 & U^2 - Y_-^2 \end{bmatrix} \qquad [7.75]$$

Note that for no magnetic field [7.75] reduces to the scalar conductivity σ given by [7.47].

The Dielectric Tensor   In Section 7.23 we showed that the dielectric constant κ and the conductivity σ are related by equation [7.61]. In a similar manner we can readily show (see Exercise 7.24.2) that the relationship between the dielectric tensor κ_{ij} and the conductivity tensor σ_{ij} is given by

$$\kappa_{ij} = \delta_{ij} + \frac{i}{\omega\epsilon_o} \sigma_{ij} \qquad [7.76]$$

Substituting the expression for the conductivity tensor given by [7.75] into [7.76] we obtain

$$\kappa_{ij} = \begin{bmatrix} 1 - \dfrac{XU}{U^2 - Y_-^2} & i\dfrac{XY_-}{U^2 - Y_-^2} & 0 \\ -i\dfrac{XY_-}{U^2 - Y_-^2} & 1 - \dfrac{XU}{U^2 - Y_-^2} & 0 \\ 0 & 0 & 1 - \dfrac{X}{U} \end{bmatrix} \qquad [7.77]$$

where

$$X = \frac{\Pi^2}{\omega^2} \qquad [7.78]$$

We therefore see that the dielectric tensor for a plasma in a magnetic field is of the form

$$\kappa_{ij} = \begin{bmatrix} S & -iD & 0 \\ iD & S & 0 \\ 0 & 0 & T \end{bmatrix} \qquad [7.79]$$

where

$$S = 1 - \frac{XU}{U^2 - Y_-^2} \qquad [7.80]$$

$$D = - \frac{XY_-}{U^2 - Y_-^2} \qquad [7.81]$$

$$T = 1 - \frac{X}{U} \qquad [7.82]$$

It is, of course, possible to derive the dielectric tensor given by [7.77] directly from the dielectric model of the plasma as was done in Section 7.22 for the dielectric constant (see Exercise 7.24.3).

Exercise 7.24.1 Verify that Y_-^{-1} is given by [7.73].

Exercise 7.24.2 Verify [7.76].

Exercise 7.24.3
(a) Since $P_i = \epsilon_0 \alpha_{ij} E_j$, show that the matrix form of the electric susceptibility tensor α_{ij} is given by

$$\alpha_{ij} = -\frac{\Pi^2}{\omega^2} Y_-^{-1}$$

where Π is the plasma frequency and Y_-^{-1} is given by [7.73].
(b) Calculate κ_{ij} from the relation [3.18] $\kappa_{ij} = \delta_{ij} + \alpha_{ij}$ and show that it agrees with [7.77].
(c) Show that the conductivity tensor σ_{ij} can be calculated from the relation $\sigma_{ij} = -i\omega\epsilon_0\alpha_{ij}$.

REFERENCES

Plasma diffusion and conductivity including ambipolar diffusion and the effect of an external magnetic field are discussed by

1 Allis, W. P. "Motions of Ions and Electrons," *Handbuch der Physik*, vol. 21, Springer-Verlag, 1956.

2 Delcroix, J. L. *Introduction to the Theory of Ionized Gases*. New York: Interscience (Wiley), 1960.

3 Rose, D. J., and M. Clark. *Plasmas and Controlled Fusion*. Cambridge, Mass., and New York: Massachusetts Institute of Technology Press and Wiley, 1961.

The dielectric model of a plasma is used extensively in the theory of ionospheric propagation as described by

4 Ratcliffe, J. A. *The Magneto-Ionic Theory and Its Applications to the Ionosphere*. London: Cambridge University Press, 1959.

5 Budden, K. G. *Radio Waves in the Ionosphere*. London: Cambridge University Press, 1961.

8

CHARGED

PARTICLE ORBITS

A major distinction can be made between a microscopic and a macroscopic description of a plasma. The previous two chapters have been concerned with the behavior of plasmas from a macroscopic point of view. A microscopic description deals with the motion of the individual particles that make up the plasma. In general this means a kinetic theory treatment, but an exception is the special case that occurs when interactions between the particles can be neglected.

This leads us to the domain of orbit theory. Orbit theory gives insight into the physical phenomena that determine plasma behavior, provided that particle interactions can be considered as playing only a minor role. In this chapter we will consider the motion of a single charged particle in the presence of electric and magnetic fields.

The equation of motion of a single charged particle is determined from the forces acting on the particle. Thus, if the forces are due to electric and magnetic fields, then Newton's second law can be written from [3.1] as

$$m \frac{d\mathbf{v}}{dt} = q\mathbf{E} + q\mathbf{v} \times \mathbf{B} \qquad [8.1]$$

Modest as it looks, this equation comprehends many complex field arrangements and its solutions are not all readily obtained. We therefore begin with simple conditions on the field quantities. Thus in Section 8.2 the equation of motion is solved for the case of static uniform fields. Various special cases are then examined in detail.

In order to relax the restrictions of static uniform fields, we must consider spatial and temporal variations in the field quantities. The spatial variation of the electric field is not of first importance because the plasma screens itself from such applied electric fields.

On the contrary, the case of an inhomogeneous magnetic field is of considerable importance. A general treatment of this case is complex, but we consider the simplification of a magnetic field gradient with a small spatial variation in Section 8.3. Several special cases are then considered.

A time varying magnetic field results in an induced electric field. The resulting motion of a charged particle in this case is discussed in Section 8.4.

Finally the motion of a charged particle in a time-varying electric field which is normal to a constant magnetic field is considered in Section 8.5. The phenomenon of cyclotron resonance is specifically treated.

8.1   THE EQUATIONS OF MOTION

Consider a particle of charge q and mass m situated in a static, uniform electric field E_i, and static, uniform magnetic field B_k. The equation of motion [8.1] can then be written in indicial notation as

$$m\dot{v}_i = q(E_i + \epsilon_{ijk}v_j B_k) \qquad [8.2]$$

where v_i is the particle velocity.

We now introduce the quantity

$$\Omega_k = -\frac{qB_k}{m} \qquad [8.3]$$

This is the *cyclotron frequency* of gyration of the particles about the magnetic field lines as can be seen by interpreting [8.9]. Equation [8.2] can then be written in the form

$$\dot{v}_i = \frac{q}{m} E_i - \epsilon_{ijk}v_j \Omega_k \qquad [8.4]$$

We can orient the field quantities in the Cartesian coordinate system in the

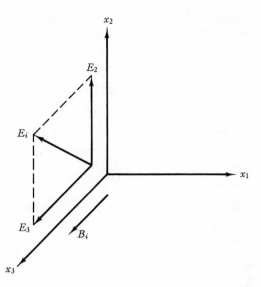

FIGURE 8.1 Orientation of Field Vectors in a Cartesian Coordinate System

way shown in Figure 8.1, without loss of generality. Then [8.4] can be written in matrix form as,

$$\begin{bmatrix} \dot{v}_1 \\ \dot{v}_2 \\ \dot{v}_3 \end{bmatrix} = \frac{q}{m} \begin{bmatrix} 0 \\ E_2 \\ E_3 \end{bmatrix} - \begin{bmatrix} v_2\Omega_3 \\ -v_1\Omega_3 \\ 0 \end{bmatrix} \qquad [8.5]$$

from which we obtain the three component equations,

$$\dot{v}_1 = -v_2\Omega_3 \qquad [8.6]$$

$$\dot{v}_2 = \frac{q}{m} E_2 + v_1\Omega_3 \qquad [8.7]$$

$$\dot{v}_3 = \frac{q}{m} E_3 \qquad [8.8]$$

Solving [8.6] and [8.7] simultaneously and integrating [8.8], we obtain for the three components of the velocity (see Exercise 8.1.1)

$$v_1 = \left(v_1^0 + \frac{qE_2}{m\Omega_3}\right) \cos \Omega_3 t - v_2^0 \sin \Omega_3 t - \frac{qE_2}{m\Omega_3} \qquad [8.9]$$

$$v_2 = \left(v_1^0 + \frac{qE_2}{m\Omega_3}\right) \sin \Omega_3 t + v_2^0 \cos \Omega_3 t \qquad [8.10]$$

$$v_3 = v_3^0 + \frac{q}{m} E_3 t \qquad [8.11]$$

where v_1^0, v_2^0 and v_3^0 are the initial values of the velocity components. Integrating [8.9] through [8.11], we obtain for the displacement of the particle the components (see Exercise 8.1.2)

$$x_1 = x_1^0 + \frac{1}{\Omega_3}\left\{v_2^0(\cos \Omega_3 t - 1) + \left(v_1^0 + \frac{qE_2}{m\Omega_3}\right)\sin \Omega_3 t - \frac{qE_2}{m}t\right\} \qquad [8.12]$$

$$x_2 = x_2^0 + \frac{1}{\Omega_3}\left\{v_2^0 \sin \Omega_3 t + \left(v_1^0 + \frac{qE_2}{m\Omega_3}\right)(1 - \cos \Omega_3 t)\right\} \qquad [8.13]$$

$$x_3 = x_3^0 + v_3^0 t + \tfrac{1}{2}\frac{q}{m}E_3 t^2 \qquad [8.14]$$

In order to understand the motion of charged particles in static, uniform electric, and magnetic fields, we will apply equations [8.9] through [8.14] to various special cases in Section 8.2.

Exercise 8.1.1   Obtain equations [8.9] and [8.10] by solving [8.6] and [8.7] simultaneously. Integrate [8.8] to obtain [8.11].

Exercise 8.1.2   Obtain equations [8.12] through [8.14] by integrating [8.9] through [8.11].

8.2 UNIFORM STATIC ELECTRIC AND MAGNETIC FIELDS

In this section we are concerned with uniform, static, electric and magnetic fields. Subdivision is made by considering the cases of no electric field, parallel electric and magnetic fields, and perpendicular electric and magnetic fields.

We find that the basic motion of a charged particle in these fields consists of a rotation around the magnetic field lines coupled with a translation of this instantaneous plane of rotation in a direction that is dependent upon the orientation of the electric field with respect to the magnetic field. The analysis of the motion in these terms is embodied in the *guiding center* concept. We can imagine the instantaneous center of rotation as being guided through the field region.

In the following sections we will see that the magnetic field produces the rotational motion (Section 8.21). When a parallel electric field is present, the guiding centers of positively and negatively charged particles move in opposite directions, thus producing space charge fields (Section 8.22). When the electric field is perpendicular to the magnetic field, the guiding centers all move together in a direction perpendicular to both the electric and magnetic field orientations (Section 8.23).

8.21   MAGNETIC FIELD ONLY

We will consider first the case in which the magnetic field is uniform and constant $B_i = (0, 0, B_3)$, and in which the electric field is zero. Consider the following set of initial conditions:

$$v_i^0 = (0, v_2^0, 0)$$

$$x_i^0 = \left(\frac{v_2^0}{\Omega_3}, 0, 0\right)$$

[8.15]

where $\Omega_3 \, [= -q(B_3/m)]$ is the cyclotron frequency (see [8.3]). Using these values in equations [8.12] to [8.14] together with the fact that $E_i = 0$, we obtain

$$x_1 = \frac{v_2^0}{\Omega_3} \cos \Omega_3 t$$

[8.16]

$$x_2 = \frac{v_2^0}{\Omega_3} \sin \Omega_3 t$$

[8.17]

$$x_3 = 0$$

[8.18]

Squaring and adding [8.16] and [8.17], we obtain

$$x_1^2 + x_2^2 = \left(\frac{v_2^0}{\Omega_3}\right)^2$$

We therefore see that a charged particle moves in a circle in the $x_1 x_2$ plane with a radius of gyration r given by

$$r = \left|\frac{v_2^0}{\Omega_3}\right| = \left|\frac{v_2^0 m}{q B_3}\right|$$

[8.19]

Consider an electron with a charge $q = -e$. Then from [8.3] the cyclotron frequency Ω_3 is,

$$\Omega_3 = \frac{e B_3}{m_-}$$

For this case [8.16] and [8.17] become

$$x_1 = \frac{v_2^0 m_-}{e B_3} \cos \left(\frac{e B_3}{m_-}\right) t$$

[8.20]

$$x_2 = \frac{v_2^0 m_-}{e B_3} \sin \left(\frac{e B_3}{m_-}\right) t$$

[8.21]

Differentiating [8.20] and [8.21] we obtain the velocity components

$$v_1 = -v_2^0 \sin\left(\frac{eB_3}{m_-}\right)t \qquad\qquad [8.22]$$

$$v_2 = v_2^0 \cos\left(\frac{eB_3}{m_-}\right)t \qquad\qquad [8.23]$$

From [8.20] to [8.23] we see that the electron gyrates about the magnetic field lines in a right-handed sense—that is, counterclockwise when looking antiparallel to the magnetic field direction or clockwise when looking parallel to the magnetic field direction as shown in Figure 8.2a.

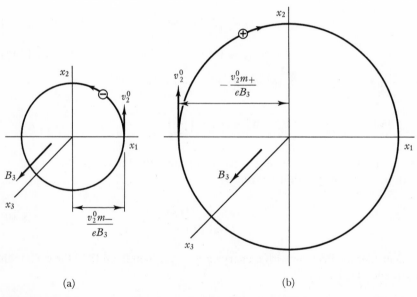

(a)   (b)

FIGURE 8.2 Orbits of Electrons and Positive Ions in Uniform, Static Magnetic Field

Similarly for a positive ion of charge $q = +e$ the cyclotron frequency is given by

$$\Omega_3 = -\frac{eB_3}{m_+}$$

so that the displacement and velocity components are given by

$$x_1 = -\frac{v_2^0 m_+}{eB_3} \cos\left(\frac{eB_3}{m_+}\right)t$$

$$x_2 = \frac{v_2^0 m_+}{eB_3} \sin\left(\frac{eB_3}{m_+}\right)t$$

$$v_1 = v_2^0 \sin\left(\frac{eB_3}{m_+}\right)t$$

$$v_2 = v_2^0 \cos\left(\frac{eB_3}{m_+}\right)t$$

It follows that a positive ion travels in a clockwise orbit when looking antiparallel to the magnetic field direction, as shown in Figure 8.2b.

In general the initial velocity will have a component along all three co-ordinate axes. The x_1 and x_2 components can be written from [8.9] and [8.10] in the form (see Exercise 8.21.3)

$$v_1 = -v_\perp \sin(\Omega_3 t - \phi) \tag{8.24}$$

$$v_2 = v_\perp \cos(\Omega_3 t - \phi) \tag{8.25}$$

where

$$v_\perp = [(v_1^0)^2 + (v_2^0)^2]^{1/2} \tag{8.26}$$

and

$$\phi = \tan^{-1}\frac{v_1^0}{v_2^0} \tag{8.27}$$

Circular motion around a line of force is one of the elemental motions of a particle moving in electric and magnetic fields. We will find it convenient to give the components of this motion a special designation which will serve our purposes in later sections of the chapter when the motion is more complicated.

To this end we will use a two-dimensional nomenclature similar to the indicial notation introduced in Chapter 2. Greek letters will be used as subscripts and will take on the values 1 and 2 only. It follows that components in the $x_1 x_2$ plane only, are represented.

We will designate the components of the circular motion as $v_1^\perp$ and $v_2^\perp$. We can then combine [8.24] and [8.25] as follows,

$$v_\alpha^\perp = \begin{bmatrix} v_1^\perp \\ v_2^\perp \end{bmatrix} = v_\perp \begin{bmatrix} -\sin(\Omega_3 t - \phi) \\ \cos(\Omega_3 t - \phi) \end{bmatrix} \tag{8.28}$$

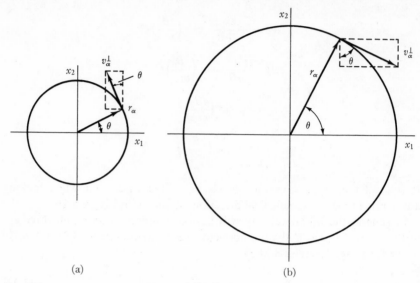

(a)   (b)

FIGURE 8.3 Radius Vector Description of Charged Particle Orbits in a Magnetic Field

We can introduce a radius vector r_α as shown in Figure 8.3 whose components are

$$r_1 = \frac{v_2^\perp}{\Omega_3} \qquad\qquad [8.29]$$

$$r_2 = -\frac{v_1^\perp}{\Omega_3} \qquad\qquad [8.30]$$

where the sign of the charge is included in Ω_3 according to [8.3].

We will also use the *two-dimensional alternating tensor* $e_{\alpha\beta}$ which is defined as follows:

$$e_{\alpha\beta} = \begin{bmatrix} +1 & \text{if } \alpha = 1 \text{ and } \beta = 2 \\ -1 & \text{if } \alpha = 2 \text{ and } \beta = 1 \\ 0 & \text{if } \alpha = \beta \end{bmatrix} \qquad [8.31]$$

with the important property that

$$e_{\alpha\beta}e_{\alpha\gamma} = \delta_{\beta\gamma} \qquad\qquad [8.32]$$

and

$$e_{\alpha\beta}e_{\gamma\alpha} = -\delta_{\beta\gamma} \qquad\qquad [8.33]$$

which follows from the definition of $e_{\alpha\beta}$.

It is now possible to combine [8.29] and [8.30] into the single vector equation

$$r_\alpha = e_{\alpha\beta} \frac{v_\beta^\perp}{\Omega_3} \qquad [8.34]$$

where repeated *Greek subscripts* are summed from one to two. If we multiply [8.34] by $e_{\alpha\gamma}$ and use [8.32], we obtain

$$e_{\alpha\gamma} r_\alpha = \delta_{\gamma\beta} \frac{v_\beta^\perp}{\Omega_3}$$

from which

$$v_\alpha^\perp = -\Omega_3 e_{\alpha\beta} r_\beta \qquad [8.35]$$

where we have changed the names of the subscripts and noted that

$$e_{\alpha\beta} = -e_{\beta\alpha}$$

Exercise 8.21.1 Show that the cyclotron frequency for an electron is $2.80 \times 10^6 B$ cycles/sec where B is given in gauss. NOTE: 1 gauss $= 10^{-4}$ weber/meter^2.

What is the cyclotron frequency in cycles per second for the following positive ions, H^+, H_2^+, He^+, He^{++} ?

Exercise 8.21.2 Draw graphs showing the variation of the radius of gyration of an electron and an atomic hydrogen ion as a function of magnetic field strength and particle energy. Show magnetic fields varying from zero to 10^5 gauss and temperatures varying from 10 to 10^8 °K.

Exercise 8.21.3 Derive equations [8.24] and [8.25] from [8.9] and [8.10].

Exercise 8.21.4 Show that an initial velocity in the x_3-direction results in a helical orbit of constant pitch.

8.22 ELECTRIC FIELD
PARALLEL TO MAGNETIC FIELD

Let us take the same initial conditions as in the previous section, thus,

$$v_i^0 = (0, v_2^0, 0)$$

$$x_i^0 = \left(\frac{v_2^0}{\Omega_3}, 0, 0 \right)$$

Using these values in equations [8.12], [8.13], and [8.14] together with the fact that $E_i = (0, 0, E_3)$, we obtain,

$$x_1 = \frac{v_2^0}{\Omega_3} \cos \Omega_3 t \qquad\qquad [8.36]$$

$$x_2 = \frac{v_2^0}{\Omega_3} \sin \Omega_3 t \qquad\qquad [8.37]$$

$$x_3 = \tfrac{1}{2} \frac{q}{m} E_3 t^2 \qquad\qquad [8.38]$$

Differentiating [8.36], [8.37], and [8.38], we obtain

$$v_1 = -v_2^0 \sin \Omega_3 t \qquad\qquad [8.39]$$

$$v_2 = v_2^0 \cos \Omega_3 t \qquad\qquad [8.40]$$

$$v_3 = \frac{q}{m} E_3 t \qquad\qquad [8.41]$$

Comparison of equations [8.36] to [8.41] with the corresponding equations in the preceding section ([8.16] to [8.18]), shows that the particle motions in the $x_1 x_2$ plane are identical. This motion is the particle gyration in a circle around the magnetic field lines at the cyclotron frequency.

The only effect of the imposed electric field is to produce an acceleration in the x_3-direction. It is clear from [8.38] that the direction of this acceleration depends upon the sign of the charge of the particle.

Figure 8:4 represents the situation for a positive ion ($+$) and an electron ($-$). In a plasma the charge separation brought about by such orbits will result in a counteracting electric field due to the net space charge. This will lead to the development of space charge sheaths.

8.23 ELECTRIC FIELD
PERPENDICULAR TO MAGNETIC FIELD

Let us consider the following conditions in which the electric and magnetic fields are perpendicular.

$$E_i = (0, E_2, 0)$$

$$B_i = (0, 0, B_3)$$

$$v_i^0 = (0, 0, 0)$$

$$x_i^0 = \left(0, \frac{-qE_2}{m\Omega_3^2}, 0\right)$$

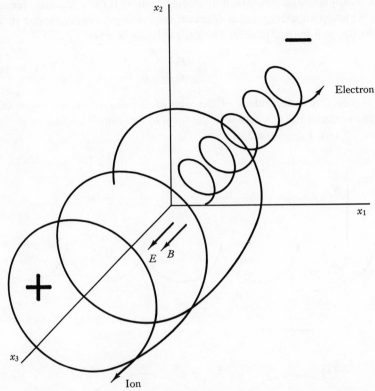

FIGURE 8.4   Orbits of Electrons and Positive Ions in Parallel Electric and Magnetic Fields

Equations [8.12], [8.13], and [8.14] then reduce to

$$x_1 = \frac{qE_2}{m\Omega_3^2} \sin \Omega_3 t - \frac{qE_2}{m\Omega_3} t$$

$$x_2 = -\frac{qE_2}{m\Omega_3^2} \cos \Omega_3 t \qquad\qquad [8.42]$$

$$x_3 = 0$$

which become, upon differentiating,

$$v_1 = \frac{qE_2}{m\Omega_3} \cos \Omega_3 t - \frac{qE_2}{m\Omega_3}$$

$$v_2 = \frac{qE_2}{m\Omega_3} \sin \Omega_3 t \qquad\qquad [8.43]$$

$$v_3 = 0$$

We therefore see from [8.42] and [8.43] that the motion takes place entirely in the $x_1 x_2$ plane and consists of a circular motion at the cyclotron frequency upon which is superimposed a constant drift motion perpendicular to both the electric and magnetic field. The drift velocity is given by

$$u_1 = -\frac{qE_2}{m\Omega_3} = \frac{E_2}{B_3} \tag{8.44}$$

and is therefore independent of the sign of the charge. The motion of the charged particles for this case is in the form of a common cycloid as shown in Figure 8.5 (see Exercise 8.23.1).

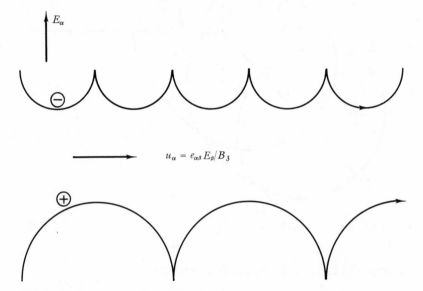

FIGURE 8.5 Orbits of Electrons and Positive Ions in Perpendicular Electric and Magnetic Fields

We can determine the drift velocity more generally in the following way. The previous special solution suggests that we can write the charged particle velocity in the $x_1 x_2$ plane as

$$v_\alpha = v_\alpha^\perp + u_\alpha \tag{8.45}$$

where $v_\alpha^\perp$ is given by [8.28] and u_α is a constant drift velocity.

The equation of motion [8.2] can be written in two-dimensional form as

$$\dot{v}_\alpha = \frac{q}{m} E_\alpha + \frac{q}{m} e_{\alpha\beta} v_\beta B_3 \tag{8.46}$$

If we substitute [8.45] into [8.46] and average over a period of the cyclotron gyration we obtain

$$0 = \frac{q}{m} E_\alpha + \frac{q}{m} e_{\alpha\beta} u_\beta B_3 \qquad [8.47]$$

Multiplying [8.47] by $e_{\alpha\gamma}$ and using [8.32] we obtain

$$0 = e_{\alpha\gamma} E_\alpha + u_\gamma B_3$$

from which, changing the names of the subscripts,

$$u_\alpha = e_{\alpha\beta} \frac{E_\beta}{B_3} \qquad [8.48]$$

Equation [8.48] should be recognized as the two-dimensional form of

$$\mathbf{u} = \frac{\mathbf{E} \times \mathbf{B}}{B^2} \qquad [8.49]$$

for the case when **B** is in the x_3-direction.

Exercise 8.23.1   Determine the position of the coordinates for the common cycloid motion shown in Figure 8.5 based on Equations [8.42] and [8.43]. Justify the shape of the curve.

Exercise 8.23.2   What is the physical reason for the drift motion in crossed electric and magnetic fields?

Exercise 8.23.3   Show that if $B_i = (0, 0, B_3)$ and $E_i = (0, E_2, 0)$ the particle motion is a straight line when $v_i^0 = v_1^0 = E_2/B_3$.

8.3   INHOMOGENEOUS
MAGNETIC FIELD

In the previous sections we have investigated the orbits which charged particles describe in the presence of static, uniform magnetic fields. We now wish to discover the effect of small spatial gradients of the magnetic field on the orbits of the charged particles.

We will assume that at the origin of a right-handed Cartesian coordinate system the magnetic field is in the x_3-direction and is given by B_3^0. All components of the magnetic field may, however, have gradients at the origin. We will further assume that the magnetic field varies sufficiently slowly in the $x_1 x_2$ plane so that at a distance equal to the radius of gyration, r, from the origin, the magnetic field can be expressed as

$$B_\alpha = r_\beta B^0_{\alpha,\beta} \qquad [8.50]$$

$$B_3 = B^0_3 + r_\beta B^0_{3,\beta} \qquad [8.51]$$

(see Exercise 8.3.1). Alternatively the cyclotron frequency can be written as

$$\Omega_\alpha = r_\beta \Omega^0_{\alpha,\beta} \qquad [8.52]$$

$$\Omega_3 = \Omega^0_3 + r_\beta \Omega^0_{3,\beta} \qquad [8.53]$$

Notice that in [8.50] and [8.51] we have explicitly considered gradients in the $x_1 x_2$ plane only. However, due to the fact that the divergence of the magnetic field vanishes—that is,

$$B_{i,i} = B_{\alpha,\alpha} + B_{3,3} = 0 \qquad [8.54]$$

it is apparent that we have also implicitly considered the gradient of B_3 in the x_3-direction. The case of gradients of B_1 and B_2 in the x_3-direction— that is, $B_{\alpha,3}$—will be considered separately in Section 8.33 on curvature drifts.

Now we assume that the motion of a charged particle consists of the circular motion described in Section 8.21 together with a motion parallel to the magnetic field and a drift velocity perpendicular to the magnetic field. We will, therefore, write the particle velocity as

$$v_i = v_\alpha + v_3 \qquad [8.55]$$

where $v_3 = v_\parallel$ is the velocity component along the magnetic field. The transverse velocity v_α can be written as

$$v_\alpha = u_\alpha + v^\perp_\alpha \qquad [8.56]$$

where $v^\perp_\alpha$ is the circular motion given by [8.35] as

$$v^\perp_\alpha = -\Omega^0_3 e_{\alpha\beta} r_\beta \qquad [8.57]$$

and u_α is the drift velocity—that is, the velocity of the guiding center in the $x_1 x_2$ plane.

Referring to [8.4], we see that the force per unit mass R_i which acts on a charged particle at any point is given by

$$R_i = \epsilon_{ijk} \Omega_j v_k$$

in the absence of an electric field. The components of R_i are then

$$R_1 = -\Omega_3 v_2 + \Omega_2 v_3 \qquad [8.58]$$

$$R_2 = \Omega_3 v_1 - \Omega_1 v_3 \qquad [8.59]$$

$$R_3 = \Omega_1 v_2 - \Omega_2 v_1 \qquad [8.60]$$

Equations [8.58] and [8.59] can be combined by making use of the properties of $e_{\alpha\beta}$ (see [8.31]). We obtain

$$R_\alpha = -e_{\alpha\beta} v_\beta \Omega_3 + e_{\alpha\beta} \Omega_\beta v_\| \qquad [8.61]$$

where $v_\| = v_3$. Also [8.60] can be written as,

$$R_\| = e_{\alpha\beta} \Omega_\alpha v_\beta \qquad [8.62]$$

Equation [8.61] gives the force per unit mass which acts on the charged particle in the transverse plane—that is, in the plane of the circular motion, while [8.62] gives the force per unit mass which acts along the magnetic field lines at the origin.

Let us consider first the transverse force R_α. Substituting [8.52], [8.53], [8.56], and [8.57] into [8.61], we obtain

$$\begin{aligned}
R_\alpha &= -e_{\alpha\beta}(u_\beta - \Omega_3^0 e_{\beta\gamma} r_\gamma)(\Omega_3^0 + r_\eta \Omega_{3,\eta}^0) \\
&\quad + e_{\alpha\beta} r_\gamma \Omega_{\beta,\gamma}^0 v_\| \\
&= -e_{\alpha\beta} u_\beta \Omega_3^0 + e_{\alpha\beta} e_{\beta\gamma} r_\gamma (\Omega_3^0)^2 - e_{\alpha\beta} u_\beta r_\eta \Omega_{3,\eta}^0 \\
&\quad + e_{\alpha\beta} e_{\beta\gamma} r_\gamma r_\eta \Omega_3^0 \Omega_{3,\eta}^0 + e_{\alpha\beta} r_\gamma \Omega_{\beta,\gamma}^0 v_\|
\end{aligned}$$

Using the property $e_{\alpha\beta} e_{\gamma\alpha} = -\delta_{\beta\gamma}$. we obtain

$$\begin{aligned}
R_\alpha &= -e_{\alpha\beta} u_\beta \Omega_3^0 - r_\alpha (\Omega_3^0)^2 - e_{\alpha\beta} u_\beta r_\eta \Omega_{3,\eta}^0 \\
&\quad - r_\alpha r_\eta \Omega_3^0 \Omega_{3,\eta}^0 + e_{\alpha\beta} r_\gamma \Omega_{\beta,\gamma}^0 v_\| \qquad [8.63]
\end{aligned}$$

Now in [8.63] some of the terms are periodic and oscillate with the cyclotron frequency. In particular, from [8.34] and [8.28] we see that r_α can be written as

$$r_\alpha = \frac{v_\perp}{\Omega_3} \begin{bmatrix} \cos(\Omega_3 t - \phi) \\ \sin(\Omega_3 t - \phi) \end{bmatrix} \qquad [8.64]$$

Since we are only interested in the transverse forces which produce drifts in the transverse plane we will average [8.63] over the period of a cyclotron gyration. From [8.64] we see that

$$\langle r_\alpha \rangle = 0 \qquad [8.65]$$

and

$$\langle r_\alpha r_\beta \rangle = \tfrac{1}{2} r^2 \delta_{\alpha\beta} \tag{8.66}$$

where

$$r^2 = \frac{v_\perp^2}{(\Omega_3^0)^2} \tag{8.67}$$

Averaging [8.63] and using [8.65] and [8.66], we obtain

$$\langle R_\alpha \rangle = -e_{\alpha\beta} u_\beta \Omega_3^0 - \tfrac{1}{2} r^2 \Omega_3^0 \Omega_{3,\alpha}^0 \tag{8.68}$$

Since

$$\Omega_3^0 \Omega_{3,\alpha}^0 = \tfrac{1}{2} (\Omega_3^0)_{,\alpha}^2$$

we can also write [8.68] as

$$\langle R_\alpha \rangle = -e_{\alpha\beta} u_\beta \Omega_3^0 - \frac{r^2}{4} (\Omega_3^0)_{,\alpha}^2 \tag{8.69}$$

Using [8.3] and [8.67] we can write [8.68] and [8.69] in terms of the magnetic field as

$$\langle R_\alpha \rangle = \frac{q}{m} B_3^0 e_{\alpha\beta} u_\beta - \frac{v_\perp^2}{2} \frac{B_{3,\alpha}^0}{B_3^0} \tag{8.70}$$

or

$$\langle R_\alpha \rangle = \frac{q}{m} B_3^0 e_{\alpha\beta} u_\beta - \frac{v_\perp^2}{4} \frac{(B_3^0)_{,\alpha}^2}{(B_3^0)^2} \tag{8.71}$$

Let us next consider the parallel force $R_\parallel$. Substituting [8.52], [8.56], and [8.57] into [8.62], we obtain

$$\begin{aligned}
R_\parallel &= e_{\alpha\beta} r_\gamma \Omega_{\alpha,\gamma}^0 (u_\beta - \Omega_3^0 e_{\beta\eta} r_\eta) \\
&= e_{\alpha\beta} r_\gamma \Omega_{\alpha,\gamma}^0 u_\beta - e_{\alpha\beta} e_{\beta\eta} r_\eta r_\gamma \Omega_{\alpha,\gamma}^0 \Omega_3^0 \\
&= e_{\alpha\beta} r_\gamma \Omega_{\alpha,\gamma}^0 u_\beta + r_\alpha r_\gamma \Omega_{\alpha,\gamma}^0 \Omega_3^0
\end{aligned} \tag{8.72}$$

where [8.33] has been used. Averaging [8.72] and using [8.65] and [8.66], we obtain

$$\langle R_\parallel \rangle = \tfrac{1}{2} r^2 \Omega_{\alpha,\alpha}^0 \Omega_3^0 \tag{8.73}$$

Using the divergence-free property of the magnetic field given by [8.54], we can write [8.73] as

$$\langle R_{\parallel} \rangle = -\tfrac{1}{2} r^2 \Omega^0_{3,3} \Omega^0_3 \qquad [8.74]$$

or, alternatively,

$$\langle R_{\parallel} \rangle = -\frac{r^2}{4} (\Omega^0_3)^2_{,3} \qquad [8.75]$$

In terms of the magnetic field [8.74] and [8.75] can be written as

$$\langle R_{\parallel} \rangle = -\frac{v^2_{\perp}}{2} \frac{B^0_{3,3}}{B^0_3} \qquad [8.76]$$

or

$$\langle R_{\parallel} \rangle = -\frac{v^2_{\perp}}{4} \frac{(B^0_3)^2_{,3}}{(B^0_3)^2} \qquad [8.77]$$

We have thus found in this section expressions for the average force per unit mass which acts on a charged particle in a slightly inhomogeneous magnetic field. This force is conveniently broken down into a transverse force given by [8.70] or [8.71] and a longitudinal force given by [8.76] or [8.77]. In the following sections we will use these expressions to investigate the special effects produced when only certain components of the magnetic field gradient exist.

Exercise 8.3.1   Write down general expressions for the incremental change in magnetic field which is experienced on moving away from an arbitrary point in the field. Show that if over a distance equal to the radius of gyration, $\Delta B \ll B$, then the magnetic field can be written in the form of [8.50] and [8.51].

8.3I L O N G I T U D I N A L   G R A D I E N T S

The components of the magnetic field gradient form the components of a second-order tensor and can be displayed in matrix form as

$$B_{i,j} = \begin{bmatrix} B_{1,1} & B_{1,2} & B_{1,3} \\ B_{2,1} & B_{2,2} & B_{2,3} \\ B_{3,1} & B_{3,2} & B_{3,3} \end{bmatrix} \qquad [8.78]$$

Let us consider in this section the main diagonal elements. The off-diagonal elements will be considered in subsequent sections.

Due to the divergence-free nature of the magnetic field, the sum of the main diagonal elements in [8.78] must vanish. We note from [8.73] and [8.74] that the existence of these terms result in an average force along the magnetic field lines. If the main diagonal elements do not vanish then the bundle of lines of force converge (or diverge) as shown in Figure 8.6.

Let us consider physically what will happen to charged particles in such a configuration. Referring to the results of Section 8.21, we see that if we look in the direction of the magnetic field, electrons will gyrate clockwise while positive ions will gyrate counterclockwise. That is, in Figure 8.6 the electron

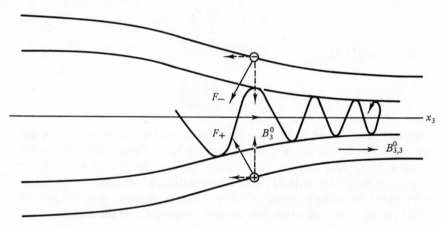

FIGURE 8.6   Orbits of Electrons and Positive Ions in a Magnetic Field with a Longitudinal Gradient

and positive ions shown are both moving out of the page. The force that acts on both charged particles therefore has a radial component directed inward, which will average to zero over a single gyration, and a parallel component directed away from regions of higher magnetic fields. The student can convince himself that this parallel force will always be in this direction regardless of the charge of the particle or where it may be located at any instant of time.

The magnitude of this parallel force is given by [8.76] as

$$\langle R_{\parallel} \rangle = -\frac{v_{\perp}^2}{2} \frac{B_{3,3}^0}{B_3^0} \qquad [8.79]$$

which is the average force per unit mass acting on the charged particle. Note that it is independent of charge and is directed away from increasing magnetic fields.

From [8.79] we can write the force equation for the charged particle as

$$m\dot{v}_\parallel = -\tfrac{1}{2}mv_\perp^2 \frac{B^0_{3,3}}{B^0_3} = -\frac{K_\perp}{B^0_3} B^0_{3,3} \qquad [8.80]$$

where

$$K_\perp = \tfrac{1}{2}mv_\perp^2 \qquad [8.81]$$

is the kinetic energy of the particle associated with its transverse motion. Since

$$\dot{v}_\parallel = \frac{dv_\parallel}{dx_3}\frac{dx_3}{dt} = v_\parallel \frac{dv_\parallel}{dx_3} = \frac{1}{2}\frac{dv_\parallel^2}{dx_3} \qquad [8.82]$$

we can write [8.80] as

$$\frac{dK_\parallel}{dx_3} = -\frac{K_\perp}{B^0_3} B^0_{3,3} \qquad [8.83]$$

where

$$K_\parallel = \tfrac{1}{2}mv_\parallel^2 \qquad [8.84]$$

is the kinetic energy of the particle associated with its longitudinal motion.
Since the total kinetic energy

$$K = K_\perp + K_\parallel$$

must remain constant, we have that

$$\frac{dK}{dx_3} = \frac{dK_\perp}{dx_3} + \frac{dK_\parallel}{dx_3} = 0$$

from which

$$\frac{dK_\parallel}{dx_3} = -\frac{dK_\perp}{dx_3} \qquad [8.85]$$

Substituting [8.85] into [8.83], we obtain

$$\frac{dK_\perp}{dx_3} = \frac{K_\perp}{B^0_3}\frac{dB^0_3}{dx_3}$$

from which

$$\frac{dK_\perp}{K_\perp} = \frac{dB_3^0}{B_3^0}$$

[8.86]

Integrating [8.86], we obtain

$$\ln\left(\frac{K_\perp}{B_3^0}\right) = \text{constant}$$

which leads to

$$\frac{K_\perp}{B_3^0} = |m_i| = \text{constant}$$

[8.87]

The quantity m_i is called the *orbital magnetic moment* of the gyrating particle (see Exercise 8.31.1). It is not strictly a constant of the motion of the particle but is called an *adiabatic invariant* since it is constant only if the change in the magnetic field over a gyromagnetic radius is small, which was the assumption on which [8.87] was derived.

From [8.87] we see that the quantity $v_\perp^2/B_3^0$ is constant. Using [8.57], this means that $B_3^0 r^2$, which is proportional to the magnetic flux linking the circular orbits, is also constant. In other words, the orbiting particle continues to encircle the same bundle of flux as shown in Figure 8.6. Such an orbiting particle can be reflected from regions of higher magnetic field strength (see Exercise 8.31.2).

Exercise 8.31.1   The orbital magnetic moment m_i of a gyrating charged particle is defined as the circulating current times the area of the loop (see Section 3.1). Show that for a charged particle in a magnetic field $|m_i| = K_\perp/B_3^0$.

Exercise 8.31.2   Since both $|m_i| = K_\perp/B_3^0$ and $K = K_\parallel + K_\perp$ must remain constant, then the transverse kinetic energy of a particle entering a region of higher field must increase while its parallel kinetic energy decreases. When all of the kinetic energy is transverse the particle will be reflected. Show that a particle whose orbit makes an angle θ with the magnetic field line B_3^0 will be reflected at a point where the magnetic field strength has increased to B_3' where $\sin^2\theta = B_3^0/B_3'$.

8.32 T R A N S V E R S E   G R A D I E N T S

We now wish to investigate the effects of some of the off-diagonal elements of [8.78]. The terms $B_{3,1}$ and $B_{3,2}$ appear in [8.70] in the form

$$\langle R_\alpha\rangle = \frac{q}{m}B_3^0 e_{\alpha\beta}u_\beta - \frac{v_\perp^2}{2}\frac{B_{3,\alpha}^0}{B_3^0}$$

[8.88]

Writing the equation of motion for the transverse forces on the particle we have

$$m\dot{v}_\alpha = qB_3^0 e_{\alpha\beta}u_\beta - \tfrac{1}{2}mv_\perp^2 \frac{B_{3,\alpha}^0}{B_3^0} \qquad [8.89]$$

Now from [8.56] and [8.57] we see that

$$v_\alpha = u_\alpha - \Omega_3^0 e_{\alpha\beta}r_\beta$$

so that

$$\dot{v}_\alpha = \dot{u}_\alpha - \dot{\Omega}_3^0 e_{\alpha\beta}r_\beta - \Omega_3^0 e_{\alpha\beta}\dot{r}_\beta$$

If we average this equation over a gyrating period, then the last two terms vanish and we see that

$$\dot{v}_\alpha = \dot{u}_\alpha \qquad [8.90]$$

Now the guiding center will only be accelerated if the magnetic field lines are curved. We will see in the next section that such a curvature results from the magnetic gradient components $B_{1,3}$ and $B_{2,3}$. For the present case we can neglect such a curvature so that $\dot{u}_\alpha = 0$ and [8.89] can be written, using [8.81] as

$$e_{\alpha\beta}u_\beta - \frac{K_\perp}{q} \frac{B_{3,\alpha}^0}{(B_3^0)^2} = 0 \qquad [8.91]$$

Multiplying [8.91] by $e_{\alpha\gamma}$ and using [8.32], we find that the velocity of the guiding center is given by

$$u_\gamma = \frac{K_\perp}{q} e_{\alpha\gamma} \frac{B_{3,\alpha}^0}{(B_3^0)^2} \qquad [8.92]$$

We therefore see that the guiding center drifts in the transverse plane at right angles to the magnetic field gradient. The direction of drift also depends on the charge of the particle.

   The physical reasons for these drifts can be seen as follows. In Figure 8.7 the magnetic field is directed out of the page and the gradient is in the x_2-direction. From [8.19] we see that the radius of the orbit of a gyrating particle decreases as the magnetic field increases. Therefore in Figure 8.7 the radius of curvature of the orbits is smaller in the regions of higher magnetic fields. However, since the electrons gyrate counterclockwise while the positive ions

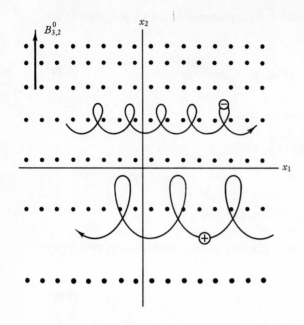

FIGURE 8.7 Orbits of Electrons and Positive Ions in a Magnetic Field with a Transverse Gradient

gyrate clockwise, the electrons will drift to the right and the positive ions will drift to the left.

From [8.92] we see that the electrons will drift with a velocity

$$u_1^- = \frac{K_\perp^-}{e} \frac{B_{3,2}^0}{(B_3^0)^2}$$

while the positive ions drift with a velocity

$$u_1^+ = -\frac{K_\perp^+}{e} \frac{B_{3,2}^0}{(B_3^0)^2}$$

Since the electrons and positive ions drift in opposite directions in Figure 8.7 we might expect a net current to flow. However, since the radii of the orbits varies in the x_2-direction, then a *magnetization current density* exists which from [3.39] is given by

$$J_\alpha^M = e_{\alpha\beta} M_{3,\beta} \qquad\qquad [8.93]$$

The *magnetization vector* M_3 can be written as (see Exercise 8.32.1)

$$M_3 = -\frac{NK_\perp}{B_3} \qquad\qquad [8.94]$$

The current density resulting from the drift of the guiding centers is, from [8.92] given by

$$J_\alpha^D = Nqu_\alpha = -NK_\perp e_{\alpha\beta} \frac{B_{3,\beta}}{B_3^2} \qquad [8.95]$$

Adding [8.93] and [8.95] and using [8.94] we find that the total current density is given by

$$J_\alpha = J_\alpha^M + J_\alpha^D$$

$$= -e_{\alpha\beta}\left[\left(\frac{NK_\perp}{B_3}\right)_{,\beta} + NK_\perp \frac{B_{3,\beta}}{B_3^2}\right]$$

$$= -e_{\alpha\beta}\left[\frac{(NK_\perp)_{,\beta}}{B_3} - \frac{NK_\perp}{B_3^2} B_{3,\beta} + \frac{NK_\perp}{B_3^2} B_{3,\beta}\right]$$

so that,

$$J_\alpha = -e_{\alpha\beta} \frac{K_\perp}{B_3} N_{,\beta} \qquad [8.96]$$

We therefore see that the current density resulting from drifts of the guiding centers is just cancelled by part of the magnetization current and that the only resultant current density is due to gradients in the particle density.

> *Exercise* 8.32.1   Show that the magnetization vector $M_3 = Nm_3$ can be written as
>
> $$M_3 = -\frac{1}{2}\frac{mNv_\perp^2}{B_3} = -\frac{NK_\perp}{B_3}$$
>
> where the orbital magnetic moment m_3 (see [3.22]) should not be confused with the mass m. What is the physical reason for the magnetization current resulting from charged particles gyrating in a magnetic field with a transverse gradient?

8.33   CURVATURE DRIFTS

In Section 8.32 we stated that the elements $B_{1,3}$ and $B_{2,3}$ of the magnetic field gradient exist when the magnetic field lines are curved. In this section we wish to show that this is true and that such a curvature produces a drift across the magnetic field lines.

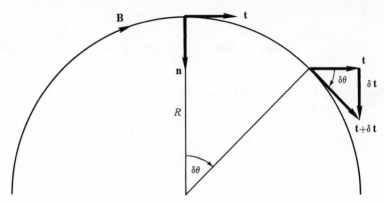

FIGURE 8.8 A Magnetic Field Line with Curvature

We begin by considering a curved magnetic field line as shown in Figure 8.8. We introduce the unit tangent vector **t** and the principal unit normal vector **n**. Since **t** is a unit vector, we see from Figure 8.8 that

$$|\delta\mathbf{t}| = \delta\theta \tag{8.97}$$

The *curvature* $\mathcal{K}$ of the magnetic field line is defined as

$$\mathcal{K} = \frac{1}{R} = \frac{d\theta}{ds}$$

where ds is the incremental distance along the circumference. Using [8.97], we see that we can express the curvature as

$$\mathcal{K} = \frac{1}{R} = \left|\frac{d\mathbf{t}}{ds}\right|$$

The direction of $d\mathbf{t}/ds$ is normal to **t**, since

$$\mathbf{t}\cdot\mathbf{t} = 1$$

so that

$$2\mathbf{t}\cdot\frac{d\mathbf{t}}{ds} = 0$$

We can therefore write

$$\frac{d\mathbf{t}}{ds} = \frac{1}{R}\mathbf{n} \tag{8.98}$$

Since the velocity of the guiding center along the magnetic field line is $v_\parallel \mathbf{t}$, we can write the acceleration $\mathbf{a}$ as

$$\mathbf{a} = \frac{d(v_\parallel \mathbf{t})}{dt} = \dot{v}_\parallel \mathbf{t} + v_\parallel \frac{d\mathbf{t}}{dt} \tag{8.99}$$

Using [8.98], we have that

$$\frac{d\mathbf{t}}{dt} = \frac{d\mathbf{t}}{ds}\frac{ds}{dt} = \frac{1}{R}\mathbf{n}v_\parallel \tag{8.100}$$

Substituting [8.100] into [8.99], we obtain

$$\mathbf{a} = \dot{v}_\parallel \mathbf{t} + \frac{v_\parallel^2}{R}\mathbf{n} \tag{8.101}$$

If at a given point we consider the magnetic field line to be directed along the x_3-axis, then $\mathbf{n}$ will lie in the $x_1 x_2$ plane. The component of the acceleration in the transverse plane can then be written from [8.101] as

$$\dot{u}_\alpha = \frac{R_\alpha}{R^2}v_\parallel^2 \tag{8.102}$$

which is the centripetal acceleration of the guiding center.

This acceleration can also be written in terms of the magnetic field gradient as follows: The magnetic field at any point in Figure 8.8 can be written as $\mathbf{B} = B\mathbf{t}$, where B is the magnitude of the field. If at a given point the unit vector $\mathbf{t}$ is in the x_3-direction, then the gradient of $\mathbf{B}$ in the x_3-direction can be broken down into a longitudinal and transverse component. That is,

$$\frac{d\mathbf{B}}{dx_3} = B_{3,3}\mathbf{t} + B_{\alpha,3}\mathbf{n}_\alpha \tag{8.103}$$

However, for this case

$$\frac{d\mathbf{B}}{dx_3} = \frac{d(B_3 \mathbf{t})}{dx_3}$$

$$= B_{3,3}\mathbf{t} + B_3 \frac{d\mathbf{t}}{dx_3}$$

$$= B_{3,3}\mathbf{t} + \frac{B_3}{R}\mathbf{n} \tag{8.104}$$

where [8.98] has been used. Since **n** is in the $x_1 x_2$ plane, we have from [8.103] and [8.104] that

$$B_{\alpha,3} = \frac{R_\alpha}{R^2} B_3$$

from which

$$\frac{R_\alpha}{R^2} = \frac{B_{\alpha,3}}{B_3} \qquad\qquad [8.105]$$

Substituting [8.105] into [8.102], we obtain

$$\dot{u}_\alpha = \frac{v_\parallel^2}{B_3} B_{\alpha,3} \qquad\qquad [8.106]$$

Now the equation of motion in the transverse plane can be written from [8.89] and [8.90] as

$$\dot{u}_\alpha = \frac{q}{m} B_3 e_{\alpha\beta} u_\beta - \tfrac{1}{2} v_\perp^2 \frac{B_{3,\alpha}}{B_3} \qquad\qquad [8.107]$$

Substituting [8.106] into [8.107], we obtain

$$e_{\alpha\beta} u_\beta = \frac{m}{q} \frac{B_{\alpha,3}}{B_3^2} v_\parallel^2 + \frac{1}{2} \frac{m}{q} v_\perp^2 \frac{B_{3,\alpha}}{B_3^2} \qquad\qquad [8.108]$$

Multiplying [8.108] by $e_{\alpha\gamma}$ and using [8.32] we obtain for the velocity of the guiding center

$$u_\gamma = \frac{m}{q B_3^2} e_{\alpha\gamma}(v_\parallel^2 B_{\alpha,3} + \tfrac{1}{2} v_\perp^2 B_{3,\alpha}) \qquad\qquad [8.109]$$

The second term of [8.109] is the drift velocity resulting from transverse gradients found in the previous section. The additional first term in [8.109] is a drift velocity resulting from the curvature of the lines of force and it depends on the magnetic gradient components $B_{1,3}$ and $B_{2,3}$. Note that the drift velocity is at right angles to these gradients—that is, the guiding center moves at right angles to both **t** and **n** in Figure 8.8.

We have now considered the effect of all of the magnetic gradient components in [8.78] except $B_{1,2}$ and $B_{2,1}$. These components exist if the bundle of lines of force twist about a center line. Although they alter the orbits slightly, as we have seen, they produce no first-order drifts of the guiding center.

Exercise 8.33.1 Show that in Figure 8.8 the direction of the electron drift is out of the page while the direction of the positive ion drift is into the page.

Exercise 8.33.2 Show that in the earth's magnetic field the direction of the drift velocity is the same for both curvature drifts and drifts due to transverse gradients.

8.4 TIME-VARYING MAGNETIC FIELD

In Section 8.21 we found that in a uniform, static magnetic field charged particles gyrated about the magnetic field lines in circular orbits. Suppose that the uniform magnetic field within these circular orbits increases with time. Then by Faraday's law [3.31] an electric field will be induced along the path of the orbit according to

$$\oint_{\text{orbit}} E_i \, ds_i = -\frac{d}{dt} \int_S B_i n_i \, dA \qquad [8.110]$$

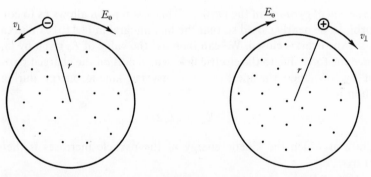

FIGURE 8.9 Electric Field Induced by a Time-Varying Magnetic Field. The magnetic field exists as a uniform magnetic field within the circular orbit and is increasing with time

Recall that the direction in which the line integral is taken in [8.110] is such that ds_i and n_i are related in a right-handed sense. Thus if the magnetic field in Figure 8.9 is directed out of the page along the x_3-axis and is increasing with time, then the induced electric field E_θ is in the direction shown. From [8.110] we then have

$$E_\theta 2\pi r = \dot{B}_3 \pi r^2$$

from which

$$E_\theta = \tfrac{1}{2}r\dot{B}_3 \qquad\qquad [8.111]$$

We see that the direction of E_θ is such as to accelerate both electrons and positive ions. This means that $v_\perp$ will increase and since

$$r = \left|\frac{mv_\perp}{qB_3}\right| \qquad\qquad [8.112]$$

we might suspect that the radius of gyration will also increase. However, since B_3 is increasing at the same time, the behavior of r will depend on the relative rates of increase of $v_\perp$ and B_3.

In order to determine what this relation is, let us calculate the rate at which the transverse kinetic energy of the particle increases. We will assume that during a single gyration the magnetic field changes sufficiently slowly so that

$$\dot{B}_3 T \ll B_3 \qquad\qquad [8.113]$$

where

$$T = \left|\frac{2\pi}{\Omega_3}\right| = \left|\frac{2\pi m}{qB_3}\right| \qquad\qquad [8.114]$$

is the *period of gyration* of the particle. This assumption allows us to consider the orbit to be nearly closed so that the line integral in [8.110] can be carried out as if the orbit is closed. We can then use the value of E_θ given by [8.111].

Since the force due to the electric field which acts on the charged particle is given by qE_θ, then the increase in transverse kinetic energy during one gyration is

$$\Delta K_\perp = qE_\theta 2\pi r \qquad\qquad [8.115]$$

The rate at which the kinetic energy of the particle increases is therefore given by

$$\frac{dK_\perp}{dt} = \frac{\Delta K_\perp}{T} = \frac{qE_\theta 2\pi r}{T} \qquad\qquad [8.116]$$

Using [8.111], [8.112], and [8.114], we can write [8.116] as

$$\frac{dK_\perp}{dt} = \frac{\tfrac{1}{2}mv_\perp^2}{B_3}\dot{B}_3 = \frac{K_\perp}{B_3}\frac{dB_3}{dt}$$

from which

$$\frac{dK_\perp}{K_\perp} = \frac{dB_3}{B_3} \qquad\qquad [8.117]$$

Integrating [8.117] we obtain

$$\ln\left(\frac{K_\perp}{B_3}\right) = \text{constant}$$

or

$$\frac{K_\perp}{B_3} = |m_i| = \text{constant} \qquad\qquad [8.118]$$

We therefore see that when the condition [8.113] holds, the orbital magnetic moment m_i is a constant, just as it was in the case of longitudinal gradients in Section 8.31.

We can now answer our question concerning the behavior of the radius of gyration r. Equation [8.118] tells us that the transverse velocity $v_\perp$ varies as $(B_3)^{1/2}$. Thus from [8.112] the radius of gyration r has a net variation which is proportional to $(B_3)^{-1/2}$. It will therefore decrease as B_3 increases as shown in Figure 8.10.

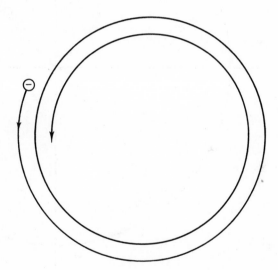

FIGURE 8.10 Electron Orbit in Time-Varying Magnetic Field. The magnetic field is directed out of the page and is increasing with time

As mentioned in Section 8.31, the constancy of the magnetic moment given by [8.118] implies that the gyrating particle continually encircles the same number of flux lines. Thus in Figure 8.10 as the magnetic field strength increases the radius of the orbit decreases in such a way that the particle always encircles the same number of flux lines.

So far in this section we have only considered changing magnetic fields that exist within the circular orbit of the gyrating particle (or are, at least, cylindrically symmetric about the center of the orbit). Clearly, if time-varying

magnetic fields exist outside the orbit in an unsymmetrical manner, then the
resultant induced electric field acting on the charged particle could considerably alter its orbit from that shown in Figure 8.10. In general the form
of such orbits can be extremely complicated. However the general idea of
what may happen can be seen by considering the following special case.

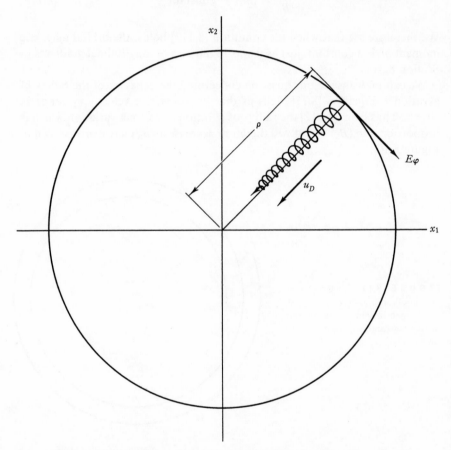

F I G U R E   8.11   Particle Orbit in an Increasing Cylindrical Magnetic Field. $\rho \gg r$.
Magnetic field directed out of the page

Consider a uniform cylindrical magnetic field that exists over a radius ρ
which is much larger than the radius of gyration r. If the magnetic field
increases as shown in Figure 8.11, then the induced electric field E_ϕ at point A
is given from Faraday's law by

$$E_\phi = \tfrac{1}{2}\rho \dot{B}_3 \qquad\qquad [8.119]$$

(Compare with [8.111].) A charged particle located at A will now be situated in a crossed electric and magnetic field such as described in Section 8.23. A drift velocity u_D directed radially inward thus results as shown in Figure 8.11 which is given by

$$u_D = \dot{\rho} = \frac{E_\phi}{B_3} = \tfrac{1}{2}\rho \, \frac{\dot{B}_3}{B_3} \qquad [8.120]$$

This situation can also be pictured as follows. As the magnetic field strength increases in Figure 8.11, the density of magnetic flux lines increases. That is, a given flux line located originally at point A appears to move radially inward with some velocity as the magnetic field strength increases. One can readily show (see Exercise 8.4.1) that this velocity is given by

$$u_F = \tfrac{1}{2}\rho \, \frac{\dot{B}_3}{B_3} \qquad [8.121]$$

which is the same as u_D in [8.120]. We therefore obtain the picture of the guiding center being attached to a given flux line. At the same time the total flux encircled by the gyrating particle remains constant so that its radius of gyration decreases as it drifts radially inward as shown in Figure 8.11.

A detailed calculation of charged particle orbits in time-varying magnetic fields requires the direct solution of the equation of motion. For more information on this treatment the student is referred to the problems and references at the end of the chapter.

Exercise 8.4.1   Show that if the magnetic field increases at the rate $\dot{B}_3$ in Figure 8.11 then a given line of flux appears to move radially inward with a velocity

$$u_F = \tfrac{1}{2}\rho \, \frac{\dot{B}_3}{B_3}$$

Exercise 8.4.2   For the situation shown in Figure 8.11 show that

$$K_\perp \rho^2 = \text{constant}$$

8.5   TIME-VARYING
ELECTRIC FIELD

In Section 8.23 we found that a static electric field perpendicular to a static magnetic field produced a drift velocity of the charged particles at right angles to both fields. We now wish to examine the orbits of the charged particles when a sinusoidal electric field is turned on abruptly at $t = 0$. We shall find that the motion of the charged particles has components at both the cyclotron frequency Ω and at the frequency of the electric field ω. It should be noted that if the electric field is turned on sufficiently slowly no component motion at the cyclotron frequency will occur (see Problem 8.4).

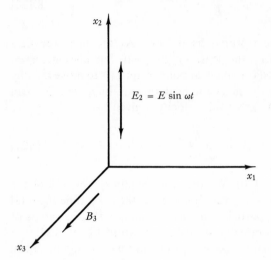

FIGURE 8.12 Orientation of Field Vectors for Time-Varying Electric Fields

We will use the coordinate axes shown in Figure 8.12 so that the only motion of interest takes place in the $x_1 x_2$ plane. The x_1- and x_2-components of the equation of motion for $t > 0$ can then be written from [8.5] as

$$\dot{v}_1 = -v_2 \Omega \qquad [8.122]$$

$$\dot{v}_2 = \alpha \sin \omega t + v_1 \Omega \qquad [8.123]$$

where

$$\alpha = \frac{qE}{m} \qquad [8.124]$$

and for convenience Ω_3 has been written as Ω.

Equations [8.122] and [8.123] can be solved simultaneously to yield (see Exercise 8.5.1)

$$v_1 = v_1^0 \cos \Omega t - v_2^0 \sin \Omega t - \frac{\alpha}{\omega^2 - \Omega^2} (\omega \sin \Omega t - \Omega \sin \omega t) \quad [8.125]$$

$$v_2 = v_1^0 \sin \Omega t + v_2^0 \cos \Omega t + \frac{\alpha \omega}{\omega^2 - \Omega^2} (\cos \Omega t - \cos \omega t) \qquad [8.126]$$

The x_1- and x_2-components of the orbit can be found by integrating [8.125] and [8.126] to give (see Exercise 8.5.2)

$$x_1 = x_1^0 + \frac{v_1^0}{\Omega} \sin \Omega t + \frac{v_2^0}{\Omega} (\cos \Omega t - 1)$$

$$- \frac{\alpha}{\Omega \omega} + \frac{\alpha}{\omega^2 - \Omega^2} \left(\frac{\omega}{\Omega} \cos \Omega t - \frac{\Omega}{\omega} \cos \omega t \right) \qquad [8.127]$$

$$x_2 = x_2^0 + \frac{v_2^0}{\Omega} \sin \Omega t - \frac{v_1^0}{\Omega} (\cos \Omega t - 1)$$

$$+ \frac{\alpha \omega}{\omega^2 - \Omega^2} \left(\frac{1}{\Omega} \sin \Omega t - \frac{1}{\omega} \sin \omega t \right) \qquad [8.128]$$

Now the first three terms on the right-hand side of [8.127] and [8.128] are concerned only with the initial displacement and velocity of the charged particle. In order to consider a specific case, let us pick the initial displacement and velocity of the particle so that we consider only the last terms in Equations [8.125] to [8.128]. We can then rewrite these equations in the form

$$v_1 = - \frac{\alpha \omega}{\omega^2 - \Omega^2} \left(\sin \Omega t - \frac{\Omega}{\omega} \sin \omega t \right) \qquad [8.129]$$

$$v_2 = \frac{\alpha \omega}{\omega^2 - \Omega^2} (\cos \Omega t - \cos \omega t) \qquad [8.130]$$

$$x_1 = \frac{\alpha}{\omega^2 - \Omega^2} \left(\frac{\omega}{\Omega} \cos \Omega t - \frac{\Omega}{\omega} \cos \omega t \right) \qquad [8.131]$$

$$x_2 = \frac{\alpha}{\omega^2 - \Omega^2} \left(\frac{\omega}{\Omega} \sin \Omega t - \sin \omega t \right) \qquad [8.132]$$

In order to discover the major characteristics of the orbits described by [8.129] to [8.132], we will consider various ranges of the ratio ω/Ω.

Low Frequency Electric Field $\omega \ll \Omega$

In the case when the electric field has a low frequency we would expect that during each half cycle of the electric field the particle would drift in a manner similar to that described in Section 8.23 for the d.c. case. Since in this case $\omega/\Omega \ll 1$, we can approximate equations [8.131] and [8.132] by

$$x_1 \approx \frac{\alpha}{\omega \Omega} \cos \omega t$$

and

$$x_2 \approx \frac{\alpha}{\Omega^2} \sin \omega t$$

We therefore see that the drift motion is in the form of an ellipse with its major axes along the x_1-axes. The ratio of the minor to the major axes of the ellipse is ω/Ω. From [8.132] we see that the ratio of the radius of gyration at the cyclotron frequency to the minor axes of the ellipse is also ω/Ω. A typical orbit for this case is shown in Figure 8.13.

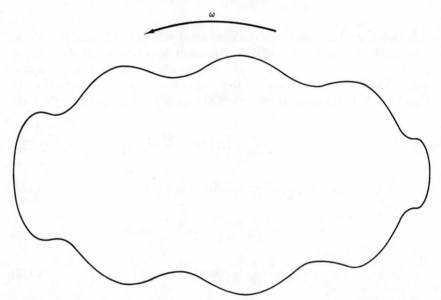

FIGURE 8.13 Electron Orbit in a Low Frequency Electric Field Perpendicular to a Static Magnetic Field $\omega \ll \Omega$. Magnetic field directed out of the page. Analog computer solution of equations (8.122) and (8.123) for the case when $\omega/\Omega = 1/10$. The major motion is elliptical at the frequency ω

High Frequency Electric Field $\omega \gg \Omega$

For this case $\Omega/\omega \ll 1$, and [8.131] and [8.132] can be approximated as

$$x_1 \approx \frac{\alpha}{\omega\Omega} \cos \Omega t$$

$$x_2 \approx \frac{\alpha}{\omega\Omega} \sin \Omega t$$

Thus the major motion is a circular motion at the low cyclotron frequency. From [8.131] and [8.132] we see that superimposed on this motion is an elliptical motion at the high signal frequency. The major axis of the ellipse is in the x_2-direction and is ω/Ω times as large as the minor axis of the ellipse. The major axis of the ellipse is only Ω/ω as large as the radius of the circle traced out at the cyclotron frequency. A typical orbit for this case is shown in Figure 8.14.

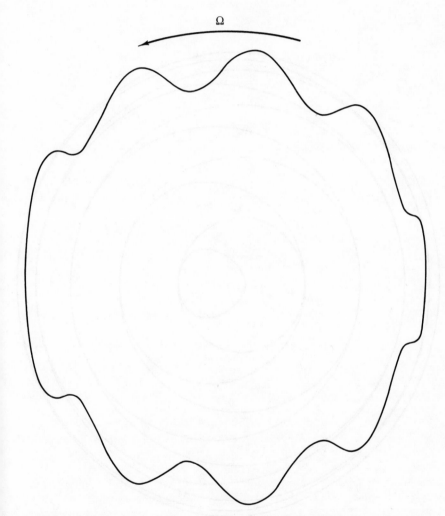

FIGURE 8.14 Electron Orbit in a High Frequency Electric Field Perpendicular to a Static Magnetic Field. $\omega \gg \Omega$. Magnetic field directed out of the page. Analog computer solution of equations (8.122) and (8.123) for the case when $\omega/\Omega = 10$. The major motion is circular at the cyclotron frequency Ω

Electric Field Frequency Close to Cyclotron Frequency $\omega \approx \Omega$

If we write $\Omega/\omega = 1 + \delta$, then [8.131] and [8.132] can be written as

$$x_1 = \frac{\alpha\omega}{\Omega(\omega^2 - \Omega^2)} [\cos \Omega t - \cos \omega t] - \frac{(\delta^2 + 2\delta)\alpha\omega}{\Omega(\omega^2 - \Omega^2)} \cos \omega t \quad [8.133]$$

$$x_2 = \frac{\alpha\omega}{\Omega(\omega^2 - \Omega^2)} [\sin \Omega t - \sin \omega t] - \delta \frac{\alpha\omega}{\Omega(\omega^2 - \Omega^2)} \sin \omega t \quad [8.134]$$

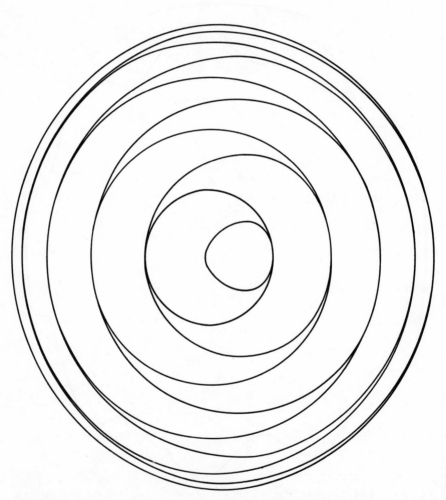

FIGURE 8.15 Electron Orbit in a Sinusoidal Electric Field Perpendicular to a Magnetic Field. $\omega \approx \Omega$. Magnetic field directed out of the page. Analog computer solution of equations (8.122) and (8.123) close to cyclotron resonance

Now if $\omega \approx \Omega$, then $\delta \ll 1$, and we can write [8.133] and [8.134] as

$$x_1 \approx \frac{2\alpha\omega}{\Omega(\omega^2 - \Omega^2)} \sin \tfrac{1}{2}(\omega - \Omega)t \sin \tfrac{1}{2}(\omega + \Omega)t \qquad [8.135]$$

$$x_2 \approx -\frac{2\alpha\omega}{\Omega(\omega^2 - \Omega^2)} \sin \tfrac{1}{2}(\omega - \Omega)t \cos \tfrac{1}{2}(\omega + \Omega)t \qquad [8.136]$$

The orbit described by [8.135] and [8.136] is a circular gyration at the frequency $(\omega + \Omega)/4\pi$ whose radius varies sinusoidally at the beat frequency $(\omega - \Omega)/4\pi$. A typical orbit is shown in Figure 8.15.

The situation when $\omega = \Omega$ represents the singular case of cyclotron resonance. This important special case will be discussed separately in the following section.

Exercise 8.5.1 Solve [8.122] and [8.123] simultaneously to obtain [8.125] and [8.126].

Exercise 8.5.2 Integrate [8.125] and [8.126] to obtain [8.127] and [8.128].

Exercise 8.5.3 Verify [8.135] and [8.136].

Exercise 8.5.4 When $\omega \approx \Omega$, what is the maximum radius of the orbit of a charged particle? At what point is the particle moving the fastest?

8.51 CYCLOTRON RESONANCE

When $\omega = \Omega$, the solution of the equation of motion given by [8.125] and [8.126] becomes indeterminate. It is therefore necessary to go back to the original equations of motion and re-solve the problem for this case.

If we set $\omega = \Omega$ in [8.123], we can write the equations of motion as

$$\dot{v}_1 = -v_2\Omega \qquad [8.137]$$

$$\dot{v}_2 = \alpha \sin \Omega t + v_1\Omega \qquad [8.138]$$

By solving these equations simultaneously, we obtain (see Exercise 8.51.1)

$$v_1 = v_1^0 \cos \Omega t - v_2^0 \sin \Omega t - \frac{\alpha}{2\Omega}(\sin \Omega t - \Omega t \cos \Omega t) \qquad [8.139]$$

$$v_2 = v_2^0 \cos \Omega t + v_1^0 \sin \Omega t + \frac{\alpha}{2}t \sin \Omega t \qquad [8.140]$$

Integrating [8.139] and [8.140], we obtain for the displacement of the particle (see Exercise 8.51.2)

$$x_1 = x_1^0 + \frac{v_1^0}{\Omega} \sin \Omega t + \frac{1}{\Omega} \left(v_2^0 + \frac{\alpha}{2\Omega} \right)(\cos \Omega t - 1) + \frac{\alpha t}{2\Omega} \sin \Omega t \quad [8.141]$$

$$x_2 = x_2^0 - \frac{v_1^0}{\Omega} (\cos \Omega t - 1) + \frac{1}{\Omega} \left(v_2^0 + \frac{\alpha}{2\Omega} \right) \sin \Omega t$$

$$- \frac{\alpha}{2\Omega} t \cos \Omega t \qquad [8.142]$$

After a sufficient length of time the last terms in [8.141] and [8.142] become dominant and the charged particles move in circles of ever increasing radii.

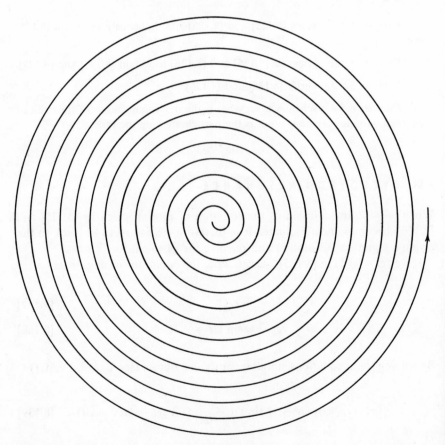

FIGURE 8.16 Electron Orbit at Cyclotron Resonance. $\omega = \Omega$. Analog computer solution of equations (8.122) and (8.123) at cyclotron resonance

During this spiral motion the velocity of the particle continually increases. Since its kinetic energy increases the particle absorbs energy from the r.f. electric field.

A typical resonant spiral is shown in Figure 8.16. In practice the size that the spiral attains will be limited by some physical factor such as the walls of a vessel.

Exercise 8.51.1 Solve [8.137] and [8.138] simultaneously to obtain [8.139] and [8.140].

Exercise 8.51.2 Integrate [8.139] and [8.140] to obtain [8.141] and [8.142].

Exercise 8.51.3 Write an expression for the kinetic energy of a charged particle at resonance as a function of time.

Problems

8.1 The particle motion under the conditions discussed in Section 8.23 is of the form of a cycloid. Show that if $v_i^0 = (v_1^0, 0, 0)$ then,

(a) for $v_1^0 > \dfrac{2E_2}{B_3}$ and for $v_1^0 < 0$ an epicycloid results.

(b) for $v_1^0 = \dfrac{2E_2}{B_3}$ or for $v_1^0 = 0$ a common cycloid results.

(c) for $\dfrac{E_2}{B_3} < v_1^0 < \dfrac{2E_2}{B_3}$ and $0 < v_1^0 < \dfrac{E_2}{B_3}$ a hypocycloid results.

(d) for $v_1^0 = \dfrac{E_2}{B_3}$ the motion is a straight line (Exercise 8.23.3).

Sketch the orbits for cases (a), (b) and (c). How can case (d) be exploited to design a mass spectrometer?

8.2 Consider a cylindrical tube which is bent into the form of a closed circular torus. The radius of the tube is 10 cm while the radius of the torus is 1 m. A coil is wound around the torus in order to produce an axial magnetic field of 10^3 gauss. For electrons and protons at a temperature of 10^4 °K calculate for each:

(a) the radius of gyration and the cyclotron frequency;
(b) the time required to travel completely around the torus;
(c) the drift velocity across the tube due to curvature drifts;
(d) the drift velocity across the tube due to transverse gradients in the magnetic field.

8.3 For a cylindrically symmetric time-varying magnetic field in the x_3-direction show that the induced electric field can be written as

$$E_\alpha = \frac{\dot{B}}{2} e_{\alpha\beta} x_\beta$$

Show that the equation of motion is then

$$\ddot{x}_\alpha = \frac{q}{m} e_{\alpha\beta} \left[\frac{\dot{B}}{2} x_\beta + B\dot{x}_\beta \right]$$

Write the equation of motion in polar coordinates. Suggest methods for solving these equations.

8.4 Let a sinusoidal electric field be normal to a static magnetic field. Show that if the electric field is turned on sufficiently slowly, charged particles will oscillate only at the frequency of the alternating electric field.

REFERENCES

Discussions of charged particle orbits can be found in

1 Rose, D. J., and M. Clark. *Plasmas and Controlled Fusion*. Cambridge, Mass., and New York: Massachusetts Institute of Technology Press and Wiley, 1961.

2 Uman, M. A. *Introduction to Plasma Physics*. New York: McGraw-Hill, 1964.

3 Spitzer, L. *Physics of Fully Ionized Gases*. 2nd ed.; New York: Interscience (Wiley), 1962.

4 Longmire, C. L. *Elementary Plasma Physics*. Interscience, 1963.

More advanced treatments with emphasis on magnetic field gradients are given by

5 Alfvén, H., and C-G. Fälthammar. *Cosmical Electrodynamics*. 2nd ed.; London: Oxford University Press, 1963.

6 Allis, W. P. "Motions of Ions and Electrons." *Handbuch der Physik*, vol. 21. Springer-Verlag, 1956.

7 Thompson, W. B. *An Introduction to Plasma Physics*. New York and Boston: Pergamon and Addison-Wesley, 1962.

Electron orbits in crossed electric and magnetic fields are treated by

8 Hemenway, C. L., R. W. Henry, and M. Caulton. *Physical Electronics*. New York: Wiley, 1962.

9 Harman, W. W. *Fundamentals of Electronic Motion*. New York: McGraw-Hill, 1953.

Methods for solving the equation of motion for the case of a time-varying magnetic field are described by

10   Gartenhaus, S. *Elements of Plasma Physics.* New York: Holt, Rinehart and Winston, 1964.

11   Haines, M. G., and D. W. Allan. "The Motion of a Charged Particle in a Time-Varying Axial Magnetic Field," *Proc. Phys. Soc.*, **81** (1963), 104–17.

The role of adiabatic invariants in describing charged particle orbits is discussed by

12   Chandrasekhar, S. *Plasma Physics.* Chicago: University of Chicago Press, 1960.

For more detail see

13   Northrop, T. G. *The Adiabatic Motion of Charged Particles.* New York: Interscience (Wiley), 1963.

A good discussion of charged particle orbits including the case of time-varying electric fields is given by

14   Linhart, J. G. *Plasma Physics.* 2nd ed.; North-Holland, 1961.

CHAPTER

9

CHARGED

PARTICLE INTERACTIONS

In Chapter 8, Charged Particle Orbits, we infer the behavior of a plasma from the behavior of individual charged particles. This assumes that each charged particle of the plasma will behave in a manner similar to that of an individual, isolated charged particle, subject to the same externally applied electric and magnetic fields. Such an assumption is clearly dependent upon the fact of a negligible interaction between the various types of particle which are present. Although this assumption may be acceptable in a few cases, it is generally untenable, and the present chapter will study these particle interactions.

In the broader context of the plasma theory we are developing, such a study implies an analysis of the right-hand side of the Boltzmann equation— that is, the term $(\partial f/\partial t)_{\text{coll}}$. We must distinguish between interactions of charged particles and interactions in which neutral particles as well as charged particles are involved. In the discussion of binary collisions in Chapter 4, we have already shown the difference between the Coulomb force which applies to charged particle interactions, and the forces that determine the interaction between a charged particle and a neutral particle. In this chapter we will go beyond the discussion of binary Coulomb interactions to

243

consider the interaction of a charged test particle with many other charged particles simultaneously. In general it is more likely that the charged test particle will suffer a large cumulative deflection in its path due to the sum of small deflections caused by many charged neighbors, than that it will suffer a single major deflection as the result of a single, binary Coulomb collision.

In considering the influence of many particles upon a test particle, we find that there is a limit to the number of particles we have to consider. Charged particles close to the test particle act as a screen between the test particle and more distant charged particles. The length parameter that marks this transition is called the *Debye length*. Charged particles situated further than a Debye length from the test particle have a negligible effect on the trajectory of the test particle.

Plasma phenomena that take place over distances greater than the Debye length cannot be described in terms of individual particle motions, but rather depend upon the collective motions of particles. Oscillations and wave phenomena belong in this category and are discussed in Chapters 11 and 12.

We begin the chapter with a discussion of some basic phenomena which pertain to individual and collective charged particle behavior. A cross section for binary Coulomb interactions is defined in terms of the scattering through angles greater than $90°$. The ability of the plasma to maintain space-charge neutrality is shown. The important Debye shielding distance is derived and the elemental plasma collective phenomenon, an oscillation at the plasma frequency, is discussed.

The presence of multiple Coulomb collisions in plasma particle interactions threatens to undermine the Boltzmann equation approach to plasma theory. This is because an equation that describes the behavior of the single-particle distribution function is basically incapable of handling nonbinary particle interactions where the correlations between particle motions are important. Indeed this problem of dealing with multiple Coulomb collisions may be considered to be a problem of central interest in the development of plasma theory. In order to provide a firm foundation for its solution it would be necessary to given an expanded treatment of Liouville's equation together with a discussion of the Fokker-Planck formulation of stochastic processes. Such a treatment is beyond the scope of this book and the reader is referred to references 5 and 6 of Chapter 5 for further discussion.

Instead, a simple concept is used to broaden the utility of the Boltzmann equation. This is to treat multiple Coulomb collisions as a succession of small-angle binary interactions. The application of this concept enables us to derive a Fokker-Planck expression to be used as the collision term of the Boltzmann equation. The coefficients involved in this Fokker-Planck equation can then be evaluated in terms of the properties of binary collisions which we developed in Chapter 4. These tasks form the subject matter of Section 9.2.

Having now assembled a more adequate artillery for the assault on plasma problems, it is appropriate to discuss the circumstances under which the different techniques must be used. The distinction to be made is between weakly ionized and strongly ionized plasmas. When multiple Coulomb interactions (and in fact all Coulomb interactions) may be ignored, the plasma is defined as being weakly ionized. We find in Section 9.3 that the distinction may be conveniently expressed in terms of the concept of a relaxation time. Applied to particle interactions, this is simply the reciprocal of the collision frequency. For several gases at various pressures and temperatures we use experimental collision cross section data to evaluate the relaxation time for electron-neutral particle collisions. This time is independent of the plasma charged particle density, but, as this density increases, we calculate that the relaxation time associated with multiple Coulomb collisions decreases and, at a certain plasma density, becomes equal to the relaxation time for electron-neutral particle collisions at a given pressure and temperature. This is the dividing line, and for further increases in plasma charged particle density the multiple Coulomb collisions increasingly dominate the collision term. In other words, the time taken for an electron to be scattered through a substantial angle due to multiple Coulomb collisions becomes much smaller than the scattering time for electron-neutral particle collisions.

9.1   INDIVIDUAL AND COLLECTIVE CHARGED PARTICLE BEHAVIOR

From the introductory discussion to this chapter it is clear that phenomena involving distances less than the Debye length must be analyzed in terms of individual particle interactions. In many instances of interest there are a large number of particles in a *Debye sphere*—that is, within a Debye length of a test particle. The question therefore arises as to how we are to analyze the interaction of a single charged particle with the many other charged particles in the Debye sphere.

In order to attempt to answer this question, we can distinguish two types of interactions which the charged particle will experience that result in a significant deflection of the particle. The first is a direct binary Coulomb collision with another charged particle. This type of interaction will be discussed in this section. The second type is a simultaneous interaction with all other charged particles in the Debye sphere. This will be discussed in Section 9.2.

The dynamics of a binary Coulomb collision were described in Chapter 4. The angle of deflection χ was given in [4.57] by

$$\tan \frac{\chi}{2} = \frac{p_c}{p} \qquad [9.1]$$

where p is the impact parameter and where, for electron-ion collisions,

$$p_c = \frac{-Ze^2}{4\pi\epsilon_0 m' g^2} \qquad [9.2]$$

is called the *critical impact parameter* and is the value of the impact parameter that will yield a deflection angle of 90°. The quantity m' is the reduced mass, g is the relative velocity, and Z is the charge number of the positive ion.

For all encounters in which the impact parameter is less than p_c, the particle will be scattered through angles greater than 90°. We define a cross section Q_{90} for such close Coulomb collisions by the relation

$$Q_{90} = \pi p_c^2 = \frac{Z^2 e^4}{16\pi\epsilon_0^2 m'^2 g^4} \qquad [9.3]$$

From [4.1] and [4.2] we can define a mean free path L_{90} and a collision frequency ν_{90} for Coulomb collisions which result in deflection angles greater than 90°. Thus

$$L_{90} = \frac{1}{Q_{90}N} = \frac{1}{\pi p_c^2 N} \qquad [9.4]$$

and

$$\nu_{90} = g Q_{90} N = g\pi p_c^2 N \qquad [9.5]$$

where N is the number density of the scatterers.

Now in the preceding discussion we have implied the arbitrary criterion that a Coulomb encounter must result in a deflection angle of at least 90° before a collision is considered to have occurred. This can be justified from the fact that a collision must result in a substantial transfer of momentum in order to contribute significantly to macroscopically observed transport properties. It might therefore appear that we could use the value of ν_{90} given by [9.5] as an effective electron-ion collision frequency in order to include Coulomb collisions in the momentum equation [6.36]. (See also [6.111]). However this results in a value of ν_{EI} that is too small to explain transport processes in strongly ionized gases. This indicates that the second type of interaction—the simultaneous interaction with other charged particles in the Debye sphere—is more significant in determining the behavior of strongly ionized plasmas than the close Coulomb collisions described in this section.

9.11 ELECTRICAL NEUTRALITY

In most plasmas a charged test particle is constantly buffeted by the Coulomb forces of the surrounding space charge. However in the interior of a quiescent plasma the microscopic space charge fields cancel each other and no net space charge exists over macroscopic distances. The plasma is said to be space charge neutral.

If we inquire into the stability of this space charge neutrality we discover three elementary properties of a plasma:

1. The plasma will not support large potential variations, or, in other words, electric fields, but seeks to maintain macroscopic space charge neutrality.

2. Such potential gradients as may exist have a characteristic length parameter equal to the Debye length.

3. These potential gradients are characterized by a natural oscillation frequency known as the plasma frequency.

These three plasma properties will be examined in this section and in the two which follow it.

The magnitude of the fluctuating potentials that may appear in a plasma due to the thermal motion of the charged particles will be limited to the potential that corresponds to a conversion of the kinetic energy of the particles into potential energy. We recollect that a potential energy of 1 eV corresponds to a kinetic temperature of 11,000°K, so that the potentials expected are modest indeed. The resultant departures from macroscopic space charge neutrality are correspondingly small as can be seen from the following example.

Let us suppose that we have plasma with a charged particle density of 10^{13} cm^{-3}. Suppose that in a spherical volume of 1 mm radius the electron density differs, instantaneously, from the density of the positive ions by 1 per cent. Then the potential at the surface of the sphere is given by

$$\psi = \frac{e(N_+ - N_-)4\pi r^3/3}{4\pi\epsilon_0 r} \text{ volts (MKS units)} \qquad [9.6]$$

so that

$$\psi = \frac{(10^{19} \times 0.01)(1.6 \times 10^{-19})10^{-6}}{3(8.8 \times 10^{-12})} \approx 600 \text{ volts}$$

Thus a 1 per cent deviation from space charge neutrality over a 1 mm radius sphere in a plasma of density 10^{13} cm^{-3} implies a plasma temperature of millions of degrees Kelvin.

Exercise 9.11.1   Draw a graph relating the plasma temperature, plasma density, and the radius of a sphere within which the charged particle density may differ by a maximum of 1 per cent from that outside. Consider the ranges of plasma temperature and density shown in Figure 1.8. Note that the average kinetic energy per particle in one direction is $\frac{1}{2}kT$.

9.12 THE DEBYE SHIELDING DISTANCE

The concept of the Debye shielding distance plays an important role in plasma theory. At the beginning of this chapter it has been discussed in terms of particle interactions, describing how it sets a bound upon the extent to which charged particles interact upon each other individually, and how it defines the onset of collective charged particle behavior. This electrostatic shielding effect is not confined to the charged particles only, but applies when any object with a fixed electric potential is introduced into the plasma. These objects may be probes that are inserted into the plasma in order to attempt to determine its properties, or they may be solid boundaries and electrodes. These are either at a predetermined electric potential, or they may acquire a certain potential. A sheath develops between the object and the plasma. Within the sheath the property of charge neutrality does not hold and the variation of the positive and negative charge densities and currents within this region depends upon the characteristics of the fixed potential object (boundary or probe) as well as those of the plasma.

The characteristic dimension of a plasma cell will be considerably greater than the Debye length. As the cell dimension becomes comparable to the Debye length, the region in which a plasma exists will shrink and finally disappear. The inequality

$$\text{Debye length} < \text{cell dimension}$$

is, in fact, an existence criterion for a plasma.

In order to calculate the Debye length, we will focus our attention on a particular positive ion which we locate at the origin of our coordinate system. This positive ion will attract neighboring electrons while at the same time repelling other positive ions. The result is that, in a region surrounding the positive ion, an excess electronic charge will exist. Thus within this region we will not have strict charge neutrality, and a space charge will be set up which is given by $\eta = e(N_+ - N_-)$. This space charge will give rise to a static electric field E_i whose potential ψ, given by $E_i = -\psi_{,i}$, will satisfy Poisson's equation $\psi_{,ii} = -\eta/\epsilon_0$.

We will assume that the ions are at rest and that the ion density N_+ is given by the average charged particle density N_0, while within the region under consideration the electron density $N_-(x_i) \neq N_+$ is some slowly varying function of x_i. We can then write Poisson's equation as

$$\psi_{,ii} = -\frac{e}{\epsilon_0} [N_0 - N_-(x_i)] \qquad [9.7]$$

In order to solve for the potential ψ in the neighborhood of the positive ion, we need to determine $N_-(x_i)$ which is given by

$$N_-(x_i) = \int f \, dc \qquad [9.8]$$

where f satisfies the Boltzmann equation

$$\frac{\partial f}{\partial t} + v_i \frac{\partial f}{\partial x_i} - \frac{eE_i}{m_-} \frac{\partial f}{\partial v_i} = \left(\frac{\partial f}{\partial t}\right)_{\text{coll}}$$

As we have seen in Section 5.5, the solution involves the Boltzmann factor and is given by

$$f = f_o \exp\left[\frac{e\psi(x_i)}{kT}\right] \qquad [9.9]$$

where f_o is the Maxwellian distribution

$$f_o = N_0 \left(\frac{m_-}{2\pi kT}\right)^{3/2} e^{-(mv_i v_i / 2kT)}$$

Substituting [9.9] into [9.8], we find that the electron density can be written as

$$N_-(x_i) = N_0 \exp\left[\frac{e\psi(x_i)}{kT}\right] \qquad [9.10]$$

If we assume that $e\psi \ll kT$, then we can approximate [9.10] by

$$N_-(x_i) \approx N_0 \left(1 + \frac{e\psi}{kT}\right) \qquad [9.11]$$

Substituting [9.11] into [9.7] we obtain

$$\psi_{,ii} = \frac{e^2 N_0}{\epsilon_0 kT} \psi = \frac{1}{h^2} \psi \qquad [9.12]$$

where

$$h = \left(\frac{\epsilon_0 kT}{N_0 e^2}\right)^{1/2} \qquad [9.13]$$

and has the dimension of length.

Since the potential will be spherically symmetric about the positive ion at the origin, we can write [9.12] in spherical coordinates with only an r-variation as

$$\frac{1}{r^2}\frac{d}{dr}\left(r^2\frac{d\psi}{dr}\right) = \frac{1}{h^2}\psi \qquad [9.14]$$

The boundary conditions on the solution to [9.14] are that the potential goes to zero when r goes to infinity and that it reduces to the Coulomb potential $\psi_c = e/(4\pi\epsilon_0 r)$ for small values of r. One can readily verify (see Exercise 9.12.1) that the solution satisfying these conditions is given by

$$\psi_s = \frac{e}{4\pi\epsilon_0 r}\exp\left(\frac{-r}{h}\right) \qquad [9.15]$$

We therefore see that the effect of the electrons which tend to swarm about a positive ion is to shield the Coulomb potential of the ion in an exponential manner. From [9.15] we see that the Coulomb potential of the positive ion is

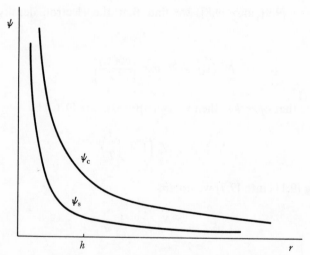

FIGURE 9.1   The Debye Shielding Distance h.
$$\psi_s = \psi_c \exp\left(-r/h\right)$$

substantially reduced at distances greater than h from the ion. The situation is shown in Figure 9.1. The quantity h, given by [9.13], is called the *Debye shielding distance*, or simply the *Debye length*. It becomes larger at higher temperatures and smaller at higher densities. From [9.13] we find that

$$h = 6.9 \left(\frac{T}{N_0}\right)^{1/2} \text{cm} \qquad [9.16]$$

if T is given in °K and N_0 in cm^{-3}.

Since the average number density of electrons (or ions) is N_0 then the number of electrons M_h (or ions) in a sphere with radius h, known as a Debye sphere, is

$$M_h = N_0 \tfrac{4}{3}\pi h^3 = 1.38 \times 10^3 \frac{T^{3/2}}{N_0^{1/2}} \qquad [9.17]$$

The Debye length and the number of particles in a Debye sphere are plotted in Figure 9.2 as a function of electron density for different temperatures.

Although this derivation of the shielded Coulomb potential was based on a simplified model of the plasma, the fact that electrostatic forces tend to shield the potential of individual charged particles is clear from physical reasoning.

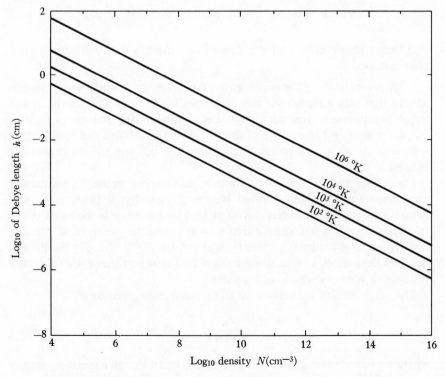

FIGURE 9.2a   The Debye Length h as a function of Plasma Parameters

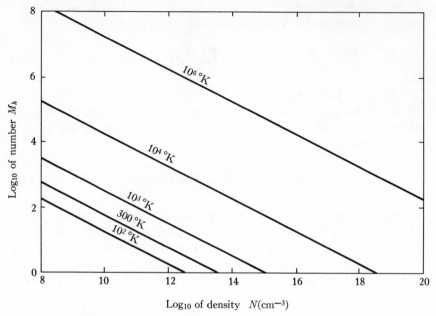

FIGURE 9.2b   Number of Particles in the Debye Sphere M_h

The Debye length gives an indication of the length which characterizes this phenomenon.

Representative Plasma Lengths   We have now mentioned several lengths that play a significant role in plasma behavior. These are the Debye length (h), the mean free path (L_{90}), and critical impact parameter (p_c) for 90° deflections in binary Coulomb collisions. In addition the interparticle separation ($d = N^{-1/3}$) and a length characteristic of a plasma cell are of interest.

Figures 9.3 and 9.4 show how these lengths depend upon plasma density and temperature. A fully ionized plasma is considered. (That is to say, neutral particles are neglected.) Also plotted for reference is the value of the Bohr radius, which will clearly give a lower bound to the classical value p_c can assume. For densities greater than about $4 \times 10^{21}T^{3/2}$ cm^{-3} the plasma becomes degenerate so that it is governed by Fermi statistics rather than the Boltzmann statistics which we are using.

The magnitude of the critical impact parameter is given by [9.2] as

$$|p_c| = \frac{Ze^2}{4\pi\epsilon_0 m'g^2} = \frac{Ze^2}{12\pi\epsilon_0 kT} = 5.55 \times 10^{-4}\frac{1}{T}\text{cm} \qquad [9.18]$$

where we have taken $Z = 1$ and g to be the mean thermal speed by setting $\frac{1}{2}m'g^2 = \frac{3}{2}kT$.

The value of L_{90} is given by [9.4] as

$$L_{90} = \frac{1}{\pi p_{\mathrm{c}}^2 N} = \frac{144\pi}{N}\left(\frac{\epsilon_0 kT}{Ze^2}\right)^2 = 1.03 \times 10^6 \frac{T^2}{N} \text{ cm} \qquad [9.19]$$

We notice that for densities less than 10^{12} cm^{-3} at room temperature (300°K) we have that

$$|p_{\mathrm{c}}| < d < h < L_{90} \qquad [9.20]$$

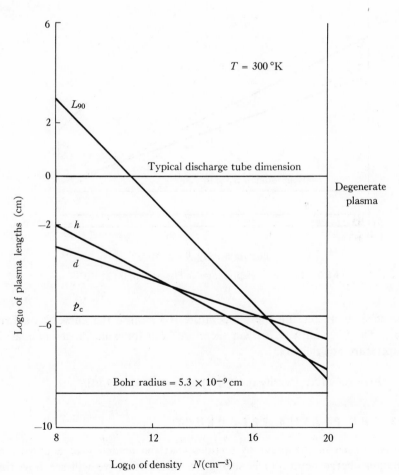

F I G U R E 9.3 Representative Plasma Lengths at 300°K

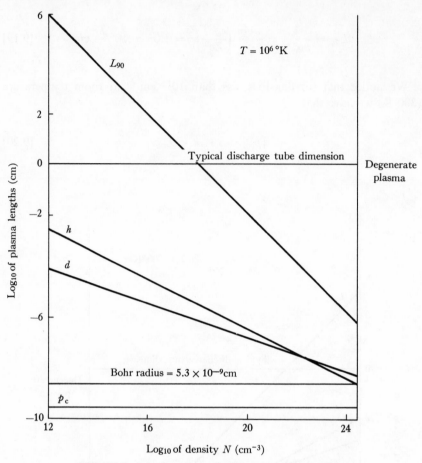

FIGURE 9.4 Representative Plasma Lengths at 10^6 °K

The effect of increasing the temperature is to cause the curves to spread apart. The inequality [9.20] will therefore hold for wide ranges of plasma temperature and density.

Exercise 9.12.1   Verify that [9.15] is a solution of [9.14].

9.13 THE PLASMA FREQUENCY

We have seen in the previous sections that the tendency of a plasma to maintain charge neutrality is strong. In this section we will see how this tendency leads to a characteristic oscillation of the plasma. Suppose that the positive ions in a plasma are fixed and do not move and consider a certain group of electrons to be displaced by some means as shown in Figure 9.5. The resulting charge separation gives rise to an electric field which is described by Poisson's equation [3.48]. This electric field will tend to accelerate the electrons back to their equilibrium position. Due to their momentum they will overshoot the equilibrium position and an electric field will then be set up in the opposite direction. The electrons will then be accelerated back in the opposite direction and will therefore tend to oscillate about their equilibrium position.

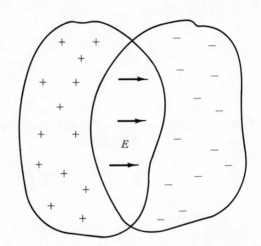

FIGURE 9.5 Charge Separation in a Plasma

In order to determine the frequency of this oscillation, we will assume that the electrons are cold (that is, their thermal motion may be neglected) and that their motion can be described by the single species equations of Chapter 6. For this case the continuity and momentum equations for the electrons can be written from [6.16] and [6.37] as

$$\frac{\partial N_-}{\partial t} + \frac{\partial (N_- \langle v_i^- \rangle)}{\partial x_i} = 0$$

$$\frac{\partial \langle v_i^- \rangle}{\partial t} + \langle v_j^- \rangle \frac{\partial \langle v_i^- \rangle}{\partial x_j} = -\frac{e}{m_-} E_i$$

[9.21]

where the effect of collisions has been ignored.

Let the number density of the positive ions N_+ be given by the constant value N_o, and let the number density of the electrons N_- be written as

$$N_- = N_o + \bar{N}_-$$

[9.22]

where N_0 is the constant equilibrium value and $\bar{N}_-$ is a small fluctuating perturbation. Under these conditions we can then write Poisson's equation [3.48] as

$$E_{i,i} = -\frac{e}{\epsilon_0}\bar{N}_- \qquad [9.23]$$

The electron velocity $\langle v_i^- \rangle$ is assumed to consist only of a small fluctuating value which we will designate by $\bar{v}_i^-$. If we then substitute [9.22] into the equations [9.21] and neglect terms involving products of the small quantities $\bar{N}_-$ and $\bar{v}_i^-$, we obtain

$$\frac{\partial \bar{N}_-}{\partial t} + N_0 \frac{\partial \bar{v}_i^-}{\partial x_i} = 0 \qquad [9.24]$$

$$\frac{\partial \bar{v}_i^-}{\partial t} = -\frac{e}{m_-} E_i \qquad [9.25]$$

If we take a time derivative of [9.24] and a spatial derivative of [9.25], we obtain, by combining the results,

$$\frac{\partial^2 \bar{N}_-}{\partial t^2} - \frac{N_0 e}{m_-} E_{i,i} = 0$$

or, using [9.23]

$$\frac{\partial^2 \bar{N}_-}{\partial t^2} + \frac{N_0 e^2}{m_- \epsilon_0} \bar{N}_- = 0$$

This equation represents a simple harmonic motion of the fluctuating density $\bar{N}_-$ at the angular frequency

$$\Pi_- = \sqrt{\frac{N_0 e^2}{m_- \epsilon_0}} \qquad [9.26]$$

which is called the *plasma frequency*. The frequency of oscillation is then given by $\Pi_-/2\pi \approx 9000\sqrt{N_0}$, where N_0 is in units of cm^{-3}.

In this section we have neglected the thermal motion of the electrons. From Figure 9.5 it is clear that if the electrons have a finite temperature, a pressure gradient of the electrons will exist which will accelerate the electrons in the same direction as does the electric field. We would therefore expect that the frequency of oscillation will increase. We will find this to be the case when we analyze this problem in Section 11.3. The effect of the positive ion motion on these oscillations will be included in Chapter 12 where we will consider plasma oscillations in detail.

9.2 THE FOKKER-PLANCK EQUATION

We found in Section 9.12 that charged particles interacting at distances less than the Debye length interact on an individual basis. Only if the impact parameter is less than p_c will the Coulomb collision result in a deflection angle greater than 90 degrees. However, since there are, in general, a large number of positive ions in a Debye sphere, an electron will be interacting with a large number of positive ions simultaneously. This simultaneous interaction can result in a cumulative deflection of the electron through an angle greater than 90 degrees. If such large angle cumulative deflections occur at a rate greater than ν_{90}, then they will be more important in determining the momentum transferred by the electrons. We shall see that this is indeed the case.

We are then faced with the problem of how to take into account the simultaneous Coulomb interactions of a charged particle with the many other charged particles in the Debye sphere. Consider a particular charged particle which we will call the *test particle*. During the time it takes the test particle to cross a Debye sphere it will have interacted with many other charged particles, which we will call the *field particles*. In order to proceed analytically we will suppose that this interaction can be thought of as a series of weak binary collisions. Our task is then to obtain an expression for the collision term of the Boltzmann equation.

Since we are considering a series of binary collisions, we will begin with the collision integral given by [5.34] which was derived for binary collisions. If $\phi(v_i)$ is some arbitrary function of velocity, then we found in Section 6.11 (see Equation [6.14]) that the collision integral could be written in the form

$$\int \phi \left(\frac{\partial f}{\partial t} \right)_{\text{coll}} dc = \int \int \int (\tilde{\phi} - \phi) f f^B g S(\chi) \, d\omega \, dc^B \, dc \qquad [9.27]$$

Now we assume that the binary collisions being considered result in only a small change in the velocity of the test particle. That is, $\tilde{v}_i = v_i + \Delta v_i$ where Δv_i is assumed to be small. Since $\tilde{\phi} = \phi(\tilde{v}_i) = \phi(v_i + \Delta v_i)$, we can expand $\tilde{\phi}$ in a Taylor series as

$$\phi(v_i + \Delta v_i) = \phi(v_i) + \frac{\partial \phi}{\partial v_i} \Delta v_i + \frac{1}{2} \frac{\partial^2 \phi}{\partial v_i dv_j} \Delta v_i \Delta v_j + \cdots$$

from which

$$\tilde{\phi} - \phi = \frac{\partial \phi}{\partial v_i} \Delta v_i + \tfrac{1}{2} \Delta v_i \Delta v_j \frac{\partial^2 \phi}{\partial v_i \partial v_j} \qquad [9.28]$$

where higher order terms have been neglected.

Substituting [9.28] into [9.27] we obtain

$$\int \phi \left(\frac{\partial f}{\partial t}\right)_{\text{coll}} dc = \iiint \left(\frac{\partial \phi}{\partial v_i} \Delta v_i + \tfrac{1}{2}\Delta v_i \, \Delta v_j \frac{\partial^2 \phi}{\partial v_i \partial v_j}\right) ff^B g S(\chi) \, d\omega \, dc^B \, dc$$

[9.29]

We would like to be able to factor out the ϕ in the bracket of [9.29]. This can be accomplished by integrating the first term in the brackets by parts once and by integrating the second term in the brackets by parts twice. In each case the integrated out terms vanish since it is assumed that f is zero at $\pm\infty$. We therefore obtain

$$\int \phi \left(\frac{\partial f}{\partial t}\right)_{\text{coll}} dc = \iiint \left[-\phi \frac{\partial}{\partial v_i} (\Delta v_i fg S(\chi) \, d\omega)\right] f^B \, dc^B \, dc$$

$$+ \iiint \left[\tfrac{1}{2}\phi \frac{\partial^2}{\partial v_i \partial v_j} (\Delta v_i \, \Delta v_j fg S(\chi) \, d\omega)\right] f^B \, dc^B \, dc$$

$$= \int \phi \left[-\frac{\partial}{\partial v_i} \left(f \iint \Delta v_i g S(\chi) \, d\omega f^B \, dc^B\right)\right] dc$$

$$+ \int \phi \left[\frac{1}{2} \frac{\partial^2}{\partial v_i \partial v_j} \left(f \iint \Delta v_i \, \Delta v_j g S(\chi) \, d\omega f^B \, dc^B\right)\right] dc$$

[9.30]

Let us define the quantities

$$\langle \Delta v_i \rangle_{\text{av}} = \iint \Delta v_i g S(\chi) \, d\omega f^B \, dc^B$$

[9.31]

and

$$\langle \Delta v_i \, \Delta v_j \rangle_{\text{av}} = \iint \Delta v_i \, \Delta v_j g S(\chi) \, d\omega f^B \, dc^B$$

[9.32]

which are modified averages over the scattering angle and the velocity distribution of the scatterers.

Then [9.30] can be written as

$$\int \phi \left(\frac{\partial f}{\partial t}\right)_{\text{coll}} dc = \int \phi \left(-\frac{\partial}{\partial v_i} f\langle \Delta v_i \rangle_{\text{av}} + \frac{1}{2} \frac{\partial^2}{\partial v_i \partial v_j} f\langle \Delta v_i \, \Delta v_j \rangle_{\text{av}}\right) dc$$

[9.33]

Since ϕ is an arbitrary function of velocity, it follows from [9.33] that we must have

$$\left(\frac{\partial f}{\partial t}\right)_{\text{coll}} = -\frac{\partial f \langle \Delta v_i \rangle_{\text{av}}}{\partial v_i} + \frac{1}{2} \frac{\partial^2 f \langle \Delta v_i \, \Delta v_j \rangle_{\text{av}}}{\partial v_i \partial v_j}$$

[9.34]

This equation is known as the *Fokker-Planck equation.*

The quantities $\langle \Delta v_i \rangle_{av}$ and $\langle \Delta v_i \Delta v_j \rangle_{av}$ are called the *Fokker-Planck coefficients*, and give the mean rate at which Δv_i and $\Delta v_i \Delta v_j$ are changed due to many small, successive, Coulomb collisions. One often refers to $\langle \Delta v_i \rangle_{av}$ as the coefficient of *dynamical friction*. Since $\langle \Delta v_i \Delta v_j \rangle_{av}$ enters [9.34] in the form of a diffusion coefficient in velocity space, it is often referred to as the *diffusion-in-velocity tensor*. These Fokker-Planck coefficients will be evaluated in the following section.

Exercise 9.2.1   Obtain [9.30] from [9.29].

9.21 THE FOKKER-PLANCK COEFFICIENTS

In this section we wish to evaluate the Fokker-Planck coefficients $\langle \Delta v_i \rangle_{av}$ and $\langle \Delta v_i \Delta v_j \rangle_{av}$. From [9.31] and [9.32] we can write

$$\langle \Delta v_i \rangle_{av} = \int \{\Delta v_i\} f^B \, dc^B \qquad [9.35]$$

and

$$\langle \Delta v_i \Delta v_j \rangle_{av} = \int \{\Delta v_i \Delta v_j\} f^B \, dc^B \qquad [9.36]$$

where the curly bracket has the special significance that,

$$\{\Delta v_i\} = \int \Delta v_i g S(\chi) \, d\omega \qquad [9.37]$$

and

$$\{\Delta v_i \Delta v_j\} = \int \Delta v_i \Delta v_j g S(\chi) \, d\omega \qquad [9.38]$$

We will proceed by calculating $\{\Delta v_i\}$ and $\{\Delta v_i \Delta v_j\}$ in the center-of-mass coordinate system. Now it will be convenient later on to consider the electrons to be deflected by the field of a stationary group of positive ions, so that there is no difference between the center-of-mass system and the laboratory system. The change in v_i in the center-of-mass system was calculated in Section 4.21. Applying the results here, we have

$$\Delta v_1 = M^B g (1 - \cos \chi) = 2 M^B g \sin^2 (\chi/2) \qquad [9.39]$$

$$\Delta v_2 = M^B g \sin \chi \cos \psi \qquad [9.40]$$

$$\Delta v_3 = M^B g \sin \chi \sin \psi \qquad [9.41]$$

where Δv_1 is the change in v_i in the direction of the initial relative velocity. We can also write the angular distribution function $S(\chi)$ for a Coulomb potential from [4.65] and [4.66] as

$$S(\chi) = \frac{p_c^2}{4 \sin^4 (\chi/2)} = \frac{p_c^2}{(1 - \cos \chi)^2} \qquad [9.42]$$

where p_c is the critical impact parameter given by [9.2].

Let us proceed to calculate $\{\Delta v_1\}$ from [9.37] by using [9.39] and [9.42]. We have that

$$\{\Delta v_1\} = \int_0^{2\pi} \int_0^\pi M^B g^2 p_c^2 \frac{\sin \chi}{1 - \cos \chi} \, d\chi \, d\psi \qquad [9.43]$$

By letting $r = 1 - \cos \chi$, we can write [9.43] as

$$\{\Delta v_i\} = 2\pi M^B g^2 p_c^2 \int_0^2 \frac{dr}{r} = 2\pi M^B g^2 p_c^2 \ln r \Big|_0^2 \qquad [9.44]$$

which clearly blows up at the lower limit. This is not surprising since the long-range effect of the Coulomb potential means that a slight deflection will result when two particles approach each other even with a very large impact parameter. However, as we have already seen, particles separated by distances greater than the Debye length are effectively shielded from one another and individual particle interactions give way to collective behavior. We will therefore avoid the divergence of the integral in [9.44] by replacing the lower limit by the value of deflection angle that corresponds to an impact parameter equal to the Debye length h.

Using [9.1], let us make the change of variables

$$u = \frac{p}{p_c} = \cot \frac{\chi}{2}, \quad \text{from which} \quad du = -\frac{d\chi}{1 - \cos \chi} \qquad [9.45]$$

From [9.45] we can readily find that $\sin \chi = 2u/(1 + u^2)$.

Now if we use this change of variables and cut off the integration at an impact parameter $p = h$ (the Debye length)—that is, at

$$u = \frac{h}{p_c} = \Lambda \qquad [9.46]$$

then [9.43] can be written

$$\begin{aligned}
\{\Delta v_1\} &= -2\pi M^B g^2 p_c^2 \int_\Lambda^0 \frac{2u}{1 + u^2} \, du \\
&= 4\pi M^B g^2 p_c^2 \int_0^\Lambda \frac{u}{1 + u^2} \, du \\
&= 2\pi M^B g^2 p_c^2 \ln (1 + \Lambda^2) \qquad [9.47]
\end{aligned}$$

We will find that in general $\Lambda \gg 1$. Using this fact together with the expression for p_c given by [9.2], we can write [9.47] as

$$\{\Delta v_1\} = \frac{M^B Z^2 e^4 \ln \Lambda}{4\pi \epsilon_0^2 m'^2 g^2} = \frac{M^B \Theta}{g^2} \qquad [9.48]$$

where

$$\Theta = \frac{Z^2 e^4 \ln \Lambda}{4\pi \epsilon_0^2 m'^2} \qquad [9.49]$$

Let us now consider $\{\Delta v_2\}$ and $\{\Delta v_3\}$. Since these quantities involve the integral of either $\cos \psi$ or $\sin \psi$ from 0 to 2π, both of these quantities are zero. Similarly we can show that (see Exercise 9.21.1a)

$$\{\Delta v_1 \Delta v_2\} = \{\Delta v_1 \Delta v_3\} = \{\Delta v_2 \Delta v_3\} = 0 \qquad [9.50]$$

Now from [9.38], [9.39], and [9.42] we can evaluate $\{(\Delta v_1)^2\}$ from

$$\{(\Delta v_1)^2\} = 2\pi (M^B)^2 g^3 p_c^2 \int_{\chi_{\min}}^{\pi} \sin \chi \, d\chi \qquad [9.51]$$

Changing variables in [9.51] according to [9.45] we obtain (see Exercise 9.21.1b),

$$\{(\Delta v_1)^2\} = -2\pi (M^B)^2 g^3 p_c^2 \int_{\Lambda}^{0} \frac{4u}{(1 + u^2)^2} \, du$$

$$= 4\pi (M^B)^2 g^3 p_c^2 \frac{\Lambda^2}{1 + \Lambda^2} \qquad [9.52]$$

For $\Lambda \gg 1$, we can write [9.52] as

$$\{(\Delta v_1)^2\} = 4\pi (M^B)^2 g^3 p_c^2 = \frac{(M^B)^2 Z^2 e^4}{4\pi \epsilon_0^2 m'^2 g} = \frac{(M^B)^2 \Theta}{g \ln \Lambda} \qquad [9.53]$$

Finally in a similar manner we can evaluate $\{(\Delta v_2)^2\}$ and $\{(\Delta v_3)^2\}$ as (see Exercise 9.21.1c)

$$\{(\Delta v_2)^2\} = \{(\Delta v_3)^2\} = 4\pi (M^B)^2 g^3 p_c^2 \int_0^{\Lambda} \frac{u^3}{(1 + u^2)^2} \, du$$

$$= 2\pi (M^B)^2 g^3 p_c^2 \left[\ln (1 + \Lambda^2) - \frac{\Lambda^2}{1 + \Lambda^2} \right] \qquad [9.54]$$

which can be written for large values of Λ, as

$$\{(\Delta v_2)^2\} = \{(\Delta v_3)^2\} = 4\pi (M^B)^2 g^3 p_c^2 \ln \Lambda$$

$$= \frac{(M^B)^2 Z^2 e^4 \ln \Lambda}{4\pi \epsilon_0^2 m'^2 g} = \frac{(M^B)^2 \Theta}{g} \qquad [9.55]$$

Now in order to evaluate the Fokker-Planck coefficients we must integrate the values of $\{\Delta v_i\}$ and $\{\Delta v_i \Delta v_j\}$ which we have just calculated over the distribution of velocities of the field particles as indicated by [9.35] and [9.36]. This procedure is, in general, quite complicated.

In order to simplify the situation, we will assume that the test particle is an electron that is colliding with a field of positive ions. We will further assume that the positive ions are motionless so that the distribution function f^B can be written as

$$f^B = N_+ \, \delta(v_i^+) \qquad [9.56]$$

where $\delta(v_i^+)$ is the Dirac delta function. Since Δv_1 is in the direction of the initial relative velocities, then substituting [9.56] into [9.35] we can write

$$\langle \Delta v_1 \rangle_{av} = \langle \Delta v_\parallel \rangle_{av} = \int \{\Delta v_1\} N_+ \, \delta(v_i^+) \, dc_+ = N_+ \{\Delta v_1\} \qquad [9.57]$$

Similarly we can write the remaining nonzero quantities pertaining to $\{\Delta v_i \Delta v_j\}$ as

$$\langle (\Delta v_1)^2 \rangle_{av} = \langle (\Delta v_\parallel)^2 \rangle_{av} = N_+ \{(\Delta v_1)^2\} \qquad [9.58]$$

and

$$\langle (\Delta v_2)^2 \rangle_{av} = \langle (\Delta v_3)^2 \rangle_{av} = \langle (\Delta v_\perp)^2 \rangle_{av} = N_+ \{(\Delta v_2)^2\} \qquad [9.59]$$

Because $m_-/m_+ \ll 1$ so that $M^B = M_+ = m_+/(m_- + m_+) \approx 1$, we can substitute [9.48] into [9.57] to obtain

$$\langle \Delta v_\parallel \rangle_{av} = \frac{N_+ \Theta}{g^2} \qquad [9.60]$$

Similarly, substituting [9.53] into [9.58], we obtain

$$\langle (\Delta v_\parallel)^2 \rangle_{av} = \frac{N_+ \Theta}{g \ln \Lambda} \qquad [9.61]$$

and, substituting [9.55] into [9.59], we obtain

$$\langle(\Delta v_\perp)^2\rangle_{av} = \frac{N_+ \Theta}{g} \qquad [9.62]$$

where (see [9.49])

$$\Theta = \frac{Z^2 e^4 \ln \Lambda}{4\pi\epsilon_0^2 m'^2} \qquad [9.63]$$

We will now apply the results of this section to investigate the concepts of relaxation times in plasmas.

Exercise 9.21.1
  (a)   Verify [9.50].
  (b)   Verify [9.52].
  (c)   Verify [9.54].

9.3 THE DISTINCTION BETWEEN WEAKLY AND STRONGLY IONIZED PLASMAS

The thermal equilibrium state of a plasma is described in kinetic theory terms by stating that each single-particle velocity distribution function is of the Maxwellian form and that all the constituent gases of the plasma are at the same temperature, which is also the temperature of the walls, if there are any. The velocities in a Maxwellian distribution are randomized (isotropic), and the time taken by a group of particles with a directed velocity to become deflected in random directions is one of the factors that determine the time required to reach equilibrium. In our treatment we will identify the relaxation time with this deflection time. So we see that if, on the average, a particle changes its momentum in a collision by an amount equal to its initial momentum (an average deflection of 90°), then the reciprocal of the collision frequency—that is, the mean free time—will be the measure of the relaxation time.

This concept of complete randomization of velocity after one collision is so useful that we seek to define the collision cross section and collision frequency in terms of it. The appropriate values in the case of binary collisions involving one neutral particle are the momentum transfer cross section and the corresponding collision frequency. For binary Coulomb collisions we somewhat arbitrarily consider a cross section for scattering through angles of at least

90°. In considering multiple, distant Coulomb interactions, we again look for the cumulative effect that will deflect the test particle through 90°. These three cases are treated in the next section. Finally (Section 9.32) these various relaxation times are compared under differing plasma conditions.

Exercise 9.3.1   Consider a three-component plasma of electrons, one species of positive ions and one species of neutral particles. Assume that each component in turn is given a velocity distribution which is far from equilibrium. Describe the important processes in the return to equilibrium in each case. List the various plasma conditions that would affect the time taken to reach equilibrium.

9.31 RELAXATION TIMES FOR ELECTRON-NEUTRAL AND COULOMB COLLISIONS

Momentum transfer collisions are the collisions that are effective in destroying any preferred motion of the electrons in the plasma. Therefore in collisions between electrons and neutral particles the important quantity is the collision frequency for momentum transfer given by

$$\nu_{EN} = gQ_M N_N \qquad [9.64]$$

where Q_M is the cross section for momentum transfer and N_N is the number density of the neutral particles. We can therefore introduce a *relaxation time* τ_{EN} as the mean time between such collisions. Thus

$$\tau_{EN} = \frac{1}{\nu_{EN}} = \frac{1}{gQ_M N_N} \qquad [9.65]$$

In order to determine the relaxation time τ_{EN} (or the collision frequency ν_{EN}), we must know the temperature of the gas and the cross section for momentum transfer. These cross sections are known from experimental measurements.

Close Coulomb Collisions   In Section 9.1 we introduced a cross section for 90° Coulomb collisions. We could then define the collision frequency ν_{90} for such collisions. If we are considering the collision of an electron with a positive ion, then from [9.3], [9.5], and [9.63] we have that

$$\nu_{90} = \frac{Z^2 e^4 N_+}{16\pi\epsilon_0^2 m'^2 g^3} = \frac{\Theta N_+}{4g^3 \ln \Lambda} \qquad [9.66]$$

We can therefore define a relaxation time τ_{90} as the mean time between collisions that result in a deflection angle greater than $90°$. From [9.66] we therefore have that

$$\tau_{90} = \frac{4g^3 \ln \Lambda}{\Theta N_+} \qquad [9.67]$$

However we will see that the relaxation time that describes distant Coulomb collisions is much shorter than τ_{90}. This means that the effect of distant Coulomb collisions will outweigh the effects of occasional close Coulomb collisions.

Distant Coulomb Collisions   We now wish to obtain a relaxation time that will characterize the distant Coulomb collisions. We recall from Section 9.2 that $\langle \Delta v_i \rangle_{av}$ and $\langle \Delta v_i \Delta v_j \rangle_{av}$ are the rates at which Δv_i and $\Delta v_i \Delta v_j$ are changed as the result of many small Coulomb collisions. We would like to know how long it takes for many of these small deflections to produce a mean cumulative deflection of $90°$. This time will then be designated as the relaxation time for this process τ_D.

We found in Section 9.21 that the mean value $\langle \Delta v_\perp \rangle$ was zero due to the symmetry of the scattering process. However the mean square value $\langle (\Delta v_\perp)^2 \rangle$ is not zero; it represents the rate at which points in velocity space diffuse in a direction perpendicular to the initial velocity. Since the mass of the positive ions has been taken to be infinite (that is, they are motionless), then $M^B = 1$, and we can take the velocity of the center-of-mass v_i^G for an electron-ion encounter to be zero. If a large number of electrons start out at a given time with a velocity v_1^0, then the diffusion of points in velocity space is illustrated in Figure 9.6.

At time $t = 0$ all electrons have the velocity $g = v_1^0$ so that $f = N_- \delta(v_i - v_1^0)$. After a time t_1 the electrons have diffused in a direction perpendicular to v_1^0. We might suspect that the particle density at any instant of time varies in the radial direction according to a Gaussian distribution as shown in Figure 9.6b.

The *Gaussian distribution* is given by

$$p(v_\perp) = \frac{1}{\sqrt{2\pi}\,\zeta} e^{-(v_\perp^2/2\zeta^2)} \qquad [9.68]$$

where ζ^2 is the variance and is a measure of the spread of the distribution (see Exercise 9.31.1). In [9.68] $p(v_\perp)$ is the probability of finding an electron at a given value of $v_\perp$.

In our case the variance ζ^2 is a function of time. The time dependence of the distribution function is given by the Fokker-Planck equation. For the

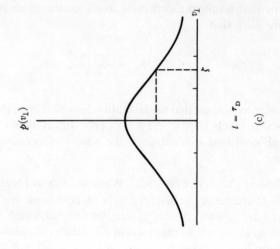

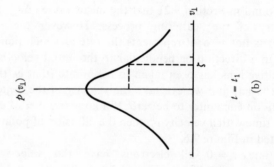

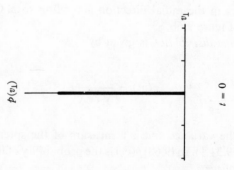

FIGURE 9.6 Diffusion of Particles in Velocity Space

special case we are considering of electrons interacting with fixed positive ions, we can consider the diffusion coefficient $\langle(\Delta v_\perp)^2\rangle$ given by [9.62] to be a constant. Then if we consider only the component of diffusion in the direction of $v_\perp$, the Fokker-Planck equation [9.34] reduces to

$$\frac{\partial f}{\partial t} = \frac{1}{2}\langle(\Delta v_\perp)^2\rangle_{av}\frac{\partial^2 f}{\partial v_\perp^2}$$

Since we can write $f(v_\perp, t) = N_-p(v_\perp, t)$ then we have that

$$\frac{\partial p}{\partial t} = \frac{1}{2}\langle(\Delta v_\perp)^2\rangle_{av}\frac{\partial^2 p}{\partial v_\perp^2} \qquad [9.69]$$

This is a diffusion equation which we hope will be satisfied by [9.68] for some appropriate time variation of ζ^2. Let us assume that ζ^2 varies linearly with time. That is,

$$\zeta^2 = kt \qquad [9.70]$$

Then [9.68] becomes

$$p(v_\perp, t) = \frac{1}{\sqrt{2\pi}\,k^{1/2}t^{1/2}}\,e^{-(v_\perp^2/2kt)} \qquad [9.71]$$

Substituting this value of $p(v_\perp, t)$ into [9.69], we readily find that [9.71] is a solution to the diffusion equation [9.69] provided that

$$k = \langle(\Delta v_\perp)^2\rangle_{av} \qquad [9.72]$$

(see Exercise 9.31.2). From [9.72] and [9.70] we see therefore that the variance of the Gaussian distributions shown in Figure 9.6 vary with time according to

$$\zeta^2 = \langle(\Delta v_\perp)^2\rangle_{av}t \qquad [9.73]$$

From Figure 9.6c we can define a mean cumulative deflection of 90° as occurring when $\zeta = g$. At this time about 68 per cent of the electrons will have perpendicular velocity components less than g while 32 per cent will have perpendicular velocity components greater than g. The original velocity distribution of the electrons will have been appreciably altered and the time required for this to happen will be identified as the relaxation time for distant encounters τ_D. Setting $\zeta = g$ in [9.73], we therefore have

$$\zeta^2 = \langle(\Delta v_\perp)^2\rangle_{av}\tau_D = g^2 \qquad [9.74]$$

Substituting the value of $\langle (\Delta v_\perp)^2 \rangle_{av}$ from [9.62] into [9.74] we see that the relaxation time τ_D can be written as

$$\tau_D = \frac{g^3}{N_+ \Theta} = \frac{(3kT/m_-)^{3/2}}{N_- \Theta} \qquad [9.75]$$

where we have set $\frac{1}{2}m_- g^2 = \frac{3}{2}kT$ and noted that $N_- = N_+$.

From [9.60] and [9.75] we see that in the time τ_D the mean change in $\Delta v_\parallel$ is

$$\langle \Delta v_\parallel \rangle_{av} \tau_D = g \qquad [9.76]$$

so that the parallel velocity components of the electrons decrease as their perpendicular velocity components increase. The time defined by [9.76] is often referred to as a *slowing down time*. The fact that it is equal to the relaxation time τ_D in our case results from our model of electrons interacting with fixed ions. If the positive ions are allowed to move, then these times are no longer identical.

If $\ln \Lambda \gg 1$, then we see from [9.61] that the coefficient $\langle (\Delta v_\parallel)^2 \rangle_{av}$ is much less than $\langle (\Delta v_\perp)^2 \rangle_{av}$. For this reason it is of less importance and is therefore generally neglected.

It is interesting to compare the value of the relaxation time for distant encounters τ_D with that for close encounters τ_{90}. From [9.67] and [9.75] we have that

$$\frac{\tau_{90}}{\tau_D} = 4 \ln \Lambda \qquad [9.77]$$

We therefore see that if $\ln \Lambda \gg 1$, the time τ_{90} is much longer than τ_D. For this reason we can generally neglect the occasional large Coulomb deflection compared with the many weak Coulomb interactions that result in a large cumulative deflection. We therefore adopt the time τ_D to describe the electron-ion collisions and write

$$\tau_D = \tau_{EI} = \frac{1}{\nu_{EI}}$$

where ν_{EI} is the *effective collision frequency for electron-ion collisions*.

In the following section we will obtain numerical values for τ_{EI} for different temperatures and densities and compare these with the relaxation times for electron-neutral collisions.

Exercise 9.31.1   Let $p(x)$ be the probability of an event occurring at x. Then

$$\int_{-\infty}^{\infty} p(x)\, dx = 1$$

The mean value of x is given by

$$\langle x \rangle = \int_{-\infty}^{\infty} xp(x)\,dx$$

The mean squared value of x is given by

$$\langle x^2 \rangle = \int_{-\infty}^{\infty} x^2 p(x)\,dx$$

The variance ζ^2 is given by

$$\zeta^2 = \langle (x - \langle x \rangle)^2 \rangle$$

(a) Show that

$$\zeta^2 = \langle x^2 \rangle - \langle x \rangle^2$$

(b) The general Gaussian distribution is given by

$$p(x) = \frac{1}{\sqrt{2\pi}\,\zeta}\, e^{-[(x - \langle x \rangle)^2/2\zeta^2]}$$

Using this value of $p(x)$, verify that

(i) $\displaystyle\int_{-\infty}^{\infty} p(x)\,dx = 1$

(ii) $\displaystyle\int_{-\infty}^{\infty} xp(x)\,dx = \langle x \rangle$

(iii) $\displaystyle\int_{-\infty}^{\infty} (x - \langle x \rangle)^2 p(x)\,dx = \zeta^2$

Exercise 9.31.2   Verify that [9.71] is a solution to [9.69] if $k = \langle (\Delta v_\perp)^2 \rangle$.

9.32 COMPARISON OF RELAXATION TIMES FOR SOME GASES

Many of the previous results depend upon the validity of the assumption that $\ln \Lambda \gg 1$. It is therefore important to calculate the value of $\ln \Lambda$ for different values of temperature and electron density.

From [9.46], [9.13], and [9.18] we have that

$$\ln \Lambda = \ln \frac{h}{p_c} = \ln \left(12.4 \times 10^3 \frac{T^{3/2}}{N_-^{1/2}} \right) \tag{9.78}$$

A quantum mechanical correction is needed for temperatures greater than about 10^5 °K, and Marshak[1] has shown that this correction can be accounted for by multiplying Λ by $(4.2 \times 10^5/T)^{1/2}$, whenever T is greater than 4.2×10^5 degrees K. From [9.78] we therefore have that

$$\ln \Lambda = 9.42 + \tfrac{3}{2} \ln T - \tfrac{1}{2} \ln N_- \qquad \text{for } T < 4.2 \times 10^5 \text{ °K} \qquad [9.79]$$

and

$$\ln \Lambda = 15.9 + \ln T - \tfrac{1}{2} \ln N_- \qquad \text{for } T > 4.2 \times 10^5 \text{ °K} \qquad [9.80]$$

Using these equations, one can readily calculate $\ln \Lambda$ for various values of temperature and electron density. Typical values are shown in Table 9.1.

TABLE 9.1.   Values of $\ln \Lambda = \ln (h/p_c)$

ELECTRON TEMPERATURE T_-, °K	ELECTRON DENSITY N_-, cm^{-3}								
	1	10^3	10^6	10^9	10^{12}	10^{15}	10^{18}	10^{21}	10^{24}
10^2	16.3	12.8	9.4	6.0					
10^3	19.7	16.3	12.8	9.4	6.0				
10^4	23.2	19.7	16.3	12.8	9.4	6.0			
10^5	26.7	23.2	19.7	16.3	12.8	9.4	6.0		
10^6	29.7	26.3	22.8	19.3	15.9	12.4	9.0	5.5	
10^7	32.0	28.5	25.1	21.6	18.1	14.7	11.2	7.8	4.4
10^8	34.3	30.9	27.4	24.0	20.5	17.0	13.6	10.1	6.7

The value of Θ can be found from [9.63] to be

$$\Theta = 8.05 \times 10^5 \ln \Lambda \frac{\text{meters}^6}{\text{sec}^4} \qquad [9.81]$$

Thus, the relaxation time τ_{EI} can be written from [9.75] as

$$\tau_{EI} = \frac{0.38 T^{3/2}}{N_- \ln \Lambda} \qquad [9.82]$$

where T is in °K and N_- is in cm^{-3}. This relaxation time is plotted in Figure 9.7 as a function of electron density for different values of electron temperature.

Now when the relaxation time τ_{EI} for electron-ion collisions is shorter than the relaxation time τ_{EN} for electron-neutral collisions, then the effects of

[1] R. Marshak, *Ann. N.Y. Acad. Science*, **41** (1941), 49.

Coulomb collisions become predominant. We define a weakly ionized gas as one in which only electron-neutral collisions are important. Similarly we define a strongly ionized gas as one in which electron-ion collisions are more important than electron-neutral collisions. We can therefore establish a boundary between these two regions as the condition that occurs when $\tau_{EI} = \tau_{EN}$. Of course, close to this boundary both electron-neutral and electron-ion collisions will be important.

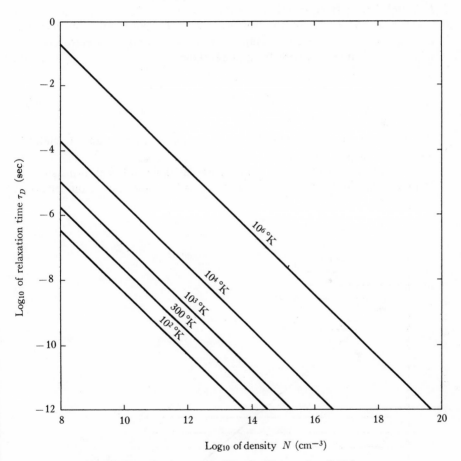

FIGURE 9.7   Relaxation Time for Electron-Ion Collisions

From [9.65] and [9.82] we find that

$$\frac{\tau_{EI}}{\tau_{EN}} = \frac{2.22 \times 10^9 Q_M T^2 N_N}{N_- \ln \Lambda} \qquad [9.83]$$

Setting this ratio equal to one we see that the boundary between weakly and strongly ionized gases occurs when

$$\frac{N_-}{N_N} = \frac{2.22 \times 10^9 Q_M T^2}{\ln \Lambda} \tag{9.84}$$

Thus by using the appropriate collision cross section data, we can find the critical percentage ionization, $N_-/(N_N + N_-)$, for a given electron temperature and density from [9.84].

For example, if one uses the cross section for H_2 at a mean electron energy corresponding to an electron temperature of 10^3 °K and an electron density of 10^{12} cm^{-3}, then one finds from [9.84] that

$$\frac{N_-}{N_N} = 0.6 \times 10^{-4} \tag{9.85}$$

We therefore see that Coulomb effects can become important at relatively low percentages of ionization.

This critical value of N_-/N_N can be represented in a different form as shown in Figure 9.8. In this figure τ_{EI} is plotted as a function of electron density at

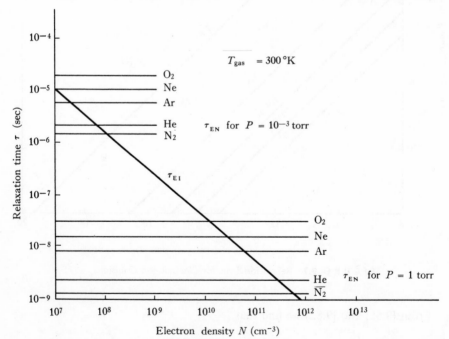

FIGURE 9.8   Relaxation Times for Electron-Neutral and Electron-Ion Interactions

a given temperature. Values of τ_{EN} are then plotted for different gases at different pressures. It is assumed that all the electrons travel with the mean thermal speed. The neutral gas in each case is assumed to be at room temperature $T_g = (300°K)$ such that $P = N_N k T_g$. For any value of N_- the relative importance of electron collisions with neutral particles and with positive ions can be ascertained by noting the relative magnitudes of τ_{EI} and τ_{EN}.

REFERENCES

General discussions of Coulomb interactions may be found in

1   Glasstone, S., and R. H. Lovberg. *Controlled Thermonuclear Reactions.* Princeton: Van Nostrand, 1960.

2   Rose, D. J., and M. Clark. *Plasmas and Controlled Fusion.* New York: Wiley, 1961.

The concept of a relaxation time is discussed in relation to gravitational fields by

3   Chandrasekhar, S. *Principles of Stellar Dynamics.* New York: Dover, 1942.

In relation to Coulomb fields relaxation times are treated in

4   Spitzer, L. *Physics of Fully Ionized Gases.* 2nd ed.; New York: Interscience, 1962, Chap. 5.

The Fokker-Planck equation was applied to the problem of Brownian motion by

5   Chandrasekhar, S. "Stochastic Problems in Physics and Astronomy." *Rev. Mod. Phys.*, **15** (1943), 1–89.

Application of the Fokker-Planck equation to Coulomb interactions is discussed by

6   Allis, W. P. "Motions of Ions and Electrons," *Handbuch der Physik*, vol. 21. Springer-Verlag, 1956.

7   Brandstatter, J. J. *An Introduction to Waves, Rays, and Radiation in Plasma Media.* New York: McGraw-Hill, 1963.

8   Cohen, R. S., L. Spitzer, and P. Routly. "The Electrical Conductivity of an Ionized Gas," *Phys. Rev.*, **90** (1950), 230–8.

9   Delcroix, J. L. *Introduction to the Theory of Ionized Gases.* New York: Interscience, 1960.

10   Linhart, J. G. *Plasma Physics*. 2nd ed.; North-Holland, 1961.

11   Rosenbluth, M. N., W. M. MacDonald, and D. L. Judd. "Fokker-Planck Equation for an Inverse-Square Force," *Phys. Rev.*, **107** (1957), 1–6.

12   Longmire, C. L. *Elementary Plasma Physics*. New York: Interscience, 1963.

CHAPTER

10

PLASMA KINETIC THEORY: THE USE OF THE BOLTZMANN EQUATION

By taking moments of the Boltzmann equation we have found that we could obtain a set of macroscopic equations that describe the time variation of the macroscopic variables. However we discovered that this description was not complete and that information was lost in the process of integrating the Boltzmann equation. Some truncation procedure was therefore necessary in order to obtain a determined set of equations.

On the other hand, if we solve the Boltzmann equation directly for the distribution function f, then all macroscopic quantities can be calculated. In this chapter we will describe a method for solving the Boltzmann equation which is applicable under certain conditions. We will assume that the plasma is weakly ionized and that only the electron motion is important. We include the effects of electron-neutral collisions and assume that the external forces acting on the plasma only slightly perturb its equilibrium distribution.

Under these conditions it is possible to expand the distribution function in spherical harmonics. If one retains only the first two terms of the series expansion, then a set of two coupled equations is obtained for the isotropic and anisotropic parts of the distribution function. This procedure is carried out in Section 10.1.

By solving these two equations, one can calculate the macroscopic currents that flow in the plasma. As a result one can obtain expressions for various transport coefficients. In Section 10.2 we will obtain expressions for the conductivity and diffusion coefficients in both isotropic and anisotropic plasmas. By assuming that the isotropic part of the distribution function is Maxwellian, we can obtain explicit expressions for these transport coefficients. However we will see in Section 10.4 that by actually calculating the isotropic part of the distribution function we are led to a nonlinear conductivity for the plasma.

10.1 SOLUTION OF
THE BOLTZMANN EQUATION

We consider a weakly ionized plasma in which only electron-neutral collisions are important. If the forces acting on the electrons arise from electric and magnetic fields then the Boltzmann equation for the electrons can be written as

$$\frac{\partial f}{\partial t} + v_i \frac{\partial f}{\partial x_i} - \frac{e}{m} E_i \frac{\partial f}{\partial v_i} - \epsilon_{ijk} v_j \Omega_k \frac{\partial f}{\partial v_i} = \left(\frac{\partial f}{\partial t}\right)_{coll} \qquad [10.1]$$

where, from Section 5.32,

$$\left(\frac{\partial f}{\partial t}\right)_{coll} = \int_{-\infty}^{\infty} \int_{0}^{2\pi} \int_{0}^{\pi} (\tilde{f}\tilde{f}^N - ff^N) g S(\chi) \sin \chi \, d\chi \, d\psi \, dc^N \qquad [10.2]$$

and f^N is the distribution function of the neutral scatterers.

Since no exact solution to this equation is known, we must try to find some type of approximate solution. We found in Section 5.4 that in the absence of external forces or spatial gradients the collisions between the particles maintained a Maxwellian distribution in the steady state. For a gas at rest this distribution is isotropic about the origin.

The effect of spatial gradients and external forces is to cause the electrons to acquire a small drift velocity. That is, the velocity distribution function will become anisotropic since more electrons will be moving in one direction than another. For this case we will assume that we can write the distribution function f as

$$f = f^0 + \phi(v_i) \qquad [10.3]$$

where f^0 is an isotropic distribution which need not be Maxwellian and $\phi(v_i)$ is a small perturbation which causes f to be anisotropic.

If the external forces and spatial gradients perturb the distribution only slightly (that is $\phi(v_i) \ll f^0$), then we will suppose that the small perturbation $\phi(v_i)$ can be written as

$$\phi(v_i) = \frac{v_i}{w} f_i' = f' \cos \Theta \qquad [10.4]$$

where

$$w^2 = v_i v_i \qquad [10.5]$$

and Θ is the angle between v_i and f_i' as shown in Figure 10.1. The vector f_i' points in the direction in which the electrons drift as the result of the external fields and spatial gradients.

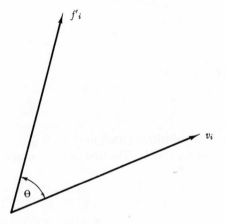

FIGURE 10.1 Orientation of the Anisotropic Part of the Electron Velocity Distribution Function (f_i')

The total distribution f can then be written from [10.3] as

$$f = f^0 + \frac{v_i}{w} f_i' \qquad [10.6]$$

This form of f can be shown to be equivalent to the first two terms of a spherical harmonic expansion of the distribution function (see Problem 10.1).

One should note carefully the meaning of the expansion [10.6]. Suppose, for example, that an electric field is applied to a plasma which has a Maxwellian distribution of velocities. The effect is to simply displace the Maxwellian distribution as shown in Figure 10.2a. On the other hand the expansion of f given by [10.6] is shown graphically in Figure 10.2b. We see that for weak field strengths the dotted curve in Figure 10.2b approximates the displaced Maxwellian in Figure 10.2a. The advantage of the spherical harmonic expansion is that one can readily include combined effects of density gradient, magnetic fields, and so forth.

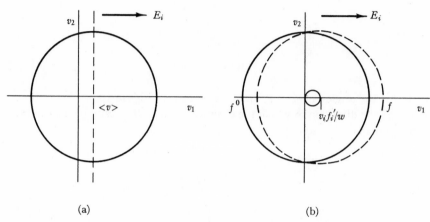

(a)   (b)

FIGURE 10.2 Illustration of the Difference Between a Displaced Maxwellian Distribution (a) and a Spherical Harmonic Expansion of the Distribution Function (b)

We now substitute [10.6] into the Boltzmann equation [10.1] and consider each term separately. The first term becomes

$$\frac{\partial f}{\partial t} = \frac{\partial f^0}{\partial t} + \frac{v_i}{w}\frac{\partial f_i'}{\partial t} \qquad [10.7]$$

The second term can be written

$$v_i\frac{\partial f}{\partial x_i} = v_i\frac{\partial f^0}{\partial x_i} + \frac{v_i v_j}{w}\frac{\partial f_j'}{\partial x_i} \qquad [10.8]$$

In treating the third term of [10.1], we note from [10.5] that

$$\frac{\partial}{\partial v_i} = \frac{\partial w}{\partial v_i}\frac{\partial}{\partial w}$$

$$= \frac{v_i}{w}\frac{\partial}{\partial w} \qquad [10.9]$$

We can then write

$$\frac{\partial f}{\partial v_i} = \frac{\partial}{\partial v_i}\left(f^0 + \frac{v_j f_j'}{w}\right)$$

$$= \frac{v_i}{w}\frac{\partial f^0}{\partial w} + \frac{\partial}{\partial v_i}\left(\frac{v_j f_j'}{w}\right)$$

$$= \frac{v_i}{w}\frac{\partial f^0}{\partial w} + \frac{f_i'}{w} + \frac{v_i v_j}{w}\frac{\partial}{\partial w}\left(\frac{f_j'}{w}\right) \qquad [10.10]$$

The magnetic field term in [10.1] is written as

$$\epsilon_{ijk}v_j\Omega_k\frac{\partial f}{\partial v_i} = \epsilon_{ijk}v_j\Omega_k\frac{\partial}{\partial v_i}\left[f^0 + \frac{v_r f_r'}{w}\right]$$

$$= \epsilon_{ijk}v_j\Omega_k\frac{v_i}{w}\frac{\partial f^0}{\partial w} + \epsilon_{ijk}v_j\Omega_k\frac{\partial}{\partial v_i}\left(\frac{v_r f_r'}{w}\right) \qquad [10.11]$$

The first term on the right-hand side of [10.11] is zero since, when the subscripts i and j are interchanged, the term is seen to be equal to the negative of itself. The remaining term can be written as

$$\epsilon_{ijk}v_j\Omega_k\frac{\partial}{\partial v_i}\left(\frac{v_r f_r'}{w}\right) = \epsilon_{ijk}v_j\Omega_k\frac{f_r'}{w}\delta_{ir} + \epsilon_{ijk}v_j\Omega_k v_r\frac{v_i}{w}\frac{\partial}{\partial w}\left(\frac{f_r'}{w}\right) \qquad [10.12]$$

Again the last term in [10.12] is zero, so that [10.11] can finally be written as

$$\epsilon_{ijk}v_j\Omega_k\frac{\partial f}{\partial v_i} = \epsilon_{ijk}v_j\Omega_k\frac{f_i'}{w} \qquad [10.13]$$

The form of the collision term in [10.1] will be treated separately in Section 10.13.

Collecting our results, we see from [10.7], [10.8], [10.10], and [10.13] that the Boltzmann equation [10.1] takes the form

$$\frac{\partial f^0}{\partial t} + \frac{v_i}{w}\frac{\partial f_i'}{\partial t} + v_i\frac{\partial f^0}{\partial x_i} + \frac{v_i v_j}{w}\frac{\partial f_j'}{\partial x_i} - \frac{e}{m}E_i\left[\frac{v_i}{w}\frac{\partial f^0}{\partial w} + \frac{f_i'}{w} + \frac{v_i v_j}{w}\frac{\partial}{\partial w}\left(\frac{f_j'}{w}\right)\right]$$

$$- \epsilon_{ijk}v_j\Omega_k\frac{f_i'}{w} = \left(\frac{\partial f}{\partial t}\right)_{coll} \qquad [10.14]$$

We will see in the following two sections that certain orthogonality relations allow us to obtain two coupled equations from [10.14]. The first describes the time-variation of the isotropic part of the distribution function f^0, while the second equation describes the time variation of the anisotropic part f_i'.

10.11 THE EQUATION
FOR THE TIME-VARIATION OF f^0

Let w, θ, and φ be the spherical coordinates of the velocity vector as shown in Figure 10.3. Then using the results of Exercise 10.11.1 we have the following orthogonality relations

$$\int_0^{2\pi} \int_0^{\pi} \sin \theta \, d\theta \, d\varphi = 4\pi \tag{10.15}$$

$$\int_0^{2\pi} \int_0^{\pi} v_i \sin \theta \, d\theta \, d\varphi = 0 \tag{10.16}$$

$$\int_0^{2\pi} \int_0^{\pi} v_i v_j \sin \theta \, d\theta \, d\varphi = \frac{4\pi}{3} w^2 \, \delta_{ij} \tag{10.17}$$

$$\int_0^{2\pi} \int_0^{\pi} v_i v_j v_k \sin \theta \, d\theta \, d\varphi = 0 \tag{10.18}$$

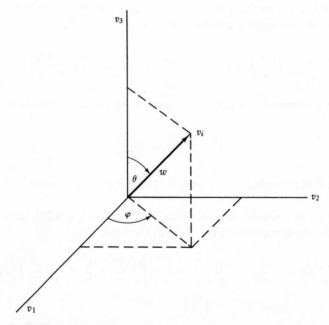

FIGURE 10.3 The Spherical Coordinates of the Velocity Vector

Using these relations, we can obtain an equation for the time-variation of f^0 by multiplying [10.14] by $\sin \theta \, d\theta \, d\varphi$ and integrating over the angles θ and

φ. The second, third, fifth, and eighth term in [10.14] will then be zero as the result of [10.16]. Using [10.15] and [10.17], the remaining terms become

$$4\pi \frac{\partial f^0}{\partial t} + \frac{4\pi}{3} w^2 \delta_{ij} \frac{1}{w} \frac{\partial f'_j}{\partial x_i} - \frac{e}{m} E_i \left[4\pi \frac{f'_i}{w} + \frac{4\pi}{3} w^2 \delta_{ij} \frac{1}{w} \frac{\partial}{\partial w} \frac{f'_j}{w} \right]$$

$$= \int_0^{2\pi} \int_0^\pi \left(\frac{\partial f}{\partial t} \right)_{coll} \sin \theta \, d\theta \, d\varphi$$

or

$$\frac{\partial f^0}{\partial t} + \frac{w}{3} \frac{\partial f'_i}{\partial x_i} - \frac{e}{m} E_i \left[\frac{f'_i}{w} + \frac{w}{3} \frac{\partial}{\partial w} \left(\frac{f'_i}{w} \right) \right] = \frac{1}{4\pi} \int_0^{2\pi} \int_0^\pi \left(\frac{\partial f}{\partial t} \right)_{coll} \sin \theta \, d\theta \, d\varphi$$

[10.19]

The two terms in the bracket in [10.19] can be written as

$$\frac{f'_i}{w} + \frac{w}{3} \frac{\partial}{\partial w} \left(\frac{f'_i}{w} \right) = \frac{f'_i}{w} + \frac{w^3}{3w^2} \frac{\partial}{\partial w} \left(\frac{f'_i}{w} \right)$$

$$= \frac{f'_i}{w} + \frac{1}{3w^2} \frac{\partial}{\partial w} \left(\frac{w^3 f'_i}{w} \right) - \frac{3w^2}{3w^2} \frac{f'_i}{w}$$

$$= \frac{1}{3w^2} \frac{\partial}{\partial w} (w^2 f'_i)$$

[10.20]

Substituting [10.20] into [10.19], we obtain the following equation for the time-variation of f^0

$$\frac{\partial f^0}{\partial t} + \frac{w}{3} \frac{\partial f'_i}{\partial x_i} - \frac{e}{m} \frac{E_i}{3w^2} \frac{\partial}{\partial w} (w^2 f'_i) = \left(\frac{\partial f^0}{\partial t} \right)_{coll}$$

[10.21]

where

$$\left(\frac{\partial f^0}{\partial t} \right)_{coll} = \frac{1}{4\pi} \int_0^{2\pi} \int_0^\pi \left(\frac{\partial f}{\partial t} \right)_{coll} \sin \theta \, d\theta \, d\varphi$$

[10.22]

We will return to the form of the collision term in Section 10.13. First, however, we will obtain an equation for f'_i in the next section.

Exercise 10.11.1 From Figure 10.3 we can write

$$v_1 = w \sin \theta \cos \varphi$$

$$v_2 = w \sin \theta \sin \varphi$$

$$v_3 = w \cos \theta$$

from which the matrix $v_i v_j$ has the following form

$$
v_i v_j = \begin{bmatrix} w^2 \sin^2 \theta \cos^2 \varphi & w^2 \sin^2 \theta \sin \varphi \cos \varphi & w^2 \sin \theta \cos \theta \cos \varphi \\ w^2 \sin^2 \theta \sin \varphi \cos \varphi & w^2 \sin^2 \theta \sin^2 \varphi & w^2 \sin \theta \cos \theta \sin \varphi \\ w^2 \sin \theta \cos \theta \cos \varphi & w^2 \sin \theta \cos \theta \sin \varphi & w^2 \cos^2 \theta \end{bmatrix}
$$

Using these values prove the orthogonality relations [10.15] to [10.18].

10.12 THE EQUATION
FOR THE TIME-VARIATION OF f_i'

As a result of the orthogonality relations [10.15] to [10.18] we can obtain an equation for the time-variation of f_i' by multiplying [10.14] by $v_r \sin \theta \, d\theta \, d\varphi$ and integrating over the angles θ and φ. In this case the first, fourth, sixth and seventh terms in [10.14] will be zero as a result of [10.16] and [10.18]. Using [10.17], the remaining terms can then be written as

$$
\frac{4\pi}{3} w^2 \delta_{ir} \frac{1}{w} \frac{\partial f_i'}{\partial t} + \frac{4\pi}{3} w^2 \delta_{ir} \frac{\partial f^0}{\partial x_i} - \frac{e}{m} E_i \frac{4\pi}{3} w^2 \delta_{ir} \frac{1}{w} \frac{\partial f^0}{\partial w} - \epsilon_{ijk} \Omega_k \frac{f_i'}{w} \frac{4\pi}{3} w^2 \delta_{jr}
$$
$$
= \int_0^{2\pi} \int_0^\pi v_r \left(\frac{\partial f}{\partial t} \right)_{\text{coll}} \sin \theta \, d\theta \, d\varphi
$$

or, dividing through by $4\pi w/3$,

$$
\frac{\partial f_r'}{\partial t} + w \frac{\partial f^0}{\partial x_r} - \frac{e}{m} E_r \frac{\partial f^0}{\partial w} - \epsilon_{irk} \Omega_k f_i' = \left(\frac{\partial f_r'}{\partial t} \right)_{\text{coll}} \tag{10.23}
$$

where

$$
\left(\frac{\partial f_r'}{\partial t} \right)_{\text{coll}} = \frac{3}{4\pi w} \int_0^{2\pi} \int_0^\pi v_r \left(\frac{\partial f}{\partial t} \right)_{\text{coll}} \sin \theta \, d\theta \, d\varphi \tag{10.24}
$$

We now turn to the evaluation of the collision terms [10.22] and [10.24].

10.13 THE COLLISION TERMS

In this section we wish to determine the form of the collision terms given by [10.22] and [10.24]. We consider only collisions between electrons and neutral particles so that the collision integral [10.2] can be written

$$
\left(\frac{\partial f}{\partial t} \right)_{\text{coll}} = \int_{-\infty}^\infty \int_0^{2\pi} \int_0^\pi (\tilde{f} \tilde{f}^N - f f^N) g S(\chi) \sin \chi \, d\chi \, d\psi \, dc^N \tag{10.25}
$$

where f is the electron distribution function and f^N is the distribution function for the neutral particles.

According to [10.6] the electron distribution function is written as

$$f = f^0(w) + \frac{v_i}{w} f_i' \qquad [10.26]$$

Note that the velocity dependence of the term $v_i f_i'/w$ is given explicitly so that f_i' is not a function of velocity and $\tilde{f}_i' = f_i'$. If we substitute [10.26] into [10.25], the factor in parenthesis becomes

$$(\tilde{f}\tilde{f}^N - ff^N) = \tilde{f}^0\tilde{f}^N - f^0 f^N + \frac{\tilde{v}_i}{\tilde{w}} f_i' \tilde{f}^N - \frac{v_i}{w} f_i' f^N \qquad [10.27]$$

Now in this section we will assume that the neutral particles are infinitely massive. That is, they are initially at rest and do not recoil as the result of collisions with the electrons. For this case

$$\tilde{w} = w \quad \text{and} \quad \tilde{f}^N = f^N \qquad [10.28]$$

Using these results we have from [10.4] that

$$\frac{v_i}{w} f_i' = f' \cos \Theta \qquad [10.29]$$

and

$$\frac{\tilde{v}_i}{\tilde{w}} f_i' = f' \cos \tilde{\Theta} \qquad [10.30]$$

where the angles Θ and $\tilde{\Theta}$ are shown in Figure 10.4. Since the neutral

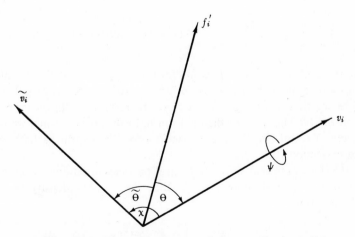

FIGURE 10.4 The Electron Velocity Before and After a Collision

particles are assumed to be infinitely massive, the angle between v_i and $\tilde{v}_i$ is simply the scattering angle χ in the center-of-mass coordinate system.

From Figure 10.5 and Exercise 10.13.1 we find that

$$\cos \tilde{\Theta} = \cos \Theta \cos \chi + \sin \Theta \sin \chi \cos \psi \qquad [10.31]$$

where ψ is the azimuthal scattering angle. Using [10.28] to [10.31] we can write the last two terms of [10.27] as

$$\frac{\tilde{v}_i}{\tilde{w}} f_i' f^N - \frac{v_i}{w} f_i' f^N = f^N f'(\cos \tilde{\Theta} - \cos \Theta)$$

$$= f^N f'[\cos \Theta(\cos \chi - 1) + \sin \Theta \sin \chi \cos \psi] \qquad [10.32]$$

Substituting [10.27] into [10.25] and using [10.32], we obtain

$$\left(\frac{\partial f}{\partial t}\right)_{\text{coll}} = \int_{-\infty}^{\infty} \int_0^{2\pi} \int_0^{\pi} (\tilde{f}^0 \tilde{f}^N - f^0 f^N) g S(\chi) \sin \chi \, d\chi \, d\psi \, dc^N$$

$$+ \int_{-\infty}^{\infty} \int_0^{2\pi} \int_0^{\pi} f^N f' \cos \Theta(\cos \chi - 1) g S(\chi) \sin \chi \, d\chi \, d\psi \, dc^N$$

$$+ \int_{-\infty}^{\infty} \int_0^{2\pi} \int_0^{\pi} f^N f' \sin \Theta \sin \chi \cos \psi g S(\chi) \sin \chi \, d\chi \, d\psi \, dc^N \qquad [10.33]$$

If we carry out the integration from 0 to 2π over the azimuthal scattering angle ψ, then the last term in [10.33] vanishes. Since we have assumed that $\tilde{w} = w$ then $\tilde{f}^0 \tilde{f}^N = f^0 f^N$ and the first term on the right-hand side of [10.33] is also zero. Using [10.28] and [10.29], we can write the remaining term in [10.33] as

$$\left(\frac{\partial f}{\partial t}\right)_{\text{coll}} = -2\pi \int_{-\infty}^{\infty} \int_0^{\pi} f^N \frac{v_i f_i'}{w} (1 - \cos \chi) g S(\chi) \sin \chi \, d\chi \, dc^N \qquad [10.34]$$

If we then substitute this expression for $(\partial f/\partial t)_{\text{coll}}$ into [10.22], we find that the collision term in the equation for f^0 is zero as a result of [10.16]. We therefore see that in the absence of recoil there is no collision term in the equation for f^0. The form of the collision term that results when we include the effects of recoil and the thermal motion of the neutral particles will be derived in Section 10.3.

In [10.34] we note that since the neutral particles are infinitely massive we can write $w = g$, and using the fact that the number density of neutral particles is given by

$$N_N = \int_{-\infty}^{\infty} f^N \, dc^N$$

we find from [10.24] and [10.34] that

$$\left(\frac{\partial f_r'}{\partial t}\right)_{coll} = -\frac{3}{4\pi w} 2\pi N_N f_i' \frac{4\pi}{3} w^2 \delta_{ir} \int_0^\pi (1 - \cos \chi) S(\chi) \sin \chi \, d\chi$$

$$= -2\pi N_N w f_r' \int_0^\pi (1 - \cos \chi) S(\chi) \sin \chi \, d\chi$$

$$= -\nu_{EN} f_r' \qquad [10.35]$$

where

$$\nu_{EN} = N_N w 2\pi \int_0^\pi (1 - \cos \chi) S(\chi) \sin \chi \, d\chi \qquad [10.36]$$

is the electron-neutral collision frequency for momentum transfer which has previously been found in Section 6.22. In this chapter we will for simplicity write the collision frequency simply as ν.

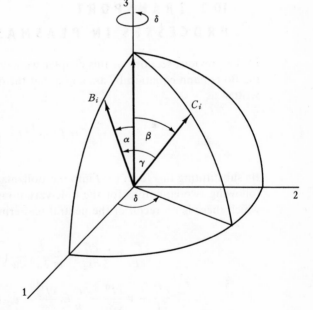

FIGURE 10.5 Definition of the Angles in the Trigonometric Relationship $\cos \gamma = \cos \alpha \cos \beta + \sin \alpha \sin \beta \cos \delta$

Using the collision term [10.35], we can then write the equation for the time-variation of f_i' from [10.23] as

$$\frac{\partial f_i'}{\partial t} + w \frac{\partial f^0}{\partial x_i} - \frac{e}{m} E_i \frac{\partial f^0}{\partial w} - \epsilon_{ijk} \Omega_j f_k' = -\nu f_i' \qquad [10.37]$$

We will see in the following sections that we can use this equation to calculate the transport coefficients in a plasma.

Exercise 10.13.1   The coordinates of B_i and C_i in Figure 10.5 are given by

$$B_i = \begin{bmatrix} \sin \alpha \\ 0 \\ \cos \alpha \end{bmatrix}, \qquad C_i = \begin{bmatrix} \sin \beta \cos \delta \\ \sin \beta \sin \delta \\ \cos \beta \end{bmatrix}$$

Using these facts show that

$$\cos \gamma = \cos \alpha \cos \beta + \sin \alpha \sin \beta \cos \delta$$

and thus verify that in Figure 10.4.

$$\cos \tilde{\Theta} = \cos \Theta \cos \chi + \sin \Theta \sin \chi \cos \psi$$

10.2 TRANSPORT PROCESSES IN PLASMAS

In the previous sections of this chapter we have approached the solution of the Boltzmann equation by assuming that the distribution function could be written as

$$f = f^0 + \frac{v_i}{w} f_i' \tag{10.38}$$

By substituting this form for f into the Boltzmann equation, we obtained the following two equations for the time-variations of f^0 and f_i' for the case in which there is no recoil of the neutral scattering particles,

$$\frac{\partial f^0}{\partial t} + \frac{w}{3} \frac{\partial f_i'}{\partial x_i} - \frac{e}{m} \frac{E_i}{3w^2} \frac{\partial}{\partial w} (w^2 f_i') = 0 \tag{10.39}$$

$$\frac{\partial f_i'}{\partial t} + w \frac{\partial f^0}{\partial x_i} - \frac{e}{m} E_i \frac{\partial f^0}{\partial w} - \epsilon_{ijk} \Omega_j f_k' = -\nu f_i' \tag{10.40}$$

In order to obtain any information about f^0, it will be necessary to include the effects of recoil of the neutral particles. This will introduce a collision term on the right-hand side of [10.39]. We will derive the form of this term in Section 10.3 and then examine the possible values of f^0 which can result in Section 10.4.

However, since f^0 is isotropic it will enter only indirectly into expressions for momentum transport processes. In order to show this, we consider the flux vector Γ_i given by

$$\Gamma_i = N\langle v_i \rangle = \int v_i f \, dc \qquad [10.41]$$

The volume element dc in spherical coordinates is

$$dc = w^2 \sin \theta \, d\theta \, d\varphi \, dw \qquad [10.42]$$

Substituting [10.38] and [10.42] into [10.41], we obtain

$$\Gamma_i = \int_0^\infty \int_0^{2\pi} \int_0^\pi v_i f^0 w^2 \sin \theta \, d\theta \, d\varphi \, dw$$
$$+ \int_0^\infty \int_0^{2\pi} \int_0^\pi v_i v_j f_j' w \sin \theta \, d\theta \, d\varphi \, dw \qquad [10.43]$$

Since f^0 is only a function of w, if we integrate [10.43] over the angles θ and φ, the first term on the right vanishes as a result of [10.16]. Applying [10.17] to the second term on the right of [10.43], we obtain

$$\Gamma_i = \tfrac{4}{3}\pi \int_0^\infty f_i' w^3 \, dw \qquad [10.44]$$

Thus the flux vector Γ_i depends directly on f_i' only. Of course we can see from [10.40] that f_i' will, in general, be some function of f^0.

Since the perturbations which produce f_i' are considered to be small, it seems reasonable that, to a first approximation, the isotropic part of the distribution function f^0 could be assumed to be Maxwellian. This is a common assumption, and we will calculate the conductivity and diffusion coefficients for a Maxwellian distribution in the following sections. We therefore defer until Section 10.4 the determination of the actual form of the isotropic part of the distribution function f^0.

10.21 ELECTRICAL CONDUCTIVITY

In this section we wish to obtain expressions for the a.c. conductivity of a weakly ionized plasma. We will assume that the plasma is homogeneous and isotropic. The effect of an external magnetic field will be discussed in Section 10.22.

For the case we are now considering the equation for f_i' can be written from [10.40] as

$$\frac{\partial f_i'}{\partial t} - \frac{e}{m} E_i \frac{\partial f^0}{\partial w} = -\nu f_i' \qquad [10.45]$$

The electric field E_i is taken to be an a.c. field which, using the usual convention, varies as $e^{-i\omega t}$. We will therefore assume that f_i' also has a time variation of the form $e^{-i\omega t}$. We can then write [10.45] as

$$-i\omega f_i' - \frac{e}{m} E_i \frac{\partial f^0}{\partial w} + \nu f_i' = 0$$

from which

$$f_i' = \frac{eE_i \, \partial f^0/\partial w}{m(\nu - i\omega)} \tag{10.46}$$

Now the current density in the plasma can be written, using [10.44] as

$$
\begin{aligned}
J_i &= -Ne\langle v_i \rangle \\
&= -e\Gamma_i \\
&= -\tfrac{4}{3}\pi e \int_0^\infty f_i' w^3 \, dw
\end{aligned}
\tag{10.47}
$$

Substituting [10.46] into [10.47], we obtain

$$
\begin{aligned}
J_i &= -\frac{4\pi e^2}{3m} E_i \int_0^\infty \frac{w^3}{(\nu - i\omega)} \frac{\partial f^0}{\partial w} \, dw \\
&= \sigma E_i
\end{aligned}
\tag{10.48}
$$

from which the electrical conductivity σ can be written as

$$\sigma = -\frac{4\pi e^2}{3m} \int_0^\infty \frac{w^3}{(\nu - i\omega)} \frac{\partial f^0}{\partial w} \, dw \tag{10.49}$$

Note that in this expression for the electrical conductivity the collision frequency ν can be a function of the electron speed w. The functional dependence of ν on w must generally be determined experimentally from cross-section measurements.

As was pointed out in the previous section, it is often assumed that f^0 is given by the Maxwellian distribution

$$f^0 = N \left(\frac{m}{2\pi kT}\right)^{3/2} e^{-(mw^2/2kT)} \tag{10.50}$$

For this case, if we let

$$u = \left(\frac{m}{2kT}\right)^{1/2} w \tag{10.51}$$

then we can readily show (see Exercise 10.21.1) that

$$w^3 \frac{\partial f^0}{\partial w} dw = -2N\pi^{-3/2} u^4 e^{-u^2} du \qquad [10.52]$$

Substituting [10.52] into [10.49], we obtain, after rationalizing,

$$\sigma = \frac{8Ne^2}{3\sqrt{\pi}\, m} \left\{ \int_0^\infty \frac{\nu u^4 e^{-u^2}}{\omega^2 + \nu^2} du + i\omega \int_0^\infty \frac{u^4 e^{-u^2}}{\omega^2 + \nu^2} du \right\}$$

$$= \sigma_R + i\sigma_I \qquad [10.53]$$

We can show (see Exercise 10.21.2) that if the collision frequency ν is independent of the electron speed w (and therefore independent of u), then the real and imaginary parts of σ in [10.53] reduce to

$$\sigma_R = \frac{\nu Ne^2}{m(\omega^2 + \nu^2)} \qquad [10.54]$$

and

$$\sigma_I = \frac{\omega Ne^2}{m(\omega^2 + \nu^2)} \qquad [10.55]$$

which are identical with the results of Section 7.2 based on the Langevin equation.

Equation [10.53] can therefore be used to calculate the electrical conductivity of a plasma based on a Maxwellian distribution for various velocity dependent collision frequencies (see, for example, Problem 10.2).

It is interesting to note that the conductivity given by [10.49] will always reduce to [10.54] and [10.55] if ν is independent of velocity regardless of whether or not f^0 is Maxwellian (see Exercise 10.21.3).

Exercise 10.21.1   Using the substitution [10.51] and the Maxwellian distribution [10.50], verify [10.52].

Exercise 10.21.2   If ν is not a function of u, verify that the real and imaginary parts of σ given by [10.53] reduce to [10.54] and [10.55].

Exercise 10.21.3

(a)   Show by integrating by parts that [10.49] can be written as

$$\sigma = \frac{4\pi e^2}{3m} \int_0^\infty f^0 \frac{d}{dw} \left(\frac{w^3}{\nu - i\omega} \right) dw \qquad [10.56]$$

Why does the integrated out part vanish?

(b)   Show that if ν is velocity independent then [10.56] reduces to [10.54] and [10.55] for any f^0.

10.22 THE CONDUCTIVITY IN A MAGNETIC FIELD

We now wish to consider the a.c. conductivity of a weakly ionized plasma in the presence of an external magnetic field. Assuming the plasma to be homogeneous, we can write the equation for the time-variation of f_i' from [10.40] as

$$\frac{\partial f_i'}{\partial t} - \frac{e}{m} E_i \frac{\partial f^0}{\partial w} - \epsilon_{ijk}\Omega_j f_k' = -\nu f_i' \qquad [10.57]$$

The electric field E_i varies harmonically in time as $e^{-i\omega t}$. Since we are only interested in that part of the current density that also varies harmonically at this frequency, we will assume that f_i' varies as $e^{-i\omega t}$ so that [10.57] can be written as

$$-i\omega f_i' - \frac{e}{m} E_i \frac{\partial f^0}{\partial w} - \epsilon_{ijk}\Omega_j f_k' + \nu f_i' = 0 \qquad [10.58]$$

If we divide [10.58] by $-i\omega$ we obtain

$$f_i' + i\frac{\nu}{\omega} f_i' - i\epsilon_{ijk}\frac{\Omega_j}{\omega} f_k' = i\frac{e}{m\omega} E_i \frac{\partial f^0}{\partial w}$$

which can be written as

$$[U\delta_{ij} + i\epsilon_{ijk}Y_k]f_j' = i\frac{e}{m\omega} E_i \frac{\partial f^0}{\partial w} \qquad [10.59]$$

where

$$U = 1 + i\frac{\nu}{\omega} \qquad [10.60]$$

$$Y_k = \frac{\Omega_k}{\omega} \qquad [10.61]$$

and the subscripts j and k in the magnetic field term were interchanged.

Let the magnetic field lie along the x_3-axis. That is, $Y_k = (0, 0, Y)$. Then we can write [10.59] as

$$M_{ij}f_j' = i\frac{e}{m\omega} E_i \frac{\partial f^0}{\partial w} \qquad [10.62]$$

where

$$M_{ij} = \begin{bmatrix} U & +iY & 0 \\ -iY & U & 0 \\ 0 & 0 & U \end{bmatrix} \qquad [10.63]$$

Let C_{ij} be the inverse of the matrix M_{ij} given by [10.63]. That is (see Exercise 10.22.1),

$$C_{ij} = \begin{bmatrix} \dfrac{U}{U^2 - Y^2} & \dfrac{-iY}{U^2 - Y^2} & 0 \\ \dfrac{+iY}{U^2 - Y^2} & \dfrac{U}{U^2 - Y^2} & 0 \\ 0 & 0 & \dfrac{1}{U} \end{bmatrix} \qquad [10.64]$$

From [10.62] we can then write f_i' as

$$f_i' = i\frac{e}{m\omega} C_{ij}E_j \frac{\partial f^0}{\partial w} \qquad [10.65]$$

Substituting [10.65] into the expression [10.47] for the current density J_i, we obtain

$$J_i = -\frac{4\pi i e^2}{3m\omega} \int_0^\infty C_{ij}E_j w^3 \frac{\partial f^0}{\partial w}\, dw$$

$$= \sigma_{ij}E_j \qquad [10.66]$$

from which the conductivity tensor σ_{ij} can be written as

$$\sigma_{ij} = -\frac{4\pi i e^2}{3m\omega} \int_0^\infty C_{ij} w^3 \frac{\partial f^0}{\partial w}\, dw \qquad [10.67]$$

where C_{ij} is given by [10.64]. Thus the conductivity tensor σ_{ij} has the form

$$\sigma_{ij} = \begin{bmatrix} \sigma_T & -\sigma_H & 0 \\ +\sigma_H & \sigma_T & 0 \\ 0 & 0 & \sigma_L \end{bmatrix} \qquad [10.68]$$

where

$$\sigma_T = -\frac{4\pi i e^2}{3m\omega} \int_0^\infty \frac{U}{U^2 - Y^2} w^3 \frac{\partial f^0}{\partial w} dw \qquad [10.69]$$

$$\sigma_H = \frac{4\pi e^2}{3m\omega} \int_0^\infty \frac{Y}{U^2 - Y^2} w^3 \frac{\partial f^0}{\partial w} dw \qquad [10.70]$$

$$\sigma_L = -\frac{4\pi i e^2}{3m\omega} \int_0^\infty \frac{1}{U} w^3 \frac{\partial f^0}{\partial w} dw \qquad [10.71]$$

Note that σ_L is the same as the conductivity of an isotropic plasma found in the previous section (see Exercise 10.22.2).

Exercise 10.22.1   Verify [10.64].

Exercise 10.22.2

(a)   Show that σ_L given by [10.71] is equivalent to the scalar conductivity σ given by [10.49].

(b)   Write expressions for σ_T, σ_H, and σ_L for the case where f^0 is Maxwellian.

(c)   What do equations [10.69] to [10.71] for σ_T, σ_H, and σ_L reduce to when ν (and therefore U) is independent of the electron speed w?

10.23   FREE ELECTRON DIFFUSION

In Section 7.1 we discussed free electron diffusion based on the single species macroscopic equations. The collision frequency that appeared in these equations was assumed to be velocity independent. In this section we wish to obtain expressions for the diffusion coefficient based on kinetic theory which will be valid for velocity-dependent collision frequencies.

For an isotropic plasma in the absence of an electric field we can write [10.40] for the time-variation of f_i' as

$$\frac{\partial f_i'}{\partial t} + w \frac{\partial f^0}{\partial x_i} = -\nu f_i' \qquad [10.72]$$

The effect of an external magnetic field will be discussed in Section 10.24.

In the steady state, [10.72] reduces to

$$f_i' = -\frac{w}{\nu} \frac{\partial f^0}{\partial x_i} \qquad [10.73]$$

If we substitute [10.73] into the expression for the flux vector Γ_i given by [10.44], we obtain

$$\Gamma_i = -\frac{4\pi}{3} \int_0^\infty \frac{w^4}{\nu} \frac{\partial f^0}{\partial x_i} dw \qquad [10.74]$$

Now the isotropic part of the distribution function f^0 will, in general, be a function of the number density N, the temperature T, and the electron speed w. For example, the Maxwellian distribution is

$$f^0 = N \left(\frac{m}{2\pi kT}\right)^{3/2} e^{-(mw^2/2kT)} \qquad [10.75]$$

Since the number density N always appears as the result of the normalization condition

$$N = 4\pi \int_0^\infty f^0 w^2 \, dw \qquad [10.76]$$

the distribution function f^0 is always of the form

$$f^0 = Ng(T, w) \qquad [10.77]$$

We will assume for the present discussion that there are no temperature gradients in the plasma. Then from [10.77] we can write

$$\frac{\partial f^0}{\partial x_i} = \frac{\partial N}{\partial x_i} g = \frac{\partial N}{\partial x_i} \frac{f^0}{N} \qquad [10.78]$$

Substituting [10.78] into [10.74] we obtain

$$\Gamma_i = -\frac{4\pi}{3} \frac{1}{N} \frac{\partial N}{\partial x_i} \int_0^\infty \frac{w^4}{\nu} f^0 \, dw$$

$$= -D \frac{\partial N}{\partial x_i} \qquad [10.79]$$

where

$$D = \frac{4\pi}{3} \frac{1}{N} \int_0^\infty \frac{w^4}{\nu} f^0 \, dw \qquad [10.80]$$

is the free electron diffusion coefficient.

If f^0 is the Maxwellian distribution, then [10.80] can be written (see Exercise 10.23.1)

$$D = \frac{8}{3\sqrt{\pi}} \frac{kT}{m} \int_0^\infty \frac{u^4}{\nu} e^{-u^2} \, du \qquad [10.81]$$

where

$$u = \left(\frac{m}{2kT}\right)^{1/2} w \qquad [10.82]$$

If the collision frequency ν is independent of the electron speed w, then [10.81] reduces to

$$D = \frac{kT}{m\nu} \qquad [10.83]$$

which was the result found in Section 7.1.

Exercise 10.23.1   Show that the free electron diffusion coefficient is given by [10.81] when f^0 is Maxwellian and reduces to [10.83] for the case of a velocity independent collision frequency.

10.24 ELECTRON DIFFUSION IN A MAGNETIC FIELD

In the previous section we considered free electron diffusion in an isotropic plasma. We now wish to include the effects of an external magnetic field on electron diffusion in a weakly ionized plasma. In the absence of an electric field the equation for the time-variation of f_i' can be written from [10.40] as

$$\frac{\partial f_i'}{\partial t} + w \frac{\partial f^0}{\partial x_i} - \epsilon_{ijk}\Omega_j f_k' = -\nu f_i' \qquad [10.84]$$

which, in the steady state, reduces to

$$(\nu\delta_{ij} + \epsilon_{ijk}\Omega_k)f_j' = -w \frac{\partial f^0}{\partial x_i} \qquad [10.85]$$

Let the magnetic field lie along the x_3-axis so that $\Omega_k = (0, 0, \Omega)$. Then [10.85] can be written as

$$N_{ij}f_j' = -w \frac{\partial f^0}{\partial x_i} \qquad [10.86]$$

where

$$N_{ij} = \begin{bmatrix} \nu & +\Omega & 0 \\ -\Omega & \nu & 0 \\ 0 & 0 & \nu \end{bmatrix} \qquad [10.87]$$

Let F_{ij} be the inverse of the matrix N_{ij}, so that

$$
F_{ij} = \begin{bmatrix}
\dfrac{\nu}{\nu^2 + \Omega^2} & -\dfrac{\Omega}{\nu^2 + \Omega^2} & 0 \\[2ex]
+\dfrac{\Omega}{\nu^2 + \Omega^2} & \dfrac{\nu}{\nu^2 + \Omega^2} & 0 \\[2ex]
0 & 0 & \dfrac{1}{\nu}
\end{bmatrix}
\qquad [10.88]
$$

Then from [10.86] we can write f_i' as

$$
f_i' = -w F_{ij} \frac{\partial f^0}{\partial x_j} \qquad [10.89]
$$

Substituting [10.89] into [10.44], we can write the flux vector Γ_i as

$$
\Gamma_i = -\frac{4\pi}{3} \int_0^\infty w^4 F_{ij} \frac{\partial f^0}{\partial x_j}\, dw \qquad [10.90]
$$

or, using [10.78], as

$$
\Gamma_i = -\frac{4\pi}{3} \frac{1}{N} \frac{\partial N}{\partial x_j} \int_0^\infty w^4 F_{ij} f^0 \, dw
$$

$$
= -D_{ij} \frac{\partial N}{\partial x_j} \qquad [10.91]
$$

from which the diffusion coefficient matrix D_{ij} is given by

$$
D_{ij} = \frac{4\pi}{3} \frac{1}{N} \int_0^\infty w^4 F_{ij} f^0 \, dw \qquad [10.92]
$$

where F_{ij} is given by [10.88]. We therefore see that D_{ij} is of the form

$$
D_{ij} = \begin{bmatrix}
D_T & -D_H & 0 \\
+D_H & D_T & 0 \\
0 & 0 & D_L
\end{bmatrix}
\qquad [10.93]
$$

where

$$
D_T = \frac{4\pi}{3} \frac{1}{N} \int_0^\infty \frac{\nu w^4}{\nu^2 + \Omega^2} f^0 \, dw \qquad [10.94]
$$

$$
D_H = \frac{4\pi}{3} \frac{1}{N} \int_0^\infty \frac{\Omega w^4}{\nu^2 + \Omega^2} f^0 \, dw \qquad [10.95]
$$

$$
D_L = \frac{4\pi}{3} \frac{1}{N} \int_0^\infty \frac{w^4}{\nu} f^0 \, dw \qquad [10.96]
$$

Note that D_L is the same as the scalar diffusion coefficient given by [10.80]. The matrix [10.93] should be compared with the diffusion coefficient matrix found in Section 7.1.

Exercise 10.24.1
(a)   Write expressions for D_T, D_H, and D_L for the case where f^0 is Maxwellian.
(b)   What do these results reduce to when v is velocity independent?

10.3 ELECTRON-NEUTRAL COLLISIONS

In the first part of this chapter we obtained equations for the isotropic and anisotropic parts of the distribution function f^0 and f_i'. We found in Section 10.13 that in the absence of recoil of the neutral particles (that is, taking $m_-/m_N = 0$) the collision terms in the equations for the time-variations of f^0 and f_i' were given by

$$\left(\frac{\partial f^0}{\partial t}\right)_{\text{coll}} = 0$$

and

$$\left(\frac{\partial f_i'}{\partial t}\right)_{\text{coll}} = -v f_i'$$

In this section we wish to include the effects of recoil by keeping terms of order m_-/m_N. Since the collision term $(\partial f_i'/\partial t)_{\text{coll}}$ describes a transfer of momentum, we will assume that it is not appreciably changed by including terms of order m_-/m_N. On the other hand the collision term $(\partial f^0/\partial t)_{\text{coll}}$ describes a transfer of energy which is zero under the assumption of Section 10.13 that $\tilde{w} = w$. We now wish to determine what this collision term will be when the electron speed changes slightly as the result of giving up a small amount of energy to the neutral particles.

From [10.22] we have that

$$\left(\frac{\partial f^0}{\partial t}\right)_{\text{coll}} = \frac{1}{4\pi} \int_0^{2\pi} \int_0^{\pi} \left(\frac{\partial f}{\partial t}\right)_{\text{coll}} \sin\theta \, d\theta \, d\varphi \qquad [10.97]$$

The expression for $(\partial f/\partial t)_{\text{coll}}$ was given in Section 10.13 by [10.33] where the first and third terms on the right were shown to be zero for the case of no recoil. However, when we allow for recoil of the neutral particle, the first term on the right of [10.33] must be retained. If we then substitute [10.33] into [10.97], the second term will vanish by using [10.29] and [10.16]. Using [10.15], the remaining term becomes

$$\left(\frac{\partial f^0}{\partial t}\right)_{\text{coll}} = 2\pi \int_{-\infty}^{\infty} \int_0^\pi (\tilde{f}^0 \tilde{f}^N - f^0 f^N) g S(\chi) \sin \chi \, d\chi \, dc^N \qquad [10.98]$$

We will now treat the collision term [10.98] in a manner similar to that described in Section 6.11. Thus we let Φ be some arbitrary function of the electron speed w. Then from [10.98] we can form

$$\int_{-\infty}^{\infty} \Phi \left(\frac{\partial f^0}{\partial t}\right)_{\text{coll}} dc = 2\pi \int_{-\infty}^{\infty} \int_{-\infty}^{\infty} \int_0^\pi \Phi(\tilde{f}^0 \tilde{f}^N - f^0 f^N) g S(\chi) \sin \chi \, d\chi \, dc^N \, dc$$

$$[10.99]$$

Now using the same argument as given in Section 6.11 we can rewrite [10.99] as

$$4\pi \int_0^\infty \Phi(w) \left(\frac{\partial f^0}{\partial t}\right)_{\text{coll}} w^2 \, dw$$
$$= 4\pi \int_0^\infty \int_{-\infty}^{\infty} \int_0^\pi 2\pi(\tilde{\Phi} - \Phi) f^0 f^N g S(\chi) \sin \chi \, d\chi \, dc^N w^2 \, dw \qquad [10.100]$$

where we have taken $dc = w^2 \sin \theta \, d\theta \, d\varphi$ and used the fact that Φ is only a function of w.

Now if we write $\tilde{w} = w + \Delta w$, then we can expand $\tilde{\Phi} = \Phi(\tilde{w})$ as

$$\tilde{\Phi} = \Phi(w + \Delta w) = \Phi(w) + \frac{\partial \Phi}{\partial w} \Delta w + \frac{1}{2} \frac{\partial^2 \Phi}{\partial w^2} (\Delta w)^2$$

so that

$$\tilde{\Phi} - \Phi = \frac{\partial \Phi}{\partial w} \Delta w + \frac{1}{2} \frac{\partial^2 \Phi}{\partial w^2} (\Delta w)^2 \qquad [10.101]$$

Substituting [10.101] into [10.100], we obtain

$$4\pi \int_0^\infty \Phi \left(\frac{\partial f^0}{\partial t}\right)_{\text{coll}} w^2 \, dw$$
$$= 4\pi \int_0^\infty \int_{-\infty}^{\infty} \int_0^\pi 2\pi \frac{\partial \Phi}{\partial w} \Delta w f^0 f^N g S(\chi) \sin \chi \, d\chi \, dc^N w^2 \, dw$$
$$+ 4\pi \int_0^\infty \int_{-\infty}^{\infty} \int_0^\pi \pi \frac{\partial^2 \Phi}{\partial w^2} (\Delta w)^2 f^0 f^N g S(\chi) \sin \chi \, d\chi \, dc^N w^2 \, dw$$

Integrating the first term on the right by parts once and the second term on the right by parts twice we obtain

$$4\pi \int_0^\infty \Phi \left(\frac{\partial f^0}{\partial t}\right)_{\text{coll}} w^2 \, dw$$

$$= -4\pi \int_0^\infty \Phi \frac{\partial}{\partial w} \left[\int_{-\infty}^\infty \int_0^\pi 2\pi w^2 g \, \Delta w f^0 S(\chi) \sin \chi \, d\chi f^N \, dc^N\right] dw$$

$$+ 4\pi \int_0^\infty \Phi \frac{\partial^2}{\partial w^2} \left[\int_{-\infty}^\infty \int_0^\pi \pi w^2 g (\Delta w)^2 f^0 S(\chi) \sin \chi \, d\chi f^N \, dc^N\right] dw$$

from which, since Φ is arbitrary

$$\left(\frac{\partial f^0}{\partial t}\right)_{\text{coll}} = -\frac{1}{w^2} \frac{\partial}{\partial w} \left[2\pi w^2 f^0 \int_{-\infty}^\infty \int_0^\pi \Delta w \, g S(\chi) \sin \chi \, d\chi f^N \, dc^N\right]$$

$$+ \frac{1}{w^2} \frac{\partial^2}{\partial w^2} \left[\pi w^2 f^0 \int_{-\infty}^\infty \int_0^\pi (\Delta w)^2 g S(\chi) \sin \chi \, d\chi f^N \, dc^N\right] \qquad [10.102]$$

In the next two sections we will use [10.102] to calculate $(\partial f^0/\partial t)_{\text{coll}}$ for the following two cases:

1. when the neutral particles are initially at rest
2. when the neutral particles have a Maxwellian velocity distribution.

10.31 RECOIL OF MOLECULES INITIALLY AT REST

We consider first the case when the neutral particles are initially at rest. The collision diagram of Figure 4.4 is then of the form shown in Figure 10.6. Since the mass of the neutral particle is much greater than the mass of the electron, the inner circle of Figure 10.6 will have a much smaller radius than the outer circle. Using this fact we can see directly from Figure 10.6 that Δw is given approximately by

$$-\Delta \omega = M_- w - M_- w \cos \chi$$

or

$$\Delta w \approx -\frac{m_-}{m_N} w(1 - \cos \chi) \qquad [10.103]$$

This result could also have been obtained by applying the law of cosines to the triangle OAB in Figure 10.6 (see Exercise 10.31.1).

Note that Δw given by [10.103] is of order m_-/m_N. Since we shall only keep terms up to order m_-/m_N, then for the case we are considering the second term on the right of [10.102] which contains $(\Delta w)^2$ may be neglected. If we

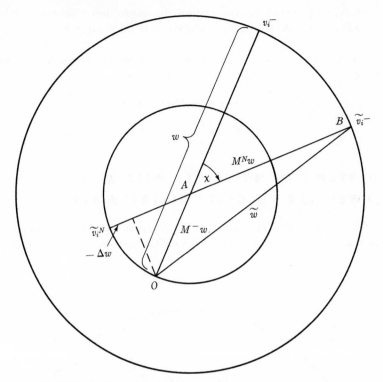

FIGURE 10.6   Velocity Diagram for Electron-Neutral Collision.
Neutral Particle Initially at Rest

now substitute the expression [10.103] for Δw into [10.102] and note that $g = w$ since the molecules are initially at rest, we obtain

$$\left(\frac{\partial f^0}{\partial t}\right)_{\text{coll}} = \frac{1}{w^2} \frac{\partial}{\partial w} \left[2\pi w^3 N_N f^0 \frac{m_-}{m_N} w \int_0^\pi (1 - \cos \chi) S(\chi) \sin \chi \, d\chi \right]$$

$$= \frac{1}{w^2} \frac{\partial}{\partial w} \left[\frac{m_-}{m_N} \nu w^3 f^0 \right] \qquad [10.104]$$

where

$$\nu = N_N w 2\pi \int_0^\pi (1 - \cos \chi) S(\chi) \sin \chi \, d\chi \qquad [10.105]$$

is the collision frequency for momentum transfer given by [10.36].

If we let $G = 2m_-/m_N$ be the *mean fractional energy loss for an electron-neutral collision* (see Section 4.41) then [10.104] can be written as

$$\left(\frac{\partial f^0}{\partial t}\right)_{\text{coll}} = \frac{1}{2w^2} \frac{\partial}{\partial w} (G\nu w^3 f^0) \qquad [10.106]$$

In the following section we will see how this expression must be modified to account for an initial Maxwellian distribution of the neutral particle velocities.

    Exercise 10.31.1   Using the law of cosines on the triangle OAB in Figure 10.6 show that to order m_-/m_N, Δw is given by

$$\Delta w = -wM_- M_N(1 - \cos \chi)$$

$$\approx -w\frac{m_-}{m_N}(1 - \cos \chi)$$

10.32 RECOIL OF MOLECULES WITH A
MAXWELLIAN VELOCITY DISTRIBUTION

We now wish to extend the results of the previous section to include the case when the neutral particles have a Maxwellian distribution of velocities. We

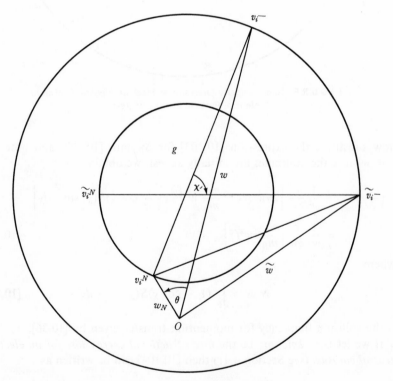

FIGURE 10.7 Velocity Diagram for Electron-Neutral Collision.
Neutral Particle Initially in Motion

must therefore calculate a new value for $\Delta w = \tilde{w} - w$ to be used in [10.102]. For this case the initial velocity of the neutral particles will not be zero as is shown in Figure 10.7. We must note carefully, however, that we want to keep w and w_N independent so that we may readily carry out the integrations in [10.102]. This means that in going from Figure 10.6 to Figure 10.7 we must keep w constant. Thus, since we have added w_N in Figure 10.7 then the relative speed g in Figure 10.7 is not equal to the relative speed $g = w$ in Figure 10.6. Since from [4.51] the angle of deflection χ is a function of the relative speed g, then the scattering angles in Figure 10.6 and Figure 10.7 will be different. We have therefore written the scattering angle in Figure 10.7 as χ'.

Our first task is then to determine an expression for Δw for the situation of Figure 10.7. We proceed by introducing a unit vector k_i which bisects the two relative velocity vectors g_i and $-\tilde{g}_i$ as shown in Figure 10.8. From this figure we obtain (see Exercise 10.32.1)

$$g_i - \tilde{g}_i = 2g_j k_j k_i \qquad\qquad [10.107]$$

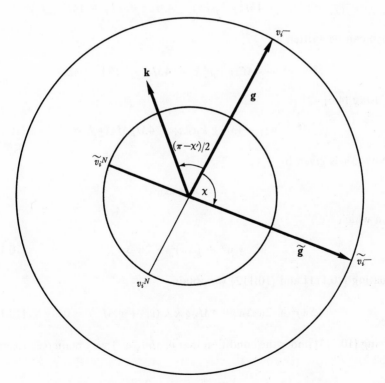

F I G U R E 10.8   Velocity Diagram Illustrating the Orientation
of the unit vector **k**

From equations [4.11] and [4.14] we can write the electron velocities before and after a collision as

$$v_i^- = v_i^G + M_N g_i \qquad [10.108]$$

and

$$\tilde{v}_i^- = v_i^G + M_N \tilde{g}_i \qquad [10.109]$$

Subtracting [10.108] from [10.109] we obtain by using [10.107]

$$\tilde{v}_i^- = v_i^- - 2M_N g_j k_j k_i \qquad [10.110]$$

Multiplying [10.110] by itself and using the fact that

$$v_i^- = v_i^N + g_i$$

we obtain

$$\tilde{v}_i^- \tilde{v}_i^- = v_i^- v_i^- - 4M_N g_j k_j v_i^N k_i - 4M_N g_j k_j g_i k_i + 4M_N^2 (g_j k_j)^2$$

which can be written as

$$\tilde{w}^2 = w^2 - 4M_N g_j k_j v_i^N k_i - 4M_N (g_j k_j)^2 (1 - M_N)$$

or, using [4.6]

$$\tilde{w}^2 = w^2 - 4M_N g_j k_j v_i^N k_i - 4M_N M_- (g_j k_j)^2 \qquad [10.111]$$

Now Δw is given by

$$\tilde{w} = w + \Delta w$$

from which

$$\tilde{w}^2 = w^2 + (\Delta w)^2 + 2w \, \Delta w \qquad [10.112]$$

Equating [10.111] and [10.112] we obtain

$$(\Delta w)^2 + 2w \, \Delta w + 4M_N g_j k_j k_i (v_i^N + g_i M_-) = 0 \qquad [10.113]$$

Solving [10.113] under the condition that $m_- / m_N \ll 1$ we obtain (see Exercise 10.32.2)

$$\Delta w \approx -\frac{2}{w} \frac{m_-}{m_N} (g_j k_j)^2 - \frac{2}{w} v_i^N k_i g_j k_j \qquad [10.114]$$

If the electrons and neutral particles are at the same temperature then $w_N = (m_-/m_N)^{1/2}w$. We therefore see that in order to keep terms of order m_-/m_N in [10.114] we will need an expression for g/w which will include terms of order $(m_-/m_N)^{1/2}$. From Figure 10.7 we can readily show (see Exercise 10.32.3) that to order $(m_-/m_N)^{1/2}$

$$g = w - w_N \cos \theta \qquad [10.115]$$

We can now write $\chi'(g) = \chi'(w - w_N \cos \theta)$ shown in Figure 10.7 in terms of $\chi(w)$ shown in Figure 10.6 by expanding χ' about $w_N = 0$. Thus,

$$\chi' = \chi - w_N \cos \theta \frac{\partial \chi}{\partial w}$$

It thus follows that to order $(m_-/m_N)^{1/2}$

$$\sin \chi' = \sin \chi - w_N \cos \theta \cos \chi \frac{\partial \chi}{\partial w}$$

$$\sin \frac{\chi'}{2} = \sin \frac{\chi}{2} - \frac{w_N}{2} \cos \theta \cos \frac{\chi}{2} \frac{\partial \chi}{\partial w}$$

$$\cos \frac{\chi'}{2} = \cos \frac{\chi}{2} + \frac{w_N}{2} \cos \theta \sin \frac{\chi}{2} \frac{\partial \chi}{\partial w} \qquad [10.116]$$

$$\sin^2 \frac{\chi'}{2} = \sin^2 \frac{\chi}{2} - \frac{w_N}{2} \cos \theta \sin \chi \frac{\partial \chi}{\partial w}$$

From Figure 10.8 we have, using [10.115],

$$g_j k_j = g \cos \tfrac{1}{2}(\pi - \chi')$$

$$= g \sin \frac{\chi'}{2}$$

$$= w \sin \frac{\chi'}{2} - w_N \cos \theta \sin \frac{\chi'}{2} \qquad [10.117]$$

If we substitute [10.117] into [10.114], use [10.116], and only keep terms up to order m_-/m_N, we obtain (see Exercise 10.32.4)

$$\Delta w = \Delta w_0 + \Delta w' \qquad [10.118]$$

where

$$\Delta w_0 = -2w \frac{m_-}{m_N} \sin^2 \frac{\chi}{2}$$

$$= -w \frac{m_-}{m_N} (1 - \cos \chi) \qquad [10.119]$$

and

$$\Delta w' = -2v_i^N k_i \left(\sin \frac{\chi}{2} - \frac{w_N}{w} \cos \theta \sin \frac{\chi}{2} - \frac{w_N}{2} \cos \theta \cos \frac{\chi}{2} \frac{\partial \chi}{\partial w} \right) \quad [10.120]$$

Note that Δw_0 is the value of Δw which results when $v_i^N = 0$ as was given by [10.103].

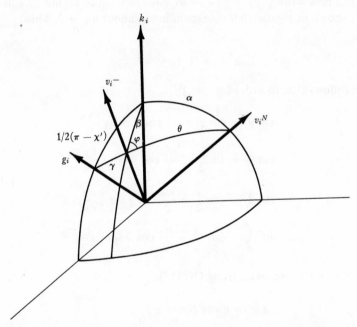

FIGURE 10.9 Angular Relations between k_i, v_i^-, v_i^N, and g_i

Let α be the angle between k_i and v_i^N as shown in Figure 10.9 so that $v_i^N k_i = w_N \cos \alpha$. From Figure 10.9 we can write $\cos \alpha$ to order $(m_-/m_N)^{1/2}$ in terms of χ', θ, and φ (see Exercise 10.32.5). Using [10.116] we can then write (see Exercise 10.32.6a)

$$v_i^N k_i = w_N \left(\sin \frac{\chi}{2} \cos \theta + \cos \frac{\chi}{2} \sin \theta \cos \varphi \right)$$

$$- \frac{w_N^2}{2} \left(\cos^2 \theta \cos \frac{\chi}{2} - \cos \theta \sin \theta \cos \varphi \sin \frac{\chi}{2} \right) \frac{\partial \chi}{\partial w}$$

$$+ \frac{w_N^2}{w} \left(\sin \theta \cos \theta \cos \varphi \cos \frac{\chi}{2} - \sin^2 \theta \cos^2 \varphi \sin \frac{\chi}{2} \right) \quad [10.121]$$

Substituting [10.121] into [10.120] and keeping terms only up to order m_-/m_N, we obtain

$$\Delta w' = -2w_N \sin^2 \frac{\chi}{2} \cos \theta + w_N^2 \cos^2 \theta \sin \chi \frac{\partial \chi}{\partial w}$$

$$+ 2 \frac{w_N^2}{w} \sin^2 \frac{\chi}{2} (\cos^2 \theta + \sin^2 \theta \cos^2 \varphi)$$

$$- 2w_N \left(\sin \frac{\chi}{2} \cos \frac{\chi}{2} - \frac{w_N}{2} \cos \theta \cos \chi \frac{\partial \chi}{\partial w} \right) \sin \theta \cos \varphi \quad [10.122]$$

We may now calculate the collision term $(\partial f^0/\partial t)_{\text{coll}}$ from [10.102]. Note that the terms in [10.102] contain the factors $g\Delta w$ and $g(\Delta w)^2$. Since Δw_0 is already of order m_-/m_N and we are only keeping terms up to order m_-/m_N, we see from [10.118] and [10.115] that

$$g\Delta w = w\Delta w_0 + (w - w_N \cos \theta) \Delta w' \quad [10.123]$$

and

$$g(\Delta w)^2 = w(\Delta w')^2 \quad [10.124]$$

If we substitute [10.119] and [10.122] into [10.123] and [10.124] and keep terms only up to order m_-/m_N, we obtain (see Exercise 10.32.6b)

$$g\Delta w = -\frac{m_-}{m_N} w^2 (1 - \cos \chi) + 2w_N^2 \sin^2 \frac{\chi}{2} (2 \cos^2 \theta + \sin^2 \theta \cos^2 \varphi)$$

$$+ ww_N^2 \cos^2 \theta \sin \chi \frac{\partial \chi}{\partial w} - 2ww_N \sin^2 \frac{\chi}{2} \cos \theta \quad [10.125]$$

$$- 2w_N(w - w_N \cos \theta) \left(\sin \frac{\chi}{2} \cos \frac{\chi}{2} - \frac{w_N}{2} \cos \theta \cos \chi \frac{\partial \chi}{\partial w} \right) \sin \theta \cos \varphi$$

and

$$g(\Delta w)^2 = 4ww_N^2 \sin^2 \frac{\chi}{2} \left(\sin^2 \frac{\chi}{2} \cos^2 \theta + \cos^2 \frac{\chi}{2} \sin^2 \theta \cos^2 \varphi \right) \quad [10.126]$$

By substituting [10.125] and [10.126] into [10.102] and taking

$$dc^N = w_N^2 \sin \theta \, d\theta \, d\varphi \, dw_N$$

we note that the last two terms in [10.125] vanish when integrated over θ and φ. We then obtain

$$\left(\frac{\partial f^0}{\partial t}\right)_{\text{coll}} = \left(\frac{\partial f^0}{\partial t}\right)_{\text{coll}}^{\text{I}} + \left(\frac{\partial f^0}{\partial t}\right)_{\text{coll}}^{\text{II}} \qquad [10.127]$$

where

$$\left(\frac{\partial f^0}{\partial t}\right)_{\text{coll}}^{\text{I}} = -\frac{1}{w^2}\frac{\partial}{\partial w}\left\{2\pi w^2 f^0 \int_0^\infty \int_0^\pi 4\pi \left[\left(-\frac{m_-}{m_N}w^2 + w_N^2\right)(1 - \cos\chi)\right.\right.$$
$$\left.\left. + \frac{1}{3}ww_N^2 \sin\chi \frac{\partial\chi}{\partial w}\right] S(\chi)\sin\chi f^N w_N^2 \, d\chi \, dw_N\right\} \quad [10.128]$$

and

$$\left(\frac{\partial f^0}{\partial t}\right)_{\text{coll}}^{\text{II}} = \frac{1}{w^2}\frac{\partial^2}{\partial w^2}\left[\pi w^2 f^0 \int_0^\infty \int_0^\pi \frac{8\pi}{3} w_N^4 w(1 - \cos\chi)S(\chi)\sin\chi \, d\chi f^N \, dw_N\right]$$
$$[10.129]$$

We now let the neutral particle distribution function f^N be the Maxwellian distribution

$$f^N = N_N\left(\frac{m_N}{2\pi kT_N}\right)^{3/2} e^{-(m_N w_N^2/2kT_N)}$$

and note that

$$N_N = 4\pi \int_0^\infty w_N^2 f^N \, dw_N \qquad [10.130]$$

and

$$\frac{N_N kT_N}{m_N} = \frac{4\pi}{3}\int_0^\infty w_N^4 f^N \, dw_N \qquad [10.131]$$

If we recall from [5.33] and [5.34] that we may replace $S(\chi)\sin\chi \, d\chi$ by $p \, dp$ in the expression for the collision frequency ν given by [10.105], then it is clear that $S(\chi)\sin\chi \, d\chi$ is not a function of w and we may write

$$\frac{\partial}{\partial w}\left(\frac{\nu}{w}\right) = N_N 2\pi \int_0^\pi \sin\chi \frac{\partial\chi}{\partial w}S(\chi)\sin\chi \, d\chi \qquad [10.132]$$

Using [10.130]–[10.132] together with [10.105], we can write [10.128] and [10.129] as

$$\left(\frac{\partial f^0}{\partial t}\right)^{\mathrm{I}}_{\mathrm{coll}} = -\frac{1}{w^2}\frac{\partial}{\partial w}\left[-\frac{m_-}{m_N}vw^3f^0 + 3vwf^0\frac{kT_N}{m_N} + w^3f^0\frac{kT_N}{m_N}\frac{\partial}{\partial w}\left(\frac{v}{w}\right)\right]$$

[10.133]

and

$$\left(\frac{\partial f^0}{\partial t}\right)^{\mathrm{II}}_{\mathrm{coll}} = \frac{1}{w^2}\frac{\partial^2}{\partial w^2}\left(vw^2f^0\frac{kT_N}{m_N}\right)$$

[10.134]

Substituting [10.133] and [10.134] into [10.127], we obtain

$$\left(\frac{\partial f^0}{\partial t}\right)_{\mathrm{coll}} = \frac{1}{w^2}\frac{\partial}{\partial w}\left(\frac{m_-}{m_N}vw^3f^0\right) - \frac{1}{w^2}\frac{\partial}{\partial w}\left(2vwf^0\frac{kT_N}{m_N}\right)$$

$$-\frac{1}{w^2}\frac{\partial}{\partial w}\left(w^2f^0\frac{kT_N}{m_N}\frac{\partial v}{\partial w}\right) + \frac{1}{w^2}\frac{\partial^2}{\partial w^2}\left(vw^2f^0\frac{kT_N}{m_N}\right) \quad [10.135]$$

If we expand the last term of [10.135] and cancel terms we obtain

$$\left(\frac{\partial f^0}{\partial t}\right)_{\mathrm{coll}} = \frac{1}{w^2}\frac{\partial}{\partial w}\left(\frac{m_-}{m_N}vw^3f^0\right) + \frac{1}{w^2}\frac{\partial}{\partial w}\left(vw^2\frac{kT_N}{m_N}\frac{\partial f^0}{\partial w}\right) \quad [10.136]$$

Note that the first term of [10.136] is just the expression for $(\partial f^0/\partial t)_{\mathrm{coll}}$ given by [10.104] for the case when the neutral particles are initially at rest.

The second term of [10.136] is the modification required when the neutral particles have a Maxwellian velocity distribution at a temperature T_N.

Equation [10.136] may be rewritten as

$$\left(\frac{\partial f^0}{\partial t}\right)_{\mathrm{coll}} = \frac{1}{w^2}\frac{\partial}{\partial w}\left(\frac{m_-}{m_N}vw^3f^0 + \frac{kT_Nv}{m_N}w^2\frac{\partial f^0}{\partial w}\right)$$

[10.137]

or alternatively, letting $G = 2m_-/m_N$

$$\left(\frac{\partial f^0}{\partial t}\right)_{\mathrm{coll}} = \frac{1}{2w^2}\frac{\partial}{\partial w}\left(Gvw^3f^0 + \frac{GvkT_N}{m_-}w^2\frac{\partial f^0}{\partial w}\right)$$

[10.138]

Now in the absence of any external forces the electron distribution function f^0 must in the steady state reduce to the Maxwellian distribution at the gas temperature T_N. That is, $(\partial f^0/\partial t)_{\mathrm{coll}}$ should be zero if

$$f^0 = N_-\left(\frac{m_-}{2\pi kT_N}\right)^{3/2}e^{-(m_-w^2/2kT_N)}$$

[10.139]

One can readily show (see Exercise 10.32.7) that this is indeed the case if [10.139] is substituted into [10.138]. In the following section we shall use the collision term [10.138] to determine the distribution of electron velocities.

Exercise 10.32.1   From Figure 10.8 show that

$$\mathbf{g} - \tilde{\mathbf{g}} = 2(\mathbf{g} \cdot \mathbf{k})\mathbf{k}$$

or, alternatively

$$g_i - \tilde{g}_i = 2g_j k_j k_i$$

Exercise 10.32.2   Show that under the condition $m_-/m_N \ll 1$ the solution of [10.113] is given by [10.114].

Exercise 10.32.3   Show that by only keeping terms up to order $(m_-/m_N)^{1/2}$ the relative speed g is given by

$$g = w - w_N \cos \theta$$

Exercise 10.32.4   Verify [10.118]–[10.120].

Exercise 10.32.5   From Figure 10.9, show that

$$\cos \alpha = \cos \beta \cos \theta + \sin \beta \sin \theta \cos \varphi$$

and

$$\sin \frac{\chi'}{2} = \cos \beta \cos \gamma - \sin \beta \sin \gamma \cos \varphi$$

From Figure 10.7, show that to order $(m_-/m_N)^{1/2}$ $\sin \gamma = (w_N/w) \sin \theta$, and $\cos \gamma = 1$. Using the above results, show that to order $(m_-/m_N)^{1/2}$

$$\cos \alpha = \sin \frac{\chi'}{2} \cos \theta + \cos \frac{\chi'}{2} \sin \theta \cos \varphi$$

$$+ (w_N/w) \sin \theta \cos \varphi \left(\cos \frac{\chi'}{2} \cos \theta - \sin \frac{\chi'}{2} \sin \theta \cos \varphi \right)$$

Exercise 10.32.6   (a) Verify [10.121] and [10.122].
                     (b) Verify [10.125] and [10.126].

Exercise 10.32.7   Show that equation [10.138] is zero when f^0 is given by [10.139].

10.4 THE DISTRIBUTION
OF ELECTRON VELOCITIES

In Section 10.2 we calculated a general expression for the a.c. conductivity of a plasma which was given in terms of the isotropic part of the distribution function f^0. We then obtained special results for the case when f^0 is Maxwellian. These results can be expected to be applicable for weak electric fields. On the other hand, as the electric field strength is increased, the isotropic part of the distribution function will not remain Maxwellian.

In order to determine f^0 we will use the expression for $(\partial f^0/\partial t)_{\text{coll}}$ which was derived in the previous section. Thus from [10.21], [10.138], and [10.37] we can write the equations for the time-variations of f^0 and f_i' as

$$\frac{\partial f^0}{\partial t} + \frac{w}{3} \frac{\partial f_i'}{\partial x_i} - \frac{eE_i}{3mw^2} \frac{\partial}{\partial w} (w^2 f_i') = \frac{1}{2w^2} \frac{\partial}{\partial w} \left(Gvw^3 f^0 + \frac{GvkT_N}{m_-} w^2 \frac{\partial f^0}{\partial w} \right)$$

[10.140]

and

$$\frac{\partial f_i'}{\partial t} + w \frac{\partial f^0}{\partial x_i} - \frac{e}{m} E_i \frac{\partial f^0}{\partial w} - \epsilon_{ijk} \Omega_j f_k' = -v f_i'$$ [10.141]

The form of the isotropic part of the distribution function for a plasma in an alternating electric field is known as the Margenau distribution and will be derived in the following section. A special case of this result is the Druyvesteyn distribution which is discussed in Section 10.42. Finally in Section 10.43 we investigate the form of f^0 for a plasma in a magnetic field.

10.41 THE MARGENAU DISTRIBUTION

Consider a homogeneous, isotropic plasma in the presence of an alternating electric field which varies as $e^{-i\omega t}$. The solution of [10.141] for f_i' is then given by [10.46] as

$$f_i' = \frac{eE_i(\partial f^0/\partial w)}{m_-(v - i\omega)}$$ [10.142]

In the absence of spatial gradients the steady-state equation for f^0 can be written from [10.140] as

$$\frac{eE_i}{3mw^2} \frac{\partial}{\partial w} (w^2 f_i') + \frac{1}{2w^2} \frac{\partial}{\partial w} \left(Gvw^2 f^0 + \frac{GvkT_N}{m_-} w^2 \frac{\partial f^0}{\partial w} \right) = 0$$ [10.143]

Note that only f_i' has a harmonic time-variation at the frequency ω. The isotropic part of the distribution function f^0 is a steady-state distribution in which the harmonic perturbations have been time averaged. Thus in [10.143] the product $E_i f_i'$ must be the time average of the product of the real parts of E_i and f_i'. That is

$$E_i f_i' = \langle \text{Re} (E_i) \, \text{Re} (f_i') \rangle_{\text{av}}$$ [10.144]

Now if

$$E_i = A_i e^{-i\omega t}$$

$$= A_i(\cos \omega t - i \sin \omega t) \qquad [10.145]$$

then

$$\text{Re}\,(E_i) = A_i \cos \omega t \qquad [10.146]$$

From [10.142] we see that

$$\text{Re}\,(f_i') = \text{Re}\left[\frac{\partial f^0}{\partial w}\,\frac{eE_i}{m_-(v^2 + w^2)}\,(v + i\omega)\right] \qquad [10.147]$$

from which, using [10.145],

$$\text{Re}\,(f_i') = \frac{eA_i}{m_-(v^2 + \omega^2)}\,\frac{\partial f^0}{\partial w}\,(v \cos \omega t + \omega \sin \omega t) \qquad [10.148]$$

Substituting [10.148] and [10.146] into [10.144], we obtain after averaging over the period of the wave (see Exercise 10.41.1)

$$E_i f_i' = \frac{eA^2 v}{2m_-(v^2 + \omega^2)}\,\frac{\partial f^0}{\partial w} \qquad [10.149]$$

where $A^2 = A_i A_i$.

If we now substitute [10.149] into [10.143], we obtain

$$\frac{1}{2w^2}\,\frac{\partial}{\partial w}\left[\frac{e^2 A^2 v w^2}{3m_-^2(v^2 + \omega^2)}\,\frac{\partial f^0}{\partial w} + Gvw^2\left(wf^0 + \frac{kT_N}{m_-}\,\frac{\partial f^0}{\partial w}\right)\right] = 0 \qquad [10.150]$$

Integrating [10.150] once, we obtain

$$w^2\left[\frac{e^2 A^2 v}{3m_-^2(v^2 + \omega^2)}\,\frac{\partial f^0}{\partial w} + Gv\left(wf^0 + \frac{kT_N}{m_-}\,\frac{\partial f^0}{\partial w}\right)\right] = 0 \qquad [10.151]$$

where the constant of integration is zero since f^0 must be Maxwellian at the temperature T_N when $A = 0$.

We can rewrite [10.151] as

$$\left[\frac{e^2 A^2}{3Gm_-(v^2 + \omega^2)} + kT_N\right]\frac{\partial f^0}{\partial w} = -m_- wf^0$$

from which

$$\frac{\partial f^0}{f^0} = -\frac{m_- w\, dw}{\left[kT_N + \dfrac{e^2 A^2}{3Gm_-(v^2 + \omega^2)} \right]} \qquad [10.152]$$

The solution of [10.152] is then

$$f^0 = C \exp \left\{ - \int_0^w \frac{m_- w\, dw}{\left[kT_N + \dfrac{e^2 A^2}{3Gm_-(v^2 + \omega^2)} \right]} \right\} \qquad [10.153]$$

where the constant C is determined by the normalization condition

$$N_- = 4\pi \int_0^\infty w^2 f^0\, dw \qquad [10.154]$$

The form of f^0 given by [10.153] is known as the Margenau distribution and is a function of the amplitude and frequency of the electric field.

We can rewrite [10.153] in the form

$$f^0 = C \exp \left[- \int_0^w \frac{m_- w\, dw}{kT_N(1 + \alpha)} \right] \qquad [10.155]$$

where

$$\alpha = \frac{e^2 A^2}{3kT_N Gm_-(\omega^2 + v^2)} \qquad [10.156]$$

For the case of weak electric fields and high frequencies such that $\alpha \ll 1$ or

$$kT_N \gg \frac{e^2 A^2}{3Gm_-(\omega^2 + v^2)} \qquad [10.157]$$

we can expand [10.155] in the form

$$\begin{aligned}
f^0 &= C \exp \left[- \int_0^w \frac{mw\, dw}{kT_N} (1 - \alpha + \alpha^2 - \cdots) \right] \\
&= C \left(\exp - \int_0^w \frac{mw\, dw}{kT_N} \right) \left(\exp \int_0^w \frac{\alpha mw\, dw}{kT_N} \right) (\cdots) \\
&\approx C e^{-(mw^2/2kT_N)} \left(1 + \int_0^\omega \frac{\alpha mw\, dw}{kT_N} \right) \qquad [10.158]
\end{aligned}$$

which shows the change in f^0 from the Maxwellian distribution due to the electric field.

If we substitute [10.158] into the expression for σ given by [10.56], we obtain a "nonlinear" conductivity which will depend on the electric field strength

$$\sigma = \frac{4\pi e^2}{3m} C \int_0^\infty e^{-(mw^2/2kT_N)} \left(1 + \int_0^w \frac{\alpha mw\,dw}{kT_N}\right) \frac{d}{dw}\left(\frac{w^3}{v - i\omega}\right) dw \quad [10.159]$$

It is interesting to note that if the collision frequency v (and therefore α) is independent of the electron speed then from [10.155] the distribution function f^0 is given by

$$f^0 = Ce^{-[mw^2/2kT_N(1+\alpha)]} \quad [10.160]$$

From the condition [10.154] we then find (see Exercise 10.41.2) that

$$C = N_- \left[\frac{m}{2\pi kT_N(1+\alpha)}\right]^{3/2} \quad [10.161]$$

Now if [10.160] and [10.161] are used in either [10.49] or [10.56] we will obtain

$$\sigma = \frac{N_- e^2}{m_-}\left(\frac{v + i\omega}{\omega^2 + v^2}\right) \quad [10.162]$$

which is the simple expression for conductivity derived from the Langevin equation (see Exercise 10.21.3). Thus we see that only for a velocity independent collision frequency will the Margenau distribution result in a conductivity independent of the electric field amplitude.

Exercise 10.41.1   Verify [10.149].

Exercise 10.41.2   Verify [10.161].

10.42 THE DRUYVESTEYN DISTRIBUTION

We have found in the previous sections that an assumption of a velocity independent collision frequency leads to a simple expression for the conductivity of a weakly ionized plasma. Since the collision frequency v is given in terms of the cross section for momentum transfer Q by

$$v = N_N wQ \quad [10.163]$$

then a constant collision frequency corresponds to a cross section which varies as $1/w$.

On the other hand we found in Section 4.4 that a hard sphere model for the gas led to a constant cross section. Since the mean free path L is given by

$$L = \frac{1}{N_N Q}$$

this case corresponds to a constant mean free path assumption. For this case we see from [10.163] that the collision frequency is proportional to the electron speed w.

Let us consider the case of strong electric fields and low frequencies so that $(\omega^2 \ll \nu^2)$ and $\alpha \gg 1$. Then we can approximate the Margenau distribution [10.153] by

$$f^0 = C \exp - \left[\int_0^w \frac{m_- w \, dw}{\left(\dfrac{e^2 A^2}{3Gm_- \nu^2} \right)} \right] \qquad [10.164]$$

If we substitute [10.163] into [10.164] and assume a constant cross section, we obtain

$$f^0 = C \exp \left(- \int_0^w \frac{3Gm_-^2 N_N^2 Q^2 w^3 \, dw}{e^2 A^2} \right)$$

from which

$$f^0 = Ce^{-(3Gm_-^2 N_N^2 Q^2 w^4 / 4e^2 A^2)} \qquad [10.165]$$

This form of f^0 is known as the Druyvesteyn distribution. It is applicable for a plasma with a constant cross section under the influence of a strong d.c. or low-frequency electric field. Notice that since f^0 in [10.165] varies as e^{-aw^4} the tail of this distribution will decrease more rapidly than the Maxwellian distribution. For a plasma with a given mean energy the Druyvesteyn distribution therefore predicts fewer high-energy electrons than does the Maxwellian distribution.

10.43 THE DISTRIBUTION FUNCTION IN THE PRESENCE OF A MAGNETIC FIELD

In Section 10.22 we found that for a plasma in a magnetic field f_i' is given by [10.65] as

$$f_i' = \frac{ie}{m\omega} C_{ij} E_j \frac{\partial f^0}{\partial w} \qquad [10.166]$$

where C_{ij} is the matrix given by [10.64]. We now wish to determine the isotropic part of the distribution function f^0 by using [10.166] in [10.143]. As in Section 10.41 we must first evaluate the quantity

$$E_i f_i' = \langle \text{Re}(E_i) \, \text{Re}(f_i') \rangle_{\text{av}} \qquad [10.167]$$

However we can not evaluate [10.167] unless we specify the relative phases of the components E_i—that is, unless we specify the polarization of E_i. It will not do to assume that the wave is linearly polarized, since we will see in Chapter 13 that this is generally not true.

Let $|E\rangle$ represent the column matrix

$$|E\rangle = \begin{bmatrix} E_1 \\ E_2 \\ E_3 \end{bmatrix} \qquad [10.168]$$

and let $\langle E|$ represent the row matrix

$$\langle E| = [E_1^* \quad E_2^* \quad E_3^*] \qquad [10.169]$$

where the stars signify complex conjugates. (For a discussion of this notation, see Appendix H.) Then it can be shown (see Exercise 10.43.1) that $E_i f_i'$ is given by

$$E_i f_i' = \langle \text{Re}(E_i) \, \text{Re}(f_i') \rangle_{\text{av}}$$

$$= \tfrac{1}{2} \, \text{Re} \, i\langle E \mid C \mid E\rangle \left(\frac{e}{m\omega} \frac{\partial f^0}{\partial w} \right) \qquad [10.170]$$

where C is the matrix C_{ij} and $\langle E \mid C \mid E \rangle$ is the scalar quantity

$$[E_1^* \quad E_2^* \quad E_3^*] \begin{bmatrix} C_{11} & C_{12} & C_{13} \\ C_{21} & C_{22} & C_{23} \\ C_{31} & C_{32} & C_{33} \end{bmatrix} \begin{bmatrix} E_1 \\ E_2 \\ E_3 \end{bmatrix} \qquad [10.171]$$

Substituting [10.170] into [10.143] we obtain

$$\frac{1}{2w^2} \frac{\partial}{\partial w} \left[\frac{e^2 H w^2}{3m_-^2 \omega} \frac{\partial f^0}{\partial w} + G v w^2 \left(w f^0 + \frac{kT_N}{m_-} \frac{\partial f^0}{\partial w} \right) \right] = 0 \qquad [10.172]$$

where

$$H = \text{Re} \, i\langle E \mid C \mid E\rangle \qquad [10.173]$$

Proceeding as in Section 10.41, we find by integrating [10.172] twice that

$$f^0 = C \exp \left[- \int_0^w \frac{m_- w \, dw}{kT_N + \dfrac{e^2 H}{3m_- Gv\omega}} \right] \qquad [10.174]$$

where the constant C is determined from the normalization condition [10.154].

Since we must know the polarization of the electric field vector in order to calculate H we see that f^0 depends not only on the electric field strength but also on its polarization.

For example, if E_i is a right-handed circularly polarized wave in the $x_1 x_2$ plane then

$$|E_R\rangle = \frac{A}{\sqrt{2}} \begin{bmatrix} 1 \\ i \\ 0 \end{bmatrix} \qquad [10.175]$$

and

$$\langle E_R| = \frac{A}{\sqrt{2}} \begin{bmatrix} 1 & -i & 0 \end{bmatrix} \qquad [10.176]$$

Using [10.175] and [10.176] in [10.173] together with the matrix $\mathbf{C}$ given by [10.64], one can show (see Exercise 10.43.2) that for a right-circular wave H is given by

$$H_R = \frac{v\omega A^2/2}{(\omega - \Omega)^2 + v^2} \qquad [10.177]$$

Similarly for a left-handed circularly polarized wave where

$$|E_L\rangle = \frac{A}{\sqrt{2}} \begin{bmatrix} 1 \\ -i \\ 0 \end{bmatrix}$$

one finds that H is given by

$$H_L = \frac{v\omega A^2/2}{(\omega + \Omega)^2 + v^2} \qquad [10.178]$$

Using [10.177] and [10.178] in [10.174], we see that for circularly polarized waves f^0 is given by

$$f^0 = C \exp \left[- \int_0^w \frac{m_- w \, dw}{kT_N + \dfrac{e^2 A^2}{6m_- G[(\omega \pm \Omega)^2 + v^2]}} \right]$$

where the plus sign is associated with the left-handed wave while the minus sign is associated with the right-handed wave.

Exercise 10.43.1   Verify [10.170].

Exercise 10.43.2   Show that for a right- and left-handed circularly polarized wave H is given by [10.177] and [10.178], respectively.

From the above results it is possible to write an expression for f^0 for an arbitrarily polarized wave $|E\rangle$ (see Problem 10.4).

Problems

10.1   Write the distribution function f as a general series expansion in spherical harmonics. Show that the form of f given by [10.6] is equivalent to retaining only the first two terms of this expansion. Under what condition is the retention of only the first two terms justified?

10.2   (a)   Show that in the high-frequency limit $\omega^2 \gg [\nu(u)]^2$ it is possible to write the a.c. plasma conductivity for the case of a velocity dependent collision frequency as

$$\sigma_R = \frac{N_- e^2 \nu_{\text{EFF}}}{m\omega^2}$$

$$\sigma_I = \frac{N_- e^2}{m\omega}$$

where

$$\nu_{\text{EFF}} = \frac{8}{3\sqrt{\pi}} \int_0^\infty u^4 \nu(u) e^{-u^2}\, du$$

(b)   Show that in the low-frequency limit $\omega^2 \ll [\nu(u)]^2$ one can write

$$\sigma_R = \frac{N_- e^2}{m\nu_{\text{EFF}}^R}$$

$$\sigma_I = \frac{N_- e^2 \omega}{m(\nu_{\text{EFF}}^I)^2}$$

where

$$(\nu_{\text{EFF}}^R)^{-1} = \frac{8}{3\sqrt{\pi}} \int_0^\infty \frac{u^4 e^{-u^2}\, du}{\nu(u)}$$

and

$$(\nu_{\text{EFF}}^I)^{-2} = \frac{8}{3\sqrt{\pi}} \int_0^\infty \frac{u^4 e^{-u^2}\, du}{\nu^2(u)}$$

(c)   For the intermediate frequency range show that one can write

$$\sigma_R = \frac{N_- e^2 \nu_{\text{EFF}}}{m(\omega^2 + \nu_{\text{EFF}}^2)} K_R\!\left(\frac{\nu_{\text{EFF}}}{\omega}\right)$$

$$\sigma_I = \frac{N_- e^2 \omega}{m(\omega^2 + \nu_{\text{EFF}}^2)} K_I\!\left(\frac{\nu_{\text{EFF}}}{\omega}\right)$$

where

$$K_R = \frac{8}{3\sqrt{\pi}}\!\left(\frac{\omega^2 + \nu_{\text{EFF}}^2}{\nu_{\text{EFF}}\,\omega^2}\right)\int_0^\infty \left[1 - \frac{\nu^2(u)}{\omega^2} + \frac{\nu^4(u)}{\omega^4}\cdots\right]\nu(u)u^4 e^{-u^2}\,du$$

$$K_I = \frac{8}{3\sqrt{\pi}}\!\left(\frac{\omega^2 + \nu_{\text{EFF}}^2}{\omega^2}\right)\int_0^\infty \left[1 - \frac{\nu^2(u)}{\omega^2} + \frac{\nu^4(u)}{\omega^4}\cdots\right]u^4 e^{-u^2}\,du$$

and ν_{EFF} is that given in part (a) for the high frequency limit.

10.3   (a)   In the presence of a d.c. electric field and spatial gradients show that

$$f_i' = \frac{eE_i}{mv}\frac{\partial f^0}{\partial w} - \frac{w}{v}\frac{\partial f^0}{\partial x_i}$$

(b)   If the electron current density J_i and total electron energy flow H_i are given by

$$J_i = -Ne\langle v_i\rangle$$

and

$$H_i = \tfrac{1}{2}mN\langle w^2 v_i\rangle$$

show that

$$J_i = -\tfrac{4}{3}\pi e \int_0^\infty f_i' w^3\,dw$$

and

$$H_i = \tfrac{2}{3}\pi m \int_0^\infty w^5 f_i'\,dw$$

(c)   If f^0 is Maxwellian, show that

$$\frac{\partial f^0}{\partial x_i} = f^0\!\left[\frac{1}{N}\frac{\partial N}{\partial x_i} + \left(\frac{mw^2}{2kT} - \frac{3}{2}\right)\frac{1}{T}\frac{\partial T}{\partial x_i}\right]$$

(d)   For a Maxwellian distribution show that one can then write

$$J_i = \sigma E_i + eD\frac{\partial N}{\partial x_i} + \alpha\frac{\partial T}{\partial x_i}$$

and

$$H_i = \beta E_i - \gamma\frac{\partial N}{\partial x_i} - K\frac{\partial T}{\partial x_i}$$

where the electrical conductivity σ is

$$\sigma = -\frac{4\pi}{3}\frac{e^2}{m}\int_0^\infty \frac{w^3}{\nu}\frac{\partial f^0}{\partial w}\,dw$$

the diffusion coefficient D is

$$D = \frac{4\pi}{3}\frac{1}{N}\int_0^\infty \frac{w^4}{\nu}f^0\,dw$$

the current flow coefficient α due to thermal gradients at constant electron density is

$$\alpha = \frac{4\pi}{3}e\int_0^\infty \frac{w^4}{\nu}\frac{1}{T}\left(\frac{mw^2}{2kT}-\frac{3}{2}\right)f^0\,dw$$

the energy flow coefficient β due to an electric field is

$$\beta = \frac{2\pi}{3}e\int_0^\infty \frac{w^5}{\nu}\frac{\partial f^0}{\partial w}\,dw$$

the energy diffusion coefficient γ is

$$\gamma = \frac{2\pi}{3}\frac{m}{N}\int_0^\infty \frac{w^6}{\nu}f^0\,dw$$

and the energy conductivity K at constant electron density is

$$K = \frac{2\pi}{3}\frac{m}{T}\int_0^\infty \frac{w^6}{\nu}\left(\frac{mw^2}{2kT}-\frac{3}{2}\right)f^0\,dw$$

(e)   From the previous results obtain the Einstein relations

$$D = \sigma\frac{kT}{Ne^2}$$

$$\gamma = -\frac{kT}{Ne}\beta$$

and the Onsager reciprocity relation

$$\beta = -\frac{3kT}{5e}\sigma - \alpha T$$

10.4 Show that for an arbitrarily polarized wave $|E\rangle$ in the plane normal to the magnetic field the isotropic part of the distribution function f^0 can be written as

$$f^0 = C\exp\left[-\int_0^w \frac{m_-w\,dw}{kT_N + \dfrac{e^2}{3m_-G}\left[\dfrac{\langle E\mid E_R\rangle\langle E_R\mid E\rangle}{(\omega-\Omega)^2+\nu^2} + \dfrac{\langle E\mid E_L\rangle\langle E_L\mid E\rangle}{(\omega+\Omega)^2+\nu^2}\right]}\right]$$

(see Appendix H and Section 13.4).

REFERENCES

Solutions of the Boltzmann equation based on a spherical harmonic expansion of the distribution function have been discussed by

1   Allis, W. P. "Motion of Ions and Electrons," *Handbuch der Physik*, vol. **21**. Springer-Verlag, 1956.

2   Ginzburg, V. L. *Propagation of Electromagnetic Waves in Plasma.* New York: Gordon and Breach, 1960.

3   Brandstatter, J. J. *An Introduction to Waves, Rays, and Radiation in Plasma Media.* New York: McGraw-Hill, 1963.

A discussion of the collision term for electron-neutral collisions can also be found in

4   Chapman, S., and T. G. Cowling. *The Mathematical Theory of Non-Uniform Gases.* London: Cambridge University Press, 1960, pp. 346 ff.

5   DuFort, E. C. "Some Nonlinear Problems in Partially Ionized Gases." *Univ. of S. California, USCEC Report* 82-217 (1964), 218-23.

The high-frequency conductivity of a plasma was derived by

6   Margenau, H. "Conduction and Dispersion of Ionized Gases at High Frequencies," *Phys. Rev.*, **69** (1946), 508-13.

Detailed calculations of the transport coefficients in a plasma including the effects of Coulomb collisions have been carried out by

7   Shkarofsky, I. P. "Values of the Transport Coefficients in a Plasma for any Degree of Ionization Based on a Maxwellian Distribution," *Can. J. Phys.*, **39** (1961), 1619-703.

CHAPTER

11

WAVE PHENOMENA
IN PLASMAS

This chapter is designed to serve as an introduction to the topic of wave propagation in plasmas, which will be treated in more detail in Chapters 12 and 13.

In analyzing the problem of waves in plasmas one can choose between two different methods of approach. The first approach is to derive a wave equation from Maxwell's equations. The plasma is then characterized as having either a conductivity or a dielectric constant as was discussed in Section 7.2. The main advantage of this approach is that one can determine general properties of wave propagation in terms of an arbitrary dielectric constant or conductivity. We will illustrate this approach in Section 11.2 for the case of a cold isotropic plasma. This approach will be extended in Chapter 13 to treat the problem of wave propagation in anisotropic plasmas. In that analysis the plasma will be characterized by a certain dielectric tensor. We will refer explicitly to the dielectric tensor which was derived from the Langevin equation in Section 7.24. However the results of the analysis will still be applicable if we use the more exact form of the dielectric tensor which was derived from the Boltzmann equation in Section 10.2.

321

The second main approach to the problem of waves in plasmas does not involve the derivation of a wave equation explicitly. One therefore does not obtain expressions for the dielectric or conductivity tensors directly. Instead one solves Maxwell's equations simultaneously with equations that describe the motion of the plasma particles. This approach is often simpler and more straightforward, particularly when including the effect on wave propagation of thermal motions and the multicomponent properties of plasmas.

In determining the equations to describe the motion of the plasma particles, several levels of approximation are possible. The simplest procedure is to consider the electron motion only and to describe this motion by the Langevin equation. The results would then be exactly the same as those obtained from a wave equation in which the conductivity or dielectric constant had been derived from the Langevin equation.

The next higher level of approximation uses the single-species plasma equations discussed in Section 6.2. If one uses the equations for the electrons only then one assumes a single-fluid theory. If the motion of both the electrons and the ions are considered then one speaks of a two-fluid theory. Likewise a three-fluid theory would include the motion of the electrons, ions, and neutral particles. We will illustrate this main approach in Section 11.3 by considering electron plasma oscillations based on a single-fluid theory. This approach will be extended in Chapter 12 when we consider plasma waves in a magnetic field based on a two-fluid theory.

A more complete description of the particle motions will be obtained if one writes a Boltzmann equation for each species. As might be expected, however, the cost of the added information is severe mathematical difficulties. In fact only certain types of wave problems involving the Boltzmann equation are mathematically tractable. The most important of these involves a "collisionless" form of the Boltzmann equation known as the Vlasov equation. This approach will be discussed briefly in Section 11.4.

We begin this chapter with a review of electromagnetic waves in free space.

11.1 ELECTROMAGNETIC WAVES IN FREE SPACE

We first wish to derive the free space wave equation. The equation will be valid for a region having no conducting, dielectric, or magnetic properties. Thus the space charge density η and the current density J_i are zero. For such a region Maxwell's equations [3.34] and [3.35] become

$$\epsilon_{ijk}E_{k,j} = -\mu_0\dot{H}_i \qquad [11.1]$$

and

$$\epsilon_{rsi} H_{i,s} = \epsilon_o \dot{E}_r \qquad [11.2]$$

Taking the time derivative of both sides of [11.2] we obtain

$$\epsilon_{rsi} \dot{H}_{i,s} = \epsilon_o \ddot{E}_r \qquad [11.3]$$

Substituting $\dot{H}_i$ from [11.1] into [11.3], we obtain $\epsilon_{irs}\epsilon_{ijk}E_{k,js} = -\mu_o\epsilon_o\ddot{E}_r$ from which $(\delta_{rj}\delta_{sk} - \delta_{rk}\delta_{sj})E_{k,js} = -\mu_o\epsilon_o\ddot{E}_r$ so that

$$E_{s,rs} - E_{r,ss} = -\mu_o\epsilon_o\ddot{E}_r \qquad [11.4]$$

Since the space charge η is zero, $E_{s,s} = 0$, so that [11.4] becomes

$$E_{r,ss} = \mu_o\epsilon_o\ddot{E}_r \qquad [11.5]$$

Equation [11.5] is the free space wave equation which has solutions of the form

$$E_r = f_r(\alpha_i x_i - ct) \qquad [11.6]$$

where the unit vector α_i has the property

$$\alpha_i\alpha_i = 1 \qquad [11.7]$$

We can verify that [11.6] is a solution of [11.5] by noting that if we write

$$f_r' = \frac{\partial f_r(\xi)}{\partial \xi}$$

then $E_{r,s} = f_r'\alpha_s$ and $E_{r,ss} = f_r''\alpha_s\alpha_s = f_r''$, also $\dot{E}_r = -cf_r'$ and $\ddot{E}_r = c^2f_r''$, so that, from [11.5], $f_r'' = \mu_o\epsilon_o c^2 f_r''$. Thus [11.6] is a solution of [11.5] if

$$c^2 = \frac{1}{\mu_o\epsilon_o} \qquad [11.8]$$

Let us now consider the solution to the wave equation given by [11.6]. At some time t_1 the locus in space of $E_r = f_r(\alpha_i x_i - ct) = $ constant, will be the locus in space of $\alpha_i x_i' - ct_1 = $ constant, which is the equation of a plane with normal α_i. A second plane at t_2 will satisfy the equation $\alpha_i x_i'' - ct_2 = $

constant. If E_r is to have the same value at both values of time, then we must have (see Figure 11.1)

$$(\alpha_i x_i' - ct_1) = (\alpha_i x_i'' - ct_2) \text{ or } \alpha_i(x_i'' - x_i') = c(t_2 - t_1) \text{ or } d = c(t_2 - t_1),$$

where d is the distance between the planes. Thus $c = d/(t_2 - t_1)$ is the velocity of propagation of the waves. Such waves are called *plane waves*.

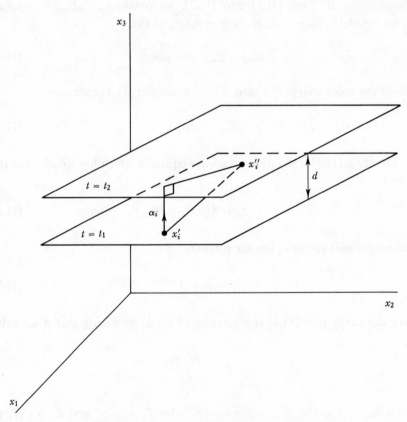

FIGURE 11.1 Propagation of Plane Waves

Thus [11.6] is a plane wave solution of [11.5] in which the velocity of propagation is

$$c = \frac{1}{\sqrt{\mu_o \epsilon_o}} \tag{11.9}$$

Substituting known values for the constants μ_o and ϵ_o in [11.9] gives a value of c equal to 3×10^8 m/sec—the velocity of light.

11.11 HARMONIC WAVES

A particularly important type of plane wave is the harmonic wave. Consider

$$E_r = A_r \cos k(\alpha_i x_i - ct) = A_r \cos (k\alpha_i x_i - \omega t) \qquad [11.10]$$

where $\omega = kc$ is the angular frequency.

If $\alpha_i = (1, 0, 0)$, the wave is traveling in the x_1-direction and

$$E_r = A_r \cos (kx_1 - \omega t).$$

The value of E_r repeats itself each time kx_1 increases by 2π. Thus k is the number of waves in a length 2π and is called the *wave number*. The length of one wave is thus $2\pi/k$ and is called the *wavelength* λ. That is,

$$\lambda = 2\pi/k \qquad [11.11]$$

Equation [11.10] can be written in complex form as

$$E_r = A_r e^{i(k\alpha_q x_q - \omega t)} \qquad [11.12]$$

where the field quantities are obtained by taking the real part of [11.12]. This complex form of E_r is an extremely useful representation for the field vectors. Care must be exercised, however, in the use of this form. The physical quantity involved is associated with the real part of the complex form. As long as the equations we use are linear equations then we can make calculations using the complex form and then take the real part of the result. If the equations are not linear, however, we cannot do this. This is due to the fact that the real part of the product of two complex quantities is not equal to the product of the real parts of the two quantities. A particularly important example of this is the calculation of the power flow of an electromagnetic wave. We will return to this topic in Section 11.13.

Equation [11.12] is a solution of the free space wave equation [11.5]. Since there is no space charge we have $E_{r,r} = 0$ or, differentiating [11.12], $E_{r,r} = A_r i k \alpha_r e^{i(k\alpha_q x_q - \omega t)} = 0$. For there to be a wave, k must be nonzero; thus we must have

$$A_r \alpha_r = 0 \qquad [11.13]$$

Equation [11.13] says that the E-field is perpendicular to the direction of propagation. That is, the E-field is transverse.

Maxwell's equation [11.1] is

$$\epsilon_{ijk} E_{k,j} = -\mu_0 \dot{H}_i \qquad [11.14]$$

Substituting [11.12] in [11.14], we obtain

$$ik\epsilon_{ijk}\alpha_j E_k = -\mu_o \dot{H}_i \qquad [11.15]$$

Integrating [11.15] with respect to time, we obtain $[ik/(-i\omega)]\epsilon_{ijk}\alpha_j E_k = -\mu_o H_i$, or

$$H_i = \frac{k}{\mu_o \omega} \epsilon_{ijk}\alpha_j E_k \qquad [11.16]$$

Since, using [11.10] and [11.9],

$$\frac{k}{\mu_o \omega} = \frac{1}{\mu_o c} = \sqrt{\frac{\epsilon_o}{\mu_o}} = \frac{1}{Z_o} \qquad [11.17]$$

[11.16] becomes

$$H_i = \sqrt{\frac{\epsilon_o}{\mu_o}} \epsilon_{ijk}\alpha_j E_k = \frac{1}{Z_o} \epsilon_{ijk}\alpha_j E_k \qquad [11.18]$$

Equation [11.18] says that H_i is also transverse and is also perpendicular to E_k. The quantity Z_0 is called the *characteristic impedance* of free space.

11.12 WAVE POLARIZATION

Consider the harmonic wave

$$E_r = a_r e^{i(kx_3-\omega t)} \qquad [11.19]$$

propagating in the x_3-direction. At the plane $x_3 = 0$ the field components are given by

$$E_r = R_e(a_r e^{-i\omega t}) \qquad [11.20]$$

The locus which the tip of the vector E_r described at a fixed location in space during a time $\tau = 2\pi/\omega$ is called the *polarization of the wave*.

The vector $a_r = A_r\underline{|\theta}$ in [11.20] will, in general, be complex. Let us assume that the wave is transverse and that the phase of $a_1 = A_1\underline{|0}$ is zero while that of $a_2 = A_2\underline{|\varphi}$ is φ. Then the x_1- and x_2-components of E_r will be given by

$$E_1 = A_1 \cos(-\omega t) \qquad [11.21]$$

$$E_2 = A_2 \cos(\varphi - \omega t) \qquad [11.22]$$

where the real quantities A_1 and A_2 are the amplitudes of the orthogonal components E_1 and E_2.

The polarization of the wave will, in general, be elliptical, depending on the values of A_1, A_2, and φ. To illustrate this, we write [11.21] and [11.22] as

$$E_1 = A_1 \cos(-\omega t) = A_1 \cos \omega t \qquad [11.23]$$

$$E_2 = A_2 \cos(\varphi - \omega t) = A_2 \cos \varphi \cos \omega t + A_2 \sin \varphi \sin \omega t \quad [11.24]$$

Squaring and adding [11.23] and [11.24] yields

$$\begin{aligned}
\frac{E_1^2}{A_1^2} + \frac{E_2^2}{A_2^2} &= \cos^2 \omega t + \cos^2 \omega t \cos^2 \varphi + \sin^2 \omega t \sin^2 \varphi \\
&\quad + 2 \cos \omega t \cos \varphi \sin \varphi \sin \omega t \\
&= \cos^2 \omega t + \cos^2 \omega t \cos^2 \varphi + \sin^2 \omega t \sin^2 \varphi \\
&\quad + 2 \cos \omega t \cos \varphi \left(\frac{E_2}{A_2} - \cos \omega t \cos \varphi \right)
\end{aligned}$$

from which, using [11.23],

$$\frac{E_1^2}{A_1^2} + \frac{E_2^2}{A_2^2} - \frac{2E_1 E_2}{A_1 A_2} \cos \varphi = \cos^2 \omega t (1 - \cos^2 \varphi) + \sin^2 \omega t \sin^2 \varphi$$

$$\frac{E_1^2}{A_1^2} + \frac{E_2^2}{A_2^2} - \frac{2E_1 E_2}{A_1 A_2} \cos \varphi = \sin^2 \varphi \qquad [11.25]$$

Equation [11.25] is the equation of an ellipse.

Consider the following special cases:

1. When $\varphi = 0$ (or $\varphi = 2n\pi$), then [11.25] becomes

$$\frac{E_1^2}{A_1^2} - \frac{2E_1 E_2}{A_1 A_2} + \frac{E_2^2}{A_2} = 0 \quad \text{or} \quad \left(\frac{E_1}{A_1} - \frac{E_2}{A_2} \right)^2 = 0,$$

from which

$$\frac{E_1}{A_1} = \frac{E_2}{A_2} \qquad [11.26]$$

Equation [11.26] is the equation of the line shown in Figure 11.2a. For this case the wave is said to be linearly polarized.

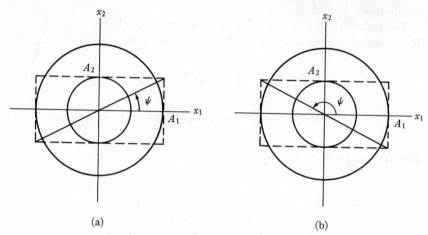

FIGURE 11.2   Representation of a Linearly Polarized Wave

2. When $\varphi = \pi$ [or $\varphi = (2n - 1)\pi$], then [11.25] reduces to

$$\frac{E_1}{A_1} + \frac{E_2}{A_2} = 0 \qquad\qquad [11.27]$$

which is the equation of the line shown in Figure 11.2b. The orientation angle ψ shown in Figure 11.2 will depend on the amplitude ratio A_2/A_1.

3. When $\varphi = \pi/2$ [or $\varphi = (2n - 1)\pi/2$], then [11.25] reduces to

$$\frac{E_1^2}{A_1^2} + \frac{E_2^2}{A_1^2} = 1 \qquad\qquad [11.28]$$

which is the equation for an ellipse whose major and minor axes lie along the directions of E_1 and E_2. The sense of rotation of the ellipse depends on whether φ is equal to $+\pi/2$ or $-\pi/2$ as illustrated in Figure 11.3. Remember that φ is the angle by which the phase of E_2 is advanced [see (11.22)]. Note also that since the time variation of E_r is of the form $e^{-i\omega t}$, then for positive φ, E_1 and E_2 are the projections on the x_1- and x_2-axes of phasors with amplitudes A_1 and A_2 rotating clockwise as shown in Figure 11.3.

Equation [11.19] represents a wave propagating in the x_3-direction. This direction is out of the page in Figure 11.3. When the wave is propagating toward the observer, as in Figure 11.3, a counterclockwise rotation of the electric field vector is called right-handed while a clockwise rotation is called left-handed.

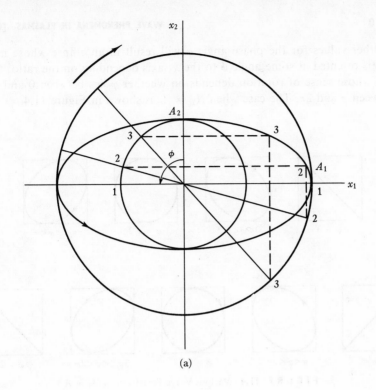

(a)

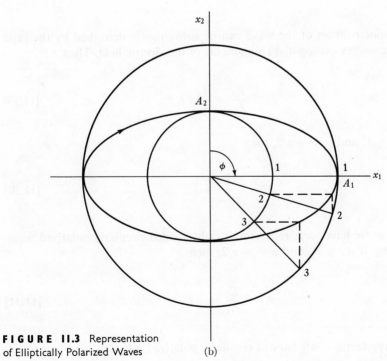

FIGURE 11.3 Representation
of Elliptically Polarized Waves

(b)

329

Other values for the phase angle φ will result in an ellipse whose major axis is oriented at some angle ψ to the x_1-axis depending on the ratio A_2/A_1 and whose sense of rotation depends on whether φ lies between 0 and π or between π and 2π. The case when $A_1 = A_2$ is shown in Figure 11.4.

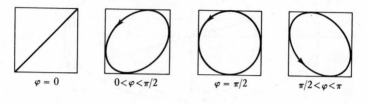

$$\varphi = 0 \qquad\qquad 0 < \varphi < \pi/2 \qquad\qquad \varphi = \pi/2 \qquad\qquad \pi/2 < \varphi < \pi$$

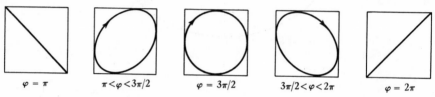

$$\varphi = \pi \qquad \pi < \varphi < 3\pi/2 \qquad \varphi = 3\pi/2 \qquad 3\pi/2 < \varphi < 2\pi \qquad \varphi = 2\pi$$

FIGURE II.4   Various Wave Polarizations ($A_1 = A_2$)

The polarization of the wave can be conveniently described by the ratio of the complex orthogonal components of the electric field. Thus

$$\frac{E_2}{E_1} = \frac{A_2}{A_1} e^{i\varphi} \qquad\qquad [11.29]$$

If $A_2 = A_1$ and $\varphi = +\pi/2$, then

$$\frac{E_2}{E_1} = i \qquad\qquad [11.30]$$

which, as we have seen, represents a right-handed circularly polarized wave. Similarly, if $A_2 = A_1$ and $\phi = -\pi/2$, then

$$\frac{E_2}{E_1} = -i \qquad\qquad [11.31]$$

which represents a left-handed circularly polarized wave.

11.13 P O W E R F L O W

We indicated in Section 11.11 that harmonic waves could be represented by a complex form. We pointed out in that section that for calculations involving the product of two complex quantities it is necessary to take the real part of the complex quantities before taking the product.

We illustrate this procedure in this section by calculating the Poynting vector given by [3.88] as

$$G_i = \epsilon_{ijk} E_j H_k \qquad [11.32]$$

for the case of a harmonic electromagnetic wave. Equation [11.32] gives the intensity of energy flow in the wave. The mean intensity of energy flow in the harmonic waves is given by

$$\langle G_i \rangle = \epsilon_{ijk} \langle \text{Re} (E_j) \, \text{Re} (H_k) \rangle \qquad [11.33]$$

where the time average is taken by integrating over a period of the harmonic wave and dividing by the period.

We write the complex form of the field vectors as

$$E_j = E_j e^{-i\omega t} = (a + ib)(\cos \omega t - i \sin \omega t) \qquad [11.34]$$

$$E_j^* = E_j^* e^{i\omega t} = (a - ib)(\cos \omega t + i \sin \omega t) \qquad [11.35]$$

$$H_k = H_k e^{-i\omega t} = (c + id)(\cos \omega t - i \sin \omega t) \qquad [11.36]$$

$$H_k^* = H_k^* e^{i\omega t} = (c - id)(\cos \omega t + i \sin \omega t) \qquad [11.37]$$

From [11.34] and [11.35] we see that

$$E_j + E_j^* = 2a \cos \omega t + 2b \sin \omega t = 2 \, \text{Re} (E_j)$$

so that

$$\text{Re} (E_j) = \tfrac{1}{2}(E_j + E_j^*) \qquad [11.38]$$

Similarly

$$\text{Re} (H_k) = \tfrac{1}{2}(H_k + H_k^*) \qquad [11.39]$$

Forming the product of [11.38] and [11.39] we obtain

$$\begin{aligned} \text{Re} (E_j) \, \text{Re} (H_k) &= \tfrac{1}{4}(E_j + E_j^*)(H_k + H_k^*) \\ &= \tfrac{1}{4}(E_j H_k + E_j^* H_k^* + E_j^* H_k + E_j H_k^*) \end{aligned} \qquad [11.40]$$

In taking the time average of [11.40], we note that the terms $E_j H_k$ and $E_j^* H_k^*$ have time variations of $e^{-i2\omega t} = \cos 2\omega t - i \sin 2\omega t$ and $e^{i2\omega t} = \cos 2\omega t + i \sin 2\omega t$, respectively, both of which vanish when integrated over a period of the wave. The last two terms of [11.40] are independent of time so that the time average of [11.40] can be written as

$$\langle \mathrm{Re}\,(E_j)\,\mathrm{Re}\,(H_k) \rangle = \tfrac{1}{4}(E_j^* H_k + E_j H_k^*) \tag{11.41}$$

From equations [11.34] to [11.37] we note that [11.41] can be written as

$$\langle \mathrm{Re}\,(E_j)\,\mathrm{Re}\,(H_k) \rangle = \tfrac{1}{2}(ac + bd) = \tfrac{1}{2}\,\mathrm{Re}\,(E_j H_k^*) \tag{11.42}$$

Substituting [11.42] in [11.33], we see that the mean intensity of the energy flow in the harmonic wave can be written as

$$\langle G_i \rangle = \tfrac{1}{2}\,\mathrm{Re}\,(\epsilon_{ijk} E_j H_k^*) \tag{11.43}$$

which is the real part of the complex vector

$$G_i^* = \tfrac{1}{2}\epsilon_{ijk} E_j H_k^* \tag{11.44}$$

II.2 ELECTROMAGNETIC WAVES IN COLD, ISOTROPIC PLASMAS

In Section 7.2 we found that a simple cold isotropic plasma could be characterized by either the complex dielectric constant κ given by

$$\kappa = 1 - \frac{\Pi^2}{\omega^2 + \nu^2} + i\,\frac{\Pi^2 \nu/\omega}{\omega^2 + \nu^2} \tag{11.45}$$

or by the complex conductivity σ given by

$$\sigma = \frac{N_- e^2}{m_-}\left(\frac{\nu}{\nu^2 + \omega^2} + i\,\frac{\omega}{\nu^2 + \omega^2}\right) \tag{11.46}$$

In the following section we will obtain a wave equation for propagation in a dielectric medium. We will then investigate the propagation properties of a plasma by using the dielectric constant given by [11.45]. In Section (11.22) we will show that the same results can be obtained by deriving a wave equation for a conducting medium and using the conductivity given by [11.46].

11.21   THE PLASMA AS A DIELECTRIC MEDIUM

Consider a region characterized by a scalar dielectric constant κ such that the electric displacement vector is

$$D_i = \epsilon_0 \kappa E_i \qquad [11.47]$$

Maxwell's equations can then be written

$$\epsilon_{ijk} E_{k,j} = -\dot{B}_i \qquad [11.48]$$

and

$$\epsilon_{ijk} B_{k,j} = \mu_0 \epsilon_0 \kappa \dot{E}_i \qquad [11.49]$$

By taking the time derivative of [11.49] and using [11.48] with the conditon that the space charge density η equal zero, we can obtain the wave equation (see Exercise 11.21.1)

$$E_{r,ss} = \mu_0 \epsilon_0 \kappa \ddot{E}_r \qquad [11.50]$$

A harmonic solution of [11.50] can be written as

$$E_r = A_r e^{ik(\alpha_q x_q - ut)} = A_r e^{i(k\alpha_q x_q - \omega t)} \qquad [11.51]$$

where u is the phase velocity given by

$$u = \frac{\omega}{k} \qquad [11.52]$$

By substituting [11.51] into [11.50], we see that

$$u^2 = \frac{1}{\mu_0 \epsilon_0 \kappa} \qquad [11.53]$$

The phase velocity in free space is given by [11.9] as $c = 1/\sqrt{\mu_0 \epsilon_0}$ so that from [11.53]

$$\kappa = \frac{c^2}{u^2} \qquad [11.54]$$

The ratio of the velocity of a wave in free space to its phase velocity in a medium is defined as the refractive index n, of the medium. That is,

$$n = \frac{c}{u} = \frac{kc}{\omega} \qquad [11.55]$$

where [11.52] has been used. Comparing [11.55] and [11.54], we see that

$$n^2 = \kappa \qquad [11.56]$$

Thus the square of the refractive index is equal to the dielectric constant.

Using the dielectric constant for a plasma given by [11.45] in [11.56] we obtain

$$n^2 = \kappa = 1 - \frac{\Pi^2}{\omega^2 + \nu^2} + i\,\frac{\Pi^2\nu/\omega}{\omega^2 + \nu^2}$$

$$= \kappa_R + i\kappa_I \qquad [11.57]$$

We see that the refractive index n will also be complex. That is

$$n = \mu + i\chi = \sqrt{\kappa} \qquad [11.58]$$

It is possible to write μ and χ in terms of κ_R and κ_I (see Exercise 11.21.2). Since the wave number k is related to the refractive index n from [11.55] by

$$k = \frac{\omega}{c}\,n \qquad [11.59]$$

then the electric field vector E_i can be written from [11.51] as

$$E_i = A_i e^{i[(\omega/c)n\alpha_q x_q - \omega t]} \qquad [11.60]$$

Substituting [11.58] into [11.60] and assuming propagation in the x_3-direction, we obtain

$$E_i = A_i e^{-(\omega/c)\chi x_3} e^{i[(\omega/c)\mu x_3 - \omega t]} \qquad [11.61]$$

This equation represents a propagating wave whose amplitude is being damped. The phase constant of the wave depends on the real part of the refractive index, while the attenuation constant depends on the imaginary part. Note that in the absence of collisions the imaginary part of the refractive index is zero so that the wave is not attenuated.

If the collision frequency is much less than the signal frequency ($\nu \ll \omega$), so that the effect of collisions can be ignored, then from [11.57] and [11.55] we can write

$$n^2 = \frac{k^2 c^2}{\omega^2} = 1 - \frac{\Pi^2}{\omega^2} \qquad [11.62]$$

from which we obtain the dispersion relation

$$\omega^2 = k^2c^2 + \Pi^2 \qquad [11.63]$$

or

$$k^2 = \frac{\omega^2 - \Pi^2}{c^2} \qquad [11.64]$$

From [11.63] we can plot ω vs. k as shown in Figure 11.5. We see that propagation occurs only when the signal frequency ω is greater than the plasma frequency Π.

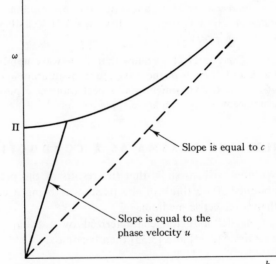

FIGURE 11.5 ω Versus k Plot for a Collisionless Plasma

Slope is equal to c

Slope is equal to the phase velocity u

Using [11.64], we can write the phase velocity u as

$$u = \frac{\omega}{k} = \frac{c}{(1 - \Pi^2/\omega^2)^{1/2}} \qquad [11.65]$$

which is always greater than c as shown in Figure 11.5.

When the signal frequency ω is less than the plasma frequency Π, then the wave number k and the refractive index n are purely imaginary (see [11.62] and [11.64]). The electric field vector E_i given by [11.51] can then be written (for propagation in the x_3-direction) as

$$E_i = A_i e^{-k_I x_3} e^{-i\omega t} \qquad [11.66]$$

where

$$k_I = \frac{1}{c}(\Pi^2 - \omega^2)^{1/2} \qquad\qquad [11.67]$$

Since E_i given by [11.66] varies harmonically in time but not in space it does not represent a propagating wave. Its amplitude is attenuated exponentially. Such a wave is called an evanescent wave. One can show (see Exercise 11.21.3) that when the wave number is purely imaginary, the E and H fields of the wave are in quadrature, and the value of the mean Poynting vector is zero. Therefore there is no net energy flow associated with this evanescent wave.

Exercise 11.21.1   Derive the wave equation [11.50].

Exercise 11.21.2   Show that the real and imaginary parts of the refractive index n are given by $\mu = [(|\kappa| + \kappa_R)/2]^{1/2}$ and $\chi = [(|\kappa| - \kappa_R)/2]^{1/2}$ where $|\kappa| = (\kappa_R^2 + \kappa_I^2)^{1/2}$.

Exercise 11.21.3   Show that if the wave number is purely imaginary then the E and H fields of the wave are in quadrature and the mean Poynting vector $\langle G_i \rangle$ is zero. Why might you expect transverse power flow associated with an evanescent wave in an anisotropic medium?

II.22 THE PLASMA AS A CONDUCTING MEDIUM

We now wish to show that the results of the previous section can also be obtained if we think of the plasma as being a conducting medium rather than a dielectric medium.

Consider a region characterized by a scalar conductivity σ. Maxwell's equations [3.34] and [3.35] then become

$$\epsilon_{krs}E_{s,r} = -\dot{B}_k \qquad\qquad [11.68]$$

and

$$\epsilon_{ijk}B_{k,j} = \mu_0\sigma E_i + \mu_0\epsilon_0\dot{E}_i \qquad\qquad [11.69]$$

Taking the time derivative of [11.69], we obtain

$$\epsilon_{ijk}\dot{B}_{k,j} = \mu_0\sigma\dot{E}_i + \mu_0\epsilon_0\ddot{E}_i \qquad\qquad [11.70]$$

Substituting B_k from [11.68] into [11.70], we obtain

$$\epsilon_{kij}\epsilon_{krs}E_{s,rj} = -\mu_0\sigma\dot{E}_i - \mu_0\epsilon_0\ddot{E}_i$$

from which

$$(\delta_{ir}\delta_{js} - \delta_{is}\delta_{jr})E_{s,rj} = -\mu_0\sigma\dot{E}_i - \mu_0\epsilon_0\ddot{E}_i$$

so that

$$E_{j,ij} - E_{i,jj} = -\mu_0\sigma\dot{E}_i - \mu_0\epsilon_0\ddot{E}_i \qquad [11.71]$$

Assuming the space charge η is zero, $E_{j,j} = 0$, and [11.71] becomes

$$E_{i,jj} = \mu_0\sigma\dot{E}_i + \mu_0\epsilon_0\ddot{E}_i \qquad [11.72]$$

Assume a wave solution for [11.72] of the form (see [11.12]),

$$E_i = A_i e^{i(k\alpha_q x_q - \omega t)} \qquad [11.73]$$

Substituting [11.73] into [11.72], we obtain

$$-k^2 E_i = \mu_0\sigma(-i\omega)E_i + \mu_0\epsilon_0(-\omega^2)E_i$$

or

$$(-k^2 + i\omega\mu_0\sigma + \mu_0\epsilon_0\omega^2)E_i = 0$$

Thus, for a wave to exist, we must have that

$$k^2 = \mu_0\epsilon_0\omega^2 + i\omega\mu_0\sigma \qquad [11.74]$$

Equation [11.74] is called the *dispersion equation* for the conducting medium. A dispersion equation relates the wave number k to the angular frequency ω. Notice that the dispersion equation does not tell what waves will exist but rather what waves may exist. That is, if the initial conditions are such that the assumed wave solution [11.73] is excited, then it will propagate according to [11.74].

We can rewrite [11.74] with the help of [11.9], [11.55], and [11.56] as

$$n^2 = \kappa = 1 + \frac{i\sigma}{\omega\epsilon_0} \qquad [11.75]$$

which relates the dielectric constant κ and the conductivity σ of the plasma. If we substitute the value of σ given by [11.46] for a plasma into [11.75], we obtain

$$n^2 = 1 - \frac{\Pi^2}{\omega^2 + \nu^2} + i\frac{\Pi^2\nu/\omega}{\omega^2 + \nu^2} \qquad [11.76]$$

which is the same expression for the refractive index as [11.57] found in the previous section. Thus the propagation properties of a plasma are the same whether it is considered to be a dielectric or a conducting medium.

11.23 WAVE PACKETS AND GROUP VELOCITY

In our discussion of waves up to now we have assumed waves of a single frequency. However in practice all waves have some finite spread in frequencies. The concept of a wave packet is particularly applicable when there is a small spread in frequencies about some central frequency ω_0. This is equivalent to a small spread in wave numbers about a central wave number k_0.

Let us consider an infinite set of harmonic waves propagating in the x_1-direction which can be represented by

$$E(x_1, t) = \int_{-\infty}^{\infty} A(k)e^{i(kx_1 - \omega t)} \, dk \qquad [11.77]$$

In this expression the weighting function $A(k)$ will be assumed to be peaked about some central wave number k_0. We have taken k to be the independent variable in [11.77] and ω is some function of k which is determined from the dispersion equation $\omega = \omega(k)$.

We could equally well have taken ω to be the independent variable in which case

$$E(x_1, t) = \int_{-\infty}^{\infty} A(\omega)e^{i(kx_1 - \omega t)} \, d\omega \qquad [11.78]$$

and the dispersion equation would give us $k = k(\omega)$. The weighting function would then be the frequency spectrum $A(\omega)$ which can be determined from the Fourier transform of $E(0, t)$. Such a frequency spectrum is often peaked about a central frequency ω_0 (see Problem 11.1).

When the functions $A(k)$ [or $A(\omega)$] are sufficiently peaked about a central value k_0 (or ω_0), then the expressions [11.77] and [11.78] are said to represent a wave packet. Let us write [11.78] as

$$E(x_1, t) = \int_{-\infty}^{\infty} A(\omega)e^{i\psi(\omega)} \, d\omega \qquad [11.79]$$

where

$$\psi(\omega) = kx_1 - \omega t \qquad [11.80]$$

Since $A(\omega)$ is peaked and has a maximum at ω_0, then the value of the integral in [11.79] will be largest when the frequencies near $\omega_0 = \omega(k_0)$ have the same phase and therefore interfere constructively. This will occur when $\psi(\omega)$ has an extremum or from [11.80] when

$$\frac{\partial \psi(\omega)}{\partial \omega} = 0 = \left(\frac{\partial k}{\partial \omega}\right)_{\omega_0} x_1 - t \qquad [11.81]$$

This result tells us that the maximum of the wave packet travels with a velocity v, known as the group velocity, and given by

$$v = \frac{dx_1}{dt} = \left(\frac{\partial \omega}{\partial k}\right)_{\omega_0} \qquad [11.82]$$

We can write the group velocity v in terms of the phase velocity u by noting from [11.52] that $\omega = uk$ so that $v = \partial \omega / \partial k = \partial (uk)/\partial k = u + k\, \partial u/\partial k$ or, using [11.11],

$$v = u - \lambda \frac{\partial u}{\partial \lambda} \qquad [11.83]$$

(see Exercise 11.23.1).

From [11.83] we can consider three possibilities. If the phase velocity is not a function of the wavelength, then the group velocity is equal to the phase velocity and the medium is said to be nondispersive. If the phase velocity increases for increasing wavelengths ($\partial u/\partial \lambda > 0$), then the group velocity is less than the phase velocity and the medium is said to exhibit normal dispersion. On the other hand, if the phase velocity decreases for increasing wavelengths ($\partial u/\partial \lambda < 0$), then the group velocity is greater than the phase velocity and one refers to this case as anomalous dispersion.

For the plasma medium considered in the previous sections we see from [11.63] that the group velocity can be written as

$$v = \frac{\partial \omega}{\partial k} = \frac{kc^2}{\omega} = \frac{c^2}{u} \qquad [11.84]$$

from which

$$uv = c^2 \qquad [11.85]$$

Substituting [11.65] into [11.84], we obtain

$$v = c \left(1 - \frac{\Pi^2}{\omega^2}\right)^{1/2} \qquad [11.86]$$

so that the group velocity is always less than c.

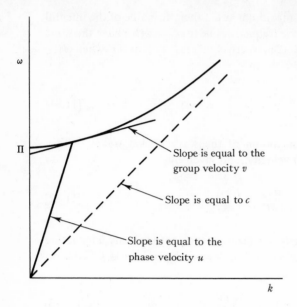

Slope is equal to the
group velocity v

Slope is equal to c

Slope is equal to the
phase velocity u

FIGURE II.6 ω Versus k Plot
Illustrating Phase and Group
Velocities

We notice from the relation $v = \partial\omega/\partial k$ that the group velocity will be equal
to the slope of the tangent to the dispersion curve in a plot of ω vs. k. This
is illustrated in Figure 11.6 where the ω-k plot for a collisionless plasma is

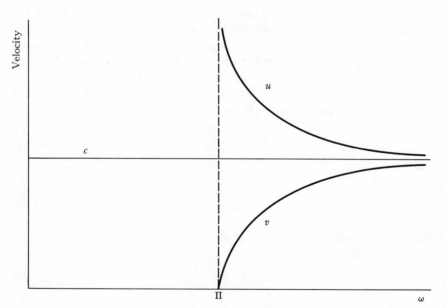

FIGURE II.7 Phase Velocity u and Group Velocity v as a Function of ω

redrawn from Figure 11.5. We see that the group velocity increases from zero to c as the frequency increases from the plasma frequency to infinity. The frequency dependence of the phase velocity and group velocity are shown in Figure 11.7.

Exercise 11.23.1 Verify [11.83].

11.3 ELECTRON
PLASMA OSCILLATIONS

We now wish to illustrate the second main approach to wave problems in plasmas by using a single-fluid model in which only the motions of the electrons are considered. We will write the appropriate continuity and momentum equations for the electrons and then solve them simultaneously with Maxwell's equations.

The purpose of this section is twofold. The first is to illustrate, with a simple case, the technique that will be used in Chapter 12 to analyze the more general case of waves in a two-fluid plasma when the effects of a magnetic field are included. The second purpose is to obtain results that describe longitudinal electron plasma oscillations.

In this section we will consider the case in which no external magnetic field exists and we will neglect the effect of collisions between the electrons and heavier particles. For this case the momentum equation for the electrons can be written from Section 6.22 in the form

$$N_- m_- \left(\frac{\partial \langle v_i^- \rangle}{\partial t} + \langle v_j^- \rangle \frac{\partial \langle v_i^- \rangle}{\partial x_j} \right) + \frac{\partial \Psi_{ij}^-}{x_j} - N_- q_- E_i = 0 \qquad [11.87]$$

Now, in general, we would not expect the pressure tensor to be isotropic for the problem of plasma oscillations in which the electron density varies in a preferred direction. Nevertheless we will assume that Ψ_{ij}^- can be written as some scalar pressure $P_- \delta_{ij}$ where the effect of the anisotropy can be included in the particular form of P_-. We can then write the momentum equation [11.87] as

$$\frac{\partial \langle v_i^- \rangle}{\partial t} + \langle v_j^- \rangle \frac{\partial \langle v_i^- \rangle}{\partial x_j} = -\frac{e}{m_-} E_i - \frac{1}{N_- m_-} \frac{\partial P_-}{\partial x_i} \qquad [11.88]$$

This equation is nonlinear and in order to proceed we will linearize it in the following way. We will assume that the wave phenomena or oscillations are adequately described as small perturbations from an equilibrium configuration. That is, we will assume that the electron velocity $\langle v_i^- \rangle$ and the electron number density N_- can be written as

$$\langle v_i^- \rangle = C_i^- + \bar{v}_i^- \qquad [11.89]$$

and

$$N_- = N_0 + \bar{N}_- \qquad [11.90]$$

where C_i^- and N_0 represent constant average values while $\bar{v}_i^-$ and $\bar{N}_-$ represent small perturbations from equilibrium. In the linearization process products of these small quantities are neglected.

Now in the pressure gradient term of [11.88] we can write

$$\frac{1}{m_-} \frac{\partial P_-}{\partial x_i} = \frac{1}{m_-} \frac{\partial P_-}{\partial \bar{N}_-} \frac{\partial \bar{N}_-}{\partial x_i} = a^2 \frac{\partial \bar{N}_-}{\partial x_i} \qquad [11.91]$$

where

$$a = \left(\frac{1}{m_-} \frac{\partial P_-}{\partial \bar{N}_-} \right)^{1/2} \qquad [11.92]$$

has the dimensions of velocity and is of the order of the thermal velocity.

For example, if we assume that the plasma is isothermal then

$$P_- = N_- kT_- = (N_0 + \bar{N}_-)kT_-$$

so that

$$a^2 = \frac{kT_-}{m_-} \qquad [11.93]$$

(There should be no confusion between Boltzmann's constant which occurs in kT and the wave number k.)

On the other hand, plasma oscillations are more likely to behave adiabatically, in which case (see Section 6.23)

$$\frac{P_-}{P_0} = \left(\frac{N_-}{N_0} \right)^{\gamma} \qquad [11.94]$$

where

$$P_0 = N_0 kT_0 = \text{const} \qquad [11.95]$$

and T_0 is the constant, average part of the electron temperature. Using [11.94] and [11.95] and the fact that $\bar{N}_- \ll N_0$, we find that

$$\frac{\partial P_-}{\partial \bar{N}_-} = N_0 kT_0 \frac{\partial}{\partial \bar{N}_-} \left(\frac{N_0 + \bar{N}_-}{N_0}\right)^\gamma = N_0 kT_0 \frac{\partial}{\partial \bar{N}_-} \left(1 + \frac{\gamma \bar{N}_-}{N_0}\right) \qquad [11.96]$$

or

$$\frac{\partial P_-}{\partial \bar{N}_-} = \gamma kT_0 \qquad [11.96]$$

so that

$$a^2 = \gamma \frac{kT_0}{m_-} \qquad [11.97]$$

Note that [11.97] differs from [11.93] only in the constant γ. For an ideal gas with three degrees of freedom we found that $\gamma = \frac{5}{3}$. However, due to the anisotropy mentioned at the beginning of this section, we can consider the plasma to have only one degree of freedom, in which case $\gamma = 3$. In any event we will use [11.91] in the momentum equation where the velocity a is of the order of the thermal velocity.

Substituting [11.89], [11.90], and [11.91] into [11.88] and neglecting terms involving the products of the small perturbations, we obtain

$$\frac{\partial \bar{v}_i^-}{\partial t} + C_j^- \frac{\partial \bar{v}_i^-}{\partial x_j} = -\frac{e}{m_-} E_i - \frac{a^2}{N_0} \frac{\partial \bar{N}_-}{\partial x_i} \qquad [11.98]$$

If we consider a plasma whose electrons have no constant average velocity, then $C_i^- = 0$, so that the only electron motion contributing to $\langle v_i^- \rangle$ is the small oscillatory motion $\bar{v}_i^-$. For this case we can then write [11.98] as

$$\frac{\partial \bar{v}_i^-}{\partial t} = -\frac{e}{m_-} E_i - \frac{a^2}{N_0} \frac{\partial \bar{N}_-}{\partial x_i} \qquad [11.99]$$

The continuity equation for the electrons is

$$\frac{\partial N_-}{\partial t} + (N_- \langle v_i^- \rangle)_{,i} = 0$$

which can be written in linearized form, using [11.89] and [11.90] with $C_i^- = 0$, as

$$\frac{\partial \bar{N}_-}{\partial t} + N_0 \bar{v}_{i,i}^- = 0 \qquad [11.100]$$

We now have Maxwell's equations

$$\epsilon_{ijk}E_{k,j} = -\dot{B}_i \qquad\qquad [11.101]$$

and

$$\epsilon_{ijk}B_{k,j} = \mu_0 J_i + \mu_0\epsilon_0\dot{E}_i \qquad\qquad [11.102]$$

where the current density J_i is given, after linearizing, by

$$J_i = -N_0 e\bar{v}_i^- \qquad\qquad [11.103]$$

Equations [11.99] to [11.103] represent a total of thirteen scalar equations in the thirteen unknowns E_i, B_i, J_i, $\bar{v}_i^-$, and $\bar{N}_-$. In the following section we will obtain a dispersion equation by assuming harmonic wave solutions for these unknown variables and solving the resultant equations simultaneously.

11.31 THE DISPERSION EQUATION

If we assume a wave solution for the quantities E_i, B_i, J_i, $\bar{v}_i^-$, and $\bar{N}_-$ of the form $e^{i(k\alpha_q x_q - \omega t)}$ then [11.99] to [11.103] can be written respectively as

$$-i\omega\bar{v}_i^- = -\frac{e}{m_-}E_i - ik\alpha_i a^2 \frac{\bar{N}_-}{N_0} \qquad\qquad [11.104]$$

$$-i\omega\bar{N}_- + ik\alpha_i N_0\bar{v}_i^- = 0 \qquad\qquad [11.105]$$

$$ik\epsilon_{ijk}\alpha_j E_k = i\omega B_i \qquad\qquad [11.106]$$

$$ik\epsilon_{ijk}\alpha_j B_k = \mu_0 J_i - i\omega\mu_0\epsilon_0 E_i \qquad\qquad [11.107]$$

$$J_i = -N_0 e\bar{v}_i^- \qquad\qquad [11.108]$$

We can write [11.106] as

$$B_k = \frac{k}{\omega}\epsilon_{krs}\alpha_r E_s \qquad\qquad [11.109]$$

Substituting [11.109] and [11.108] into [11.107] and using $c^2 = 1/(\mu_0\epsilon_0)$ we obtain

$$\frac{ik^2}{\omega}\epsilon_{ijk}\epsilon_{krs}\alpha_j\alpha_r E_s = -\mu_0 N_0 e\bar{v}_i^- - i\omega\mu_0\epsilon_0 E_i$$

or,

$$\epsilon_{kij}\epsilon_{krs}\alpha_j\alpha_r E_s = \frac{i\omega\mu_o N_o e}{k^2}\,\bar{v}_i^{\,-} - \frac{\omega^2}{k^2 c^2}\,E_i$$

whence,

$$(\delta_{ir}\delta_{js} - \delta_{is}\delta_{jr})\alpha_j\alpha_r E_s = \frac{i\omega\mu_o N_o e}{k^2}\,\bar{v}_i^{\,-} - \frac{\omega^2}{k^2 c^2}\,E_i$$

and,

$$\alpha_j\alpha_i E_j - \alpha_j\alpha_j E_i + \frac{\omega^2}{k^2 c^2}\,E_i = \frac{i\omega\mu_o N_o e}{k^2}\,\bar{v}_i^{\,-}$$

or, since $\alpha_j\alpha_j = 1$,

$$\bar{v}_i^{\,-} = \frac{k^2}{i\omega\mu_o N_o e}\left[\alpha_i\alpha_j - \delta_{ij}\left(1 - \frac{\omega^2}{k^2 c^2}\right)\right]E_j \qquad [11.110]$$

We still have equations [11.104] and [11.105] to use. From [11.105] we can write

$$\bar{N}_- = \frac{k}{\omega}\,N_o\alpha_j\bar{v}_j^{\,-} \qquad\qquad\qquad [11.111]$$

Substituting [11.111] into [11.104], we obtain

$$\bar{v}_i^{\,-} = -\,\frac{ie}{m_-\omega}\,E_i + \frac{k^2 a^2}{\omega^2}\,\alpha_i\alpha_j\bar{v}_j^{\,-}$$

from which

$$-\,\frac{ie}{m_-\omega}\,E_i = \left(\delta_{ij} - \frac{k^2 a^2}{\omega^2}\,\alpha_i\alpha_j\right)\bar{v}_j^{\,-} \qquad [11.112]$$

Finally, if we substitute [11.110] into [11.112], we obtain

$$\frac{N_o e^2}{m_-\epsilon_o}\,\frac{\mu_o\epsilon_o}{k^2}\,E_i = \left(\delta_{ij} - \frac{k^2 a^2}{\omega^2}\,\alpha_i\alpha_j\right)\left[\alpha_j\alpha_k - \delta_{jk}\left(1 - \frac{\omega^2}{k^2 c^2}\right)\right]E_k$$

$$\frac{\Pi^2}{k^2 c^2}\,E_i = \left[\alpha_i\alpha_k - \delta_{ik}\left(1 - \frac{\omega^2}{k^2 c^2}\right) - \frac{k^2 a^2}{\omega^2}\,\alpha_i\alpha_k + \alpha_i\alpha_k\,\frac{k^2 a^2}{\omega^2}\left(1 - \frac{\omega^2}{k^2 c^2}\right)\right]E_k$$

$$= \left[\alpha_i\alpha_k\left(1 - \frac{a^2}{c^2}\right) - \delta_{ik}\left(1 - \frac{\omega^2}{k^2 c^2}\right)\right]E_k$$

from which

$$\left[\delta_{ik}\left(1 - \frac{\omega^2}{k^2 c^2} + \frac{\Pi^2}{k^2 c^2}\right) - \alpha_i \alpha_k \left(1 - \frac{a^2}{c^2}\right)\right] E_k = 0 \qquad [11.113]$$

If we now assume that the wave is propagating in the x_3-direction so that $\alpha_i = (0, 0, 1)$ then

$$\alpha_i \alpha_k = \begin{bmatrix} 0 & 0 & 0 \\ 0 & 0 & 0 \\ 0 & 0 & 1 \end{bmatrix}$$

and [11.113] can be written in matrix form as

$$\begin{bmatrix} \left(1 - \frac{\omega^2}{k^2 c^2} + \frac{\Pi^2}{k^2 c^2}\right) & 0 & 0 \\ 0 & \left(1 - \frac{\omega^2}{k^2 c^2} + \frac{\Pi^2}{k^2 c^2}\right) & 0 \\ 0 & 0 & \left(\frac{a^2}{c^2} - \frac{\omega^2}{k^2 c^2} + \frac{\Pi^2}{k^2 c^2}\right) \end{bmatrix} \begin{bmatrix} E_1 \\ E_2 \\ E_3 \end{bmatrix} = 0$$

$$[11.114]$$

from which

$$\left(1 - \frac{\omega^2}{k^2 c^2} + \frac{\Pi^2}{k^2 c^2}\right) E_1 = 0 \qquad [11.115]$$

$$\left(1 - \frac{\omega^2}{k^2 c^2} + \frac{\Pi^2}{k^2 c^2}\right) E_2 = 0 \qquad [11.116]$$

$$\left(\frac{a^2}{c^2} - \frac{\omega^2}{k^2 c^2} + \frac{\Pi^2}{k^2 c^2}\right) E_3 = 0 \qquad [11.117]$$

For the fields E_1, E_2, and E_3 to exist, the coefficients in each case must vanish. From [11.115] and [11.116] we see that the dispersion equation for the transverse fields E_1 and E_2 is

$$\omega^2 = \Pi^2 + k^2 c^2 \qquad [11.118]$$

which is the same as that found in Section 11.21 (see [11.63]). However from [11.117] we see that we can also have a longitudinal wave in which the E-field is in the direction of propagation and that the dispersion equation for this wave is given by

$$\omega^2 = \Pi^2 + k^2 a^2 \qquad [11.119]$$

We note that this dispersion equation is of the same form as [11.118] for the transverse waves where the thermal speed a replaces the speed of light c. The properties of this wave and the conditions under which it can propagate will be discussed in the following chapter in Section 12.21.

11.4 THE VLASOV EQUATION

In this section we wish to introduce the manner in which the Boltzmann equation can be used, together with Maxwell's equations, to describe wave phenomena in plasmas. Let us consider the Boltzmann equation in the form

$$\frac{\partial f}{\partial t} + v_i \frac{\partial f}{\partial x_i} + \frac{q}{m} E_i \frac{\partial f}{\partial v_i} = \left(\frac{\partial f}{\partial t}\right)_{\text{coll}} \qquad [11.120]$$

where we have neglected any forces due to magnetic fields. Various forms of the collision term on the right-hand side of [11.120] have been considered in previous chapters. Thus electron-neutral collisions could be described in terms of the binary collision integral. On the other hand, Coulomb collisions were treated in Chapter 9 by a term of the Fokker-Planck type. In that case we found that the effect of Coulomb shielding led us to cut off our integrations at impact parameters equal to the Debye length.

The question now arises as to how we can include in [11.120] interactions between charged particles separated by distances greater than the Debye length. It is clear from our considerations of Coulomb shielding that such charged particles do not interact with each other on an individual basis. Rather, macroscopic space charge fields can be set up as the result of fluctuations in the charged particle densities. These space charge fields will, in turn, influence the motion of the charged particles. It is by this means of "collective oscillations" that charged particles separated by distances greater than a Debye length "interact."

The method of analyzing this collective behavior by means of the Boltzmann equation was first considered by Vlasov. For this case the collision term on the right-hand side of [11.120] is neglected entirely and the electric field on the left-hand side is taken to be the space charge field that exists within the plasma. If we restrict ourselves to longitudinal modes of propagation then the electric field E_i can be expressed as the gradient of a scalar potential $(E_i = -\psi_{,i})$ which is determined from Poisson's equation

$$E_{i,i} = -\psi_{,ii} = \frac{\eta}{\epsilon_o} \qquad [11.121]$$

(see Exercise 11.4.1). The charge density η is given by [3.4] as

$$\eta = e(N_+ - N_-) \qquad [11.122]$$

Let us consider the electron motion only and assume that the ions form a neutralizing background charge with an average number density N_0. Neglecting the collision term, the Boltzmann equation for the electrons can be written from [11.120] as

$$\frac{\partial f_-}{\partial t} + v_i \frac{\partial f_-}{\partial x_i} - \frac{e}{m} E_i \frac{\partial f_-}{\partial v_i} = 0 \qquad [11.123]$$

We will now linearize this equation by letting

$$f_- = f^0 + \tilde{f} \qquad [11.124]$$

where f^0 is the stationary distribution and $\tilde{f}$ is the small fluctuating term. Substituting [11.124] into [11.123] and neglecting the product $E_i \, \partial \tilde{f}/\partial v_i$, we obtain

$$\frac{\partial \tilde{f}}{\partial t} + v_i \frac{\partial \tilde{f}}{\partial x_i} - \frac{e}{m} E_i \frac{\partial f^0}{\partial v_i} = 0 \qquad [11.125]$$

The electron density N_- is given by

$$N_- = \int f_- \, dc = \int f^0 \, dc + \int \tilde{f} \, dc = N_0 + \int \tilde{f} \, dc \qquad [11.126]$$

so that the charge density η from [11.122] becomes

$$\eta = -e \int \tilde{f} \, dc \qquad [11.127]$$

Substituting [11.127] into [11.121], we find that

$$E_{i,i} = -\frac{e}{\epsilon_0} \int \tilde{f} \, dc \qquad [11.128]$$

The simultaneous solution of [11.125] and [11.128] for $\tilde{f}$ and E_i represents a self-consistent solution in which the electric field that determines the distribution function is itself determined by the distribution function.

The "collisionless" form of the Boltzmann equation when used in this way is often referred to as the Vlasov equation. Vlasov originally looked for stationary solutions by assuming wave solutions of the form $e^{i(k\alpha_q x_q - \omega t)}$ for both E_i and $\tilde{f}$ in [11.125] and [11.128]. This procedure leads to the dispersion equation (see Exercise 11.4.2)

$$\frac{e^2}{m\epsilon_0 k} \int \frac{\alpha_i \, \partial f^0/\partial v_i}{(k\alpha_i v_i - \omega)} \, dc = 1 \qquad [11.129]$$

However the integration in [11.129] cannot be carried out directly since the denominator in the integrand vanishes for certain values of v_i. This difficulty was pointed out by Landau who sought to remedy the situation by letting ω be complex. In so doing he found that under certain conditions the oscillations became severely damped. We will discuss these conditions for Landau damping in Chapter 12.

Much effort has subsequently been directed toward the proper way of solving [11.125] and [11.128] and in carrying out the integrations. We will not pursue this matter further, but the interested student may consult the references at the end of the chapter.

Exercise 11.4.1 Show that if one considers only longitudinal modes of propagation, then it is sufficient to use Poisson's equation rather than the full Maxwell equations in the wave treatment of this section.

Exercise 11.4.2 Show that the substitution method of assuming harmonic wave solutions for E_i and f leads to the dispersion equation [11.129].

Problem

11.1 Consider a pulsed carrier of frequency $\omega_0/2\pi$ and pulse width T. Evaluate the Fourier transform for this case and show that the frequency spectrum is peaked about ω_0 when $2\pi/\omega_0 \ll T$.

REFERENCES

Electromagnetic waves in free space are discussed in any text on electromagnetic theory. See, for example, the references at the end of Chapter 3. References on plasma waves based on the macroscopic equations and the wave equation approach are given at the end of Chapters 12 and 13.
Electron plasma oscillations are treated by means of the Vlasov equation by

1   Berg, F. "On the Theory of Plasma Waves," *Proc. Phys. Soc. B*, **69** (1956), 939–52.

2   Bohm, D., and E. P. Gross. "Theory of Plasma Oscillations—A. Origin of Medium-Like Behavior," *Phys. Rev.*, **75** (1949), 1851.

3   Bohm, D., and E. P. Gross. "Theory of Plasma Oscillations—B. Excitation and Damping of Oscillations," *Phys. Rev.*, **75** (1949), 1864.

4   Gartenhaus, S. *Elements of Plasma Physics*. New York: Holt, Rinehart and Winston, 1964.

5　　Jackson, J. D. "Longitudinal Plasma Oscillations," *J. Nucl. Energy*, Part C: Plasma Physics, **1** (1960), 171–89.

6　　Stix, T. H. *The Theory of Plasma Waves*. New York: McGraw-Hill, 1962.

7　　Van Kampen, N. G. "On the Theory of Stationary Waves in Plasmas," *Physica*, **21** (1955), 949–63.

12

PLASMA OSCILLATIONS

In the previous chapter the topic of wave phenomena in plasmas was introduced. We pointed out that two main approaches to the problem were possible depending upon whether a wave equation was explicitly derived. In Section 11.3 we discussed electron plasma oscillations by solving the macroscopic equations for electrons simultaneously with Maxwell's equations. We now wish to generalize that approach by including the effects of positive ion motion and an external magnetic field.

A general dispersion equation will be obtained in Section 12.1 after the plasma equations are linearized. This general dispersion equation includes the effects of the thermal motion of the electrons and ions. We look at the special cases of propagation along and normal to the magnetic field in Sections 12.2 and 12.3 respectively. In particular we will look in detail at the propagation of longitudinal waves along the magnetic field. The propagation of transverse waves is discussed only briefly where the connection with the more detailed treatment given in Chapter 13 is noted.

12.1 GENERAL TREATMENT OF THE PLASMA EQUATIONS

In this section we write down the equations describing a two-fluid plasma composed of electrons and positive ions. The continuity equations for the electrons and ions are from [6.16]

$$\frac{\partial N_-}{\partial t} + \frac{\partial N_-\langle v_i^- \rangle}{\partial x_i} = 0 \qquad [12.1]$$

and

$$\frac{\partial N_+}{\partial t} + \frac{\partial N_+\langle v_i^+ \rangle}{\partial x_i} = 0 \qquad [12.2]$$

The momentum equations for the electrons and ions can be written from [6.37] as

$$\frac{\partial \langle v_i^- \rangle}{\partial t} + \langle v_j^- \rangle \frac{\partial \langle v_i^- \rangle}{\partial x_j} = -\frac{e}{m_-} [E_i + \epsilon_{ijk}\langle v_j^- \rangle B_k]$$
$$- \frac{1}{N_- m_-} \frac{\partial P_-}{\partial x_i} - \nu_{\mathrm{EI}}[\langle v_i^- \rangle - \langle v_i^+ \rangle] \qquad [12.3]$$

and

$$\frac{\partial \langle v_i^+ \rangle}{\partial t} + \langle v_j^+ \rangle \frac{\partial \langle v_i^+ \rangle}{\partial x_j} = \frac{e}{m_+} [E_i + \epsilon_{ijk}\langle v_j^+ \rangle B_k]$$
$$- \frac{1}{N_+ m_+} \frac{\partial P_+}{\partial x_i} + \nu_{\mathrm{IE}}[\langle v_i^- \rangle - \langle v_i^+ \rangle] \qquad [12.4]$$

where ν_{EI} and ν_{IE} are effective collision frequencies for momentum transfer between electrons and ions.

To these equations we must add Maxwell's equations

$$\epsilon_{ijk}E_{k,j} = -\dot{B}_i \qquad [12.5]$$

and

$$\epsilon_{ijk}B_{k,j} = \mu_o J_i + \mu_o \epsilon_o \dot{E}_i \qquad [12.6]$$

where the current density J_i is given by

$$J_i = e[N_+\langle v_i^+ \rangle - N_-\langle v_i^- \rangle] \qquad [12.7]$$

Equations [12.1] to [12.7] represent a set of coupled nonlinear equations. We will linearize these equations in the following section after which we will look for wave solutions of the linearized equations.

12.11 THE LINEARIZED PLASMA EQUATIONS

In order to linearize the equations of the previous section, we first assume that the electron and ion densities $N_\pm$ consist of the same constant average value N_0 plus a small perturbation $\overline{N}_\pm$. Thus we will write

$$N_\pm = N_0 + \overline{N}_\pm \qquad [12.8]$$

Similarly we will write the mean electron and ion velocities $\langle v_i^\pm \rangle$ as

$$\langle v_i^\pm \rangle = C_i^\pm + \bar{v}_i^\pm \qquad [12.9]$$

where $C_i^\pm$ is a constant average velocity and $\bar{v}_i^\pm$ is a small perturbation. Finally the magnetic induction B_i will be written as the sum of a constant field vector B_i° plus a small perturbation b_i, that is

$$B_i = B_i^\circ + b_i \qquad [12.10]$$

The electric field E_i is assumed to have no constant part.

We now substitute Equations [12.8] to [12.10] into Equations [12.1] to [12.7] and neglect terms that contain products of the small perturbations. The continuity equations [12.1] and [12.2] then become

$$\frac{\partial \overline{N}_-}{\partial t} + N_0 \frac{\partial \bar{v}_i^-}{\partial x_i} + C_i^- \frac{\partial \overline{N}_-}{\partial x_i} = 0 \qquad [12.11]$$

and

$$\frac{\partial \overline{N}_+}{\partial t} + N_0 \frac{\partial \bar{v}_i^+}{\partial x_i} + C_i^+ \frac{\partial \overline{N}_+}{\partial x_i} = 0 \qquad [12.12]$$

In the momentum equations the pressure terms become

$$\frac{1}{N_\pm m_\pm} \frac{\partial P_\pm}{\partial x_i} = \frac{a_\pm^2}{N_0} \frac{\partial \overline{N}_\pm}{\partial x_i} \qquad [12.13]$$

where $a_\pm$ is a velocity given by

$$a_\pm^2 = \frac{1}{m_\pm} \frac{\partial P_\pm}{\partial \overline{N}_\pm} \qquad [12.14]$$

which is of the order of the thermal velocity as discussed in Section 11.3. The linearized momentum equations for the electrons and ions can then be written as

$$\frac{\partial \bar{v}_i^-}{\partial t} + C_j^- \frac{\partial \bar{v}_i^-}{\partial x_j} + \frac{e}{m_-} [E_i + \epsilon_{ijk}(C_j^- B_k^0 + C_j^- b_k + \bar{v}_j^- B_k^0)]$$
$$+ \frac{a_-^2}{N_o} \frac{\partial \bar{N}_-}{\partial x_i} + \nu_{EI}[C_i^- - C_i^+ + \bar{v}_i^- - \bar{v}_i^+] = 0 \qquad [12.15]$$

and

$$\frac{\partial \bar{v}_i^+}{\partial t} + C_j^+ \frac{\partial \bar{v}_i^+}{\partial x_j} - \frac{e}{m_+} [E_i + \epsilon_{ijk}(C_j^+ B_k^0 + C_j^+ b_k + \bar{v}_j^+ B_k^0)]$$
$$+ \frac{a_+^2}{N_o} \frac{\partial \bar{N}_+}{\partial x_i} - \nu_{IE}[C_i^- - C_i^+ + \bar{v}_i^- - \bar{v}_i^+] = 0 \qquad [12.16]$$

Maxwell's equations [12.5] and [12.6] take the form

$$\epsilon_{ijk} E_{k,j} = -\dot{b}_i \qquad [12.17]$$

and

$$\epsilon_{ijk} b_{k,j} = \mu_o J_i + \mu_o \epsilon_o \dot{E}_i \qquad [12.18]$$

Finally the linearized form of the current density J_i from [12.7] is

$$J_i = eN_o(C_i^+ - C_i^-) + eN_o(\bar{v}_i^+ - \bar{v}_i^-) + e(\bar{N}_+ C_i^+ - \bar{N}_- C_i^-) \qquad [12.19]$$

Our plan is to obtain a set of homogeneous equations involving the perturbed quantities. However this is not possible with the present set of equations since the momentum equations and the equation for J_i contain constant terms not involving the perturbed quantities. The resulting set of equations for the perturbed quantities will therefore be inhomogeneous.

In order to circumvent this difficulty we will set $C_i^\pm = 0$. That is, there is no constant motion of the electrons and ions. For simplicity we will also neglect electron-ion collisions; that is, we will set ν_{EI} and ν_{IE} equal to zero.

Under these conditions we then have the following set of linearized equations: the continuity equations

$$\frac{\partial \bar{N}_-}{\partial t} + N_o \frac{\partial \bar{v}_i^-}{\partial x_i} = 0 \qquad [12.20]$$

and

$$\frac{\partial \bar{N}_+}{\partial t} + N_o \frac{\partial \bar{v}_i^+}{\partial x_i} = 0 \qquad [12.21]$$

the momentum equations

$$\frac{\partial \bar{v}_i^-}{\partial t} + \frac{e}{m_-} [E_i + \epsilon_{ijk} \bar{v}_j^- B_k^o] + \frac{a_-^2}{N_o} \frac{\partial \bar{N}_-}{\partial x_i} = 0 \qquad [12.22]$$

and

$$\frac{\partial \bar{v}_i^+}{\partial t} - \frac{e}{m_+} [E_i + \epsilon_{ijk} \bar{v}_j^+ B_k^o] + \frac{a_+^2}{N_o} \frac{\partial \bar{N}_+}{\partial x_i} = 0 \qquad [12.23]$$

Maxwell's equations

$$\epsilon_{ijk} E_{k,j} = -\dot{b}_i \qquad [12.24]$$

and

$$\epsilon_{ijk} b_{k,j} = \mu_o J_i + \mu_o \epsilon_o \dot{E}_i \qquad [12.25]$$

and the current density

$$J_i = eN_o(\bar{v}_i^+ - \bar{v}_i^-) \qquad [12.26]$$

Wave solutions to this set of equations will be considered in the following section.

12.12   WAVE SOLUTIONS

We now assume that the perturbed quantities E_i, b_i, $\bar{v}_i^\pm$, and $\bar{N}_\pm$ have harmonic variations of the form $\exp[i(k\alpha_q x_q - \omega t)]$. Under this condition the time and spatial derivatives in equations [12.20] to [12.26] can be written as $\partial/\partial t = -i\omega$ and $\partial/\partial x_i = ik\alpha_i$. Introducing the cyclotron frequency

$$\Omega_k^\pm = -\frac{q^\pm B_k^o}{m_\pm} \qquad [12.27]$$

we then obtain the following set of linearized equations: The continuity equations

$$-i\omega \bar{N}_- + ikN_o\alpha_i \bar{v}_i^- = 0 \qquad [12.28]$$

and

$$-i\omega \bar{N}_+ + ikN_o\alpha_i \bar{v}_i^+ = 0 \qquad [12.29]$$

the momentum equations

$$-i\omega \bar{v}_i^- + \frac{e}{m_-} E_i + \epsilon_{ijk}\bar{v}_j^- \Omega_k^- + ik\alpha_i \bar{N}_- \frac{a_-^2}{N_o} = 0 \qquad [12.30]$$

and

$$-i\omega \bar{v}_i^+ - \frac{e}{m_+} E_i + \epsilon_{ijk}\bar{v}_j^+ \Omega_k^+ + ik\alpha_i \bar{N}_+ \frac{a_+^2}{N_o} = 0 \qquad [12.31]$$

Maxwell's equations

$$ik\epsilon_{ijk}\alpha_j E_k = i\omega b_i \qquad [12.32]$$

and

$$ik\epsilon_{ijk}\alpha_j b_k = \mu_o J_i - i\omega\mu_o\epsilon_o E_i \qquad [12.33]$$

and the current density

$$J_i = eN_o(\bar{v}_i^+ - \bar{v}_i^-) \qquad [12.34]$$

Equations [12.28] to [12.34] represent a total of seventeen scalar equations in the seventeen unknowns $\bar{N}_+$, $\bar{N}_-$, $\bar{v}_i^+$, $\bar{v}_i^-$, E_i, b_i, and J_i (each of the vector quantities have three scalar components). We would like to combine these equations in such a way as to eliminate all of the unknowns except the three components of the electric field E_i. We would then have a set of three homogeneous equations in the three unknowns E_1, E_2, and E_3 and the dispersion equation could then be found by setting the determinant of the coefficients equal to zero.

From [12.32] we can write the magnetic field vector as

$$b_k = \frac{k}{\omega} \epsilon_{krs}\alpha_r E_s \qquad [12.35]$$

We can then eliminate b_k and J_i from our set of equations by substituting [12.35] and [12.34] into [12.33], from which we obtain

$$\frac{ik^2}{\omega} \epsilon_{kij}\epsilon_{krs}\alpha_j\alpha_r E_s = \mu_o eN_o(\bar{v}_i^+ - \bar{v}_i^-) - i\omega\mu_o\epsilon_o E_i$$

or, using [2.27], and setting $\mu_o\epsilon_o = 1/c^2$

$$(\delta_{ir}\delta_{js} - \delta_{is}\delta_{jr})\alpha_j\alpha_r E_s = -i\frac{\omega\mu_o eN_o}{k^2}(\bar{v}_i^+ - \bar{v}_i^-) - \frac{\omega^2}{k^2c^2} E_i$$

from which

$$\alpha_j\alpha_i E_j - \alpha_j\alpha_j E_i + \frac{\omega^2}{k^2 c^2} E_i = -\frac{i\omega\mu_o e N_o}{k^2}(\bar{v}_i^+ - \bar{v}_i^-)$$

which, since $\alpha_j\alpha_j = 1$, can be written as

$$\left[\delta_{ij}\left(1 - \frac{\omega^2}{k^2 c^2}\right) - \alpha_i\alpha_j\right] E_j = \frac{i\omega\mu_o e N_o}{k^2}(\bar{v}_i^+ - \bar{v}_i^-) \qquad [12.36]$$

which is a type of wave equation involving the electric field E_j and the electron and ion velocities $\bar{v}_i^+$ and $\bar{v}_i^-$.

Now from the continuity equations [12.28] and [12.29] we can write the number densities $\bar{N}_\pm$ as

$$\bar{N}_- = \frac{k}{\omega} N_o \alpha_j \bar{v}_j^- \qquad [12.37]$$

and

$$\bar{N}_+ = \frac{k}{\omega} N_o \alpha_j \bar{v}_j^+ \qquad [12.38]$$

Substituting [12.37] and [12.38] into the momentum equations [12.30] and [12.31], we obtain

$$\bar{v}_i^- + \frac{ie}{m_-\omega} E_i + \frac{i}{\omega} \epsilon_{ijk}\bar{v}_j^- \Omega_k^- - \frac{k^2 a_-^2}{\omega^2} \alpha_i\alpha_j \bar{v}_j^- = 0 \qquad [12.39]$$

and

$$\bar{v}_i^+ - \frac{ie}{m_+\omega} E_i + \frac{i}{\omega} \epsilon_{ijk}\bar{v}_j^+ \Omega_k^+ - \frac{k^2 a_+^2}{\omega^2} \alpha_i\alpha_j \bar{v}_j^+ = 0 \qquad [12.40]$$

If we let

$$Y_k^\pm = \frac{\Omega_k^\pm}{\omega} \qquad [12.41]$$

then we can write [12.39] and [12.40] as

$$\left[\delta_{ij} + i\epsilon_{ijk} Y_k^- - \frac{k^2 a_-^2}{\omega^2} \alpha_i\alpha_j\right] \bar{v}_j^- = -\frac{ie}{m_-\omega} E_i \qquad [12.42]$$

and

$$\left[\delta_{ij} + i\epsilon_{ijk} Y_k^+ - \frac{k^2 a_+^2}{\omega^2} \alpha_i \alpha_j\right] \bar{v}_j^+ = \frac{ie}{m_+\omega} E_i \qquad [12.43]$$

Note from [12.41] and [12.27] that the sign of $Y_k^{\pm}$ depends on the sign of the charge.

We have now reduced our set of equations to the three vector equations [12.36], [12.42], and [12.43] involving the quantities E_i, $\bar{v}_i^+$, and $\bar{v}_i^-$. We will reduce this set still further to a single vector equation involving only the components E_i in the following section.

12.13 THE DISPERSION EQUATION

In the previous section we found that we could describe wave phenomena in a two-component electron-ion plasma by means of the three equations [12.36], [12.42], and [12.43]. These three equations for E_i, $\bar{v}_i^+$, and $\bar{v}_i^-$ can be written

$$\mathsf{AE} = \frac{i\omega\mu_o e N_o}{k^2} (\mathsf{V}_+ - \mathsf{V}_-) \qquad [12.44]$$

$$\mathsf{B}_-\mathsf{V}_- = -\frac{ie}{m_-\omega} \mathsf{E} \qquad [12.45]$$

$$\mathsf{B}_+\mathsf{V}_+ = \frac{ie}{m_+\omega} \mathsf{E} \qquad [12.46]$$

where

$$\mathsf{A} = A_{ij} = \left[\delta_{ij}\left(1 - \frac{\omega^2}{k^2 c^2}\right) - \alpha_i \alpha_j\right] \qquad [12.47]$$

and

$$\mathsf{B}_{\pm} = B_{ij}^{\pm} = \left[\delta_{ij} + i\epsilon_{ijk} Y_k^{\pm} - \frac{k^2 a_{\pm}^2}{\omega^2} \alpha_i \alpha_j\right] \qquad [12.48]$$

From [12.45] and [12.46] we can write

$$\mathsf{V}_- = -\frac{ie}{m_-\omega} \mathsf{B}_-^{-1}\mathsf{E} \qquad [12.49]$$

and

$$\mathsf{V}_+ = \frac{ie}{m_+\omega} \mathsf{B}_+^{-1}\mathsf{E} \qquad [12.50]$$

Substituting [12.49] and [12.50] into [12.44], we obtain

$$AE = -\frac{N_o e^2}{k^2 c^2 \epsilon_o}\left[\frac{1}{m_+}B_+^{-1} + \frac{1}{m_-}B_-^{-1}\right]E$$

or

$$\left[A + \frac{\Pi_+^2}{k^2 c^2}B_+^{-1} + \frac{\Pi_-^2}{k^2 c^2}B_-^{-1}\right]E = 0 \qquad [12.51]$$

where

$$\Pi_\pm^2 = \frac{N_o e^2}{m_\pm \epsilon_o} \qquad [12.52]$$

is the electron or ion plasma frequency. Since the refractive index n is given by

$$n = \frac{kc}{\omega} \qquad [12.53]$$

we can write [12.51] in the alternative form

$$[An^2 + X_+ B_+^{-1} + X_- B_-^{-1}]E = 0 \qquad [12.54]$$

where

$$X_\pm = \frac{\Pi_\pm^2}{\omega^2} \qquad [12.55]$$

Now equation [12.54] is of the form

$$C_{ij}E_j = 0 \qquad [12.56]$$

which is a set of three homogeneous equations for E_1, E_2, and E_3. A non-trivial solution will exist only if the determinant of C_{ij} is equal to zero. By setting this determinant equal to zero we will obtain the dispersion equation.

In order to determine the form of C_{ij}, let us investigate the forms of the matrices A and B. We will orient the coordinate system so that the d.c. magnetic field B_k^0 lies along the x_3-axis and the normal to the plane wave front α_i lies in the x_2-x_3 plane as shown in Figure 12.1. We therefore have that

$$Y_k^\pm = (0, 0, Y_\pm)$$

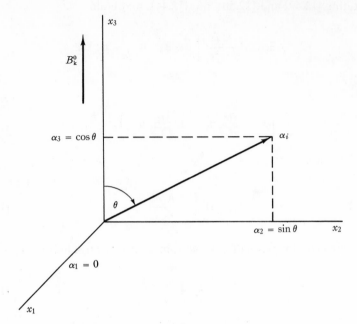

F I G U R E 12.1   Orientation of Coordinate System

and

$$\alpha_i = (0,\ \sin\ \theta,\ \cos\ \theta)$$

where θ is the angle between the direction of propagation and the direction of the magnetic field. Under these conditions we can write the matrix A from [12.47] as

$$A = \frac{1}{n^2}\begin{bmatrix} n^2 - 1 & 0 & 0 \\ 0 & n^2 \cos^2 \theta - 1 & -n^2 \sin \theta \cos \theta \\ 0 & -n^2 \sin \theta \cos \theta & n^2 \sin^2 \theta - 1 \end{bmatrix} \qquad [12.57]$$

Note that the form of the matrix A depends on the angle of propagation θ. Similarly the matrix $B_\pm$ given by [12.48] can be written as

$$B_\pm = \begin{bmatrix} 1 & iY_\pm & 0 \\ -iY_\pm & 1 - \dfrac{k^2 a_\pm^2}{\omega^2} \sin^2 \theta & -\dfrac{k^2 a_\pm^2}{\omega^2} \sin \theta \cos \theta \\ 0 & -\dfrac{k^2 a_\pm^2}{\omega^2} \sin \theta \cos \theta & 1 - \dfrac{k^2 a_\pm^2}{\omega^2} \cos^2 \theta \end{bmatrix} \qquad [12.58]$$

Note that the matrix $B_\pm$ includes the effects of the magnetic field and the thermal motions of the electrons and ions.

We see from [12.54] that in order to obtain the dispersion equation we need to take the inverse of $B_\pm$. The dispersion equation is then obtained by setting the determinant of the matrix

$$C = An^2 + X_+ B_+^{-1} + X_- B_-^{-1} \qquad [12.59]$$

equal to zero. In the following sections we will examine the dispersion equation for various special cases.

12.2 PROPAGATION OF WAVES ALONG THE MAGNETIC FIELD

We will begin our discussion of the dispersion equation by considering the case of propagation along the magnetic field. For this case $\theta = 0$ and from [12.57] we have that

$$An^2 = \begin{bmatrix} n^2 - 1 & 0 & 0 \\ 0 & n^2 - 1 & 0 \\ 0 & 0 & -1 \end{bmatrix} \qquad [12.60]$$

while from [12.58] we obtain

$$B_\pm = \begin{bmatrix} 1 & iY_\pm & 0 \\ -iY_\pm & 1 & 0 \\ 0 & 0 & 1 - \dfrac{k^2 a_\pm^2}{\omega^2} \end{bmatrix} \qquad [12.61]$$

The inverse of [12.61] is given by

$$B_\pm^{-1} = \begin{bmatrix} \dfrac{1}{1 - Y_\pm^2} & \dfrac{-iY_\pm}{1 - Y_\pm^2} & 0 \\ \dfrac{iY_\pm}{1 - Y_\pm^2} & \dfrac{1}{1 - Y_\pm^2} & 0 \\ 0 & 0 & \dfrac{1}{1 - (k^2 a_\pm^2/\omega^2)} \end{bmatrix} \qquad [12.62]$$

By using [12.60] and [12.62] we can write [12.54] in matrix form as

$$
\begin{bmatrix}
n^2 - 1 + \dfrac{X_+}{1 - Y_+^2} + \dfrac{X_-}{1 - Y_-^2} & -i\left(\dfrac{X_+ Y_+}{1 - Y_+^2} + \dfrac{X_- Y_-}{1 - Y_-^2}\right) \\[3mm]
i\left(\dfrac{X_+ Y_+}{1 - Y_+^2} + \dfrac{X_- Y_-}{1 - Y_-^2}\right) & n^2 - 1 + \dfrac{X_+}{1 - Y_+^2} + \dfrac{X_-}{1 - Y_-^2} \\[3mm]
0 & 0
\end{bmatrix}
$$

$$
\left.\begin{matrix}
0 \\[3mm]
0 \\[3mm]
\dfrac{X_+}{1 - (k^2 a_+^2/\omega^2)} + \dfrac{X_-}{1 - (k^2 a_-^2/\omega^2)} - 1
\end{matrix}\right]
\begin{bmatrix}
E_1 \\[3mm]
E_2 \\[3mm]
E_3
\end{bmatrix} = 0 \quad [12.63]
$$

From this equation we see that the transverse components of the electric field E_1 and E_2 are coupled due to the magnetic field. These transverse waves will be discussed in Section 12.24.

We will first consider the third equation of [12.63] which involves only the longitudinal component of the electric field E_3 and is written as

$$
\left(\frac{X_+}{1 - (k^2 a_+^2/\omega^2)} + \frac{X_-}{1 - (k^2 a_-^2/\omega^2)} - 1\right) E_3 = 0 \qquad [12.64]
$$

In order for a longitudinal wave E_3 to exist the coefficient in [12.64] must be zero. Setting this coefficient equal to zero we obtain the dispersion equation for the longitudinal waves

$$
X_+\left(1 - \frac{k^2 a_-^2}{\omega^2}\right) + X_-\left(1 - \frac{k^2 a_+^2}{\omega^2}\right) - \left(1 - \frac{k^2 a_-^2}{\omega^2}\right)\left(1 - \frac{k^2 a_+^2}{\omega^2}\right) = 0
$$

$$[12.65]$$

We note from this equation that longitudinal waves propagating in the direction of the magnetic field are not affected by the magnetic field.

We can write [12.65] in terms of the phase velocity $u = \omega/k$ as

$$
X_+\left(1 - \frac{a_-^2}{u^2}\right) + X_-\left(1 - \frac{a_+^2}{u^2}\right) - \left(1 - \frac{a_-^2}{u^2}\right)\left(1 - \frac{a_+^2}{u^2}\right) = 0 \qquad [12.66]
$$

Introducing

$$
X_0 = X_+ + X_- = \frac{\Pi_+^2 + \Pi_-^2}{\omega^2} \qquad [12.67]
$$

we can write [12.66] as

$$X_o - \frac{1}{u^2}(X_+ a_-^2 + X_- a_+^2) - \left(1 - \frac{a_-^2}{u^2}\right)\left(1 - \frac{a_+^2}{u^2}\right) = 0$$

or

$$X_o\left(1 - \frac{a_o^2}{u^2}\right) - \left(1 - \frac{a_-^2}{u^2}\right)\left(1 - \frac{a_+^2}{u^2}\right) = 0 \qquad [12.68]$$

where

$$a_o^2 = \frac{X_+ a_-^2 + X_- a_+^2}{X_+ + X_-} \qquad [12.69]$$

Since [12.68] is a quadratic equation in u^2 then in general two longitudinal modes of propagation are possible,

Using [12.55] it is possible (see Exercise 12.2.1) to write the dispersion equation [12.65] in the alternate form

$$(\omega^2 - k^2 a_+^2 - \Pi_+^2)(\omega^2 - k^2 a_-^2 - \Pi_-^2) - \Pi_-^2 \Pi_+^2 = 0 \qquad [12.70]$$

The electron and ion velocities are given in terms of the electric field by [12.49] and [12.50]. Thus, using [12.62], the electron and ion velocities in the x_3-direction are given by

$$\bar{v}_3^- = -\frac{ie}{m_- \omega} \frac{1}{[1 - (k^2 a_-^2/\omega^2)]} E_3$$

and

$$\bar{v}_3^+ = \frac{ie}{m_+ \omega} \frac{1}{[1 - (k^2 a_+^2/\omega^2)]} E_3$$

so that the ratio of ion to electron speed is

$$\frac{\bar{v}_3^+}{\bar{v}_3^-} = -\frac{m_-}{m_+} \frac{[1 - (k^2 a_-^2/\omega^2)]}{[1 - (k^2 a_+^2/\omega^2)]} \qquad [12.71]$$

We will now investigate the longitudinal modes of propagation which arise in various limiting cases.

Exercise 12.2.1   Show that the dispersion equation [12.65] can be written in the form given by [12.70].

12.21 ELECTRON WAVES

Let us first consider high frequency oscillations such that

$$\omega^2 \gg \Pi_+^2 \qquad\qquad [12.72]$$

and

$$\omega^2 \gg k^2 a_+^2 \qquad\qquad [12.73]$$

The condition [12.73] implies that the phase velocity $u = \omega/k$ is much larger than the ion thermal speed. Under these conditions the dispersion equation [12.70] can be approximated by

$$\omega^2 - k^2 a_-^2 - \Pi_-^2 \approx 0 \qquad\qquad [12.74]$$

This is the same as the dispersion equation for electron oscillations which was found in Section 11.3. We will call these waves electron waves. A plot of ω vs. k for the dispersion equation [12.74] is shown in Figure 12.2. Let us consider under what conditions such an electron wave is possible.

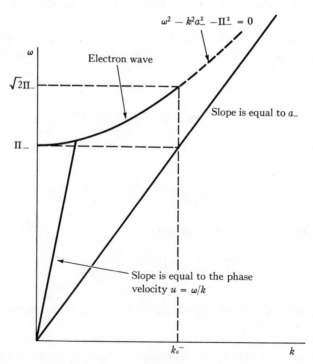

FIGURE 12.2 ω-k Diagram for Electron Waves

The wavelength $\lambda = 2\pi/k$ is the distance which the wave travels during one oscillation. In order for the oscillation to exist, it is necessary that the thermal speed of the electrons be small enough so that the electrons do not travel a distance equal to a wavelength during the time of one oscillation. Otherwise the space charge fields which drive the oscillation could not develop. Stated another way, it is necessary that the time of one oscillation be less than the time for an electron to travel a distance λ at its thermal speed. That is, if the frequency of oscillation is the plasma frequency Π_-, then the condition for an electron wave to exist is

$$\frac{2\pi}{\Pi_-} < \frac{\lambda}{a_-} = \frac{2\pi}{ka_-} \qquad [12.75]$$

or

$$k < \frac{\Pi_-}{a_-} \qquad [12.76]$$

We can therefore define a critical wave number k_c^- by

$$k_c^- = \frac{\Pi_-}{a_-} \qquad [12.77]$$

such that electron waves can only exist if $k < k_c^-$. The critical wave number k_c^- is shown in Figure 12.2 and that portion of the dispersion curve which corresponds to possible electron waves ($k < k_c^-$) is shown as a solid line. We also note from the dispersion equation that the maximum frequency corresponding to $k = k_c^- = \Pi_-/a_-$ is given by $\sqrt{2}\,\Pi$. Thus the possible frequencies of electron waves cannot greatly exceed the plasma frequency.

The condition [12.75] can also be written, using [11.97], as

$$\lambda > 2\pi \frac{a_-}{\Pi_-} = 2\pi\gamma^{1/2} h \qquad [12.78]$$

where h is the Debye length given by [9.13]. Thus the wavelength must be greater than the Debye length in order for electron waves to exist. One must not consider the boundary at k_c^- in Figure 12.2 to be a sharp cut-off, but rather in reality the boundary is somewhat diffused.

We note from Figure 12.2 that the phase velocity $u = \omega/k$ of the electron wave is much greater than the thermal speed a_-. Therefore, if we picture ourselves as riding along with the wave at the phase velocity u, the electrons will appear to be moving past us very rapidly. In fact most of the electrons will be moving past us so rapidly that they will be influenced by the wave only very slightly. However due to the thermal spread of the electron velocities there will be some electrons, which are moving in the same direction as the wave, whose velocity relative to the wave is not too great. These electrons will be alternately accelerated and decelerated as they move past the potential maxima and minima of the wave. The resulting velocity modulation of these electrons is the mechanism responsible for maintaining the oscillation.

We see from Figure 12.2 that as the phase velocity decreases it tends to approach the thermal speed a_-. That is, it begins to move into the tail of the electron velocity distribution as shown in Figure 12.3. There are now a

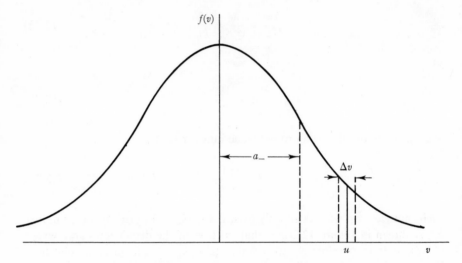

FIGURE 12.3 Velocity Distribution of Electrons

substantial number of electrons moving with velocities close to the phase velocity of the wave u. These electrons do not have sufficient kinetic energy relative to the wave to overcome the potential barrier of the electron oscillations. As a result they become trapped in the potential wells of the electron wave. If there are more electrons moving slightly slower than u than there are moving slightly faster than u, as is the case in Figure 12.3, then one can show that there is a net transfer of energy from the wave into the trapped electrons. The wave therefore becomes damped, and the phenomena is known as Landau damping.

The proper treatment of Landau damping requires the use of the Boltzmann equation rather than the macroscopic equations used in this chapter. Such an analysis will not be carried out here. The results of such an analysis, however, indicate that waves for which $k \gtrsim k_c^-$ are severely damped. These waves correspond to the dashed portion of the dispersion curve of Figure 12.2 which we have already ruled out as being unable to develop.

Let us finally consider the ratio of ion to electron speed for these electron waves. Using the condition [12.73] for electron waves and the dispersion equation [12.74], we see from [12.71] that for the electron waves

$$\frac{\bar{v}_3^+}{\bar{v}_3^-} \approx -\frac{m_-}{m_+}\frac{\Pi_-^2}{\omega^2} \qquad [12.79]$$

Thus the positive ions are practically immobile and oscillate out of phase with the electrons.

In the following section we will consider longitudinal waves dominated by the ions.

12.22 ION WAVES

In the previous section we found that in the high-frequency limit longitudinal waves can exist in a plasma in the form of electron waves. In this section we turn our attention to the low-frequency limit where

$$\omega^2 \ll \Pi_-^2 \qquad [12.80]$$

and

$$\omega^2 \ll k^2 a_-^2 \qquad [12.81]$$

Under these conditions the dispersion equation [12.70] reduces to

$$\omega^2 - k^2 a_+^2 - \Pi_+^2 = -\frac{\Pi_-^2\,\Pi_+^2}{\Pi_-^2 + k^2 a_-^2} \qquad [12.82]$$

We can now distinguish two possible cases depending upon whether $k^2 a_-^2 \gg \Pi_-^2$ or $k^2 a_-^2 \ll \Pi_-^2$. The first case corresponds to waves whose wave numbers are greater than Π_-^2/a_-^2. These waves will be discussed in this section. The second case corresponding to waves with wave numbers less than Π_-^2/a_-^2 will be treated in Section 12.23.

If

$$k^2 a_-^2 \gg \Pi_-^2 \qquad [12.83]$$

then [12.82] can be written approximately as

$$\omega^2 - k^2 a_+^2 - \Pi_+^2 \approx 0 \qquad [12.84]$$

Note that this dispersion equation is of the same form as [12.74] for the electron waves except that the quantities a_+^2 and Π_+^2 are referred to the positive ions. For this reason we will refer to waves described by [12.84] as *ion waves*.

The same conditions can be imposed for the existence of these ion waves as were imposed on the electron waves in the previous section. Thus the ion waves can only exist if the wave number k is less than a critical wave number k_c^+ given by

$$k_c^+ = \frac{\Pi_+}{a_+} \tag{12.85}$$

This equation corresponds to [12.77] of the previous section. However the condition [12.83] can be written as

$$k > \frac{\Pi_-}{a_-} = k_c^- \tag{12.86}$$

so that the ion wave can only exist when

$$k_c^- < k < k_c^+ \tag{12.87}$$

For this condition to be possible it is necessary for k_c^- to be much less than k_c^+. From [12.77], [12.85], and [11.97] we have, assuming $\gamma^+ = \gamma^-$,

$$\frac{k_c^+}{k_c^-} = \frac{\Pi_+ a_-}{\Pi_- a_+} = \left(\frac{T_-}{T_+}\right)^{1/2} \tag{12.88}$$

so that ion waves will only be possible if the electron temperature is much higher than the ion temperature.

Using the condition [12.81] and the dispersion equation [12.84] we can write the ratio of ion to electron speed from [12.71] as

$$\frac{\bar{v}_3^+}{\bar{v}_3^-} = \frac{m_-}{m_+} \frac{k^2 a_-^2}{\Pi_+^2} \tag{12.89}$$

Noting that

$$\Pi_-^2 = \frac{m_+}{m_-} \Pi_+^2$$

and using [12.77], we can write [12.89] as

$$\frac{\bar{v}_3^+}{\bar{v}_3^-} = \left(\frac{k}{k_c^-}\right)^2 \tag{12.90}$$

Since for the ion wave $k \gg k_c^-$, the ion velocity $\bar{v}_3^+$ greatly exceeds the electron velocity $\bar{v}_3^-$. Thus the electrons are at such a high temperature that they do not "feel" the ion wave.

12.23 PSEUDOSONIC WAVES

We now consider the dispersion equation [12.82] of the previous section for the case when

$$k^2 a_-^2 \ll \Pi_-^2 \qquad [12.91]$$

or

$$k \ll k_c^- \qquad [12.92]$$

The dispersion equation can then be written as

$$\omega^2 - k^2 a_+^2 - \Pi_+^2 = -\frac{\Pi_+^2}{1 + (k^2 a_-^2 / \Pi_-^2)}$$

$$\approx -\Pi_+^2 [1 - (k^2 a_-^2 / \Pi_-^2)]$$

or

$$\omega^2 = k^2 [a_+^2 + (a_-^2 \Pi_+^2 / \Pi_-^2)] \qquad [12.93]$$

Since

$$\Pi_+^2 + \Pi_-^2 = \Pi_-^2 \left(1 + \frac{m_-}{m_+} \right)$$

$$\approx \Pi_-^2$$

then [12.93] is given approximately by

$$\omega^2 = k^2 a_0^2 \qquad [12.94]$$

where a_0^2 is given by [12.69]. One can further show (see Exercise 12.23.1) that

$$a_0^2 \approx a_+^2 \left(1 + \frac{T_-}{T_+} \right) \qquad [12.95]$$

We therefore see from [12.94] that for $k \ll k_c^-$ the wave is nondispersive with a phase velocity equal to a_0. This wave will be called a pseudosonic wave and a_0 will be referred to as the speed of sound in the plasma. One can show (see Exercise 12.23.2) that for the pseudosonic wave the electrons and ions tend to move together. The plasma motion is thus somewhat analogous to ambipolar diffusion. Equation [12.95] for the velocity of propagation of pseudosonic waves should be compared with [7.23] for the ambipolar diffusion coefficient.

The longitudinal waves for propagation along the magnetic field (or in the absence of a magnetic field) are summarized in Figure 12.4. An unrealistic mass ratio m_+/m_- of 4 is chosen for convenience in plotting the dispersion curves. Note that when $T_- = T_+$ only electron waves and pseudosonic waves

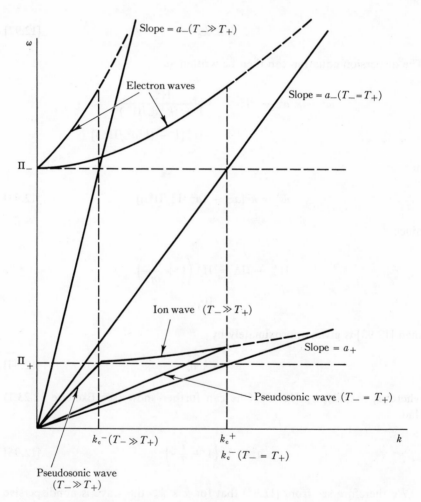

FIGURE 12.4 ω-k Diagram for Electron, Ion and Pseudosonic Waves

can exist since $k_c^- = k_c^+$. Only when we raise the electron temperature above the ion temperature will $k_c^- \ll k_c^+$ so that an ion wave can exist. It should be noted that the actual dispersion curves will differ somewhat from those in Figure 12.4 since we have only considered the limiting cases.

   Exercise 12.23.1   Verify [12.94] and [12.95].

   Exercise 12.23.2   From [12.71] show that for the pseudosonic waves $\bar{v}_3^+ \approx \bar{v}_3^-$.

12.24 TRANSVERSE WAVES

The matrix equation [12.63] describes wave propagation along the magnetic field. We have already discussed the longitudinal waves described by the third equation of [12.63]. The transverse waves are given by the first two equations which can be written as

$$\begin{bmatrix} n^2 - S & iD \\ -iD & n^2 - S \end{bmatrix} \begin{bmatrix} E_1 \\ E_2 \end{bmatrix} = 0 \qquad [12.96]$$

where

$$S = 1 - \frac{X_+}{1 - Y_+^2} - \frac{X_-}{1 - Y_-^2} \qquad [12.97]$$

and

$$D = -\left(\frac{X_+ Y_+}{1 - Y_+^2} + \frac{X_- Y_-}{1 - Y_-^2} \right) \qquad [12.98]$$

We see that the transverse waves and the longitudinal waves are uncoupled and that the thermal motions of the electrons and ions do not affect the transverse waves. This is a consequence of using a scalar pressure in the momentum equations for the electrons and ions. If, instead, a pressure tensor is used, then first-order temperature terms which affect the propagation of the transverse waves may be included by solving the second-order moment equation for the time variation of the pressure tensor.

   The dispersion equation is obtained by setting the determinant of the coefficients in [12.96] equal to zero. We then obtain

$$n^4 - 2Sn^2 + S^2 - D^2 = 0 \qquad [12.99]$$

If we let

$$R = S + D \qquad [12.100]$$

and

$$L = S - D \qquad\qquad [12.101]$$

then [12.99] can be written as

$$n^4 - (R + L)n^2 + RL = 0$$

or

$$(n^2 - R)(n^2 - L) = 0 \qquad\qquad [12.102]$$

We therefore see that two transverse modes can propagate along the magnetic field with refractive indices $n^2 = R$ and $n^2 = L$.

From the first equation of [12.96] we obtain

$$\frac{E_2}{E_1} = \frac{S - n^2}{iD} \qquad\qquad [12.103]$$

Using [12.100] we see that when $n^2 = R$

$$\frac{E_2}{E_1} = i$$

which represents a right-handed circularly polarized wave (see Section 11.12). On the other hand, when $n^2 = L$

$$\frac{E_2}{E_1} = -i$$

which represents a left-handed circularly polarized wave. We therefore see that two circularly polarized waves can propagate along the magnetic field. The right-handed wave propagates with a refractive index given by

$$n_+^2 = R = 1 - \frac{X_+}{1 - Y_+} - \frac{X_-}{1 - Y_-} \qquad\qquad [12.104]$$

while the left-handed wave propagates with a refractive index given by

$$n_-^2 = L = 1 - \frac{X_+}{1 + Y_+} - \frac{X_-}{1 + Y_-} \qquad\qquad [12.105]$$

(See Exercise 12.24.1).

Recall from [12.27] and [12.41] that the sign of $Y_\pm$ depends on the sign of the charge. Thus $Y_- > 0$ while $Y_+ < 0$. We therefore note that since the electrons gyrate in the right-handed sense, R will become resonant when ω is equal to the electron cyclotron frequency ($Y_- = 1$). On the other hand, since the positive ions gyrate in the left-handed sense, L will become resonant when ω is equal to the ion cyclotron frequency ($Y_+ = -1$).

From [12.52] and [12.27] we see that

$$\frac{\Pi_+^2}{\Pi_-^2} = -\frac{\Omega_+}{\Omega_-} = \frac{m_-}{m_+} \qquad [12.106]$$

Using [12.106] one can show (see Exercise 12.24.2) that by neglecting m_-/m_+ compared with unity the quantities R and L given by [12.104] and [12.105] can be written in the form

$$R = 1 - \frac{\Pi_-^2}{(\omega - \Omega_-)(\omega - \Omega_+)} \qquad [12.107]$$

and

$$L = 1 - \frac{\Pi_-^2}{(\omega + \Omega_-)(\omega + \Omega_+)} \qquad [12.108]$$

Let us consider the limiting cases of high and low frequencies.

High-Frequency Waves If we consider high frequencies such that $\omega \gg \Omega_+$, then [12.107] and [12.108] can be approximated by

$$R \approx 1 - \frac{\Pi_-^2}{\omega(\omega - \Omega_-)} \qquad [12.109]$$

and

$$L \approx 1 - \frac{\Pi_-^2}{\omega(\omega + \Omega_-)} \qquad [12.110]$$

It should be noted that these expressions for R and L are the same as one would obtain if the ion motion were neglected altogether. This model of the plasma in which only the electron motion is important is used extensively in studies of ionospheric propagation. We will study this case in detail in Chapter 13.

The treatment in Chapter 13 is based on the wave equation approach rather than on the macroscopic equations used in this chapter. The thermal motion of the electrons is not included in Chapter 13.

Low-Frequency Waves   If we consider very low-frequency waves such that

$$\omega \ll \Omega_+ \ll \Omega_-$$

then [12.107] and [12.108] reduce to

$$n_{\pm}^2 = R = L = 1 - \frac{\Pi_-^2}{\Omega_- \Omega_+} = 1 + \frac{N_0 m_+}{\epsilon_0 B_0^2} \qquad [12.111]$$

If we write the average mass density ρ_0 as

$$\rho_0 = N_0 m_+ + N_0 m_- \approx N_0 m_+$$

then, using $c^2 = 1/\mu_0 \epsilon_0$, we can write [12.111] as

$$n^2 = 1 + \frac{\mu_0 \rho_0 c^2}{B_0^2}$$

or

$$\frac{k^2 c^2}{\omega^2} = 1 + \frac{c^2}{A^2} \qquad [12.112]$$

where

$$A = \left(\frac{B_0^2}{\mu_0 \rho_0} \right)^{1/2} \qquad [12.113]$$

is called the Alfvén velocity (see Section 14.4).

From [12.112] we see that in the low-frequency limit the plasma is non-dispersive and waves travel with the phase velocity

$$u = \frac{c}{\sqrt{1 + c^2/A^2}} \qquad [12.114]$$

For plasmas in which the density ρ_0 is high or the magnetic field B_0 is weak such that $A^2 \ll c^2$, then [12.114] reduces to

$$u = A \qquad [12.115]$$

and corresponds to the Alfvén wave which will be discussed in detail in Chapter 14.

Note from [12.111] that since the refractive indices for the right and left-handed waves are identical, then in this low-frequency limit a linearly polarized wave will be capable of propagating unaltered.

Exercise 12.24.1   Show that R and L can be written in the form of [12.104] and [12.105].

Exercise 12.24.2   Show that if the ratio m_-/m_+ is neglected compared with unity then R and L can be given by [12.107] and [12.108].

12.3 PROPAGATION OF WAVES NORMAL TO THE MAGNETIC FIELD

In Section 12.1 we obtained a general dispersion equation for wave propagation in a plasma in a magnetic field. The thermal motions of the electrons and positive ions were included but particle collisions were neglected. We considered the case of propagation along the magnetic field in Section 12.2 with emphasis on the longitudinal modes of propagation. We will conclude this chapter by looking briefly at propagation across the magnetic field.

If we set $\theta = \pi/2$ in [12.57] and [12.58], we obtain

$$A n^2 = \begin{bmatrix} n^2 - 1 & 0 & 0 \\ 0 & -1 & 0 \\ 0 & 0 & n^2 - 1 \end{bmatrix} \qquad [12.116]$$

and

$$B_\pm = \begin{bmatrix} 1 & iY_\pm & 0 \\ -iY_\pm & 1 - \dfrac{k^2 a_\pm^2}{\omega^2} & 0 \\ 0 & 0 & 1 \end{bmatrix} \qquad [12.117]$$

By taking the inverse of [12.117] and using [12.116], we can then write [12.54] in the form (see Exercise 12.3.1)

$$\begin{bmatrix} n^2 - S_I & iD_I & 0 \\ -iD_I & -S_{II} & 0 \\ 0 & 0 & n^2 - T \end{bmatrix} \begin{bmatrix} E_1 \\ E_2 \\ E_3 \end{bmatrix} = 0 \qquad [12.118]$$

where

$$S_I = 1 - \frac{X_+[1 - (k^2 a_+^2/\omega^2)]}{1 - Y_+^2 - (k^2 a_+^2/\omega^2)} - \frac{X_-[1 - (k^2 a_-^2/\omega^2)]}{1 - Y_-^2 - (k^2 a_-^2/\omega^2)} \quad [12.119]$$

$$S_{II} = 1 - \frac{X_+}{1 - Y_+^2 - (k^2 a_+^2/\omega^2)} - \frac{X_-}{1 - Y_-^2 - (k^2 a_-^2/\omega^2)} \quad [12.120]$$

$$D_I = -\left[\frac{X_+ Y_+}{1 - Y_+^2 - (k^2 a_+^2/\omega^2)} + \frac{X_- Y_-}{1 - Y_-^2 - (k^2 a_-^2/\omega^2)}\right] \quad [12.121]$$

$$T = 1 - X_+ - X_- \quad [12.122]$$

From [12.118] we see that the transverse field E_3, directed along the magnetic field, is uncoupled from the components E_1 and E_2. The refractive index for this mode of propagation is

$$n^2 = T = 1 - X_+ - X_- \quad [12.123]$$

This wave is called the *ordinary wave* since it is not affected by the magnetic field.

The dispersion equation for the second mode, found by setting the determinant of the coefficients of E_1 and E_2 in [12.118] equal to zero, is given by

$$n^2 = \frac{S_I S_{II} - D_I^2}{S_{II}} \quad [12.124]$$

It is seen from [12.119] to [12.121] that this dispersion equation is extremely complicated. The transverse and longitudinal fields are coupled due to the magnetic field. If we neglect the thermal motions of the ions and electrons by setting $a_+ = a_- = 0$, then from [12.119] to [12.121] we see that $S_I = S_{II} = S$ and $D_I = D$, where S and D are given by [12.97] and [12.98]. For this case [12.124] reduces to

$$n^2 = \frac{S^2 - D^2}{S} = \frac{RL}{S} \quad [12.125]$$

where $R = S + D$ and $L = S - D$ as in Section 12.24. This wave is called the *extraordinary wave* and is discussed in more detail in Chapter 13 where the positive ion motion is neglected.

Exercise 12.3.1 Show that the matrix equation describing propagation across the magnetic field is given by [12.118].

REFERENCES

Treatments of plasma oscillations based on the macroscopic equations are given by

1   Oster, L. "Linearized Theory of Plasma Oscillations," *Rev. of Mod. Phys.*, **32** (1960) 141.

2   Bernstein, I. B., and S. K. Trehan. "Plasma Oscillations (I)." *Nuclear Fusion*, **1** (1960) 3.

3   Denisse, J. F., and J. L. Delcroix. *Plasma Waves.* New York: Interscience (Wiley), 1963.

Related topics on waves in plasmas may be found in

4   Allis, W. P., S. J. Buchsbaum, and A. Bers. *Waves in Anisotropic Plasmas.* Cambridge: Massachusetts Institute of Technology Press, 1963.

5   Ginzburg, V. L. *Propagation of Electromagnetic Waves in Plasma.* New York: Gordon and Breach, 1960.

6   Stix, T. H. *The Theory of Plasma Waves.* New York: McGraw-Hill, 1962.

13

ELECTROMAGNETIC WAVES IN ANISOTROPIC PLASMAS

The propagation of electromagnetic waves through plasmas immersed in a magnetic field has been an important topic for some time. Early interest in the problem during the thirties centered on the propagation of radio waves in the ionosphere. Analysis of the effect of radio waves on the motion of the electrons in the ionosphere led to the famous Appleton-Hartree equation.

As interest in space communications and plasma diagnostics grew, the theoretical formulations of this problem became more refined. Among the factors that have been taken into account are the effects of special geometries, the motions of several gas species, and the presence of density gradients and finite (instead of zero) temperatures in the plasma medium.

Despite this sophistication a basic formulation of the problem can be obtained in terms of electromagnetic wave propagation in a cold, infinite, uniform, anisotropic plasma in which the motion of the electrons only is considered. We will find that the treatment of this problem gives us considerable insight into the solution of the more general problem.

In Section 13.1 we derive the dispersion equation from Maxwell's equations

379

and in Section 13.11 show how the Appleton-Hartree equation is derived from the dispersion equation.

The several surfaces that characterize waves are discussed in Section 13.2. An alternative derivation of the dispersion equation is obtained by considering the equation for the wave normal surface. In this second derivation we work in the principal coordinate system in which the dielectric tensor assumes a diagonal form and the components of a field vector of the wave become uncoupled and correspond to the wave modes that can propagate independently in the plasma.

A catalogue of the modes of wave propagation is made in Section 13.3. In Section 13.31 the helpful Clemmow-Mullaly-Allis diagram is developed, and in Section 13.32 the shapes of the wave normal surfaces which pertain to this diagram are derived. At this point a broad perspective of the various wave modes possible under widely varying plasma conditions is obtained.

An important application of the concept of independent wave modes is made in Section 13.4 in the treatment of Faraday rotation. This is the problem of electromagnetic wave propagation parallel to the applied magnetic field. We find that a wave of arbitrary polarization can be described as consisting of the sum of two components, one in each of the characteristic wave modes that apply to this case. The plasma affects the two components differently, resulting in the phenomenon of Faraday rotation as the wave progresses.

A characteristic of propagation in anisotropic plasmas is the fact that the direction of the wave normal and the direction in which a wave packet travels do not, in general, coincide. This topic is treated in Section 13.5 and is applied to the theory of atmospheric whistlers in Section 13.53.

13.1   THE DISPERSION EQUATION

A dispersion equation describes how the propagation of a wave in a certain medium depends upon the frequency of the wave. In describing electromagnetic waves, we use Maxwell's equations, and we will adopt a dielectric model to describe the plasma medium.

In this case Maxwell's equations can be written

$$\epsilon_{ijk}E_{k,j} = -\mu_0\dot{H}_i \qquad\qquad [13.1]$$

$$\epsilon_{ijk}H_{k,j} = \dot{D}_i \qquad\qquad [13.2]$$

$$D_{i,i} = 0 \qquad\qquad [13.3]$$

$$H_{i,i} = 0 \qquad\qquad [13.4]$$

where we have assumed the plasma to have a permeability equal to that of free space (see Exercise 13.1.1).

Assuming a plane wave solution of the form $e^{i(k\alpha_q x_q - \omega t)}$, where α_q is a unit vector normal to the wave front, these equations become

$$\frac{k}{\omega\mu_o} \epsilon_{ijk}\alpha_j E_k = H_i \qquad\qquad\qquad [13.5]$$

$$-\frac{k}{\omega} \epsilon_{ijk}\alpha_j H_k = D_i \qquad\qquad\qquad [13.6]$$

$$\alpha_i D_i = 0 \qquad\qquad\qquad [13.7]$$

$$\alpha_i H_i = 0 \qquad\qquad\qquad [13.8]$$

Substituting H_i from [13.5] into [13.6], we obtain

$$-\frac{k^2}{\mu_o\omega^2} \epsilon_{ijk}\epsilon_{krs}\alpha_j\alpha_r E_s = D_i$$

or

$$-\frac{k^2}{\mu_o\omega^2} (\delta_{ir}\delta_{js} - \delta_{is}\delta_{jr})\alpha_j\alpha_r E_s = D_i$$

whence

$$-\alpha_i\alpha_s E_s + \alpha_r\alpha_r E_i = \mu_o \frac{\omega^2}{k^2} D_i \qquad\qquad [13.9]$$

The phase velocity u of the wave is given by

$$u = \frac{\omega}{k} \qquad\qquad\qquad [13.10]$$

If we also bear in mind that $\alpha_r\alpha_r = 1$, we can write [13.9] as

$$\mu_o u^2 D_i = E_i - \alpha_i\alpha_s E_s \qquad\qquad [13.11]$$

This equation tells us that in general D_i and E_i are not in the same direction. They will only be in the same direction when the divergence of E_i (that is, $\alpha_s E_s$) is zero. This is generally not the case for an anisotropic medium.

From [13.8] we see that H_i is normal to α_i, while from [13.7] and [13.6] we see that D_i is normal to both α_i and H_i. We can conclude from [13.5] that E_i lies in the plane containing α_i and D_i. The situation is shown in Figure 13.1. We also note from this figure that the direction of the Poynting vector G_i, which lies in the plane containing α_i and D_i, is not the same as the direction of the normal to the wave front α_i.

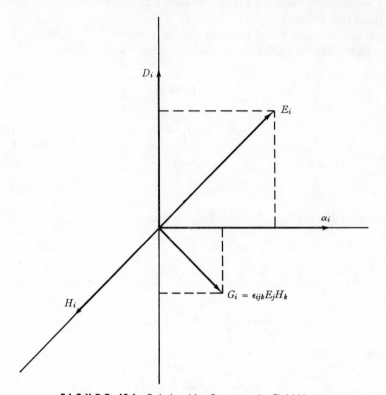

FIGURE 13.1 Relationships Between the Field Vectors

Now $D_i = \epsilon_0 \kappa_{ij} E_j$, where κ_{ij} was obtained in Section 7.24 for a cold uniform plasma immersed in a magnetic field directed along the x_3-axis as

$$\kappa_{ij} = \begin{bmatrix} S & -iD & 0 \\ iD & S & 0 \\ 0 & 0 & T \end{bmatrix} \qquad [13.12]$$

where

$$S = 1 - \frac{XU}{U^2 - Y^2} \qquad [13.13]$$

$$D = -\frac{XY}{U^2 - Y^2} \qquad [13.14]$$

$$T = 1 - \frac{X}{U} \qquad [13.15]$$

and, for convenience, we recapitulate further that

$$X = \frac{\Pi^2}{\omega^2}, \qquad \Pi = \frac{N_- e^2}{m\epsilon_0}$$

$$Y = \frac{\Omega}{\omega}, \qquad \Omega = \Omega_3 = \frac{eB_3}{m}$$

$$U = 1 + iZ, \qquad Z = \frac{\nu_{EN}}{\omega}$$

Equation [13.11] can therefore be written as

$$[\kappa_{ij} + n^2(\alpha_i\alpha_j - \delta_{ij})]E_j = 0 \qquad\qquad [13.16]$$

where the refractive index n is defined by

$$n = \frac{c}{u} \qquad\qquad [13.17]$$

If the angle between the magnetic field and the direction of propagation is denoted by θ, then from Figure 13.2 we see that

$$\alpha_1 = 0, \quad \alpha_2 = \sin\theta, \quad \alpha_3 = \cos\theta \qquad\qquad [13.18]$$

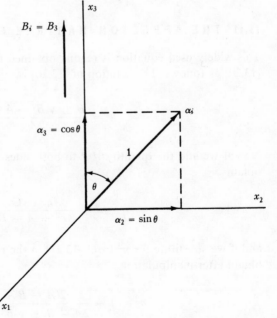

FIGURE 13.2   Relationship
Between α_i and B_i

Using these values of α_i in [13.16], we obtain

$$\begin{bmatrix} S - n^2 & -iD & 0 \\ iD & S - n^2 \cos^2 \theta & n^2 \sin \theta \cos \theta \\ 0 & n^2 \sin \theta \cos \theta & T - n^2 \sin^2 \theta \end{bmatrix} \begin{bmatrix} E_1 \\ E_2 \\ E_3 \end{bmatrix} = 0 \qquad [13.19]$$

These equations have a nontrivial solution only when the determinant of the coefficients is zero. Evaluating this determinant, we obtain

$$An^4 - Bn^2 + C = 0 \qquad [13.20]$$

where

$$A = S \sin^2 \theta + T \cos^2 \theta$$

$$B = RL \sin^2 \theta + TS(1 + \cos^2 \theta)$$

$$C = TRL$$

$$R = S + D$$

$$L = S - D$$

This is the dispersion equation.

Exercise 13.1.1   Why is $D_{i,i} = 0$ for the dielectric model of the plasma?

13.11 THE APPLETON-HARTREE EQUATION

This widely used equation is readily obtained from the dispersion equation [13.20] as follows. The solution of [13.20] is,

$$n^2 = \frac{B \pm \sqrt{B^2 - 4AC}}{2A} \qquad [13.21]$$

Now if we add the quantity An^2 to both sides of [13.20] and rearrange, we obtain

$$n^2 = \frac{An^2 - C}{An^2 + A - B} \qquad [13.22]$$

and if we substitute for n^2 from [13.21] in the right-hand side of [13.22], we obtain after manipulation

$$n^2 = 1 - \frac{2(A - B + C)}{2A - B \pm \sqrt{B^2 - 4AC}} \qquad [13.23]$$

Substituting for A, B, and C from [13.20] and then further substituting for S, D, and T from [13.13] to [13.15], we obtain

$$n^2 = 1 - \cfrac{X}{U - \cfrac{Y^2 \sin^2 \theta}{2(U - X)} \pm \left[\cfrac{Y^4 \sin^4 \theta}{4(U - X)^2} + Y^2 \cos^2 \theta \right]^{1/2}} \qquad [13.24]$$

This is the Appleton-Hartree equation. If collisions can be neglected U is written as unity in [13.24].

13.2 WAVES IN THE PRINCIPAL COORDINATE SYSTEM

In the previous section we have obtained the dispersion equation [13.20] and the Appleton-Hartree equation [13.24] based on the dielectric tensor given by [13.12]. From the form of this dielectric tensor we see that the E_1 and E_2 components of the electric field vector are coupled. This coupling is the primary source of the difficulty that arises when dealing with anisotropic plasmas. Some of this difficulty may be eliminated by recognizing that certain vectors, called *eigenvectors*, exist which are uncoupled; that is, if they are multiplied by the matrix [13.12] they are changed only in length.

In Appendix H we show that for the problem of wave propagation in magnetoplasmas three eigenvectors exist, two of which are complex vectors. If we multiply these eigenvectors by the time factor $e^{-i\omega t}$, then the two complex vectors represent unit vectors which rotate in a right- and left-handed sense in the plane normal to the magnetic field. The third eigenvector lies in the direction of the magnetic field.

We can talk about a principal coordinate system in which the three base vectors are the three eigenvectors discussed above. In this coordinate system the dielectric tensor assumes a diagonal form. As a result the components of the field vectors are uncoupled. For this reason it is often convenient to work in this principal coordinate system, as we will demonstrate in the following two sections.

13.21 WAVE NORMAL AND REFRACTIVE INDEX SURFACES

Since the electromagnetic properties of an anisotropic plasma depend upon the direction in which a wave is traveling, then the phase velocity u of the wave will also be dependent upon the direction of propagation of the wave.

We can therefore define a wave normal surface as that surface formed by letting the radius to each point be equal to

$$\frac{u}{c} = \frac{1}{n}$$

[13.25]

where c is the velocity of light and n is the refractive index of the plasma. It is also possible to define an inverse wave normal surface or a refractive index surface as that surface formed by letting the radius to each point be equal to

$$n = \frac{c}{u}$$

[13.26]

In this section we wish to utilize the properties of the principal coordinate system in order to obtain expressions which describe these surfaces.

Since the components of the unit vector α_i are real, we can represent this vector in the following form

$$|\alpha\rangle = \begin{bmatrix} \alpha_1 \\ \alpha_2 \\ \alpha_3 \end{bmatrix}, \quad \langle\alpha| = \begin{bmatrix} \alpha_1 & \alpha_2 & \alpha_3 \end{bmatrix}$$

(See the discussion of this notation in Appendix H.) Referring to (H. 22), we can write the components of the unit vector α_i in the principal coordinate system as

$$|\tilde{\alpha}\rangle = \begin{bmatrix} \dfrac{1}{\sqrt{2}}(\alpha_1 - i\alpha_2) \\ \dfrac{1}{\sqrt{2}}(\alpha_1 + i\alpha_2) \\ \alpha_3 \end{bmatrix}$$

$$\langle\tilde{\alpha}| = \begin{bmatrix} \dfrac{1}{\sqrt{2}}(\alpha_1 + i\alpha_2) & \dfrac{1}{\sqrt{2}}(\alpha_1 - i\alpha_2) & \alpha_3 \end{bmatrix}$$

In the principal coordinate system the electric field vector can be written as

$$|\tilde{E}\rangle = \begin{bmatrix} \dfrac{1}{\sqrt{2}}(E_1 - iE_2) \\ \dfrac{1}{\sqrt{2}}(E_1 + iE_2) \\ E_3 \end{bmatrix}$$

so that we can form

$$\langle \tilde{\alpha}|\tilde{E}\rangle = \left[\frac{1}{\sqrt{2}}(\alpha_1 + i\alpha_2) \quad \frac{1}{\sqrt{2}}(\alpha_1 - i\alpha_2) \quad \alpha_3\right] \begin{bmatrix} \frac{1}{\sqrt{2}}(E_1 - iE_2) \\ \frac{1}{\sqrt{2}}(E_1 + iE_2) \\ E_3 \end{bmatrix}$$

$$= \alpha_1 E_1 + \alpha_2 E_2 + \alpha_3 E_3$$

or

$$\langle \tilde{\alpha}|\tilde{E}\rangle = \langle \alpha|E\rangle \qquad [13.27]$$

Using [13.27], it is clear that we can write [13.11] in the principal coordinate system as

$$\mu_0 u^2|\tilde{D}\rangle = |\tilde{E}\rangle - |\tilde{\alpha}\rangle\langle\alpha|E\rangle \qquad [13.28]$$

From (H. 31) and (H. 34) we have that

$$|\tilde{E}\rangle = \frac{1}{\epsilon_0}\tilde{K}^{-1}|\tilde{D}\rangle \qquad [13.29]$$

where K is used to indicate the matrix of the dielectric tensor and where

$$\tilde{K}^{-1} = \begin{bmatrix} \frac{1}{R} & 0 & 0 \\ 0 & \frac{1}{L} & 0 \\ 0 & 0 & \frac{1}{T} \end{bmatrix} \qquad [13.30]$$

Substituting [13.29] into [13.28] and noting that $c^2 = 1/\mu_0\epsilon_0$,

$$(c^2\tilde{K}^{-1} - u^2\,I)|\tilde{D}\rangle = |\tilde{\alpha}\rangle\langle\alpha|E\rangle\frac{1}{\mu_0} \qquad [13.31]$$

where I represents the unit matrix. This can also be written, using [13.25], as

$$\left(\tilde{K}^{-1} - \frac{1}{n^2}\,I\right)|\tilde{D}\rangle = |\tilde{\alpha}\rangle\langle\alpha|E\rangle\epsilon_0 \qquad [13.32]$$

Substituting [13.30] into [13.31] and [13.32], we can write the components of $|\tilde{D}\rangle$ as

$$\tilde{D}_1 = \frac{\tilde{\alpha}_1}{u_R^2 - u^2} \langle \alpha | E \rangle \frac{1}{\mu_0} = \frac{\tilde{\alpha}_1}{(1/R) - (1/n^2)} \langle \alpha | E \rangle \epsilon_0 \qquad [13.33]$$

$$\tilde{D}_2 = \frac{\tilde{\alpha}_2}{u_L^2 - u^2} \langle \alpha | E \rangle \frac{1}{\mu_0} = \frac{\tilde{\alpha}_2}{(1/L) - (1/n^2)} \langle \alpha | E \rangle \epsilon_0 \qquad [13.34]$$

$$\tilde{D}_3 = \frac{\tilde{\alpha}_3}{u_T^2 - u^2} \langle \alpha | E \rangle \frac{1}{\mu_0} = \frac{\tilde{\alpha}_3}{(1/T) - (1/n^2)} \langle \alpha | E \rangle \epsilon_0 \qquad [13.35]$$

where

$$u_R^2 = \frac{c^2}{R}, \quad u_L^2 = \frac{c^2}{L}, \quad u_T^2 = \frac{c^2}{T} \qquad [13.36]$$

Now from [13.7] and [13.27] it follows that

$$\langle \tilde{\alpha} | \tilde{D} \rangle = \tilde{\alpha}_1^* \tilde{D}_1 + \tilde{\alpha}_2^* \tilde{D}_2 + \tilde{\alpha}_3^* \tilde{D}_3 = 0 \qquad [13.37]$$

where the asterisk signifies the complex conjugate.

Substituting for the components of $|\tilde{D}\rangle$, we obtain

$$\left(\frac{\tilde{\alpha}_1^* \tilde{\alpha}_1}{u_R^2 - u^2} + \frac{\tilde{\alpha}_2^* \tilde{\alpha}_2}{u_L^2 - u^2} + \frac{\tilde{\alpha}_3^* \tilde{\alpha}_3}{u_T^2 - u^2} \right) \langle \alpha | E \rangle \frac{1}{\mu_0} = 0 \qquad [13.38]$$

and

$$\left[\frac{\tilde{\alpha}_1^* \tilde{\alpha}_1}{(1/R) - (1/n^2)} + \frac{\tilde{\alpha}_2^* \tilde{\alpha}_2}{(1/L) - (1/n^2)} + \frac{\tilde{\alpha}_3^* \tilde{\alpha}_3}{(1/T) - (1/n^2)} \right] \langle \alpha | E \rangle \epsilon_0 = 0$$

$$[13.39]$$

In order to convert back into the regular coordinate system we note that

$$\tilde{\alpha}_1^* \tilde{\alpha}_1 = \tfrac{1}{2}(\alpha_1^2 + \alpha_2^2)$$

$$\tilde{\alpha}_2^* \tilde{\alpha}_2 = \tfrac{1}{2}(\alpha_1^2 + \alpha_2^2) \qquad [13.40]$$

$$\tilde{\alpha}_3^* \tilde{\alpha}_3 = \alpha_3^2$$

and remembering that for an anisotropic medium $\langle \alpha | E \rangle \neq 0$, [13.38] and [13.39] become

$$\frac{\tfrac{1}{2}(\alpha_1^2 + \alpha_2^2)}{u_R^2 - u^2} + \frac{\tfrac{1}{2}(\alpha_1^2 + \alpha_2^2)}{u_L^2 - u^2} + \frac{\alpha_3^2}{u_T^2 - u^2} = 0 \qquad [13.41]$$

and

$$\frac{\frac{1}{2}(\alpha_1^2 + \alpha_2^2)}{(1/R) - (1/n^2)} + \frac{\frac{1}{2}(\alpha_1^2 + \alpha_2^2)}{(1/L) - (1/n^2)} + \frac{\alpha_3^2}{(1/T) - (1/n^2)} = 0 \qquad [13.42]$$

A given direction of propagation is specified by the three direction cosines α_1, α_2, and α_3. Thus [13.41] can be used to plot the wave normal surfaces while [13.42] can be used to plot the refractive index surfaces. In general these surfaces will be complex. Wave normal surfaces for a collisionless plasma will be discussed in Section 13.32.

Note that [13.41] is quadratic in u^2. Therefore in any given direction there will be, in general, two possible phase velocities corresponding to the two modes of propagation.

Note from [13.25] and [13.10] that

$$n = \frac{c}{u} = \frac{kc}{\omega} \qquad [13.43]$$

Thus [13.42] can be thought of as a dispersion equation which relates ω and k for any given direction of propagation. We will discuss this dispersion relation in more detail in Section 13.3. First we will consider the concept of a ray surface.

13.22 THE RAY SURFACE

In the preceding section we derived equations from which one could plot the refractive index surface and the wave normal surface. For an anisotropic medium it is possible to define another surface called the ray surface. From Figure 13.1 we see that the Poynting vector G_i is not in the same direction as the wave normal α_i. Let β_i be a unit vector in the direction of G_i which defines the ray direction.

Consider a plane wave whose normal is α_i moving with a phase velocity u. The situation is shown in Figure 13.3 where Figure 13.1 has been redrawn with H_i directed out of the paper. From this figure it is clear that

$$\alpha_i D_i = 0 \qquad [13.44]$$

and

$$\beta_i E_i = 0 \qquad [13.45]$$

Now in a unit time the wave-front travels a distance u in the direction of α_i while it travels a distance w in the direction of β_i (see Figure 13.3). The quantity w is called the *ray velocity*. It is the velocity with which a ray must

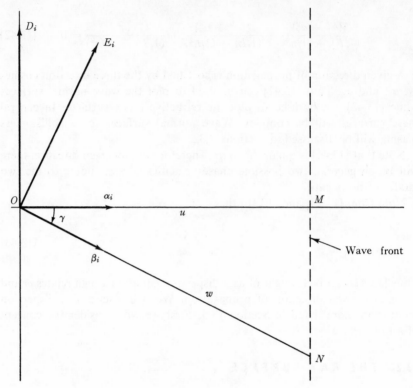

FIGURE 13.3 The Ray Direction

travel in order to stay in phase with the rest of the wave-front. The ray surface is then defined as that surface formed by letting the radius to each point be equal to w/c.

From Figure 13.3 we see that

$$\alpha_i \beta_i = \cos \gamma = \frac{u}{w} \qquad [13.46]$$

Now the relation between α_i, E_i, and D_i is given from [13.11] by

$$\mu_0 u^2 D_i = E_i - \alpha_i \alpha_s E_s \qquad [13.47]$$

Let us try to find a corresponding relation between β_i, D_i, and E_i. By analogy we assume the form

$$p E_i = D_i - \beta_i q \qquad [13.48]$$

where p and q are coefficients which are to be determined.

If we multiply [13.48] by β_i and note that $\beta_i E_i = 0$ and $\beta_i \beta_i = 1$, then we find that

$$q = \beta_i D_i = \beta_s D_s \qquad [13.49]$$

We can therefore write [13.48] as

$$p E_i = D_i - \beta_i \beta_s D_s \qquad [13.50]$$

If we multiply [13.47] by β_i, we obtain

$$\mu_0 u^2 D_i \beta_i = -\alpha_i \beta_i \alpha_s E_s \qquad [13.51]$$

while if we multiply [13.50] by α_i, we obtain

$$p E_i \alpha_i = -\alpha_i \beta_i \beta_s D_s \qquad [13.52]$$

Substituting $\alpha_s E_s$ from [13.52] into [13.51], we find that

$$p \mu_0 u^2 = (\alpha_i \beta_i)^2 \qquad [13.53]$$

from which, using [13.46],

$$p = \frac{1}{\mu_0 w^2} \qquad [13.54]$$

Therefore [13.50] can be written

$$\frac{1}{\mu_0 w^2} E_i = D_i - \beta_i \beta_s D_s \qquad [13.55]$$

which is the "dual" to [13.47].

An equation for the ray surface can now be found by the same technique that was used in Section 13.21. Thus in the principal coordinate system [13.55] can be written as

$$\frac{1}{\mu_0 w^2} |\tilde{E}\rangle = |\tilde{D}\rangle - |\tilde{\beta}\rangle\langle\beta|D\rangle \qquad [13.56]$$

Substituting $|\tilde{D}\rangle = \epsilon_0 \tilde{K}|\tilde{E}\rangle$ into [13.56] we obtain

$$\left(\frac{1}{c^2}\tilde{K} - \frac{1}{w^2}\mathbb{1}\right)|\tilde{E}\rangle = |\tilde{\beta}\rangle\langle\beta|D\rangle\mu_0 \qquad [13.57]$$

which is analogous to [13.31].

Using the matrix form of $\tilde{K}$ with R, L, T replaced from [13.36], we can write the components of $|\tilde{E}\rangle$ from [13.57] as

$$\tilde{E}_1 = \frac{\tilde{\beta}_1}{(1/u_R^2) - (1/w^2)} \langle \beta|D\rangle \mu_0 \qquad [13.58]$$

$$\tilde{E}_2 = \frac{\tilde{\beta}_2}{(1/u_L^2) - (1/w^2)} \langle \beta|D\rangle \mu_0 \qquad [13.59]$$

$$\tilde{E}_3 = \frac{\tilde{\beta}_3}{(1/u_T^2) - (1/w^2)} \langle \beta|D\rangle \mu_0 \qquad [13.60]$$

Now if we use these component values in the equation for the ray surface $\langle \tilde{\beta}|\tilde{E}\rangle = \tilde{\beta}_1^*\tilde{E}_1 + \tilde{\beta}_2^*\tilde{E}_2 + \tilde{\beta}_3^*\tilde{E}_3 = 0$, together with fact that $\tilde{\beta}_1^*\tilde{\beta}_1 = \tilde{\beta}_2^*\tilde{\beta}_2 = \frac{1}{2}(\beta_1^2 + \beta_2^2)$ and $\tilde{\beta}_3^*\tilde{\beta}_3 = \beta_3^2$, we find that the equation for the ray surface can be written as

$$\frac{\frac{1}{2}(\beta_1^2 + \beta_2^2)}{(1/u_R^2) - (1/w^2)} + \frac{\frac{1}{2}(\beta_1^2 + \beta_2^2)}{(1/u_L^2) - (1/w^2)} + \frac{\beta_3^2}{(1/u_T^2) - (1/w^2)} = 0 \quad [13.61]$$

By now it is clear that a close dual relationship exists between the ray surface and the refractive index surface. We will find in Section 13.52 that these are reciprocal surfaces and that one can be determined from the other by a geometrical construction. We will also find in Section 13.5 that the group velocity propagates in the ray direction.

13.3 MODES OF WAVE PROPAGATION

The effect of a magnetoplasma on an electromagnetic wave is described by the dispersion equation. The form of the dispersion equation given by [13.42] includes the refractive index of the plasma and permits the principal regimes of wave propagation to be delineated. For example, when the refractive index is zero, the wave is cut-off, and when the refractive index is infinite, a resonance condition exists. These transition values of refractive index depend upon the strength of the magnetic field, the density of the plasma, and the frequency of the electromagnetic wave and are predicted by [13.42]. The Clemmow-Mullaly-Allis diagram is one way of presenting these principal regimes of wave propagation (Section 13.31). The shape of the wave normal surface describes the wave behavior within each regime, and this is discussed in Section 13.32.

Equation [13.42] was written as

$$\frac{\frac{1}{2}(\alpha_1^2 + \alpha_2^2)}{(1/R) - (1/n^2)} + \frac{\frac{1}{2}(\alpha_1^2 + \alpha_2^2)}{(1/L) - (1/n^2)} + \frac{\alpha_3^2}{(1/T) - (1/n^2)} = 0 \qquad [13.62]$$

Without loss of generality we can let the unit vector α_i lie in the x_2-x_3 plane as shown in Figure 13.2.

If the angle between the magnetic field and the direction of propagation is denoted by θ, then from Figure 13.2 we see that

$$\alpha_1 = 0, \quad \alpha_2 = \sin\theta, \quad \alpha_3 = \cos\theta \qquad [13.63]$$

It is possible by using [13.63] to write [13.62] as (see Exercise 13.3.1)

$$\tan^2\theta = \frac{-T(n^2 - R)(n^2 - L)}{(Sn^2 - RL)(n^2 - T)} \qquad [13.64]$$

Alternatively it is also possible using [13.63] to write [13.62] in the form

$$An^4 - Bn^2 + C = 0 \qquad [13.65]$$

where

$$A = S\sin^2\theta + T\cos^2\theta \qquad [13.66]$$

$$B = RL\sin^2\theta + TS(1 + \cos^2\theta) \qquad [13.67]$$

$$C = TRL \qquad [13.68]$$

$$S = \tfrac{1}{2}(R + L) \qquad [13.69]$$

which is the result obtained in [13.20].

Now from the dispersion relation [13.64] note that for propagation along the magnetic field, $\theta = 0$, and the square of the refractive index can have the values

$$n_+^2 = R \qquad [13.70]$$

or

$$n_-^2 = L \qquad [13.71]$$

These values are equal to the eigenvalues whose eigenvectors are the right- and left-handed rotating unit vectors. (See Appendix H.) Thus the two possible modes that can propagate along the magnetic field are waves which are circularly polarized in either the right- or left-handed sense. The right-handed wave propagates through a medium with a refractive index equal to $\sqrt{R}$, while the left-handed wave propagates through a medium with a refractive index equal to $\sqrt{L}$.

Alternatively we have from [13.19]

$$
\begin{bmatrix}
S - n^2 & -iD & 0 \\
iD & S - n^2 \cos^2 \theta & n^2 \sin \theta \cos \theta \\
0 & n^2 \sin \theta \cos \theta & T - n^2 \sin^2 \theta
\end{bmatrix}
\begin{bmatrix}
E_1 \\
E_2 \\
E_3
\end{bmatrix} = 0 \qquad [13.72]
$$

From the first equation of [13.72] we see that we can write the ratio of the E_2 component of the wave to the E_1 component as

$$
\frac{E_2}{E_1} = \frac{S - n^2}{iD} \qquad [13.73]
$$

Using the value $n^2 = R$ from [13.70] for propagation along the magnetic field and recalling that $R = S + D$, we find from [13.73] that

$$
\frac{E_2}{E_1} = i \qquad [13.74]
$$

which is a right-handed circularly polarized wave as we expected. Similarly substituting $n^2 = L$ into [13.73] we find that

$$
\frac{E_2}{E_1} = -i \qquad [13.75]
$$

which is a left-handed circularly polarized wave. We will continue our study of wave propagation in anisotropic plasmas by considering the various cut-offs and resonances which can occur.

Exercise 13.3.1 Verify [13.64].

13.31 THE CLEMMOW-MULLALY-ALLIS DIAGRAM

In this and the following section we will neglect the effects of collisions. Then in [13.13] to [13.15] the value of U is set equal to one. We therefore have

$$S = 1 - \frac{X}{1 - Y^2} \qquad [13.76]$$

$$D = -\frac{XY}{1 - Y^2} \qquad [13.77]$$

$$T = 1 - X \qquad [13.78]$$

Since $R = S + D$ and $L = S - D$, we find that

$$R = 1 - \frac{X}{1 - Y} \qquad [13.79]$$

$$L = 1 - \frac{X}{1 + Y} \qquad [13.80]$$

A cut-off occurs when the refractive index n is equal to zero. From [13.65] and [13.68] we see that the refractive index is zero only when

$$T = 0 \quad \text{or} \quad R = 0 \quad \text{or} \quad L = 0 \qquad [13.81]$$

Thus from [13.78] to [13.80] we see that these cases correspond to

$$X = 1, \quad X = 1 - Y, \quad X = 1 + Y \qquad [13.82]$$

These cut-offs are shown as dashed lines in Figure 13.4, where Y^2 is plotted as a function of X. In this diagram the magnetic field increases in the vertical direction, the plasma electron density increases in the horizontal direction, and the frequency of the electromagnetic wave decreases in the radial direction.

A resonance occurs when the refractive index becomes infinite. From [13.64] we see that at an infinity of the refractive index

$$\tan^2 \theta = -\frac{T}{S} \qquad [13.83]$$

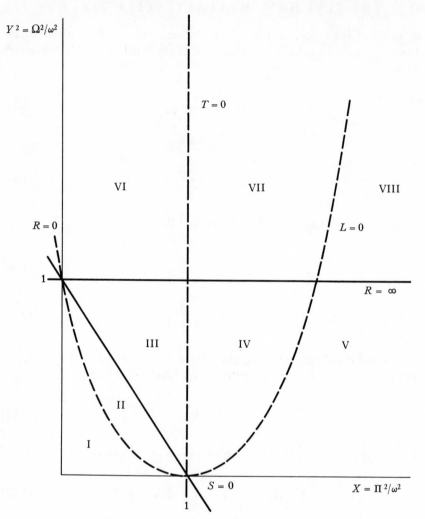

FIGURE 13.4 Cut-offs and Principal Resonances

The principal resonances are defined as the resonances which occur at $\theta = 0$ and $\theta = \pi/2$. From [13.83] we see that these occur when $S = \infty$ and $S = 0$. (Note that $T = 0$ is a cut-off given by [13.81]). Now referring to [13.69] and [13.79] we see that $S = \infty$ when $R = \infty$ or $Y = 1$. We also see from [13.76] that $S = 0$ when $X = 1 - Y^2$. These principal resonances are plotted as solid lines in Figure 13.4.

The lines representing the cut-offs and principal resonances divide the parameter space of Figure 13.4 into eight regions. We will see in the following section that the general shape of the wave normal surface for a given mode of propagation can only be changed by crossing one of the cut-offs or principal resonances in Figure 13.4.

13.32 THE SHAPE OF THE WAVE NORMAL SURFACES

We now wish to determine the shape of the wave normal surfaces that can exist in each of the eight regions of Figure 13.4. For a given set of parameters it would be possible to use [13.41] to plot the phase velocity for various directions of propagation. However in order to determine the shape of the wave normal surface in the various regions of Figure 13.4, it is convenient to proceed in a different way.

Let us consider first the case when $Y < 1$. That is, the cyclotron frequency is less than the signal frequency. For propagation along the magnetic field the refractive index can be written from [13.70], [13.71], [13.79], and [13.80] as

$$n_\pm^2 = 1 - \frac{X}{1 \mp Y} \qquad [13.84]$$

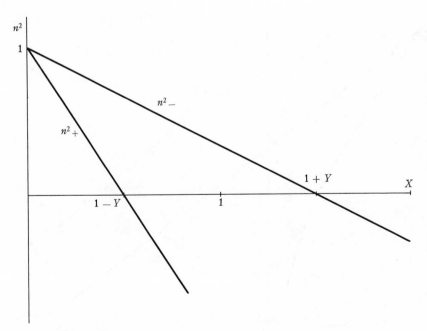

FIGURE 13.5 The Refractive Index for Propagation along the Magnetic Field

If we plot n^2 as a function of X from [13.84], we obtain the two straight lines shown in Figure 13.5. Note that since $Y < 1$, then $1 - Y$ is always positive.

For propagation across the magnetic field, $\theta = \pi/2$, and from [13.64] we see that n^2 can have the values

$$n^2_{\text{ord}} = T \qquad\qquad [13.85]$$

and

$$n^2_{\text{ex}} = \frac{RL}{S} \qquad\qquad [13.86]$$

Using [13.76] to [13.80], we can write these as

$$n^2_{\text{ord}} = 1 - X \qquad\qquad [13.87]$$

and

$$n^2_{\text{ex}} = 1 - \frac{X(1 - X)}{1 - X - Y^2} \qquad\qquad [13.88]$$

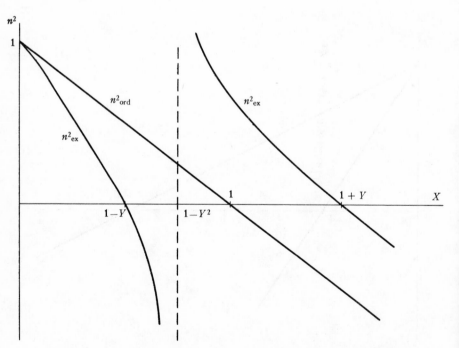

FIGURE 13.6 The Refractive Index for Propagation across the Magnetic Field

Since the refractive index given by [13.87] is the same as that for propagation without a magnetic field, this mode of propagation is called the *ordinary wave*. The mode of propagation characterized by the refractive index of [13.88] is called the *extraordinary wave*. The ordinary wave is linearly polarized in the direction of the magnetic field, while the transverse component of the extraordinary wave is normal to the magnetic field.

From [13.88] we see that n_{ex}^2 has zeros at $X = 1 \pm Y$ and goes to infinity at $X = 1 - Y^2$. Equations [13.87] and [13.88] are plotted in Figure 13.6. Note that since $Y < 1$, then $1 - Y^2$ lies between $1 - Y$ and 1.

For directions of propagation between 0 and 90° to the magnetic field the curves of n^2 vs. X must lie somewhere between those of Figure 13.5 and Figure 13.6. If the angle between the direction of propagation and the magnetic field is continuously changed from 0 to 90°, then the curves of Figure 13.5 must change continuously into those of Figure 13.6. Figure 13.7 shows how this change occurs.

Since only positive values of n^2 correspond to propagation we need only consider the upper half of Figure 13.7 where the five regions shown are the same five regions as in the lower part of Figure 13.4.

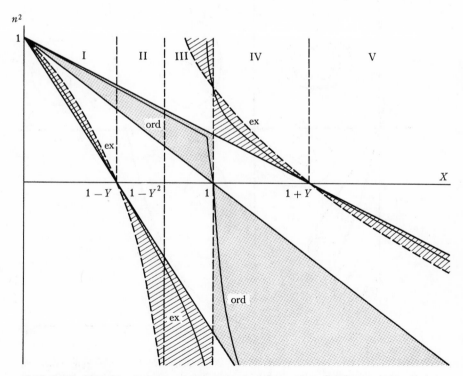

FIGURE 13.7 The Refractive Index for Various Directions of Propagation $Y < 1$

From Figure 13.7 it is clear that both modes propagate in Region I for all directions. In Region II only the ordinary mode propagates. A peculiar situation occurs in Region III. The ordinary mode propagates in all directions while for the extraordinary mode the refractive index becomes infinite for values of θ close to zero. Since the phase velocity is proportional to $1/n$, this means that the phase velocity goes to zero for angles in this "resonant cone." In Region IV only the extraordinary mode propagates, while in Region V neither mode can propagate.

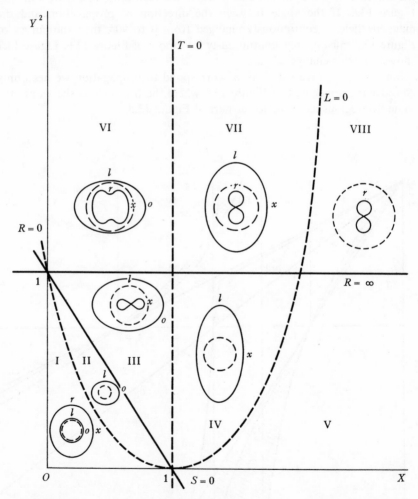

FIGURE 13.8 The Clemmow-Mullaly-Allis Diagram. Reprinted from *Waves in Anisotropic Plasmas* by Allis, Buchsbaum, and Bers by permission of The M.I.T. Press

Since the phase velocity u is equal to c/n, we can, from Figure 13.7, sketch the wave normal surfaces for the five regions as shown in Figure 13.8.

The wave normal surfaces shown in Regions VI, VII, and VIII can be obtained in a similar fashion by constructing a diagram similar to Figure 13.7 for the case when $Y > 1$. Such a diagram is shown in Figure 13.9.

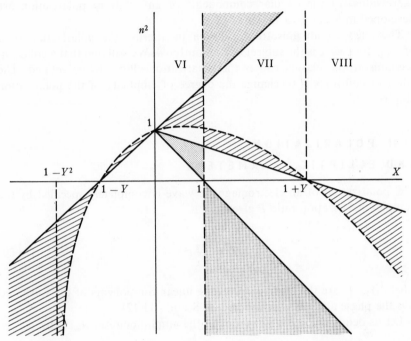

FIGURE 13.9 The Refractive Index for Various Directions of Propagation $Y > 1$

Exercise 13.32.1 Construct Figure 13.9 step-by-step and verify the shapes of the wave normal surfaces in Regions VI, VII, and VIII.

13.4 FARADAY ROTATION

As we have seen, the right- and left-handed circularly polarized waves are the characteristic waves capable of propagating along the magnetic field in an anisotropic plasma. If a wave of any other polarization is incident on the plasma with a direction of propagation along the magnetic field, it will be split into these two characteristic waves, which will then propagate independently. Since the propagation constants (or refractive indices) for the right and left circular waves are different, the resultant polarization of the wave propagating through the plasma will be continually altered. It is the purpose of this section to determine how this polarization is changed.

Since an arbitrary polarization is split into its circular components, we must find a method for determining these circular components. In order to do this, we will first develop some general properties of elliptical polarizations. The concept of orthogonal polarizations is introduced in Section 13.42 and expressions for the circular components of an arbitrary polarization are developed in Section 13.43.

The effect of an anisotropic plasma in altering the polarization of a propagating wave is the subject of Section 13.44. We will find that a collisionless anisotropic plasma causes the polarization ellipse to be rotated. The effect of collisions is to change the degree of ellipticity of the polarization ellipse.

13.41 POLARIZATION
AND ELLIPTIC PARAMETERS

The polarization of an electromagnetic wave is completely specified by the complex polarization ratio P given by,

$$P = \frac{A_2}{A_1} e^{i\phi} \qquad [13.89]$$

where A_1, A_2 are the magnitudes of the linear components of the wave and ϕ is the phase angle between them (see Section 11.12).

Let us define the angle θ in terms of the amplitude ratio A_2/A_1 by

$$\frac{A_2}{A_1} = \tan \tfrac{1}{2}\theta \qquad [13.90]$$

Then the polarization ratio can be written as

$$P = \tan \tfrac{1}{2}\theta e^{i\phi} \qquad [13.91]$$

Therefore, the state of polarization can be specified by giving the angles

$$\theta \qquad 0 < \theta < \pi$$

and

$$\phi \qquad 0 < \phi < 2\pi$$

The angles θ and ϕ will be called the *polarization parameters*.

It is also possible to specify the polarization of a wave by giving its orientation angle, its axial ratio, and its sense of rotation. We wish to relate this description to the polarization parameters θ and ϕ described above. The polarization ellipse is shown in Figure 13.10. The angle $\theta/2$ is related to

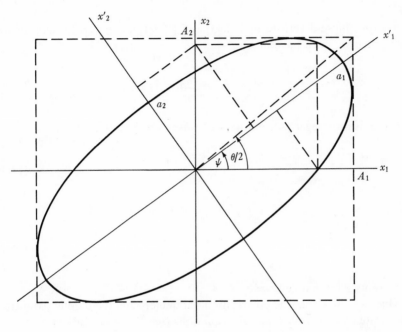

FIGURE 13.10   The Polarization Ellipse

the amplitude ratio according to [13.90]. The principal axes x_1'-x_2' are directed along the major and minor axes of the ellipse and are inclined at the angle ψ to the fixed coordinate axes x_1-x_2. The orientation angle ψ lies between 0 and π.

The axial ratio of the ellipse is given by a_2/a_1. Let the angle λ be defined in terms of this ratio by the expression

$$\tan \lambda = \frac{a_2}{a_1} \qquad\qquad [13.92]$$

The angle λ is taken to lie between $-45°$ and $+45°$. Positive values of $\tan \lambda$ correspond to a right-handed sense of rotation, while negative values correspond to a left-handed sense of rotation. The angles λ and ψ will be called the *elliptic parameters*.

Now from Figure 13.10 we can write the harmonic electric field components referred to the principal axes as

$$E_1' = E_1 \cos \psi + E_2 \sin \psi = a_1 \cos (\phi_1' - \omega t) \qquad [13.93]$$

$$E_2' = -E_1 \sin \psi + E_2 \cos \psi = a_2 \cos (\phi_2' - \omega t) \qquad [13.94]$$

Since the ellipse described by [13.93] and [13.94] is referred to the principal axes, then we must have that

$$\phi_2' - \phi_1' = (2n - 1)\frac{\pi}{2} \qquad [13.95]$$

where n is an integer. A right-handed wave is represented by

$$\phi_2' - \phi_1' = \frac{\pi}{2} \qquad [13.96]$$

while

$$\phi_2' - \phi_1' = -\frac{\pi}{2} \qquad [13.97]$$

represents a left-handed wave.

One can show that the polarization parameters and the elliptic parameters are related by the following four equations (see Exercise 13.41.1)

$$\tan 2\psi = \tan \theta \cos \phi \qquad [13.98]$$

$$\sin 2\lambda = \sin \theta \sin \phi \qquad [13.99]$$

$$\cos \theta = \cos 2\lambda \cos 2\psi \qquad [13.100]$$

$$\tan \phi = \tan 2\lambda \csc 2\psi \qquad [13.101]$$

Exercise 13.41.1 Verify Equations [13.98] to [13.101]. HINT: (a) From [13.90] and [13.92] show that

$$\sin \theta = \frac{2A_1 A_2}{A_1^2 + A_2^2} \qquad \sin 2\lambda = \frac{2a_1 a_2}{a_1^2 + a_2^2}$$

$$\cos \theta = \frac{A_1^2 - A_2^2}{A_1^2 + A_2^2} \qquad \cos 2\lambda = \frac{a_1^2 - a_2^2}{a_1^2 + a_2^2} \qquad [13.102]$$

$$\tan \theta = \frac{2A_1 A_2}{A_1^2 - A_2^2} \qquad \tan 2\lambda = \frac{2a_1 a_2}{a_1^2 - a_2^2}$$

(b) By substituting $E_1 = A_1 \cos(-\omega t)$ and $E_2 = A_2 \cos(\phi - \omega t)$ into [13.93] and [13.94], equating coefficients of $\cos \omega t$ and $\sin \omega t$, and using [13.96] and [13.97], obtain the relations

$$A_1 \cos \psi + A_2 \cos \phi \sin \psi = a_1 \cos \phi_1' \qquad [13.103]$$

$$A_2 \sin \phi \sin \psi = a_1 \sin \phi_1' \qquad [13.104]$$

$$-A_1 \sin \psi + A_2 \cos \phi \cos \psi = a_2 \cos \phi_2' = \mp a_2 \sin \phi_1' \qquad [13.105]$$

$$A_2 \sin \phi \cos \psi = a_2 \sin \phi_2' = \pm a_2 \cos \phi_1' \qquad [13.106]$$

where the upper sign is associated with the right-handed wave.

(c) By squaring and adding first [13.103] and [13.104] and then [13.105] and [13.106] and then by adding and subtracting the results, show that

$$A_1^2 + A_2^2 = a_1^2 + a_2^2 \qquad [13.107]$$

and

$$a_1^2 - a_2^2 = (A_1^2 - A_2^2) \cos 2\psi + 2A_1 A_2 \sin 2\psi \cos \phi \qquad [13.108]$$

(d) By multiplying [13.103] by [13.105] and [13.104] by [13.106] and adding the results, show that

$$\tan 2\psi = \frac{2A_1 A_2}{A_1^2 - A_2^2} \cos \phi \qquad [13.109]$$

By multiplying [13.103] by [13.106] and [13.104] by [13.105] and adding the results, show that

$$\pm a_1 a_2 = A_1 A_2 \sin \phi \qquad [13.110]$$

(e) Obtain equations [13.98] to [13.101] by using [13.102] together with [13.107] to [13.110].

13.42 ORTHOGONAL POLARIZATIONS

In this section we wish to determine the conditions under which two polarizations are orthogonal. We saw in Section 11.1 that the polarization of a wave can be written as a column matrix whose elements are the E_1 and E_2 components of the wave. Let us write this matrix in terms of the polarization ratio P as

$$|\pi\rangle = \frac{1}{\sqrt{1 + PP^*}} \begin{bmatrix} 1 \\ P \end{bmatrix} \qquad [13.111]$$

The complex conjugate is given by the row matrix

$$\langle \pi | = \frac{1}{\sqrt{1 + PP^*}} [1 \quad P^*] \tag{13.112}$$

These polarizations are normalized so that

$$\langle \pi | \pi \rangle = 1 \tag{13.113}$$

Using the value of P given by [13.91], we can write [13.111] and [13.112] as

$$| \pi \rangle = \begin{bmatrix} \cos \frac{1}{2}\theta \\ \sin \frac{1}{2}\theta e^{i\phi} \end{bmatrix} \tag{13.114}$$

and

$$\langle \pi | = [\cos \tfrac{1}{2}\theta \quad \sin \tfrac{1}{2}\theta e^{-i\phi}] \tag{13.115}$$

Let us consider the two polarizations

$$| \pi_1 \rangle = \begin{bmatrix} \cos \frac{1}{2}\theta_1 \\ \sin \frac{1}{2}\theta_1 e^{i\phi_1} \end{bmatrix} \tag{13.116}$$

and

$$| \pi_2 \rangle = \begin{bmatrix} \cos \frac{1}{2}\theta_2 \\ \sin \frac{1}{2}\theta_2 e^{i\phi_2} \end{bmatrix} \tag{13.117}$$

These two polarizations are said to be orthogonal if

$$\langle \pi_1 | \pi_2 \rangle = \langle \pi_2 | \pi_1 \rangle = 0 \tag{13.118}$$

Referring to [13.114] and [13.115], we see that

$$\langle \pi_1 | \pi_2 \rangle = (\cos \tfrac{1}{2}\theta_1 \cos \tfrac{1}{2}\theta_2 + \sin \tfrac{1}{2}\theta_1 \sin \tfrac{1}{2}\theta_2 e^{i(\phi_2 - \phi_1)}) \tag{13.119}$$

and

$$\langle \pi_2 | \pi_1 \rangle = (\cos \tfrac{1}{2}\theta_1 \cos \tfrac{1}{2}\theta_2 + \sin \tfrac{1}{2}\theta_1 \sin \tfrac{1}{2}\theta_2 e^{-i(\phi_2 - \phi_1)}) \tag{13.120}$$

The conditions for [13.119] and [13.120] to be zero are found to be (see Exercise 13.42.1)

$$\phi_2 - \phi_1 = \pm \pi \tag{13.121}$$

and

$$\cos \theta_1 = -\cos \theta_2$$

from which

$$\theta_2 = \pi - \theta_1 \qquad [13.122]$$

Remember that θ lies between 0 and π. From [13.121] and [13.122] we can show that orthogonal polarizations have the same axial ratio, opposite senses of rotation, and their major axes are normal to each other.

If from [13.116] we represent a given polarization by

$$|\pi\rangle = \begin{bmatrix} \cos \tfrac{1}{2}\theta \\ \sin \tfrac{1}{2}\theta e^{i\phi} \end{bmatrix} \qquad [13.123]$$

then from [13.117], [13.121], and [13.122] we can represent the polarization which is orthogonal to [13.123] by

$$|\bar{\pi}\rangle = \begin{bmatrix} \sin \tfrac{1}{2}\theta \\ -\cos \tfrac{1}{2}\theta e^{i\phi} \end{bmatrix} \qquad [13.124]$$

Now from [13.123] and [13.124] let us form the quantities

$$|\pi\rangle\langle\pi| = \begin{bmatrix} \cos^2 \tfrac{1}{2}\theta & \cos \tfrac{1}{2}\theta \sin \tfrac{1}{2}\theta e^{-i\phi} \\ \cos \tfrac{1}{2}\theta \sin \tfrac{1}{2}\theta e^{i\phi} & \sin^2 \tfrac{1}{2}\theta \end{bmatrix} \qquad [13.125]$$

and

$$|\bar{\pi}\rangle\langle\bar{\pi}| = \begin{bmatrix} \sin^2 \tfrac{1}{2}\theta & -\cos \tfrac{1}{2}\theta \sin \tfrac{1}{2}\theta e^{-i\phi} \\ -\cos \tfrac{1}{2}\theta \sin \tfrac{1}{2}\theta e^{i\phi} & \cos^2 \tfrac{1}{2}\theta \end{bmatrix} \qquad [13.126]$$

from which we obtain the important property that

$$|\pi\rangle\langle\pi| + |\bar{\pi}\rangle\langle\bar{\pi}| = \mathsf{I} \qquad [13.127]$$

where I is the unit matrix.

Exercise 13.42.1   Verify that the conditions for the orthogonality of two polarizations are given by [13.121] and [13.122]. Show that orthogonal polarizations have the same axial ratio and opposite senses of rotation and that their major axes are normal to each other.

13.43 CIRCULAR COMPONENTS
OF AN ARBITRARY POLARIZATION

In this section we will show that any arbitrary polarization can be synthesized from any pair of orthogonal elliptical polarizations. We will then consider the special case in which the orthogonal polarizations are the right and left circular polarizations.

Suppose we wish to form the arbitrary polarization

$$|a\rangle = \begin{bmatrix} \cos\frac{1}{2}\theta \\ \sin\frac{1}{2}\theta e^{i\phi} \end{bmatrix} \qquad [13.128]$$

from the two orthogonal polarizations $|\pi\rangle$ and $|\bar{\pi}\rangle$.

We can write

$$|a\rangle = 1\,|a\rangle \qquad [13.129]$$

and if we substitute [13.127] into [13.129], we obtain

$$|a\rangle = |\pi\rangle\langle\pi|a\rangle + |\bar{\pi}\rangle\langle\bar{\pi}|a\rangle \qquad [13.130]$$
$$= |\pi\rangle C + |\bar{\pi}\rangle\overline{C}$$

In [13.130] the arbitrary polarization $|a\rangle$ is given as the sum of the two orthogonal polarizations $|\pi\rangle$ and $|\bar{\pi}\rangle$ where the contribution from each is determined by the coefficients

$$C = \langle\pi|a\rangle \qquad [13.131]$$

and

$$\overline{C} = \langle\bar{\pi}|a\rangle \qquad [13.132]$$

Let us consider the special case in which the orthogonal polarizations are the right and left-handed circular polarizations. We will represent these two polarizations as

$$|r\rangle = \frac{1}{\sqrt{2}}\begin{bmatrix} 1 \\ i \end{bmatrix} \qquad [13.133]$$

and

$$|l\rangle = \frac{1}{\sqrt{2}}\begin{bmatrix} 1 \\ -i \end{bmatrix} \qquad [13.134]$$

From [13.130] to [13.132] we see that the arbitrary polarization $|a\rangle$ can be written as

$$|a\rangle = |r\rangle C_r + |l\rangle C_l \qquad [13.135]$$

where

$$C_r = \langle r|a\rangle \qquad [13.136]$$

and

$$C_l = \langle l|a\rangle \qquad [13.137]$$

Using [13.128] and [13.133], we see that [13.136] becomes

$$C_r = \frac{1}{\sqrt{2}}[1 - i]\begin{bmatrix} \cos\tfrac{1}{2}\theta \\ \sin\tfrac{1}{2}\theta e^{i\phi} \end{bmatrix}$$

$$= \frac{1}{\sqrt{2}}(\cos\tfrac{1}{2}\theta - i\sin\tfrac{1}{2}\theta e^{i\phi})$$

or

$$C_r = \frac{1}{\sqrt{2}}(\cos\tfrac{1}{2}\theta + \sin\tfrac{1}{2}\theta\sin\phi - i\sin\tfrac{1}{2}\theta\cos\phi) \qquad [13.138]$$

Similarly, using [13.128] and [13.134], we can write [13.137] as

$$C_l = \frac{1}{\sqrt{2}}(\cos\tfrac{1}{2}\theta - \sin\tfrac{1}{2}\theta\sin\phi + i\sin\tfrac{1}{2}\theta\cos\phi) \qquad [13.139]$$

13.44 POLARIZATION TRANSFORMING PROPERTIES OF ANISOTROPIC PLASMAS

We now wish to determine how the polarization of a wave is changed as it propagates along the magnetic field in an anisotropic plasma. We have seen that the only modes that can propagate along the magnetic field are the right and left circular waves. From the results of Section 13.3 we see that the right circular component C_r propagates with a wave number

$$k_+ = \frac{\omega}{c}n_+ = \frac{\omega}{c}\sqrt{R} \qquad [13.140]$$

while the left circular component C_1 propagates with a wave number

$$k_- = \frac{\omega}{c} n_- = \frac{\omega}{c} \sqrt{L} \qquad \text{[13.141]}$$

Therefore at any point along the magnetic field the right and left circular components of the wave will be given by

$$C'_r = C_r e^{ik_+ x_3} \qquad \text{[13.142]}$$

and

$$C'_1 = C_1 e^{ik_- x_3} \qquad \text{[13.143]}$$

so that the ratio of the left-handed component and the right-handed component at any point is given by

$$\frac{C'_1}{C'_r} = \frac{C_1}{C_r} e^{-i(k_+ - k_-)x_3} \qquad \text{[13.144]}$$

For any arbitrary initial polarization the ratio C_1/C_r can be determined from [13.138] and [13.139]. This description is in terms of the polarization parameters. We will now show that the ratio C_1/C_r can conveniently be represented in terms of the elliptic parameters.

From [13.138] and [13.139] we form the ratio

$$s = \frac{C_1}{C_r} = \frac{\cos \frac{1}{2}\theta - \sin \frac{1}{2}\theta \sin \phi + i \sin \frac{1}{2}\theta \cos \phi}{\cos \frac{1}{2}\theta + \sin \frac{1}{2}\theta \sin \phi - i \sin \frac{1}{2}\theta \cos \phi} \qquad \text{[13.145]}$$

which can be written, after rationalizing, as

$$s = \frac{\cos \theta + i \sin \theta \cos \phi}{(\cos \frac{1}{2}\theta + \sin \frac{1}{2}\theta \sin \phi)^2 + (\sin \frac{1}{2}\theta \cos \phi)^2} = |s| e^{i\gamma} \qquad \text{[13.146]}$$

Now from [13.146] we see that

$$\tan \gamma = \frac{\sin \theta \cos \phi}{\cos \theta} = \tan \theta \cos \phi \qquad \text{[13.147]}$$

Comparing [13.147] with [13.98], we see that

$$\gamma = 2\psi \qquad \text{[13.148]}$$

Also from [13.146] we see that

$$|s| = \frac{(\cos^2 \theta + \sin^2 \theta \cos^2 \phi)^{1/2}}{(\cos \tfrac{1}{2}\theta + \sin \tfrac{1}{2}\theta \sin \phi)^2 + (\sin \tfrac{1}{2}\theta \cos \phi)^2}$$

or

$$|s| = \frac{(\cos^2 \theta + \sin^2 \theta \cos^2 \phi)^{1/2}}{1 + \sin \theta \sin \phi} \qquad [13.149]$$

Substituting [13.100], [13.101], and [13.99] into [13.149], we obtain

$$|s| = \frac{(\cos^2 2\lambda \cos^2 2\psi + \cos^2 2\lambda \sin^2 2\psi)^{1/2}}{1 + \sin 2\lambda}$$

$$= \frac{\cos^2 \lambda - \sin^2 \lambda}{(\cos \lambda + \sin \lambda)^2}$$

$$= \frac{\cos \lambda - \sin \lambda}{\cos \lambda + \sin \lambda}$$

or

$$|s| = \frac{1 - \tan \lambda}{1 + \tan \lambda} \qquad [13.150]$$

Thus, using [13.148] and [13.150] in [13.146] we find that

$$s = \frac{C_1}{C_r} = \frac{1 - \tan \lambda}{1 + \tan \lambda} e^{i2\psi} = \frac{a_1 - a_2}{a_1 + a_2} e^{i2\psi} \qquad [13.151]$$

where [13.92] has been used.
  We can use [13.151] to write the transformation relation [13.144] as

$$\frac{1 - \tan \lambda'}{1 + \tan \lambda'} e^{i2\psi'} = \frac{1 - \tan \lambda}{1 + \tan \lambda} e^{i[2\psi - (k_+ - k_-)x_3]} \qquad [13.152]$$

  Suppose that the initial polarization is linearly polarized in the horizontal direction. Then $\tan \lambda = \psi = 0$ and [13.152] becomes

$$\frac{1 - \tan \lambda'}{1 + \tan \lambda'} e^{i2\psi'} = e^{-i(k_+ - k_-)x_3} \qquad [13.153]$$

Now, in general, if the effects of collisions are included, k_+ and k_- will be complex. Let us write

$$k_\pm = \beta_\pm + i\alpha_\pm \qquad [13.154]$$

Substituting [13.154] into [13.153], we obtain

$$\frac{1 - \tan \lambda'}{1 + \tan \lambda'} e^{i2\psi'} = e^{(\alpha_+ - \alpha_-)x_3} e^{-i(\beta_+ - \beta_-)x_3} \qquad [13.155]$$

From [13.155] we see that if collisions are neglected so that $\alpha_+ = \alpha_- = 0$, then $\tan \lambda' = 0$ so that the original linearly polarized wave remains linearly polarized and is rotated through the angle

$$\psi' = -\tfrac{1}{2}(\beta_+ - \beta_-)x_3 \qquad [13.156]$$

This phenomenon is known as Faraday rotation.

If collisions occur in the plasma then α_+ and α_- are not zero and the original linearly polarized wave not only becomes rotated through an angle ψ' but it also becomes elliptical. The axial ratio of the ellipse is, from [13.155], obtained from the relation

$$\frac{1 - \tan \lambda'}{1 + \tan \lambda'} = e^{(\alpha_+ - \alpha_-)x_3} \qquad [13.157]$$

We note from [13.156] and [13.157] that the angle of rotation is determined from the real part of $k_\pm$, while the axial ratio is determined from the imaginary part of $k_\pm$. It is therefore possible to use a measurement of the output polarization as a diagnostic technique in which the angle of rotation and the change in axial ratio determine the electron density and the electron collision frequency of a plasma.

13.5 GROUP VELOCITY
IN ANISOTROPIC MEDIA

The concepts of group velocity were discussed in Section 11.23. We associated the group velocity with the velocity with which the amplitude of a wave packet travels in a dispersive medium. We found that the location of the wave packet at any time t was determined from the condition that the phase in the integral

$$E(x_i, t) = \int_{-\infty}^{\infty} A(k)e^{i(k\alpha_q x_q - \omega t)} \, dk \qquad [13.158]$$

be constant with respect to variations in ω (or k).

Now, in general, the amplitude function $A(k)$ will depend on the direction of propagation as well as the frequency. Thus, if the direction of α_i is given by the angles θ and φ as shown in Figure 13.11, so that

$$\alpha_i x_i = \alpha_1 x_1 + \alpha_2 x_2 + \alpha_3 x_3$$

$$= \sin \theta (x_1 \cos \varphi + x_2 \sin \varphi) + x_3 \cos \theta \qquad [13.159]$$

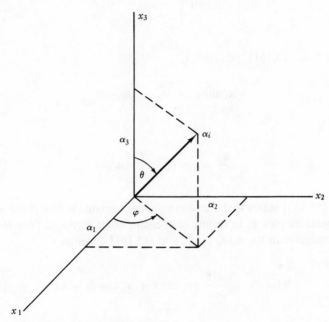

FIGURE 13.11   The Direction of α_i

then [13.158] can be written as

$$E(x_i, t) = \int_0^{2\pi} \int_0^{\pi} \int_{-\infty}^{\infty} A(\omega, \theta, \varphi) e^{i\Psi(\omega, \theta, \varphi)} \, d\omega \, d\theta \, d\varphi \qquad [13.160]$$

where

$$\Psi(\omega, \theta, \varphi) = \left\{ \frac{\omega n(\theta)}{c} \left[\sin \theta (x_1 \cos \varphi + x_2 \sin \varphi) + x_3 \cos \theta \right] - \omega t \right\}$$

$$[13.161]$$

and where $n(\theta)$ is the refractive index of the plasma given by the Appleton-Hartree equation.

We now proceed as we did in Section 11.23 recognizing that $A(k, \theta, \varphi)$ will have a maximum value for some particular values k_0, θ_0, and φ_0. The values θ_0 and φ_0 will correspond to the direction in which the wave packet travels in the absence of a plasma. The value of the integral [13.160] will be largest when the phase $\Psi(\omega, \theta, \varphi)$ is constant with respect to variations in θ, φ, and ω near the values θ_0, φ_0, and k_0. We consider each of these variations in turn.

From the condition

$$\left.\frac{\partial \Psi}{\partial \varphi}\right|_{\varphi_0} = 0 \qquad\qquad [13.162]$$

we obtain from [13.161] the relation

$$-x_1 \sin \varphi_0 + x_2 \cos \varphi_0 = 0$$

from which

$$\frac{x_2}{x_1} = \tan \varphi_0 = \text{const} \qquad\qquad [13.163]$$

Equation [13.163] states that the wave packet remains in the plane $\varphi = \varphi_0$. We can therefore pick φ_0 to be any convenient angle, say $\pi/2$. Then the wave packet propagates in the x_2-x_3 plane and [13.161] becomes

$$\Psi(\omega, \theta) = \frac{\omega n(\theta)}{c}(x_2 \sin \theta + x_3 \cos \theta) - \omega t \qquad\qquad [13.164]$$

Let us now consider variations with respect to θ. From the condition

$$\left.\frac{\partial \Psi}{\partial \theta}\right|_{\theta_0} = 0 \qquad\qquad [13.165]$$

we find from [13.164] that

$$\left.\frac{\partial n(\theta)}{\partial \theta}\right|_{\theta_0}(x_2 \sin \theta_0 + x_3 \cos \theta_0) + n(\theta_0)(x_2 \cos \theta_0 - x_3 \sin \theta_0) = 0$$

$$[13.166]$$

Now θ_0 is the angle between α_i and the x_3-axis (that is, the direction of the magnetic field). The values of x_2 and x_3 in [13.166] are the coordinates of the wave packet position at some time t. The wave packet will not, in general, propagate in the direction of α_i. Let the direction in which the wave packet travels be given by the unit vector β_i which is inclined at an angle γ from α_i as shown in Figure 13.12. It will turn out that the unit vector β_i and the angle γ are the same as those quantities in Figure 13.3.

If in a time t the wave packet has traveled a distance r_o in the direction of β_i, then from Figure 13.12 the coordinates of the wave packet are

$$x_2 = r_o \sin (\theta_o - \gamma) = r_o(\sin \theta_o \cos \gamma - \sin \gamma \cos \theta_o)$$

$$x_3 = r_o \cos (\theta_o - \gamma) = r_o(\cos \theta_o \cos \gamma + \sin \gamma \sin \theta_o)$$

$$[13.167]$$

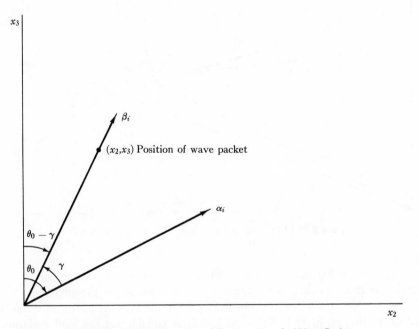

FIGURE 13.12   Direction of Propagation of a Wave Packet

Substituting [13.167] into [13.166], we obtain, after canceling terms,

$$\frac{\partial n(\theta)}{\partial \theta}\bigg|_{\theta_o} \cos \gamma - n(\theta_o) \sin \gamma = 0$$

from which we have the important result that

$$\tan \gamma = \frac{1}{n} \frac{\partial n}{\partial \theta}\bigg|_{\theta_o} \qquad [13.168]$$

Consider a segment of the refractive index surface shown in Figure 13.13. Writing [13.168] as

$$\tan \gamma = \frac{\delta n}{n \delta \theta} \qquad [13.169]$$

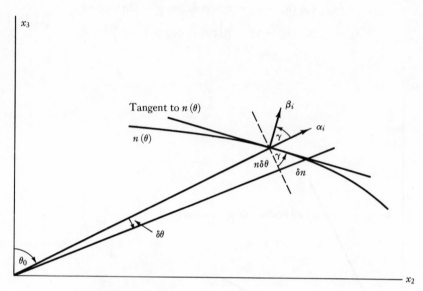

FIGURE 13.13   Properties of the Refractive Index Surface

it is clear from Figure 13.13 that γ is the angle between a line tangent to the refractive index surface and a line normal to α_i. Since γ is the angle between α_i and β_i, this means that β_i is normal to the refractive index surface. We will return to this property in Section 13.52 after considering the final variation of Ψ (with respect to ω) in the next section.

13.51   GROUP VELOCITY AND RAY VELOCITY

In the previous section we considered the consequences of taking the phase factor Ψ to be constant with respect to variations of φ and θ. We finally wish to consider the result of requiring Ψ to be constant with respect to variations in ω.

If we substitute [13.167] into [13.164], then from the condition

$$\left. \frac{\partial \Psi}{\partial \omega} \right|_{\omega_o} = 0 \qquad [13.170]$$

we obtain

$$\frac{r_o \cos \gamma}{c} \frac{\partial(\omega n)}{\partial \omega}\bigg|_{\omega_o} - t = 0$$

or

$$ct = r_o \cos \gamma \frac{\partial(\omega n)}{\partial \omega}\bigg|_{\omega_o} = r_o n' \cos \gamma \qquad [13.171]$$

where

$$n' = \frac{\partial(\omega n)}{\partial \omega}\bigg|_{\omega_o} \qquad [13.172]$$

is called the *group refractive index*.

From [13.171] we see that the wave packet travels with the group velocity v given by

$$v = \frac{dr_o}{dt} = \frac{c}{n' \cos \gamma} \qquad [13.173]$$

Note that for an anisotropic medium

$$n' = \frac{c}{v \cos \gamma} \qquad [13.174]$$

The ray surface was discussed in Section 13.22. From [13.46] the ray velocity w is given by

$$w = \frac{u}{\cos \gamma} = \frac{c}{n \cos \gamma} \qquad [13.175]$$

It is possible to define a quantity

$$m = n \cos \gamma = \frac{c}{w} \qquad [13.176]$$

which is called the *ray refractive index*.

From [13.174] we can also define the quantity

$$m' = n' \cos \gamma = \frac{c}{v} \qquad [13.177]$$

which is called the *group-ray refractive index*.

13.52 RECIPROCAL PROPERTIES OF
THE RAY AND REFRACTIVE INDEX SURFACES

It is now instructive to summarize the results of the previous sections in a graphical fashion. In Section 13.21 we defined the refractive index surface and the wave normal surface. Thus a given point on the wave normal surface is found by moving in the direction of α_i a distance equal to u/c. The corresponding point on the refractive index surface is found by moving in the direction of α_i a distance equal to $n = c/u$. Thus in a sense the refractive index surface is an inverse wave normal surface.

Now for each point on the wave normal surface and the refractive index surface there corresponds a point on the ray surface defined in Section 13.22 which is found by moving in the direction of β_i a distance equal to w/c. This point corresponds to the point reached by the wave front in the direction of β_i in a unit time. But since the normal to the wave front is in the direction of

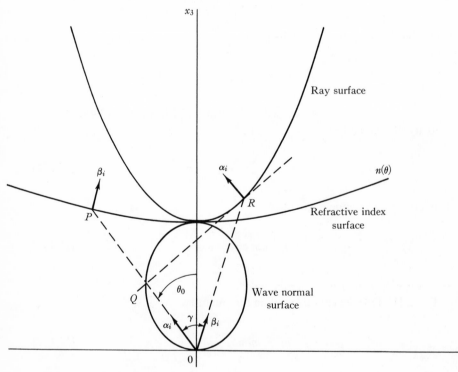

FIGURE 13.14 Properties of the Wave Normal, Refractive Index, and Ray Surfaces

α_i, then the normal to the ray surface at each point must be in the direction of α_i. This is made clear in Figure 13.14.

In Figure 13.3 the direction of β_i is the direction of the Poynting vector G_i. As we have seen for a plasma in a magnetic field the electric field vector E_i can have a component in the direction of α_i while the magnetic field vector H_i cannot. Since the polarization of the wave is, in general, elliptical, the direction of the Poynting vector continually changes over a cycle. The direction β_i is the direction of the mean Poynting vector given by [11.43]. This is then the direction in which the mean intensity of energy flows.

The direction of β_i in Figure 13.12 is the direction in which a wave packet moves—that is, the direction of the group velocity. It can be shown (see Problem 13.1) that for the case of a collisionless plasma the group velocity is in the direction of the mean Poynting vector. Thus from Figure 13.13 we see that the ray direction β_i is normal to the refractive index surface.

We can therefore state the following reciprocal properties of the ray surface and refractive index surface shown in Figure 13.14. For every point Q on the wave normal surface there exists a point P on the refractive index surface and a point R on the ray surface. The normal to the refractive index surface at P is in the direction of β_i (that is, parallel to the line OR) and the normal to the ray surface at R is in the direction of α_i (that is, parallel to the line OQP).

The properties of the group velocity in anisotropic media will be used in the following section to explain the phenomena of atmospheric whistlers.

13.53   THE THEORY OF WHISTLERS

We now want to apply the theory of group velocity in anisotropic media to explain the phenomenon of whistlers. If a loudspeaker is connected through amplifiers to an appropriate antenna it is possible at times to hear a type of atmospherics which is in the form of a descending audio tone. This audio tone, which may last for several seconds, is called a *whistler*.

The theory is that whistlers originate with a lightning flash. A pulse of electromagnetic energy is produced which contains a wide range of frequencies. This pulse or wave packet moves up through the ionosphere and is guided by the earth's magnetic field to a point on another part of the earth's surface. If the whistler is detected at this point it is called a *short whistler*. However the signal may be reflected by the earth at this point and return along the earth's magnetic field to a point close to where it originated. In such a case the whistler is called a *long whistler*. For this case both the lightning flash and the whistler can be detected. The difference between long and short whistlers is shown in Figure 13.15.

The frequencies of interest are in the audio range between 0.5 and 10 kc. The value of the plasma frequency $\Pi/2\pi$ along the path of the signal can

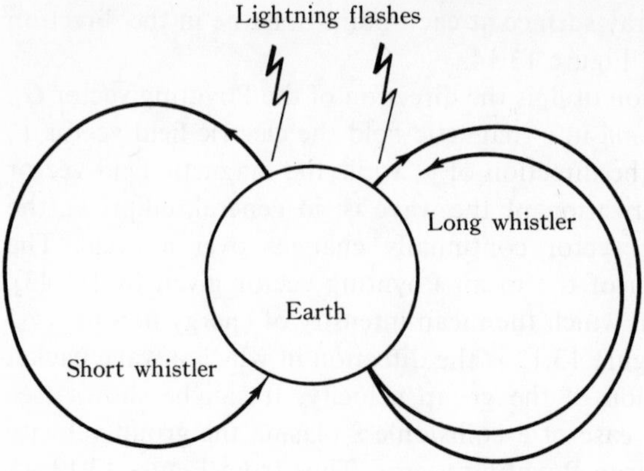

Lightning flashes

Long whistler

Earth

Short whistler

FIGURE 13.15   The Propagation of Whistlers

FIGURE 13.15   The Propagation of Whistlers

be between 0 and 10 mc. The value of the cyclotron frequency $\Omega/2\pi$ is between 1.5 and 0.1 mc. Thus the parameters X and Y can have the following values

$$X:\ \ 0 \text{ to } 4 \times 10^8$$

$$Y:\ \ 10 \text{ to } 3000$$

$$X/Y:\ \ 0 \text{ to } 10^5$$

At the great heights being considered for most of the journey of the signal (> 80 km) the collision frequency ν_{EN} is negligible.

Based on these values of the parameters we shall attempt to explain whistlers in terms of the right-circular mode in Region VIII of Figure 13.8. The theory must be able to answer the following two questions. (1) Why does the signal follow the magnetic lines of force? (2) Why is the received signal heard as a descending whistle? These questions will be answered on the basis of a simplified analysis in what follows.

Angular Confinement of Rays   From the Appleton-Hartree equation [13.24] we see that for propagation nearly along the magnetic field lines $\left(Y\cos\theta \gg \dfrac{Y^2\sin^2\theta}{2(1-X)}\right)$ we can write, in the collisionless case,

$$n^2 \approx 1 - \frac{X}{1 - Y\cos\theta} \qquad\qquad [13.178]$$

This mode of propagation is often referred to as the quasi-longitudinal mode.
If $Y\cos\theta \gg 1$, we can write [13.178] as

$$n^2 \approx 1 + \frac{X}{Y\cos\theta} \qquad\qquad [13.179]$$

and if we further have that $X/Y \gg 1$, then [13.179] can be written as

$$n^2 \approx \frac{X}{Y \cos \theta} \qquad [13.180]$$

For our analysis of whistlers we will therefore assume that the refractive index n is given by

$$n = \left(\frac{X}{Y \cos \theta}\right)^{1/2} \qquad [13.181]$$

Now since the energy from the lightning flash is in the form of a wave packet, it will travel in the direction β_i, which is inclined at an angle γ from α_i as shown in Figure 13.12. From [13.168] we have that

$$\tan \gamma = \frac{1}{n} \frac{\partial n}{\partial \theta}\bigg|_{\theta_0} \qquad [13.182]$$

From [13.181] we can write

$$\frac{\partial n}{\partial \theta} = \frac{1}{2}\sqrt{\frac{X}{Y}} \frac{\sin \theta}{(\cos \theta)^{3/2}} \qquad [13.183]$$

Using [13.181] and [13.183] in [13.182], we obtain

$$\tan \gamma = \tfrac{1}{2} \tan \theta_0 \qquad [13.184]$$

The direction β_i in which the wave packet moves is inclined to the direction of the magnetic field by an angle $(\theta_0 - \gamma)$. From the relation

$$\tan (\theta_0 - \gamma) = \frac{\tan \theta_0 - \tan \gamma}{1 + \tan \theta_0 \tan \gamma} \qquad [13.185]$$

we obtain by using [13.184]

$$\tan (\theta_0 - \gamma) = \frac{\tfrac{1}{2} \tan \theta_0}{1 + \tfrac{1}{2} \tan^2 \theta_0} \qquad [13.186]$$

The wave normal surface in Region VIII of Figure 13.8 is of the general shape of the wave normal surface shown in Figure 13.14. This surface has a resonant cone—that is, there is a maximum value which the angle θ_0 may have. When θ_0 is maximum the angle $(\theta_0 - \gamma)$ between the magnetic field and β_i is also maximum. This angle represents the maximum angular deviation of the ray surface from the direction of the magnetic field. That is, it represents the maximum angular deviation from the magnetic field of the direction in which a wave packet can travel.

From [13.186] we find that the maximum value of $\tan(\theta_o - \gamma)$ occurs when

$$\frac{\partial \tan(\theta_o - \gamma)}{\partial \theta_o} = \frac{(1 + \frac{1}{2}\tan^2\theta_o)^{\frac{1}{2}}\sec^2\theta_o - \frac{1}{2}\tan^2\theta_o\sec^2\theta_o}{(1 + \frac{1}{2}\tan^2\theta_o)^2} = 0$$

that is, when

$$\tan\theta_o = \sqrt{2} \qquad\qquad [13.187]$$

or

$$\theta_{o_{MAX}} = 54°44' \qquad\qquad [13.188]$$

Substituting [13.187] into [13.186] we find the maximum value of $\tan(\theta_o - \gamma)$ is

$$\tan(\theta_o - \gamma)_{MAX} = \frac{1}{\sqrt{8}} \qquad\qquad [13.189]$$

from which the maximum value of $(\theta_o - \gamma)$ is

$$(\theta_o - \gamma)_{MAX} = 19°29' \qquad\qquad [13.190]$$

Thus the wave packet is confined to a narrow beam of less than 20° about the magnetic field lines. The wave packet is thus said to be guided by the magnetic field.

Variation of Frequency   We now wish to determine why the received signal is in the form of a descending whistle. The wave packet travels with the group velocity v given by [13.173] as

$$v = \frac{dr_o}{dt} = \frac{c}{n'\cos\gamma} \qquad\qquad [13.191]$$

where

$$n' = \frac{\partial(\omega n)}{\partial\omega}\bigg|_{\omega_o} \qquad\qquad [13.192]$$

is the group refractive index.

From [13.181] we can write

$$\omega n = \left(\frac{\omega \Pi^2}{\Omega \cos \theta}\right)^{1/2} \qquad [13.193]$$

from which

$$n' = \left.\frac{\partial(\omega n)}{\partial \omega}\right|_{\omega_0} = \frac{1}{2}\left(\frac{\Pi^2}{\omega_0 \Omega \cos \theta}\right)^{1/2} = \frac{n}{2} \qquad [13.194]$$

Substituting [13.194] into [13.191], we obtain for the group velocity

$$v = \frac{2c\sqrt{\Omega \cos \theta}}{\Pi \cos \gamma} \omega_0^{1/2} \qquad [13.195]$$

Since the group velocity is proportional to the square root of the frequency, the higher frequencies will arrive slightly ahead of the lower frequencies. Thus the received signal will have a descending pitch.

Many experiments on whistlers have been carried out which verify the frequency dependence of the group velocity given by [13.195]. For more information on whistlers the student may consult the references at the end of the chapter.

Problem

13.1 Show that in a collisionless anisotropic plasma the direction of the mean Poynting vector $\langle G_i \rangle$ given by [11.43] is the same as the direction in which a wave packet moves as given by [13.168] [Ref. 9].

REFERENCES

The theory of radio wave propagation in the ionosphere based on the Appleton-Hartree equation is treated in detail by

1   Ratcliffe, J. A. *The Magneto-ionic Theory and its Applications to the Ionosphere.* London: Cambridge University Press, 1959.

2   Budden, K. G. *Radio Waves in the Ionosphere.* London: Cambridge University Press, 1961.

Treatments of wave propagation in anisotropic plasmas based on the principal coordinate system can be found in

3   Brandstatter, J. J. *An Introduction to Waves, Rays and Radiation in Plasma Media.* New York: McGraw-Hill, 1963.

4   Turner, C. H. M. "Birefringence in Crystals and in the Ionosphere," *Can. J. Phys.*, **32** (1954), 16–31.

5   Westfold, K. C. "The Wave Equations for Electromagnetic Radiation in an Ionized Medium in a Magnetic Field," *Australian J. Sci. Research*, Ser. A, **2** (1949), 169–83.

Discussions of wave normal surfaces and the Clemmow-Mullaly-Allis diagram of Figure 13.8 can be found in

6   Allis, W. P., S. J. Buchsbaum, and A. Bers. *Waves in Anisotropic Plasmas*. Cambridge, Mass.: Massachusetts Institute of Technology Press, 1963.

7   Allis, W. P. "Propagation of Waves in a Plasma in a Magnetic Field," *I.R.E. Trans.*, Vol. MTT-9 (1961), 79–82.

8   Stix, T. H. *The Theory of Plasma Waves*. New York: McGraw-Hill, 1962.

The fact that wave packets travel in the same direction as that of the energy flow was demonstrated by

9   Hines, C. O. "Wave Packets, The Poynting Vector, and Energy Flow," *J. Geophys. Res.*, **56** (1951), 63, 197, 207, 535.

A comprehensive treatment of whistlers is given by

10   Storey, L. R. O. "An Investigation of Whistling Atmospherics," *Phil. Trans. Roy. Soc.*, Ser. A, **246** (1953), 113.

General treatments of electromagnetic wave propagation in plasmas can be found in

11   Denisse, J. F., and J. L. Delcroix. *Theorie des Ondes dans les Plasmas*. Paris: Dunod, 1961; translated as *Plasma Waves*, New York: Interscience (Wiley), 1963.

12   Ginzburg, V. L. *Propagation of Electromagnetic Waves in Plasmas*. New York: Gordon and Breach, 1960.

14

MAGNETO-
FLUID DYNAMICS

A particular area of plasma dynamics in which there is widespread interest is that area in which the plasma is considered to be a conducting fluid. The equations for a conducting fluid have already been developed in Chapter 6 and the application of these equations forms the subject matter of magneto-fluid dynamics.

We found in Sections 6.4 and 6.5 that the equations for a conducting fluid could be divided into two groups. The first group contains the moment equations which describe the time variation of the fluid dynamic or state variables. These moment equations include the continuity equation from [6.73]

$$\frac{\partial \rho}{\partial t} + \frac{\partial \rho v_i^*}{\partial x_i} = 0 \qquad [14.1]$$

the momentum equation from [6.81]

$$\rho \frac{D v_i^*}{Dt} = \eta E_i + \epsilon_{ijk} J_j B_k - \frac{\partial \Psi_{ij}^*}{\partial x_j} \qquad [14.2]$$

and the energy equation from [6.91]

$$\frac{D\mathscr{E}^*}{Dt} + \mathscr{E}^* \frac{\partial v_i^*}{\partial x_i} + \frac{\partial Q_i^*}{\partial x_i} + \Psi_{ij}^* \frac{\partial v_j^*}{\partial x_i} = J_i' E_i' \qquad [14.3]$$

As we have pointed out, the moment equations must be truncated by making some assumption about the heat flux vector Q_i^*.

The second group of equations needed to complete the description of a conducting fluid are the electrodynamic equations involving the electrodynamic variables E_i, B_i, η, and J_i. These are, from Section 6.5, the Maxwell equations

$$\epsilon_{ijk} E_{k,j} = -\dot{B}_i \qquad [14.4]$$

$$\epsilon_{ijk} B_{k,j} = \mu_0 J_i + \mu_0 \epsilon_0 \dot{E}_i \qquad [14.5]$$

The equation of continuity of charge

$$\frac{\partial \eta}{\partial t} = -J_{i,i} \qquad [14.6]$$

and for the case of an electron-ion plasma with zero space charge density, the generalized Ohm's law

$$J_i + \frac{1}{\nu_{EI}} \epsilon_{ijk} J_j \Omega_k^- + \frac{1}{\nu_{EI}} \frac{\partial J_i}{\partial t} = \sigma'(E_i + \epsilon_{ijk} v_j^* B_k) + \frac{\sigma' e}{m_-} \frac{\partial}{\partial x_j} \left(\Psi_{ij}^- - \frac{m_-}{m_+} \Psi_{ij}^+ \right)$$

$$[14.7]$$

These equations for a conducting fluid are, in their present form, far too difficult to solve. We must, therefore, proceed to simplify them in order to obtain equations which we can handle. By considering the relative orders of magnitude of various terms it will be possible to obtain a simplified set of equations applicable under certain conditions.

14.1 DIMENSIONAL CONSIDERATIONS

The generalized Ohm's law [14.7] is applicable when the space charge density η is equal to zero. We have found in Section 9.1 that there is a strong tendency for the plasma to remain electrically neutral. One can show (see Problem 3.2) that if any space charge develops in a medium with conductivity σ, it will decay exponentially with a time constant equal to ϵ_0/σ.

We found in Section 6.51 that if $|\Omega_k^-| \ll \nu_{\mathrm{EI}}$, then we can neglect the Hall current. If we further neglect the pressure gradient terms then, in the steady state, Ohm's law is given by [6.116] as

$$J_i = \sigma(E_i + \epsilon_{ijk}v_j^* B_k) \qquad [14.8]$$

In this chapter we will assume that the current density is given by [14.8] where σ (where we drop the prime) is the appropriate conductivity of the conducting fluid.

Since we have assumed charge neutrality so that $\eta = 0$, there is no convection current ηv_i^*. In general, η will not vanish, but we can show that its effect is often negligible by the following dimensional considerations. Let $\{L\}$ be the order of magnitude of a characteristic length of the conducting fluid. It is a typical length over which variations in the fluid motion occur. In laboratory plasmas it could be the dimensions of the vessel—that is, a few centimeters—while in cosmic problems it could range anywhere from the radius of the earth to many light-years. Similarly let $\{T\}$ be the order of magnitude of a representative time. This time could range from a small fraction of a second in laboratory plasmas to days or even years in cosmic plasmas. Finally the representative velocity $\{V\} = \{L\}/\{T\}$.

The space charge η which exists in a plasma is given in terms of the electric field by $E_{i,i} = \eta/\epsilon_0$. Thus, the order of magnitude of η is

$$\{\eta\} = \left\{\frac{\epsilon_0 E}{L}\right\}$$

We therefore see that the ratio of the convection current ηv_i^* to the conduction current σE_i is of the order

$$\left\{\frac{\eta V}{\sigma E}\right\} = \left\{\frac{\epsilon_0 E V}{L \sigma E}\right\} = \left\{\frac{\epsilon_0}{\sigma T}\right\} \qquad [14.9]$$

which is just the ratio of the space charge decay time to the characteristic time of the fluid motion. For many cosmic problems this ratio can be as small as 10^{-22}. Thus the convection current is extremely small and is neglected.

Using [14.8], we can now write the Maxwell equation [14.5] as

$$\epsilon_{ijk}B_{k,j} = \mu_0 \sigma E_i + \mu_0 \sigma \epsilon_{ijk}v_j^* B_k + \mu_0 \epsilon_0 \dot{E}_i \qquad [14.10]$$

The ratio of the displacement current $\epsilon_0 \dot{E}_i$ to the conduction current σE is of the order

$$\left\{\frac{\epsilon_0 E}{T \sigma E}\right\} = \left\{\frac{\epsilon_0}{\sigma T}\right\} \qquad [14.11]$$

which is the same as [14.9] and is thus extremely small for many cosmic problems. Therefore in magneto-fluid dynamics the displacement current is generally neglected.

From the Maxwell equation [14.4] we see that the ratio of E_i to B_i is of the order

$$\left\{\frac{E}{B}\right\} = \left\{\frac{L}{T}\right\} = \{V\} \tag{14.12}$$

which is the characteristic velocity of the fluid. Using [14.12] we see that the ratio of the conduction current σE_i to the induction current $\sigma \epsilon_{ijk} v_j^* B_k$ in [14.10] is of the order

$$\left\{\frac{\sigma E}{\sigma V B}\right\} = \{1\} \tag{14.13}$$

so that the conduction current and the induction current are of the same order of magnitude.

Finally, one can show (see Exercise 14.1.1) that for many problems of interest the electric field term ηE_i in [14.2] is many orders of magnitude smaller than the magnetic field term $\epsilon_{ijk} J_j B_k$ so that the electric field term may be neglected.

In magneto-fluid dynamics the pressure tensor Ψ_{ij}^* in [14.2] is assumed to be isotropic and given by $P^* \delta_{ij}$. Under certain conditions discussed in Section 6.43 the pressure P^* and the density ρ can be related by the adiabatic law [6.92]. We shall represent this functional relation as

$$P^* = P^*(\rho) \tag{14.14}$$

In view of the dimensional considerations discussed above, the remaining equations for a conducting fluid take the following form: the continuity equation

$$\frac{\partial \rho}{\partial t} + \frac{\partial (\rho v_i^*)}{\partial x_i} = 0 \tag{14.15}$$

the momentum equation

$$\rho \left(\frac{\partial v_i^*}{\partial t} + v_j^* \frac{\partial v_i^*}{\partial x_j} \right) = \epsilon_{ijk} J_j B_k - \frac{\partial P^*}{\partial x_i} \tag{14.16}$$

Maxwell's equations

$$\epsilon_{ijk} E_{k,j} = -\dot{B}_i \tag{14.17}$$

and

$$\epsilon_{ijk} B_{k,j} = \mu_0 J_i \qquad [14.18]$$

where

$$J_i = \sigma(E_i + \epsilon_{ijk} v_j^* B_k) \qquad [14.19]$$

Equations [14.14] to [14.19] represent a total of fourteen scalar equations in the fourteen unknowns v_i^*, B_i, E_i, J_i, P^*, and ρ. In order to discuss these magneto-fluid dynamic equations, we will reduce this set in the following section to eight scalar equations by eliminating the electric field E_i and the current density J_i.

Exercise 14.1.1   Under what conditions is the electric field term ηE_i much smaller than the magnetic field term $\epsilon_{ijk} J_j B_k$ in [14.2]?

14.11 THE MAGNETO-FLUID DYNAMIC EQUATIONS

Equations [14.14] to [14.19] of the previous section can be somewhat simplified by eliminating J_i and E_i. If we substitute J_i from [14.18] into [14.16], we obtain

$$
\begin{aligned}
\rho \frac{Dv_i^*}{Dt} &= \frac{1}{\mu_0} \epsilon_{ijk}\epsilon_{jmn} B_{n,m} B_k - \frac{\partial P^*}{\partial x_i} \\
&= \frac{1}{\mu_0} (\delta_{km}\delta_{in} - \delta_{kn}\delta_{im}) B_{n,m} B_k - \frac{\partial P^*}{\partial x_i} \\
&= \frac{1}{\mu_0} (B_{i,k} B_k - B_{k,i} B_k) - \frac{\partial P^*}{\partial x_i} \qquad [14.20]
\end{aligned}
$$

Since $B_{k,i} B_k = \frac{1}{2}(B^2)_{,i}$ where $B^2 = B_k B_k$, then we can write [14.20] as

$$
\begin{aligned}
\rho \frac{Dv_i^*}{Dt} &= -P_{,i}^* + \frac{1}{\mu_0} (B_{i,k} B_k - B_{k,i} B_k) \\
&= -\left(P^* + \frac{B^2}{2\mu_0}\right)_{,i} + \frac{1}{\mu_0} B_{i,k} B_k \qquad [14.21]
\end{aligned}
$$

If we substitute J_i from [14.18] into [14.19] and solve for E_i, we obtain

$$E_i = \epsilon_{ijk}\left(\frac{1}{\mu_0 \sigma} B_{k,j} - v_j^* B_k\right) \qquad [14.22]$$

Substituting [14.22] into [14.17], we obtain

$$-\dot{B}_i = \epsilon_{ijk}\epsilon_{kmn}\left(\frac{1}{\mu_o\sigma}B_{n,m} - v_m^*B_n\right)_{,j}$$

$$= (\delta_{im}\delta_{jn} - \delta_{in}\delta_{jm})\left(\frac{1}{\mu_o\sigma}B_{n,mj} - v_{m,j}^*B_n - v_m^*B_{n,j}\right)$$

from which, noting that $B_{j,j} = 0$,

$$-\dot{B}_i = -\frac{1}{\mu_o\sigma}B_{i,jj} + v_{j,j}^*B_i - v_{i,j}^*B_j + v_j^*B_{i,j}$$

which can be written in terms of the substantial derivative [6.75] as

$$\frac{DB_i}{Dt} + B_iv_{j,j}^* - B_jv_{i,j}^* = \frac{1}{\mu_o\sigma}B_{i,jj} \qquad [14.23]$$

We therefore see that the magneto-fluid dynamic equations [14.14] to [14.19] reduce to the following set involving only v_i^*, B_i, ρ, and P^*,

$$\frac{\partial\rho}{\partial t} + \frac{\partial\rho v_i^*}{\partial x_i} = 0 \qquad [14.24]$$

$$\rho\frac{Dv_i^*}{Dt} = -P_{,i}^* + \frac{1}{\mu_o}(B_{i,k}B_k - B_{k,i}B_k)$$

$$= -\left(P^* + \frac{B^2}{2\mu_o}\right)_{,i} + \frac{1}{\mu_o}B_{i,k}B_k \qquad [14.25]$$

$$\frac{DB_i}{Dt} + B_iv_{j,j}^* - B_jv_{i,j}^* = \frac{1}{\mu_o\sigma}B_{i,jj} \qquad [14.26]$$

$$P^* = P^*(\rho) \qquad [14.27]$$

Notice that if the conductivity σ is infinite, the term on the right-hand side of [14.26] is zero. We showed in Section 3.4 that for this case the magnetic field lines are "frozen" into the fluid and move along with the fluid.

Let us consider the case of a finite conductivity. We can write [14.26] as

$$\frac{\partial B_i}{\partial t} + v_j^*B_{i,j} + B_iv_{j,j}^* - B_jv_{i,j}^* = \frac{1}{\mu_o\sigma}B_{i,jj} \qquad [14.28]$$

The second, third, and fourth terms in [14.28] are all of order $\{VB/L\}$ while the term on the right-hand side of [14.28] is of the order $\{B/(\mu_o\sigma L^2)\}$. The ratio of the three terms on the left to the term on the right is thus of order

$$\{\mu_o\sigma VL\} = \{R_M\} \qquad [14.29]$$

where R_M is called the *magnetic Reynolds number*. When this number is much greater than unity, the right-hand side of [14.28] is negligible and the magnetic field can be considered to be "frozen" in the conducting fluid. On the other hand when R_M is much less than unity then [14.28] reduces to

$$\frac{\partial B_i}{\partial t} = \frac{1}{\mu_0 \sigma} B_{i,jj} \qquad [14.30]$$

which is a diffusion equation describing the diffusion of the magnetic field lines through the conducting fluid. If L is associated with the diffusion length then [14.30] can be put in the form

$$\frac{\partial B_i}{\partial t} = \frac{1}{\mu_0 \sigma L^2} B_i \qquad [14.31]$$

from which we see that the magnetic field decays exponentially in time with a time constant τ_{DIFF} given by

$$\tau_{\text{DIFF}} = \mu_0 \sigma L^2 \qquad [14.32]$$

Note that the ratio of the diffusion time τ_{DIFF} to the characteristic time $T = L/V$ is

$$\frac{\tau_{\text{DIFF}}}{T} = \mu_0 \sigma V L = R_M \qquad [14.33]$$

Thus the magnetic Reynolds number is a measure of the coupling between the motion of the magnetic field lines and the motion of the conducting fluid.

We therefore see that the basic equations of magneto-fluid dynamics can be simplified when the magnetic Reynolds number is sufficiently large. This is almost always the case in cosmic plasmas where there is a strong coupling between the magnetic field and the conducting fluid. Other simplifications are also possible. The fluid is said to be incompressible when the density ρ is a constant. From [14.24] this implies that the fluid velocity is divergence-free, that is $v^*_{i,i} = 0$.

In the following sections we will investigate the consequences of the basic magneto-fluid dynamic equations [14.24] to [14.27] for the static case ($v^*_i = 0$) and for the steady-state case ($\partial/\partial t = 0$). We will conclude this chapter with a treatment of wave motion in both an incompressible and a compressible conducting fluid.

14.2 MAGNETOHYDROSTATICS

We consider first the static case when the fluid velocity is zero. Setting $v_i^* = 0$ in [14.25] and [14.26] we obtain

$$\left(P^* + \frac{B^2}{2\mu_0}\right)_{,i} = \frac{1}{\mu_0} B_{i,k} B_k \qquad [14.34]$$

and

$$\frac{\partial B_i}{\partial t} = \frac{1}{\mu_0 \sigma} B_{i,jj} \qquad [14.35]$$

The second of these equations indicates that for a finite conductivity the magnetic field diffuses through the fluid as discussed in the previous section.

The equilibrium forces acting on the fluid are given by [14.34]. From [14.16] we see that this equation is equivalent to

$$\epsilon_{ijk} J_j B_k = P_{,i}^* \qquad [14.36]$$

We recall from Section 3.5 that for the case we are considering we can write [14.36] in terms of the magnetic stress tensor T_{ij}^M as

$$T_{ij,j}^M = P_{,i}^* \qquad [14.37]$$

where, from [3.96]

$$T_{ij}^M = \frac{1}{\mu_0} (B_i B_j - \tfrac{1}{2} B^2 \, \delta_{ij}) \qquad [14.38]$$

Equation [14.37] is clearly identical to [14.34].

The left-hand side of [14.37] is the body force per unit volume acting on the fluid due to the magnetic field. The total force acting on a volume V bounded by the closed surface S with unit outward normal n_i is then

$$\int_V T_{ij,j}^M \, d\tau = \int_S T_{ij}^M n_j \, dA \qquad [14.39]$$

where the divergence theorem has been used. Using [14.38] the surface force acting on a unit area is then

$$T_{ij}^M n_j = \frac{1}{\mu_0} B_i B_j n_j - \frac{B^2}{2\mu_0} n_i \qquad [14.40]$$

which is the sum of two terms: a tension $(1/\mu_o)B_iB_jn_j$ directed along the magnetic field lines, and a pressure $(B^2/2\mu_o)n_i$ directed inward along the normal to the surface.

We notice from [14.34] that although a tension and pressure are always associated with magnetic lines of force, there will be no force exerted on the fluid unless there is a spatial derivative of the magnetic field. For example, the term $B_{i,k}B_k$ exists when the magnetic field line is curved. The magnetic tension will tend to straighten the line of force which acts much like a taut bow. The term $(B^2/2\mu_o)_{,i}$ exists when there is a bunching of the magnetic field lines and the magnetic pressure tends to keep the lines of force apart.

It is clear from [14.34] that under certain special conditions a balance between the pressure forces and the magnetic forces could maintain a plasma in static equilibrium. The equilibrium state may or may not be stable and the stability of the configuration to small disturbances must always be examined.

If the pressure forces are negligible compared with the magnetic forces then [14.34] can still be satisfied if the magnetic field itself produces no net force on the plasma. From [14.34] and [14.36] we see that this condition implies that

$$\epsilon_{ijk}J_jB_k = \frac{1}{\mu_o} B_{i,k}B_k - \left(\frac{B^2}{2\mu_o}\right)_{,i} = 0 \qquad [14.41]$$

Such force-free magnetic fields thus represent a balance between the forces due to magnetic tension and those due to magnetic pressure. Note in this case that the current is always directed along the magnetic field lines. Many of the magnetic fields which exist throughout the universe are thought to be force-free since one can show that these fields represent a minimum magnetic energy and are thus stable.

14.3 MAGNETOHYDRODYNAMIC FLOWS

In the previous section we considered the static case where $v_i^* = 0$. Let us now consider steady flows such that $\partial/\partial t = 0$. The magneto-fluid dynamic equations [14.24] to [14.27] then become

$$(\rho v_i^*)_{,i} = 0 \qquad [14.42]$$

$$\rho v_j^* v_{i,j}^* = -\left(P^* + \frac{B^2}{2\mu_o}\right)_{,i} + \frac{1}{\mu_o} B_{i,k}B_k \qquad [14.43]$$

$$v_j^* B_{i,j} + B_i v_{j,j}^* - B_j v_{i,j}^* = \frac{1}{\mu_o\sigma} B_{i,jj} \qquad [14.44]$$

$$P^* = P^*(\rho) \qquad [14.45]$$

Throughout our discussion of magneto-fluid dynamics we have neglected any effects due to viscosity or gravitational forces. These effects can be accounted for by adding appropriate terms in the equation of motion of the fluid. In many magneto-fluid dynamic (MFD) problems, however, these effects are negligible.

Steady flows represent an important class of problems in ordinary fluid dynamics. In magneto-fluid dynamics, however, we will see that several effects arise that complicate the situation. First we should note that it is not possible to obtain a general solution of Equations [14.42] to [14.45]. In attempting to simplify these equations, we see that two main regimes exist depending upon whether the magnetic Reynolds number R_M is much greater than or much less than unity.

The case when $R_M \ll 1$ corresponds to low conductivity flows. For this case the magnetic field is not greatly affected by the fluid motion. This is the situation for most laboratory plasmas such as the MHD generator and for this case it is more convenient to go back to Equations [14.14] to [14.19] and assume that the magnetic field is a given external magnetic field. The current density J_i is then determined by the conductivity σ according to [14.19].

On the other hand when $R_M \gg 1$ the magnetic field and the plasma are strongly coupled. This is the situation for most cosmic plasmas and for this case the current density J_i is determined from [14.18]. As the conductivity becomes infinite the magnetic field lines become frozen into the conducting fluid. Thus as the fluid moves it will pull the magnetic field lines with it. If this motion bends the magnetic field lines the magnetic tension will tend to impede and even reverse this fluid motion. We would therefore expect that in this case steady flows would give way to wave motions. The remainder of this chapter will be devoted to investigating these wave motions.

14.4 WAVES IN AN INCOMPRESSIBLE CONDUCTING FLUID

In this section we wish to show that the tension in a magnetic line of force can cause waves to propagate in an incompressible, infinitely conducting fluid. Suppose that a small volume of fluid is displaced in a direction normal to the magnetic field. If the fluid has an infinite conductivity the magnetic field lines, being "frozen" in the fluid, will also be displaced as shown in Figure 14.1.

In order to analyze the motion of the fluid we will write the magnetic field as

$$B_i = B_i^\circ + b_i \qquad\qquad [14.46]$$

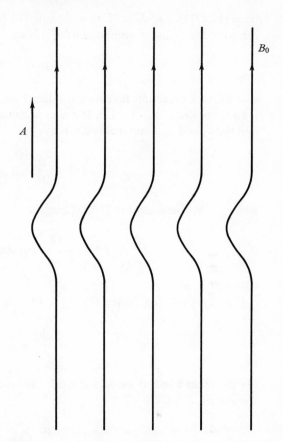

FIGURE 14.1 Propagation of Alfvén Waves

where $B_i^0 = (0, 0, B_o)$ is the constant magnetic field and b_i is the perturbation of the magnetic field due to the fluid motion. We consider the fluid to be incompressible (ρ = constant) so that from [14.24]

$$v^*_{i,i} = 0 \qquad [14.47]$$

Using [14.47] and assuming the conductivity σ to be infinite we can write [14.25] and [14.26] as

$$\rho(\dot{v}^*_i + v^*_j v^*_{i,j}) = -P^*_{,i} + \frac{1}{\mu_o}(B_{i,k}B_k - B_{k,i}B_k) \qquad [14.48]$$

and

$$\dot{B}_i + v^*_j B_{i,j} - B_j v^*_{i,j} = 0 \qquad [14.49]$$

We assume that the plasma is of infinite extent and that the only spatial variations are in the x_3-direction—that is, $\partial/\partial x_1 = \partial/\partial x_2 = 0$. We then see from [14.47] that $v_3^* = 0$. If we substitute [14.46] into [14.49], we see that we can write the x_1 and x_2 components of this vector equation as

$$\dot{b}_\alpha = B_0 v_{\alpha,3}^* \qquad [14.50]$$

where Greek subscripts take on the values 1 and 2 only. The x_3 component of [14.49] indicates that $b_3 = 0$. If we now substitute [14.46] into [14.48], we find the x_1 and x_2 components given by

$$\rho \dot{v}_\alpha^* = \frac{B_0}{\mu_0} b_{\alpha,3} \qquad [14.51]$$

while the x_3 component of [14.48] leads to

$$P^* + \frac{b^2}{2\mu_0} = \text{constant} \qquad [14.52]$$

where $b^2 = b_1^2 + b_2^2$.

If we take the time derivative of [14.50] and use [14.51] we obtain

$$\ddot{b}_\alpha = \frac{B_0^2}{\mu_0 \rho} b_{\alpha,33} \qquad [14.53]$$

On the other hand, if we take the time derivative of [14.51] and use [14.50] we obtain

$$\ddot{v}_\alpha^* = \frac{B_0^2}{\mu_0 \rho} v_{\alpha,33} \qquad [14.54]$$

We therefore see that both b_α and v_α^* satisfy wave equations that have the wave solutions

$$b_\alpha = b_\alpha^0 e^{ik(x_3 - At)} \qquad [14.55]$$

and

$$v_\alpha^* = (v_\alpha^*)^0 e^{ik(x_3 - At)} \qquad [14.56]$$

where

$$A = \left(\frac{B_0^2}{\mu_0 \rho} \right)^{1/2} \qquad [14.57]$$

is called the *Alfvén velocity*. The transverse disturbances b_α and v_α^* thus propagate along the magnetic field in the x_3-direction with a phase velocity A

given by [14.57]. These waves are called *Alfvén waves*. Note that these waves can have a finite amplitude since under the assumptions made we did not have to linearize the equations by assuming that v_i^* was small. If we substitute the solutions [14.55] and [14.56] into [14.50], we see that

$$b_\alpha = -\sqrt{\mu_0\rho} \; v_\alpha \qquad [14.58]$$

The effect of a finite conductivity on the propagation of the Alfvén waves can be considered by including the term on the right-hand side of [14.26]. In the present case this would result in [14.50] having the form

$$\dot{b}_\alpha = B_0 v_{\alpha,3}^* + \frac{1}{\mu_0\sigma} b_{\alpha,33} \qquad [14.59]$$

Taking the time derivative of [14.59] and using [14.51], we obtain

$$\ddot{b}_\alpha = \frac{B_0^2}{\mu_0\rho} b_{\alpha,33} + \frac{1}{\mu_0\sigma} \dot{b}_{\alpha,33} \qquad [14.60]$$

If we assume a wave solution of [14.60] of the form

$$b_\alpha = b_\alpha^0 e^{i(kx_3 - \omega t)} \qquad [14.61]$$

we obtain, by substituting [14.61] into [14.60] and using [14.57]

$$\left(\omega^2 - k^2 A^2 + \frac{i\omega k^2}{\mu_0\sigma}\right)b_\alpha = 0$$

from which we find that if $i\omega \ll \mu_0\sigma A^2$, then k is given by

$$k = \frac{\omega}{A} + i\frac{\omega^2}{2\mu_0\sigma A^3} \qquad [14.62]$$

By substituting [14.62] into [14.61], we see that the effect of a finite conductivity is to cause the Alfvén wave to be attenuated to $1/e$ of its initial amplitude in a distance x_3' given by

$$x_3' = \frac{2\mu_0\sigma A^3}{\omega^2} = \frac{\mu_0\sigma A\lambda^2}{2\pi^2} \qquad [14.63]$$

where $\lambda = 2\pi/k = 2\pi A/\omega$ is the wavelength of the wave.

In order for the Alfvén wave to exist, it is necessary for the wavelength to be much less than the distance over which the wave is damped. That is, from [14.63] we must have that

$$\frac{x'_3}{\lambda} = \frac{\mu_o \sigma A \lambda}{2\pi^2} = \frac{\mu_o^{1/2} \sigma B_o \lambda}{2\pi^2 \rho^{1/2}} \gg 1 \qquad [14.64]$$

This ratio is sometimes referred to as the *Lundquist number*.

In this section we have considered transverse waves which propagate along the magnetic field in an incompressible conducting fluid. In the following section we will find when the fluid is compressible, that, in addition to the transverse Alfvén wave, magnetoacoustic waves can propagate which, in general, are neither purely longitudinal nor transverse.

14.5 WAVES IN A COMPRESSIBLE CONDUCTING FLUID

We consider a compressible conducting fluid with infinite conductivity and write the MFD equations [14.24] to [14.27] as

$$\dot{\rho} + (\rho v_i^*)_{,i} = 0 \qquad [14.65]$$

$$\rho(\dot{v}_i^* + v_j^* v_{i,j}^*) = -P_{,i}^* + \frac{1}{\mu_o}(B_{i,k}B_k - B_{k,i}B_k) \qquad [14.66]$$

$$\dot{B}_i + v_j^* B_{i,j} + B_i v_{j,j}^* - B_j v_{i,j}^* = 0 \qquad [14.67]$$

$$P^* = P^*(\rho) \qquad [14.68]$$

In order to linearize this set of nonlinear equations, we will write the variables in the form

$$\rho = \rho_o + \bar{\rho} \qquad [14.69]$$

$$P^* = P_o + \bar{P} \qquad [14.70]$$

$$B_i = B_i^o + b \qquad [14.71]$$

$$v_i^* = \bar{v}_i \qquad [14.72]$$

where ρ_0, P_0, and B_i^0 are constant average values and $\bar{\rho}$, $\bar{P}$, b, and $\bar{v}_i$ are small perturbations.

If we substitute [14.69] to [14.72] into [14.65] to [14.67] and neglect terms involving the product of the small perturbations, we obtain

$$\dot{\bar{\rho}} + \rho_0 \bar{v}_{i,i} = 0 \tag{14.73}$$

$$\rho_0 \dot{\bar{v}}_i = -\bar{P}_{,i} + \frac{1}{\mu_0}(B_k^0 b_{i,k} - B_k^0 b_{k,i}) \tag{14.74}$$

$$\dot{b}_i + B_i^0 \bar{v}_{j,j} - B_j^0 \bar{v}_{i,j} = 0 \tag{14.75}$$

We further write

$$\bar{P}_{,i} = \left(\frac{\partial \bar{P}}{\partial \rho}\right)\bar{\rho}_{,i} = a^2 \bar{\rho}_{,i} \tag{14.76}$$

where $a = (\partial \bar{P}/\partial \rho)^{1/2}$ is the speed of sound in the fluid.

If we assume that all the perturbed quantities vary as $e^{i(k\alpha_q x_q - \omega t)}$ and use [14.76], then [14.73] to [14.75] become

$$-i\omega\bar{\rho} + ik\rho_0\alpha_i\bar{v}_i = 0 \tag{14.77}$$

$$-i\omega\rho_0\bar{v}_i = -ika^2\alpha_i\bar{\rho} + \frac{ik}{\mu_0}(B_k^0\alpha_k b_i - B_k^0\alpha_i b_k) \tag{14.78}$$

$$-i\omega b_i + ikB_i^0\alpha_j\bar{v}_j - ikB_j^0\alpha_j\bar{v}_i = 0 \tag{14.79}$$

From [14.77] and [14.79] we obtain

$$\bar{\rho} = \frac{k}{\omega}\rho_0\alpha_i\bar{v}_i \tag{14.80}$$

and

$$b_i = \frac{k}{\omega}(B_i^0\alpha_j - B_m^0\alpha_m\delta_{ij})\bar{v}_j \tag{14.81}$$

Substituting [14.80] into [14.78], we obtain

$$\left(\delta_{ij} - \frac{k^2 a^2}{\omega^2}\alpha_i\alpha_j\right)\bar{v}_j + \frac{k}{\omega\mu_0\rho_0}(B_r^0\alpha_r\delta_{ik} - B_k^0\alpha_i)b_k = 0 \tag{14.82}$$

Substituting [14.81] into [14.82] and noting that $B_i^o B_i^o = B_o^2$ and $B_r^o \alpha_r = B_o \cos \theta$, where θ is the angle between the direction of propagation and the magnetic field, we obtain

$$\left(\delta_{ij} - \frac{k^2 a^2}{\omega^2} \alpha_i \alpha_j \right) \bar{v}_j + \frac{k^2}{\omega^2 \mu_o \rho_o} (B_r^o \alpha_r \delta_{ik} - B_k^o \alpha_i)(B_k^o \alpha_j - B_m^o \alpha_m \delta_{kj}) \bar{v}_j = 0$$

$$\left\{ \delta_{ij} - \frac{k^2 a^2}{\omega^2} \alpha_i \alpha_j \right.$$

$$\left. + \frac{k^2}{\omega^2 \mu_o \rho_o} [B_i^o B_r^o \alpha_r \alpha_j - \delta_{ij}(B_r^o \alpha_r)^2 - B_o^2 \alpha_i \alpha_j + B_m^o \alpha_m B_j^o \alpha_i] \right\} \bar{v}_j = 0$$

$$\left[\delta_{ij} \left(1 - \frac{k^2 B_o^2 \cos^2 \theta}{\omega^2 \mu_o \rho_o} \right) \right.$$

$$\left. - \frac{k^2}{\omega^2} \left(a^2 + \frac{B_o^2}{\mu_o \rho_o} \right) \alpha_i \alpha_j + \frac{k^2 B_o \cos \theta}{\omega^2 \mu_o \rho_o} (B_i^o \alpha_j + B_j^o \alpha_i) \right] \bar{v}_j = 0$$

or

$$\left[\delta_{ij} \left(1 - \frac{k^2 A^2 \cos^2 \theta}{\omega^2} \right) \right.$$

$$\left. - \frac{k^2}{\omega^2} (a^2 + A^2) \alpha_i \alpha_j + \frac{k^2 A^2 \cos \theta}{\omega^2 B_o} (B_i^o \alpha_j + B_j^o \alpha_i) \right] \bar{v}_j = 0 \quad [14.83]$$

where A is the Alfvén velocity given by [14.57].

Equation [14.83] is a set of three homogeneous equations in the three unknowns $\bar{v}_1$, $\bar{v}_2$, and $\bar{v}_3$. A nontrivial solution exists only if the determinant of the coefficients vanishes. Thus the dispersion equation for the hydromagnetic waves can be obtained by setting the determinant of the coefficients in [14.83] equal to zero. If we orient the coordinate system as shown in Figure 14.2 so that the magnetic field is in the x_3-direction and α_i is in the x_2-x_3 plane, then one can readily show (see Exercise 14.5.1) that the matrix form of [14.83] is

$$\begin{bmatrix} 1 - \dfrac{k^2 A^2 \cos^2 \theta}{\omega^2} & 0 & 0 \\ 0 & 1 - \dfrac{k^2}{\omega^2} (A^2 + a^2 \sin^2 \theta) & -\dfrac{k^2}{\omega^2} a^2 \sin \theta \cos \theta \\ 0 & -\dfrac{k^2}{\omega^2} a^2 \sin \theta \cos \theta & 1 - \dfrac{k^2}{\omega^2} a^2 \cos^2 \theta \end{bmatrix} \begin{bmatrix} \bar{v}_1 \\ \bar{v}_2 \\ \bar{v}_3 \end{bmatrix} = 0$$

$$[14.84]$$

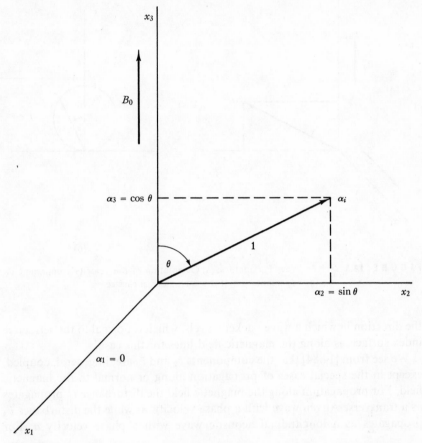

FIGURE 14.2   Orientation of Coordinate System for Propagation of Hydromagnetic
Waves

From this matrix equation we see at once that $\bar{v}_1$ is uncoupled from $\bar{v}_2$ and
$\bar{v}_3$ and that these transverse disturbances in the x_1-direction propagate with a
phase velocity

$$u = \frac{\omega}{k} = A \cos \theta \qquad [14.85]$$

as shown in Figure 14.3. This is just the Alfvén wave discussed in the previous
section. Note that the wave normal surface is a circle in the x_2-x_3 plane.
From the discussion in Section 13.52 this means that the refractive index
surface is a straight line in the x_2-x_3 plane normal to the magnetic field. Thus

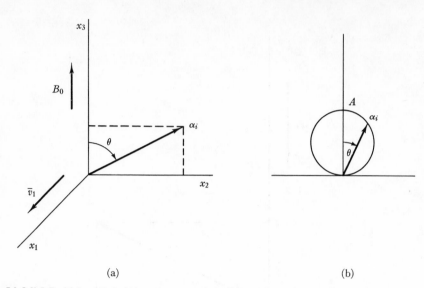

(a)   (b)

FIGURE 14.3   Alfvén Wave Parameters: (a) Orientation of the velocity component $\bar{v}_1$.
(b) Representation of the wave normal surface

the direction in which a wave packet travels, which is normal to the refractive index surface, is along the magnetic field lines for this case.

We see from [14.84] that the components $\bar{v}_2$ and $\bar{v}_3$ are, in general, coupled, except in the special cases of propagation along or normal to the magnetic field. For propagation along the magnetic field the disturbance $\bar{v}_2$ propagates as a transverse Alfvén wave with a phase velocity A, while the disturbance $\bar{v}_3$ propagates as a longitudinal acoustic wave with a phase velocity a. For

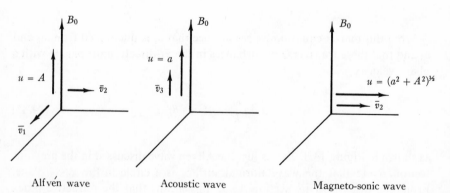

Alfvén wave   Acoustic wave   Magneto-sonic wave

FIGURE 14.4   Orientation of Velocity Components of Hydromagnetic Waves

propagation across the magnetic field only the disturbance $\bar{v}_2$ propagates as a longitudinal magnetosonic wave with a phase velocity $(a^2 + A^2)^{1/2}$. These waves are summarized in Figure 14.4.

For arbitrary directions of propagation we can write the equations for $\bar{v}_2$ and $\bar{v}_3$ from [14.84] as

$$\begin{bmatrix} u^2 - (A^2 + a^2 \sin^2 \theta) & -a^2 \sin \theta \cos \theta \\ -a^2 \sin \theta \cos \theta & u^2 - a^2 \cos^2 \theta \end{bmatrix} \begin{bmatrix} \bar{v}_2 \\ \bar{v}_3 \end{bmatrix} = 0 \qquad [14.86]$$

where $u = \omega/k$ is the phase velocity. Setting the determinant of the coefficients in [14.86] equal to zero we obtain (see Exercise 14.5.2)

$$u^4 - (A^2 + a^2)u^2 + A^2 a^2 \cos^2 \theta = 0 \qquad [14.87]$$

This dispersion equation is quadratic in u^2. We therefore see that, in general, two modes can propagate. These are called the *modified hydromagnetic wave* and the *modified acoustic wave*, and the shape of their wave normal surfaces depends upon whether A is greater or less than a as shown in Figure 14.5.

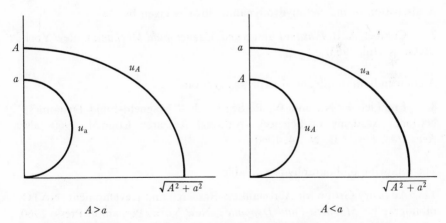

FIGURE 14.5 Wave Normal Surfaces for Modified Hydromagnetic Wave u_A, and Modified Acoustic Wave u_α

Exercise 14.5.1   Show that [14.84] is the matrix form of [14.83] when the coordinate axes are oriented as in Figure 14.2.

Exercise 14.5.2   Verify [14.87].

REFERENCES

Further discussion of the first section of this chapter can be found in

1   Elsasser, W. M. "Dimensional Relations in Magneto-hydrodynamics," *Phys. Rev.*, **95** (1954), 1–5.

A general introduction to this field is given in

2   Elsasser, W. M. "Hydromagnetism. I. A Review," *Amer. J. Phys.*, **23** (1955), 590–609.

3   Cowling, T. G. *Magnetohydrodynamics*. New York: Interscience, 1957.

4   Ferraro, V. C. A., and C. Plumpton. *An Introduction to Magneto-Fluid Mechanics*. New York: Oxford University Press, 1961.

5   Thompson, W. B. *An Introduction to Plasma Physics*. Reading, Mass.: Addison-Wesley, 1962.

6   Alfvén, H., and C-G. Fälthammar. *Cosmical Electrodynamics*. 2nd ed. Oxford: The Clarendon Press, 1963.

A discussion of magnetohydrodynamic flows is given by

7   Cambel, A. B. *Plasma Physics and Magnetofluid Mechanics*. New York: McGraw-Hill, 1963.

A compendium of advanced papers is given in

8   Frenkiel, F. N., and W. R. Sears, eds. "Magneto-Fluid Dynamics," National Academy of Sciences—National Research Council, 1960, also *Rev. Mod. Phys.*, **32**, No. 4, 1960.

The following bibliography is available

9   Advisory Group for Aeronautical Research and Development, NATO, Bibliography: *Magneto-Fluid-Dynamics*. New York: Pergamon Press, 1960.

CHAPTER

15

ELECTRONIC PROCESSES

IN PLASMAS:

PLASMA GENERATION

The mainstream of this book has consisted of the development of the theoretical foundations of plasma dynamics. In the first discussion of particle interactions we restricted ourselves to the properties of elastic collisions (Chapter 4), because such a treatment was sufficient to enable us to lay the groundwork of kinetic theory. We might have followed Chapter 4 with a chapter on inelastic collision processes, but we preferred not to interrupt the major thrust of our development.

Nevertheless the topic of inelastic collision processes is very much a part of the foundations of our subject. It includes those particle interactions that result in the gain and loss of charged particles in gases and that are, therefore, essential to the existence of the plasma medium. The matter becomes very specific in the laboratory, where we are faced with the necessity of generating the plasma we wish to study and maintaining its degree of ionization in accordance with the objectives of our work.

In attempting a general discussion of particle interactions and plasma generation in this chapter, we cannot maintain the depth of treatment which

445

has been possible in the rest of the book. Rather our purpose is to introduce the reader to the large variety of phenomena involved, in order to alert him to his need for further knowledge. We begin with a discussion in broad perspectives of the interactions of particles in gases, followed by a similar discussion of the interactions of particles at surfaces. We next inquire into the methods of plasma generation. We discuss the application of heat energy to a gas in general terms. The consequences of the application of an electric field to a gas are described, with derivations of ionization and breakdown equations. Finally we present a descriptive review of some types of laboratory plasma devices.

15.1 INTERACTIONS
OF PARTICLES IN GASES

The study of particle reactions forms the subject of chemical kinetics which provides a quantitative description of particle reactions including those involving ionization. The *reaction rate* is described in terms of the concentrations of the reactants by

(reaction rate) = (rate constant) × (product of the concentrations)   [15.1]

and the dependence on temperature and other factors is hidden in the rate constant. So for a reaction represented by the chemical equation

$$A + B \rightleftarrows C + D \qquad [15.2]$$

there is a forward (left to right) rate and a reverse rate. In the steady state the forward and reverse rate constants are related by

$$(k_R)_{\text{forward}}[A][B] = (k_R)_{\text{reverse}}[C][D] \qquad [15.3]$$

where the brackets represent concentrations. When all the reactants and reaction products are at the same temperature an *equilibrium constant K* may be defined as

$$K = \frac{[C][D]}{[A][B]} = \frac{(k_R)_{\text{forward}}}{(k_R)_{\text{reverse}}} \qquad [15.4]$$

The temperature dependence of the rate constant is found experimentally to be given by

$$k_R = A \exp\left(-E_a/kT\right) \qquad [15.5]$$

where A and E_a are essentially independent of temperature,[1] and E_a is called the *activation energy.*

The activation energy is the energy necessary to trigger the reaction and its relationship to the difference in potential energy before and after the reaction is illustrated by Figure 15.1. We notice that the activation energy may be

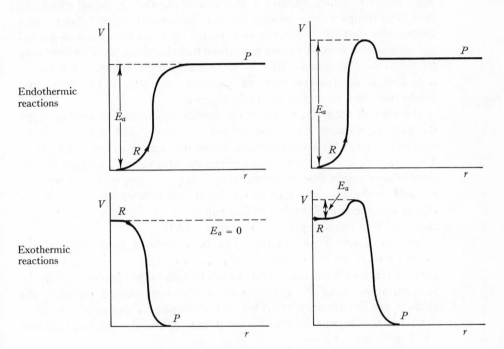

F I G U R E   15.1   The Activation Energy E_a in Chemical Reactions
          V—potential of interaction
          r—interaction distance parameter
          R—reactants
          P—products of the reaction
Endothermic reactions result in a net absorption of kinetic energy and exothermic reactions result in a net release of kinetic energy

zero. The term $e^{-E_a/kT}$ is the average probability that a particle has an energy greater than E_a and so has the possibility of initiating the reaction. The probability that a colliding particle will actually participate in a reaction (P_R) is less than this and is given by

$$P_R = p_s e^{-E_a/kT} \qquad\qquad [15.6]$$

[1] Although [15.5] expresses the gross temperature dependence of k_R, there is a mild dependence on temperature in the "constant" A. For a reaction of the type described by [15.2], the constant A is essentially the frequency of collisions of reactant molecules, and this varies with the square root of temperature. In a typical case, however, A varies over a ten-degree interval by a few per cent, while the exponential factor varies by 100 per cent.

where p_s is the *steric factor*. This is a geometrical factor which depends upon the orientation of the molecules with respect to each other and varies from approximately 0.01 to 1.0.

In chemical kinetics it is assumed that all processes except the chemical reaction are equilibrated. This means, for example, that the several participants in the reactions all have a Maxwellian distribution of velocities and there is an equipartition of energy between the participants. In other words a temperature may be assigned to each particle gas and each particle gas has the same temperature. It should be realized that this places a severe limitation on the type of situation that can be handled with confidence. We are, in fact, able to describe the state of a system only after it has come into equilibrium with respect to external influences.

The over-all requirement which the equilibrium condition imposes upon the particle reactions can be expressed as follows. The existence of an activation energy for most reactions means that energetic molecules play a dominant role in the reactions. To retain the Maxwellian distribution it is, therefore, necessary that the nonreacting, energy-sharing collisions between energetic molecules and other molecules, be much more frequent than the rate at which energetic molecules participate in reactions and thus become converted into reaction products (Exercise 15.1.1).

For our purposes all reactions can be considered reversible and the equilibrium condition requires that the forward and reverse rates be equal for each reaction. Thus from [15.4] we see that chemical kinetics predicts the concentrations of all the components of a gaseous plasma including the electron and ion densities, provided that chemical equilibrium is attained.

We will now summarize the electron producing and electron loss reactions which can occur in gases.

Impact Ionization and Three-Body Recombination

$$X + Y \rightleftarrows X^+ + e + Y \qquad [15.7]$$

In the case where Y represents an electron, we have electron impact ionization. In the presence of an electric field this is described by the first Townsend ionization coefficient (see Section 15.31). In the reverse process the three-body recombination involves an electron as the third body.

The special case of the forward reaction when Y is a metastable atom and X is an atom with an ionization potential which is lower than the metastable level of Y, represents an important effect in rare gas discharges where it is known as the *Penning effect*.

This is an example of a *collision of the second kind*. In this type of collision one of the particles has an excited electronic level. Normally such levels have a lifetime of about 10^{-8} sec before radiating, so that the number of collisions of the second kind is restricted. However in the case of metastables the lifetime may be 10^{-2} sec because radiation is forbidden and return to the ground state requires a collision with another particle. For example, the ionization potential of oxygen and nitrogen is below the metastable level of helium (19.7 eV) and neon (16 eV) so that in both of these gases the metastable level can ionize oxygen and nitrogen particles which may be present as impurities. This is one of the reasons for taking stringent precautions against impurities when studying gaseous plasmas. At a pressure of 1 Torr a metastable atom may make 10^8 collisions during its lifetime. This means that it makes 100 collisions even with an impurity which is present to only one part in a million.

Associative Ionization and Dissociative Recombination

$$X + Y \rightleftarrows XY^+ + e \qquad [15.8]$$

Dissociative recombination is always an important electron loss mechanism whenever it can occur because of its relatively large cross section.

Photoionization and Radiative Recombination

$$X + hv \rightleftarrows X^+ + e \qquad [15.9]$$

In this reaction h is *Planck's constant* and v is the frequency associated with the photon. The forward reaction requires hv to be greater than the ionization energy of the atom or molecule represented by X. The reverse reaction, radiative recombination, has a small cross section and will be swamped by the previously mentioned recombination reactions if they are present.

Photo-detachment and Radiative Attachment

$$X^- + hv \rightleftarrows X + e \qquad [15.10]$$

Collisional Detachment and Three Body Attachment

$$X^- + Y \rightleftarrows X + e + Y \qquad [15.11]$$

Associative Detachment and Dissociative Attachment

$$X^- + Y \rightleftarrows XY + e \qquad [15.12]$$

The above three reactions involve negative ions. Such ions are formed by hydrogen, oxygen, and the halogens. Nitrogen and the rare gases including helium do not form negative ions which are stable enough to play a significant role in plasma behavior. Even when present, negative ions usually play a subordinate role.

Autoionization and Dielectronic Recombination

$$X^{**} \rightleftarrows X^+ + e \qquad [15.13]$$

X^{**} represents an atom or molecule in which two electrons are in excited states, the total potential energy exceeding the ionization energy. The process is possible in metal vapor. The forward reaction is very fast, occurring in about 10^{-13} sec. The reverse reaction is therefore improbable because the reaction product X^{**} must be stabilized (for example, by a radiative transition to a new level which is not subject to autoionization) before autoionization has a chance to occur.

Charge Transfer

$$X^+ + Y \rightleftarrows X + Y^+ \qquad [15.14]$$

Cross sections for these reactions may be large so that they play an important role in the behavior of the ions. In the case of ions subject to an electric field the mechanism of charge transfer changes a fast ion into a fast neutral particle, leaving a slow ion behind. The effective ionic drift velocity is therefore reduced. Charge-exchange cross sections increase as the difference in potential energy of the ions X^+ and Y^+ decreases. When ions travel in their parent gas the cross section is a maximum and a resonance effect occurs. Combined with the reduced drift velocity we can say that a *resonance trapping* occurs.

Rearrangement of Charged Species

$$XY^+ + WZ \rightleftarrows XW^+ + YZ \qquad [15.15]$$

These reactions may have cross sections considerably larger even than the charge transfer cross sections. They are particularly important in the oxygen–nitrogen system.

Trapping of Resonance Radiation

$$X + h\nu \rightleftarrows X^* \qquad [15.16]$$

To the list of reactions involving charged particles we add this effect which influences the passage of photons, with an energy equal to an excitation level of the particles, through the gas. Because of the minimal difference between the photon energy and the energy of the excited particle the cross section shows a resonance. The reverse reaction follows the forward reaction within about 10^{-8} sec. Instead of thinking of the photon as simply traveling with the speed of light until it is absorbed, it is now the case that the resonance photon proceeds through the gas at a greatly reduced effective velocity.

We began this section with a discussion of particle reactions in terms of the rate constant k_R and the concentrations of the particles. Now the reaction rate can be described as the reaction rate of a particle of type 1 multiplied by its concentration. Using this concept, we can relate the rate constant to the collision frequency and collision cross section introduced in Chapter 4.

Let the collision frequency of a particle of type 1 be v_c^1 and its collision cross section Q_c^1. Then the mean free path between collisions with particles of type 2 and concentration N_2 is

$$L_1 = \frac{1}{Q_c^1 N_2} \tag{15.17}$$

(compare [4.2]). If the relative speed of the two reacting particles is g, then the collision frequency is given by

$$v_c^1 = \frac{g}{L_1} = gQ_c^1 N_2 \tag{15.18}$$

(compare [4.1]). From [15.6] the reaction rate of one particle of type 1 is $v_c^1 p_s \exp(-E_a/kT)$ and so the total reaction rate is $v_c^1 p_s \exp(-E_a/kT)N_1$. Equating this with the reaction rate defined by [15.3] gives

$$v_c^1 p_s \exp(-E_a/kT)N_1 = k_R N_1 N_2 \tag{15.19}$$

so that, using [15.6], we obtain

$$v_c^1 P_R = k_R N_2 \tag{15.20}$$

From [15.18] the cross section is related to the reaction constant by

$$k_R = gP_R Q_c \tag{15.21}$$

Now the reactants have a distribution in velocities and the cross section Q_c is a function of the relative velocity g. The reaction constant is the average value of $gP_R Q_c$ where the product gQ_c is integrated over velocity space. P_R is already an average value. This gives

$$k_R = \frac{P_R}{N_1 N_2} \int\int f^1 f^2 gQ_c \, dc^1 \, dc^2 \tag{15.22}$$

Exercise 15.1.1   Justify the statement that the maintenance of a Maxwellian velocity distribution among the particles of a gas requires that $v_{EP} \gg v_{ER}$, where v_{EP} is the frequency of collisions of energetic particles (possessing an energy greater than the activation energy) with other particles in which chemical reactions do not occur and ν_{ER} is the frequency of collisions of energetic particles in situations where chemical reactions do occur, resulting in the removal of the energetic particles from their place in the velocity distribution.

15.2 INTERACTIONS OF PARTICLES AT SURFACES

The objective of this section is to list and summarize the various particle reactions that take place at surfaces so that the student is alerted to those phenomena that affect the study of plasmas. Their full understanding requires a knowledge of the physics of the solid state, and the details must be left to the independent work of the interested student.

In plasma study we are concerned with electrons, ions, and neutral particles. The neutrals may be excited but we can neglect the excited neutral particle in this section because of its short lifetime. However we have to make an exception for the long-lived excited state which is known as the *metastable state*. Thus we are concerned with four types of particles. In principle any of these may bombard a surface causing the emission of any or all of the others. In addition any or all of these particles may be emitted from a surface due to the application of an electric field, the heating of the surface, or by absorption of photons. Any particular effect is sensitive to the type and condition of the material comprising the surface, the type of gas of which the bombarding particle consists, and the energy of the bombarding particles. There are therefore a very large number of cases to be considered in a comprehensive treatment.

In general these surface problems have not been completely solved by an appropriate quantum theory. Predictions of behavior must rely upon experimental results which are themselves not always complete. We will discuss those effects known to be important in plasma study. However, as the experimental and theoretical work develops, other effects may turn out to be more important than is presently realized.

Emission of Electrons from Surfaces   The emission of electrons is the most important surface effect in plasma study. Electrons may be emitted from surfaces by providing them with sufficient energy to overcome the surface potential barrier. Alternatively the barrier may be modified to increase the probability of escape by high-energy electrons. Electrons may be emitted by electrons themselves, positive ions, neutrals, and metastables. They may also be omitted by photon absorption, surface heating (thermionic emission), and by the application of an electric field. We will consider briefly these seven mechanisms in the order listed.

ELECTRON EMISSION BY ELECTRON BOMBARDMENT   If a primary beam of electrons is incident upon a metal surface it is found that the electrons that scatter away from the surface consist of four groups. A fairly large number may be electrons from the primary beam which are reflected elastically from the surface. A small group of the primary electrons may suffer one inelastic collision with the electrons of the metal and also be reflected. Their energy will be only a few electron volts less than the energy of the primary beam. Another large group possess an energy in the range 1–5 eV and are true secondary electrons. At energies between 5 eV and the energy of the primary beam the scattered electrons consist of primary electrons which have undergone multiple inelastic scattering reactions in the metal surface, together with a few secondary electrons which form the high energy tail of the secondary electron distribution.

The true secondary electrons do not appear at primary electron energies less than 10–20 eV so that a plasma must be at a high temperature before this effect is operative. The yield of secondaries rises to a maximum of about unity (one secondary for each incident primary) for most metals at incident energies of several hundred volts. This secondary electron effect is exploited in electron multiplier tubes for a variety of applications. Of the various other parameters that may change the coefficient of emission, the most significant is the angle of incidence of the primary electrons. A grazing incidence produces more secondaries because the interactions of the primary electrons occur with the electrons of the metal which are nearer the surface and therefore more likely to escape. Larger emission coefficients may apply to metallic compounds. Abnormally high coefficients (up to 1000) are obtained when a metal is covered with a thin insulating film with a further conducting layer covering the thin film. If the outer layer has an electron emission coefficient greater than unity it becomes positively charged and emission from the base metal is enhanced by field emission. This is known as the *Malter effect*. When enhanced secondary emission, due to an electric field established across an insulating film (which may be of dust particles or oxides) on the cathode, results in abnormally low breakdown voltages, the effect is known as the *Paetow effect*.

ELECTRON EMISSION BY POSITIVE ION BOMBARDMENT   High-energy positive ions cause the emission of electrons from surfaces by intense local heating. Slow ions, which are of more interest to us, cause electron emission in a two-step process in which they first capture an electron from the surface and become neutralized in an excited state. The excitation energy is then absorbed by a second surface electron which can escape if its energy is greater than the surface work function. The coefficient of *secondary electron emission by positive ion bombardment* γ is the number of electrons emitted per incident ion. The large effect of the state of the surface on the value of γ, has led to discrepancies between the results of different experimenters when studying supposedly the same type of surface and the same type of incident ion. Values of γ for slow ions are generally considerably less than unity.

ELECTRON EMISSION BY NEUTRAL PARTICLE BOMBARDMENT It is not expected that electrons will be emitted from a surface due to the incidence of low (thermal) energy neutral particles. However fast neutrals result in electron ejection and this effect has been used as a detector of neutral particles.

ELECTRON EMISSION BY METASTABLE PARTICLE BOMBARDMENT In general excited neutrals in the metastable state produce secondary electrons at surfaces. The rare gas metastable atoms are particularly effective and have emission efficiencies of from 20 to 70 per cent. The mechanism of emission is that of step two of the process previously described for positive ions. The physical concepts can be made clear by citing the results of the study of helium metastables on a magnesium surface. The helium metastable level is at 19.7 volts and the work function of magnesium is 3.01 volts. Thus we would expect secondary electrons to be emitted with a maximum energy of 16.7 volts, which is confirmed experimentally.

ELECTRON EMISSION BY PHOTON ABSORPTION Electrons may also be emitted from surfaces by an incident beam of radiation or photons. The condition for this process is that the energy of the incident photons $h\nu$ be greater than the surface work function. The photoelectric yield (number of electrons per incident quantum) is normally much less than unity but insufficient measurements are available to permit a ready comparison of the relative importance of this secondary mechanism and the emission of electrons by positive ion bombardment from metal surfaces. However these secondary mechanisms can be separated by time-resolved studies of current growth in discharge gaps. The photoelectric yield is greater from the surfaces of semiconductor materials and the exploitation of the photoelectric effect has led to the development of special surfaces with yields greater than unity, some of which rely on the Malter effect.

ELECTRON EMISSION BY SURFACE HEATING—THERMIONIC EMISSION When the temperature of a metallic surface is raised, it is found that electrons are copiously emitted even when the rate of evaporation of atoms from the surface is very small. The amount of electron emission is dependent upon the number of electrons in the metal with thermal energies greater than the surface work function. In the additional presence of an electric field the electron emission is enhanced—an effect studied by Schottky who showed that the explanation is in terms of a lowering of the effective work function by the applied electric field.

ELECTRON EMISSION BY THE APPLICATION OF AN ELECTRIC FIELD This is a quantum tunneling effect and for currents in the microampere range, requires fields of the order 10^7–10^8 volts/cm. However significant emission is commonly found at fields of 10^6 volts/cm, which is ascribed to surface contamination resulting in a low effective work function or surface roughness resulting in a higher effective electric fields at the tips of small surface projections.

In all the above-mentioned mechanisms of electron emission from surfaces the phenomenon of back diffusion of electrons may substantially reduce the number of secondary electrons which participate in the plasma phenomena. This is a dominant factor at a positively charged surface.

Surface Interactions Involving Positive Ions and Neutral Particles

POSITIVE ION EMISSION   While under extreme conditions many of the mechanisms which result in electron emission may also give rise to positive ion emission, this effect is not normally considered to be significant in electrical discharge phenomena. For example, thermionic emission of positive ions occurs at temperatures near the boiling point of metals so that it need be considered only in this situation.

EMISSION OF NEUTRAL PARTICLES—SPUTTERING   When positive ions bombard a surface electrons, positive ions, and neutral atoms are released. The positive ions emitted instantly gain an electron from the surface and so contribute to the yield of neutrals. Some of the neutrals may be in a metastable state but the resultant effect upon a discharge is not normally considered significant. The yield of neutrals is called *sputtering*. In a low-pressure gas the sputtered particles will travel to the walls of the container and form a surface layer. Suitable sputtered materials have a strong pumping action on the gas in the container. There may well be an indirect effect, therefore, on a plasma in the container.

LIBERATION OF ADSORBED GAS LAYERS BY POSITIVE ION BOMBARDMENT   A plasma cell that has not been baked out under vacuum contains adsorbed gas in large quantities in the walls. This gas is released by positive ion bombardment with a consequent contamination of the plasma gas.

CONTACT IONIZATION   If a cell contains a gas with an ionization potential which is less than the work function of the surface of the walls, the gas atoms will be ionized upon contact with the walls. Thus cesium vapor (ionization potential = 3.9 volts) ionizes in contact with a tungsten surface (work function = 4.5 volts). Other similar combinations of vapor and metallic surface produce the same effect.

If this metal surface is, at the same time, heated to thermionic emission temperature, electrons will be emitted which will form a plasma with the positive ions. This technique permits attaining a highly ionized, low energy plasma.

NEUTRALIZATION AND REFLECTION OF POSITIVE IONS AT SURFACES   A positive ion incident upon a surface may be reflected, neutralized in the ground state of the atom or neutralized into a metastable state of the atom.

The reflection coefficient of low energy positive ions on surfaces is small enough to be generally neglected. On the contrary the probability of neutralization is very high, and it may generally be assumed that a positive ion which diffuses to the wall is lost to the plasma. The probability of neutralization into a metastable state may be an important effect in the rare gases. The lack of experimental data creates an uncertainty at this point.

15.3   PLASMA GENERATION

The three principal sources of energy for plasma generation are heat, electric fields, and electromagnetic radiation. Each of these sources is important, both in nature and in the laboratory. In nature the sun is an example of a heat source which produces plasma in its vicinity. Heat is generated in combustible gases in the laboratory in order to create the plasma for a magnetohydrodynamic generator. The electrical energy generated in the earth's atmosphere creates lightning discharges, and electrical discharges in gases have long been studied in the laboratory. The radiation energy emitted by the sun is partially absorbed in the upper atmosphere of the earth where it produces the ionosphere. In the laboratory laser beams have been observed to create plasma in a gas, and radiation sources are used to trigger electrical discharges.

Plasma Generation by a Heat Source   If a gas is progressively heated, the energy absorbed is shared between the various degrees of freedom of the molecules. We will illustrate this process by considering a sample of nitrogen gas which is progressively heated, but at a slow rate, so that the gas can always be described as being at a certain temperature. At very low temperatures the energy of the gas molecules will be in the form of kinetic energy distributed between the three translational degrees of freedom. At about 10°K the rotational energy levels are excited, and at about 1000°K the vibrational states of the molecules are excited. At 5000°K dissociation becomes important, and at 10000°K there is a significant amount of ionization.

If the gas is subjected to a large, instantaneous increase in energy input, there is a time lag before the various degrees of freedom come into equilibrium. The time lag associated with each degree of freedom is called its *relaxation time*. In a time comparable with the shortest relaxation time the molecules acquire high translational energies. Thereafter the rotational states are quickly excited and come into equilibrium after only a few collisions. The vibrational energy levels are populated more slowly but, at energies below 8000°K in the case of nitrogen, for example, will come into equilibrium before there is appreciable dissociation. If the energy source is above 8000°K the population of the vibrational levels overlaps the dissociation phenomena. Finally the ionization reactions come into equilibrium and result in a degree of ionization which is given by the Saha equation.

Sudden changes in the level of the energy input to a gas are characteristic of shock wave phenomena. This is an important consideration in the reentry problem, when a plasma layer is formed around a space vehicle as it reenters the earth's atmosphere, and in laboratory shock tubes. Two extreme types of flow can be defined. If the length of time associated with the flow problem is short compared to the relaxation times for dissociation and ionization, then the composition of the gas can be assumed to be constant. This is the definition of *frozen flow*. On the other hand, if the flow time is long compared to the relaxation time, the problem becomes one in *equilibrium flow* and comes within the province of chemical kinetics. Many problems fall between these two categories and are correspondingly difficult to solve.

THE OXYGEN-NITROGEN SYSTEM   In order to illustrate the application of the gas interaction processes described in Section 15.1 to the type of problem we are discussing, we will consider an oxygen–nitrogen molecular system which is subject to a step-function increase of energy. So far as particle reactions are concerned, dissociation begins first. Then, when atomic concentrations become appreciable, atom-molecule and atom-atom interactions become important.

Ionizing phenomena may be divided into two categories. Ionization of particles which are otherwise unchanged in the reaction takes place in the following principal reactions

$$
\begin{aligned}
N_2 + M &\to N_2^+ + e + M \quad &(15.58 \text{ eV}) \\
O_2 + M &\to O_2^+ + e + M \quad &(12.08 \text{ eV}) \\
N + M &\to N^+ + e + M \quad &(14.54 \text{ eV}) \\
O + M &\to O^+ + e + M \quad &(13.61 \text{ eV})
\end{aligned}
$$

[15.23]

where M stands for any atom, molecule, or electron in the gas and the activation energy is shown in the brackets.

Now the associative ionization reactions are

$$
\begin{aligned}
N + O &\to NO^+ + e \quad &(2.76 \text{ eV}) \\
N + N &\to N_2^+ + e \quad &(5.82 \text{ eV}) \\
O + O &\to O_2^+ + e \quad &(6.96 \text{ eV})
\end{aligned}
$$

[15.24]

We see that the energies of the reactions of [15.24] are smaller than those for [15.23]. The relative importance of the two processes is determined both by the relative concentration of molecules and atoms, and also by the activation energies. When the activation energies differ markedly, the process with smaller E_a predominates, even though the concentrations are small. The reactions in [15.23] and [15.24] are endothermic so that the activation energy may be as low as the energy of the reaction.

In the oxygen-nitrogen system it is indeed the case that the reactions [15.24] predominate once dissociation is well under way. Thus, this system is an example of the importance of associative ionization in preference to impact ionization.

The equilibrium electron density is, of course, a balance between ionizing and deionizing processes. The dominant process depends upon the conditions. For example, in the E-layer of the ionosphere where the majority of ions are NO^+ with some O_2^+, the principle deionizing reaction is the dissociative recombinations of NO^+—that is,

$$NO^+ + e \rightarrow N + O \qquad [15.25]$$

15.31 IONIZATION AND BREAKDOWN IN AN ELECTRIC FIELD

The most important mechanism by which the population of free electrons grows in a gas which is subject to an electric field is the mechanism of ionization of atoms and molecules by electron impact. This is known as *primary ionization*, and the electrons produced thereby are called *primary electrons*. Several coefficients are used to give this phenomenon a quantitative description, and we will begin by defining the *first Townsend ionization coefficient*, α. This is the number of ion pairs produced by an electron during the time in which it drifts 1 cm in the direction of the electric field.

A specific situation is shown in Figure 15.2. A pair of electrodes carry an applied potential and create a uniform electric field in the gap between them. So far as a coordinate axis OX is concerned, the field is uniform in the transverse plane. In a steady state condition with a fixed current flowing in the circuit let n_x be the number of electrons per second crossing a unit area of the transverse plane located at position x between the electrodes. Here we are ignoring the thermal motion of the electrons and considering only their drift motion in the applied electric field. Then in a further distance dx along OX the increase in the flow of electrons dn_x due to primary ionization, will be equal to the number of ionizing events caused by these n_x electrons. From the definition of α, this number is given by

$$dn_x = n_x \alpha \, dx$$

from which, upon integration,

$$n_x = n_0 e^{\alpha x} \qquad [15.26]$$

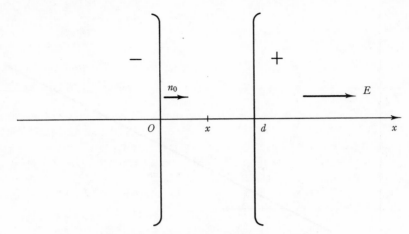

FIGURE 15.2 Primary Ionization in a Gas

where n_o is the number of electrons emitted at the cathode per unit area per second. To realize such an electron emission in practice it is customary to illuminate the cathode with a beam of radiation. The conditions can be arranged so that the photoionization in the gas is negligible. The coefficient α is assumed to be independent of x and n_x. At the anode,

$$n = n_o e^{\alpha d} \qquad [15.27]$$

The steady current in the circuit I corresponds to fixed values of n_o and α. At the anode surface this current will be carried by the electrons alone so that it is given by n multiplied by the electronic charge and the area of the anodes, or, using [15.27],

$$I = I_o e^{\alpha d} \qquad [15.28]$$

from which

$$\ln \frac{I}{I_o} = \alpha d \qquad [15.29]$$

It is clear from [15.29] that if we vary d while keeping α constant, we can measure α by plotting $\ln (I/I_o)$ vs. d as shown in Figure 15.3. Experimentally it is found that α can be held constant if the voltage applied to the electrodes is increased by the amount necessary to keep the electric field E constant as d is increased. It is assumed that the gas pressure is kept constant.

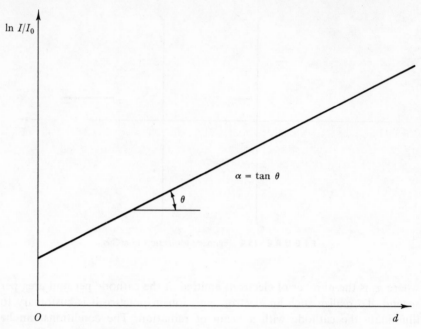

FIGURE 15.3 Measurement of Primary Ionization Coefficient

Alternatively we can describe the primary ionization process by a coefficient η which is defined as the number of ion pairs produced by an electron when it falls through a potential difference of 1 volt. The correspondence between α and η can be seen by considering the number of ion pairs produced by an electron in crossing the gap. This number is

$$\alpha d = \eta V = \eta E d$$

or

$$\alpha = \eta E \qquad\qquad\qquad [15.30]$$

where V is the voltage between the electrodes.

A third coefficient for the primary ionization processes is the rate of ionization ν_I. This is the number of ion pairs produced by an electron per second. It is related to the previous coefficients by the drift velocity v_d of the electrons in the electric field. Thus,

$$\nu_I = \alpha v_d$$

or, in terms of the mobility μ

$$\nu_I = \alpha\mu E$$

from which, using [15.30]

$$\nu_I = \eta\mu E^2 \qquad [15.31]$$

A qualitative theory of the primary ionization process can be developed as follows. The average energy gained by an electron between collisions is eEL, where L is the electron mean free path. Now L is inversely proportional to the gas pressure P so that the average energy is proportional to E/P provided the temperature remains constant. It follows that the proportion of ionizing collisions to the total number of collisions will remain unchanged under an increase of pressure, provided that the electric field is adjusted to keep E/P constant. However the total number of collisions will increase proportionately to the increase of pressure, and it follows that the number of ionizing collisions increases in similar proportion. Expressed mathematically we have

$$\alpha \propto P\big|_{E/P \text{ constant}}$$

or

$$\frac{\alpha}{P} = f\left(\frac{E}{P}\right) \qquad [15.32]$$

where f represents a function which has to be determined.

Secondary electrons are defined as those produced as a consequence of the primary ionization process. Several mechanisms by which such secondary electrons may be produced have been discussed earlier in the chapter. Unexpectedly, the ionization of atoms and molecules by positive ion impact in the gas is unimportant. It is found that appreciable ionization of this type occurs only when the positive ion velocity is comparable to that velocity of the electrons which causes ionization. Simple collisional considerations indicate that this condition will not be met by a significant number of positive ions during the process of the growth of ionization (see Exercise 15.31.1). However the impact of positive ions at the cathode, thereby releasing electrons, is a major secondary mechanism. The coefficient γ describes this process and is defined as the number of electrons released at the cathode by one incident positive ion. As this number is frequently less than unity, we can, alternatively, consider γ to be the probability that an incident positive ion will cause the release of an electron at the cathode surface.

The situation illustrated by Figure 15.2 and discussed above in terms of primary ionization is now complicated by this secondary mechanism of electron production. At the cathode surface n_o electrons are produced by the beam of radiation, and, in addition, a number of secondary electrons are produced by the bombardment of the positive ions. Let n_o' be the total number of electrons produced at the cathode by both mechanisms (Figure 15.4). As before, n is the number of electrons per unit area per second entering

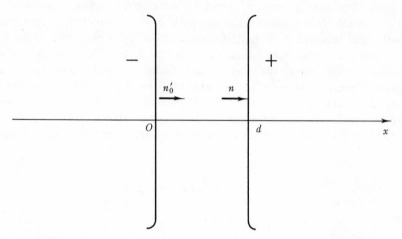

FIGURE 15.4 Secondary Ionization by Positive Ion Impact at the Cathode

the anode. Then it is clear that the primary ionization has produced a flow of $n - n_o'$ electrons at the anode and, because positive ions are produced in equal amount and we are discussing a steady state condition, there is a flux of $n - n_o'$ positive ions at the cathode. This results in a flow of $\gamma(n - n_o')$ secondary electrons from the cathode. Thus

$$n_o' = n_o + \gamma(n - n_o') \quad \text{or} \quad n_o' = \frac{n_o + \gamma n}{1 + \gamma} \qquad [15.33]$$

Now the primary ionization has multiplied the electron flow at the cathode, n_o', to a value of n at the anode. Therefore from [15.27]

$$n = n_o' e^{\alpha d} \qquad [15.34]$$

Substituting for n_o', from [15.33],

$$n = \frac{n_o + \gamma n}{1 + \gamma} e^{\alpha d} \quad \text{or} \quad n(1 + \gamma - \gamma e^{\alpha d}) = n_o e^{\alpha d}$$

from which

$$n = n_0 \frac{e^{\alpha d}}{1 - \gamma(e^{\alpha d} - 1)} \qquad [15.35]$$

Multiplying by the electronic charge and the electrode area we have

$$I = I_0 \frac{e^{\alpha d}}{1 - \gamma(e^{\alpha d} - 1)} \qquad [15.36]$$

The presence of a secondary ionization process can be detected by measuring the current in the circuit as d is varied with α held constant as discussed in connection with Figure 15.3. Experimentally a curve of the form shown in Figure 15.5 is obtained. At small gap lengths a straight line is obtained

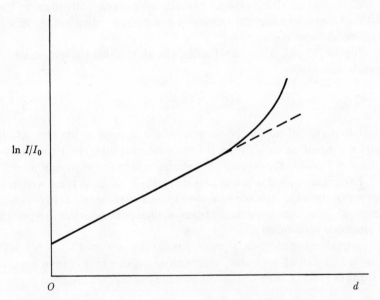

FIGURE 15.5 Simultaneous Primary and Secondary Ionization Processes

indicating that primary ionization alone is significant. At larger gap lengths an increase in current demonstrates the presence of secondary mechanisms.

In general it is found that the curve can be fitted by an equation of the form

$$I = I_0 \frac{e^{\alpha d}}{1 - C(e^{\alpha d} - 1)} \qquad [15.37]$$

where α is obtained from the slope of the straight section of the plot and C is chosen to give the best fit to the curved section.

One can show that other secondary mechanisms in addition to the γ mechanism lead to equations of the form of [15.36]. Therefore the interpretation of the value of C which has been obtained from an experiment, is dependent upon additional knowledge about the secondary mechanisms. The data of Figure 15.5 alone do not permit discrimination between secondary mechanisms to be made.

Breakdown Criteria   If a gas is steadily heated to a temperature of tens of thousands of degrees Kelvin, it passes from the neutral to the conducting (plasma) state in a smooth transition. However if a gas is subjected to a steadily increasing electric field, there are wide ranges of gas pressure and source frequency over which the transition to the conducting state is abrupt. The occurrence of an electric spark marks this transition under certain conditions.

We will begin this discussion of breakdown criteria with the d.c. case. We will then consider effects of frequency and pressure that will identify the principal breakdown regimes.

Referring to [15.36], we see that when the electric field gives values of α and γ such that

$$\gamma(e^{\alpha d} - 1) = 1 \qquad\qquad [15.38]$$

it is clear that [15.36] no longer determines the current in the gap. Mathematically the equation calls for an infinite current. Physically there must be other factors beyond the α and γ processes which intervene to limit the current. Experimentally it is found that if [15.38] is taken as the criterion for breakdown of the gap, then the predicted breakdown electric field is close to the measured value over important ranges of such parameters as gas pressure P and electrode separation d.

If we generalize the secondary process, using the symbol C as in [15.37] to stand for the sum of all secondary mechanisms leading to a current equation of the form of [15.37], then it is found that the breakdown criterion

$$C(e^{\alpha d} - 1) = 1 \qquad\qquad [15.39]$$

applies to wider ranges of conditions than does [15.38].

Let us interpret [15.38] in terms of the physical processes in the discharge gap. From [15.27] it is clear that one electron, starting from the cathode, has produced a primary avalanche of $e^{\alpha d}$ electrons at the anode. So that $(e^{\alpha d} - 1)$ is the number of positive ions in the primary avalanche. These all drift back to the cathode where the probability that one positive ion results in the emission of a secondary electron is given by γ. The probability that $(e^{\alpha d} - 1)$

positive ions give a secondary electron is then $\gamma(e^{\alpha d} - 1)$, and if this probability is unity then the whole process begins over again with the secondary electron from the primary avalanche triggering a new primary avalanche which in its turn gives rise to a further secondary electron.

If the condition [15.38] has been reached by steadily increasing the applied electric field it is clear that, at this point, if the energy source producing I_o electrons at the cathode is turned off, then the current will be self-maintaining. The condition [15.38] therefore defines the onset of a self-maintained current in the gap. So far as the current growth equation [15.36] is concerned it can give us no further insight into the discharge process.

The key to the further events which lead to an electric spark in the discharge gap is the role of accumulating space charge in producing enhanced electric fields in the gap without any increase in the strength of the applied field.

If the applied electric field is alternating in time we can expect the breakdown field strength to change if the period of alternation is short enough to interrupt the processes we have just discussed. For example, if the γ mechanism is the effective secondary mechanism, the principal time element associated with the current development is the transit time for positive ions to cross the gap. As the frequency of the applied field is increased, we would expect a discontinuity in the value of the breakdown field when a critical frequency is reached which causes the positive ions to be trapped and to oscillate in the gap. A further discontinuity (lower value) in the breakdown field strength would be expected when the frequency is two or three orders of magnitude higher so that the field reversal time coincides with the transit time for the primary avalanche. Both these effects have been found experimentally. In terms of a hypothetical discharge gap with $d = 1$ mm, $P = 0.1$ atmospheres, these two critical frequencies are of the order of hundreds of kilocycles and one hundred magacycles respectively.

At low gas pressures (below about 10^{-3} Torr for dimensions of the order of 1 cm), when the electron mean free path is of the order of the gap dimension, the breakdown field strength of the high frequency discharge becomes independent of the type of gas. Electrode or wall processes determine the current growth as the electrons travel first to one electrode, then to the other. At higher pressures (about 1 Torr) a breakdown field discontinuity occurs when the amplitude of electron oscillation in the field is equal to the gap dimension. In this breakdown regime the gas type is significant and the electron transit time is a drift time.

Exercise 15.31.1   Compare the growth of ionization in a gas immersed in an electric field due to electrons and positive ions. Show that impact ionization by positive ions is negligible compared to electron impact ionization by considering

(a)   The relative rate of energy increase of the two particles
(b)   The relative rate of energy loss in elastic collisions
(c)   The energy required for ionization (refer to experimental data).

15.4 SOME TYPES
OF LABORATORY PLASMAS

The principal d.c. discharges are the dark or Townsend discharge, the glow, and the arc discharges. The voltage-current characteristics of these discharges are shown in Figure 15.6.

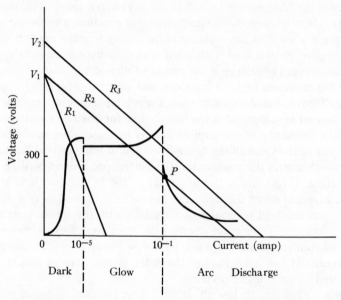

FIGURE 15.6 Typical Electrical Characteristics of the Principal D-C Discharges

In Section 15.31 we discussed the Townsend ionization coefficients which determine the characteristics of the dark, non-self-sustained discharge

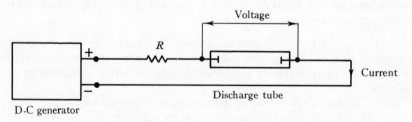

FIGURE 15.7 Operation of a D-C Discharge Tube

regime. By the term non-self-sustained it is meant that the discharge current is dependent upon a source of initiating electrons as well as upon the voltage. In this regime increased current requires increased voltage. In terms of the behavior of the d.c. circuit shown in Figure 15.7 the operating point is determined by the intersection of the resistance line R_1 with the discharge characteristic.

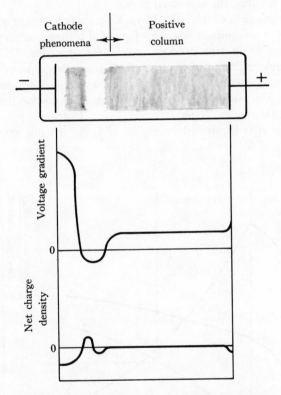

F I G U R E 15.8 Properties of the Glow Discharge

The transition from the dark discharge to the glow discharge is characterized by an electric spark with a breakdown criterion as discussed in Section 15.31. The glow discharge at a pressure of about 1 Torr has the voltage-current characteristic shown in Figure 15.6 and the distribution of electric field and charge density shown in Figure 15.8. The electric charges are generated by electron impact ionization in the high field region near the cathode. The voltage drop across the discharge tube occurs mostly at the cathode and is comparable to that required for spark breakdown in the tube. In the positive column even the small voltage gradient present leads to electron temperature of the order of 20,000°K while the heavy particles are within a few hundred degrees of room temperature. In the normal glow region (the constant voltage part of the characteristic) the current density is constant and the discharge adjusts to a variation in the total current by varying the active area of the cathode. If the voltage is increased after the cathode area is fully covered by the discharge (for example to V_2 with a series resistance of R_2 in Figure 15.6) then the current density increases and this part of the characteristic is called the abnormal glow.

The arc discharge is characterized by a cathode fall voltage which is more than an order of magnitude less than that of the glow discharge. Clearly a new mechanism of electron production becomes operative. This mechanism is the thermionic emission of electrons from the cathode. In contrast to the abrupt and uncontrolled breakdown which marks the dark-to-glow transition, the glow-to-arc transition can be quite well controlled when the usual high-melting-point electrodes are used.

This transition is illustrated in Figure 15.9. As the discharge current is

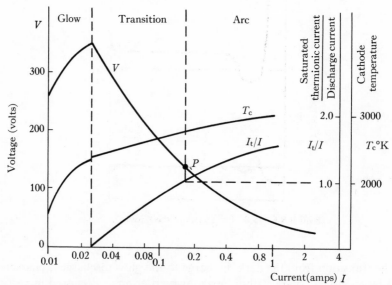

FIGURE 15.9 Glow-to-Arc Transition for Tungsten Electrodes in Nitrogen Gas

V—discharge potential
T_c—cathode temperature
I_t—saturated thermionic current
I—discharge current

After J. D. Cobine, *Gaseous Conductors*, McGraw-Hill, 1941

increased in the abnormal glow region, the cathode temperature rises rapidly. When the cathode temperature is sufficient to cause significant thermionic emission the discharge voltage, which was previously steadily rising, immediately begins to fall. There is a small current range in which the discharge is unstable but a new stable mode is soon established which has the falling voltage characteristic which is typical of the arc discharge. With continued increasing discharge current (R being reduced in the circuit of Figure 15.7) the cathode temperature rises until the saturation thermionic emission current is equal to the discharge current. This is point P on Figure 15.9. The arc mode is now fully established. The cathode fall voltage in the arc mode is of the order of the first ionization potential of the metal vapor or gas which fills the discharge tube. The thermionic electrons make enough ionizing collisions to provide the positive ion density needed by the discharge.

The arc discharge operates over a wide pressure range. The arc at atmospheric pressure is termed a high pressure arc. In this case the various gaseous constituents in the arc column are in thermal equilibrium with each other. For arcs at reduced pressures the thermal (collisional) coupling between the electron gas and the heavy particles is insufficient to maintain this thermal equilibrium. The electron gas, gaining energy from the electric field, acquires

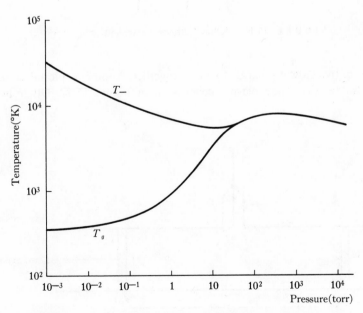

FIGURE 15.10 General relationships between the electron gas temperature (T_-) and the neutral gas temperature (T_g) in the arc discharge. After W. Elenbaas, *De Ingenieur*, **50**, E83, 1935

a temperature which may be considerably higher than the temperature of the gas atoms. This effect is shown in Figure 15.10. The arc column at low pressures bears resemblance to the positive column of the glow discharge.

An unexpectedly high level of ionization occurs in a d.c. electrode configuration known as the hollow cathode. One form of this configuration is shown in Figure 15.11, where the use of ring anode permits the cathode

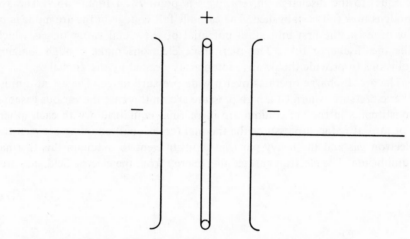

F I G U R E 15.11   Hollow Cathode Electrode Configuration

regions of two glow discharges to merge together. Another exploitation of this effect is the waveguide plasma cell shown in Figure 15.12. Other hollow

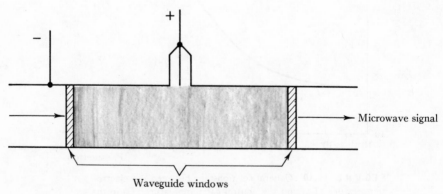

Waveguide windows

F I G U R E 15.12   Hollow Cathode Waveguide Plasma Cell

(a)   (b)   (c)

FIGURE 15.13   Various Types of Hollow Cathode: (a) Rectangular box with open side. (b) Sphere with small opening. (c) Open mesh

cathode shapes are shown in Figure 15.13. When a high negative potential is applied to these electrodes, a discharge forms within the hollow cathode and may result in the emission of a highly focused electron beam.

Further enhancement of the strength of the discharge in the electrode configuration of Figure 15.11, may be obtained by adding a magnetic field, oriented parallel to a line joining the two cathodes as shown in Figure 15.14.

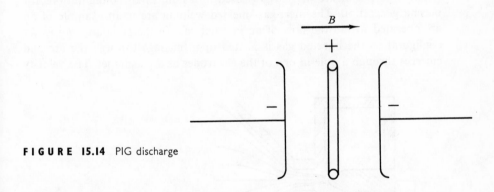

FIGURE 15.14   PIG discharge

The reason for this is that charged particle diffusion perpendicular to the field lines is inhibited as has been shown in Section 7.13. The lifetime of electrons in the discharge is therefore extended. Such an arrangement will operate at pressures as low as 10^{-7} Torr. When it is used as a vacuum gauge, it is called a *Philips* or *Penning ionization gauge*. Plasma devices using this configuration are known as PIG discharges.

If an alternating electric field is applied to a gas its frequency determines the type of discharge which will be generated. In Section 15.31 the principal regimes of high frequency discharges have been delineated in terms of the breakdown mechanisms involved. Electrode configurations for r.f. discharges are shown in Figure 15.15.

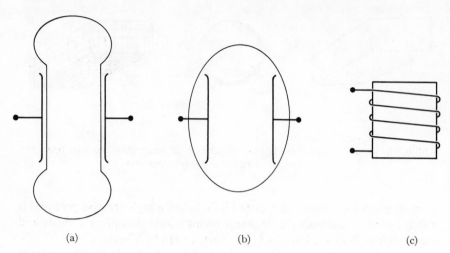

FIGURE 15.15 Types of r.f. Discharge: (a) and (b) Capacitive, and (c) Inductive Types

The high power arc discharge is used in a number of configurations for plasma generation. The inert-gas-shielded welding arc is an example of an arc operated within the flow of an injected gas. In the standard *plasma jet* configuration the injected gas is heated upon passage through the arc and emerges through a hole in one of the electrodes as a plasma jet. The velocity

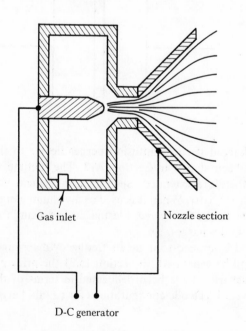

Gas inlet   Nozzle section

FIGURE 15.16 The Electro-thermal Plasma Engine

D-C generator

of the plasma jet can be optimized by the use of a nozzle section as illustrated in Figure 15.16. Such a device is called an *electrothermal plasma engine* because it converts the electrically generated heat energy of the gas into the directed velocity of the plasma jet. An electromagnetic plasma accelerator can be built by adding a flow section to the electrothermal engine which contains crossed electric and magnetic fields.

This brief review of some types of laboratory plasmas concludes this chapter and the book. Other books which are oriented toward particular plasma applications will help the reader to apply the basic knowledge he has now learnt to whichever part of the plasma field is of interest to him.

REFERENCES

Basic processes of gaseous electronics are treated by

1   Massey, H. S. W., and E. H. S. Burhop. *Electronic and Ionic Impact Phenomena.* London: Oxford, 1952.

2   Bates, D. R. *Atomic and Molecular Processes.* New York: Academic Press, 1962.

3   McDaniel, E. W. *Collision Phenomena in Ionized Gases.* New York: Wiley, 1964.

4   Loeb, L. B. *Basic Processes of Gaseous Electronics.* Berkeley: University of California Press, 1955.

5   Brown, S. C. *Basic Data of Plasma Physics.* Cambridge, Mass., and New York: Massachusetts Institute of Technology Press and Wiley, 1959.

6   Hasted, J. B. *The Theory of Atomic Collisions.* London: Butterworth, 1964.

7   Field, F. H., and J. L. Franklin. *Electron Impact Phenomena.* New York: Academic Press, 1957.

Discussion of the thermodynamic consequences of ionization in a gas is given by

8   Cambel, A. B., D. P. Duclos, and T. P. Anderson. *Real Gases.* New York: Academic Press, 1963.

9   Cambel, A. B. *Plasma Physics and Magneto-fluid-mechanics.* New York: McGraw-Hill, 1963.

Treatments of various types of gas discharges are given by

10   Penning, F. M. *Electrical Discharges in Gases*. New York: Macmillan, 1957.

11   Llewellyn-Jones, F. *Ionization and Breakdown in Gases*. New York: Methuen (Wiley), 1957.

12   Von Engel, A. *Ionized Gases*. London: Oxford University Press, 1955.

13   Cobine, J. D. *Gaseous Conductors*. New York: McGraw-Hill, 1941 (also Dover).

14   Francis, G. *Ionization Phenomena in Gases*. London: Butterworth, 1960.

15   Meek, J. M., and J. D. Craggs. *Electrical Breakdown in Gases*. London: Oxford University Press, 1953.

16   Acton, J. R., and J. D. Swift. *Cold Cathode Discharge Tubes*. New York: Academic Press, 1963.

Plasma measurements are treated by

17   Heald, M. A., and C. B. Wharton. *Plasma Diagnostics with Microwaves*. New York: Wiley, 1964.

18   Huddlestone, R. H., and S. L. Leonard. *Plasma Diagnostics*. New York: Academic Press, 1965.

Advanced treatments of the topics of this chapter are given in

19   *Electron Emission—Gas Discharges I* and *Gas Discharges II* which are, respectively, volumes 21 and 22 of the *Handbuch der Physik*, Springer-Verlag, 1956.

A discussion of the chemical kinetic reactions important in plasmas is given by

20   Bortner, M. H. "Chemical Kinetics in a Reentry Flow Field." *General Electric Space Sciences Laboratory*, Report No. R63SD63, 1963.

APPENDICES

A

PRINCIPAL
USE OF SYMBOLS

A	Alfvén velocity	M_h	Number of electrons in a Debye sphere
B_i	Magnetic induction		
C_i	Total current density	$N, N^{(s)},$ $N_-,$ etc.	Particle number density
D_i	Electric displacement		
$D_-, D_+,$ $D_A,$ etc.	Diffusion coefficients	P	Pressure
		P_i	Polarization
E_i	Electric field intensity	Q	Cross section
G_i	Poynting vector	Q_i	Heat flux vector
H_i	Magnetic field intensity	R_i	Force per unit mass
J_i	Electric current density	$S(\chi)$	Angular distribution function
L	Mean free path		
L_{ik}^*	Electro-kinetic stress tensor	T	Temperature
		T_{ij}	Electromagnetic stress tensor
M_i	Magnetization vector		

U	$1 + iZ$	Γ_i	Particle flux
$U_i^{(s)}$	Peculiar velocity relative to the mean mass velocity	Λ	h/p_c
V_i	Peculiar velocity	Π	Plasma frequency, $Ne^2/m\epsilon_0$
W	Peculiar speed	Ψ_{ij}	Pressure tensor
X	Normalized plasma frequency, Π^2/ω^2	Ω	Cyclotron frequency
Y	Normalized cyclotron frequency, Ω/ω	α	First Townsend ionization coefficient
Z	Normalized collision frequency, ν/ω	α	Recombination coefficient
		α_{ij}	Electric susceptibility tensor
a	Thermal speed	γ	Secondary ionization coefficient
c	Speed of light	γ	Ratio of specific heats
d	Interparticle separation	γ_i	Angular momentum
e	Electronic charge	δ_{ij}	Kronecker delta
$e_{\alpha\beta}$	Two-dimensional alternating tensor	ϵ	Permittivity
f	Velocity distribution function	ϵ_0	Permittivity of free space
g	Relative speed	ϵ_{ijk}	Alternating unit tensor
h	Debye length	η	Charge density
i	$\sqrt{-1}$	κ	Dielectric constant
k	Boltzmann's constant	κ_{ij}	Dielectric tensor
k	Wave number	λ	Wavelength
m	Particle mass	μ	Mobility
m'	Reduced mass, $m^A m^B/(m^A + m^B)$	μ_0	Permeability of free space
m_i	Magnetic dipole moment	μ_{ij}	Permeability tensor
n	Refractive index	$\nu,\ \nu_{EI},$ $\nu_{90},$ etc.	Collision frequency
p	Impact parameter	ρ	Mass density
p_c	Critical impact parameter	σ	Conductivity
q	Charge	σ_{ij}	Conductivity tensor
t	Time	τ	Relaxation time
u	Phase velocity	χ	Deflection angle in center-of-mass system
v	Group velocity	χ_{ij}	Magnetic susceptibility tensor
v_i	Particle velocity	ω	Angular frequency
w	Ray velocity	$\mathscr{E}$	Thermal energy density
w	Particle speed		

B

TRANSFORMATION PROPERTIES OF CARTESIAN TENSORS

In Chapter 2 we introduced the notation of Cartesian tensors by indicating the relationship between the indicial and symbolic vector notations. We will now show how vectors and tensors may be defined in terms of their transformation properties.

Consider the coordinate system 123 shown in Figure B.1. Let the projections of the line segment OP on the axes of this coordinate system be x_1, x_2, and x_3 as shown.

Now consider a second coordinate system $1'2'3'$ which is rotated with respect to the first coordinate system as shown in Figure B.2. We ask: What are the projections x_1', x_2', and x_3' of the line segment OP on the axes of this new coordinate system $1'2'3'$? Consider first the projection x_1'. This will be equal to the sum of the projections of x_1, x_2, and x_3 on the 1'-axis. Thus, if $\cos(x_1, x_1')$ is the cosine of the angle between the 01 and 01' axes, $\cos(x_2, x_1')$ the angle between the 02 and 01' axes, and so forth, then we have that

$$x_1' = x_1 \cos(x_1, x_1') + x_2 \cos(x_2, x_1') + x_3 \cos(x_3, x_1')$$

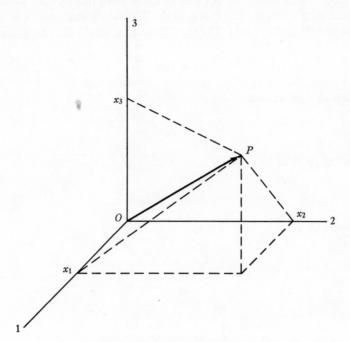

FIGURE B.I   Cartesian Coordinate System

In a similar manner

$$x_2' = x_1 \cos (x_1, x_2') + x_2 \cos (x_2, x_2') + x_3 \cos (x_3, x_2')$$
$$x_3' = x_1 \cos (x_1, x_3') + x_2 \cos (x_2, x_3') + x_3 \cos (x_3, x_3')$$

These three equations may be written in matrix form as

$$\begin{bmatrix} x_1' \\ x_2' \\ x_3' \end{bmatrix} = \begin{bmatrix} \cos (x_1, x_1') & \cos (x_2, x_1') & \cos (x_3, x_1') \\ \cos (x_1, x_2') & \cos (x_2, x_2') & \cos (x_3, x_2') \\ \cos (x_1, x_3') & \cos (x_2, x_3') & \cos (x_3, x_3') \end{bmatrix} \begin{bmatrix} x_1 \\ x_2 \\ x_3 \end{bmatrix} \qquad \text{[B.1]}$$

Let the matrix containing the nine direction cosines be denoted by

$$\cos (x_i, x_j') = l_{ij}$$

Then [B.1] can be written in indicial notation as

$$x_j' = l_{ij} x_i \qquad \text{[B.2]}$$

We could write another set of equations similar to [B.1] for x_1, x_2, and x_3 in terms of x'_1, x'_2, and x'_3. For this case the direction cosine matrix would be the transpose of that in [B.1]. The transformation would thus be given by

$$x_j = l_{ji}x'_i$$

which can also be written

$$x_i = l_{ik}x'_k \qquad \text{[B.3]}$$

Substituting [B.3] in [B.2] gives

$$x'_j = l_{ij}l_{ik}x'_k = \delta_{jk}x'_k$$

from which

$$l_{ij}l_{ik} = \delta_{jk} \qquad \text{[B.4]}$$

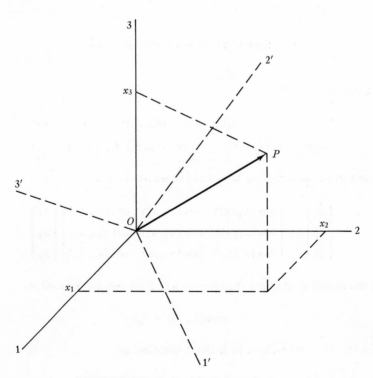

FIGURE B.2 Rotated Coordinate System

The physical meaning of [B.4] is clear if we remember that $l_{ij} = \cos(x_i, x_j')$ are the components in the x_i coordinate system of a vector one unit long lying along the x_j' axes. Since these axes are orthogonal, the dot product of l_{ij} with l_{ik} can only yield 1 or 0 according to [B.4].

We may now define vectors and tensors in the following manner.

Definition 1 Let A_i be a set of three quantities associated with the coordinate system x_k; let A_i' be a set of three quantities associated with any other coordinate system x_k'. Then A_i are said to form the components of a vector or tensor of order one if and only if

$$A_j' = l_{ij}A_i \qquad [B.5]$$

Definition 2 Let $K_{ij\ldots k}$ be a set of 3^n quantities depending on n independent subscripts in the x_p coordinate system. $K_{rs\ldots t}'$ are the corresponding 3^n quantities in any other x_p' coordinate system. Then $K_{ij\ldots k}$ form the components of a tensor of order n if and only if

$$K_{rs\ldots t}' = l_{ir}l_{js}\ldots l_{kt}K_{ij\ldots k} \qquad [B.6]$$

In order to invert [B.6] we multiply both sides by $l_{ar}l_{bs}\ldots l_{ct}$. Thus

$$l_{ar}l_{bs}\ldots l_{ct}K_{rs\ldots t}' = l_{ir}l_{ar}l_{js}l_{bs}\ldots l_{kt}l_{ct}K_{ij\ldots k} \qquad [B.7]$$

Using [B.4] in [B.7] we obtain

$$l_{ar}l_{bs}\ldots l_{ct}K_{rs\ldots t}' = \delta_{ia}\delta_{jb}\ldots \delta_{kc}K_{ij\ldots k}$$

from which

$$K_{ab\ldots c} = l_{ar}l_{bs}\ldots l_{ct}K_{rs\ldots t}' \qquad [B.8]$$

C

INTEGRAL THEOREMS

The integral theorems of Green and Stokes are important because of their usefulness in deriving various equations. Green's theorem relates a volume integral to an integral over the bounding surface, while Stokes' theorem relates the integral over an open surface to an integral around the bounding curve. For a more detailed treatment of these theorems, the reader is referred to the references at the end of Chapter 2.

GREEN'S THEOREM

Let n_i be the outward normal to the surface S bounding the volume V as in Figure C.1.

If F is a continuously differentiable tensor field, then Green's theorem states that

$$\iiint_V F_{,i} \, d\tau = \iint_S Fn_i \, dA \qquad \text{[C.1]}$$

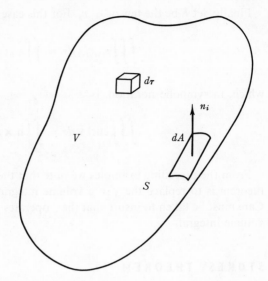

FIGURE C.I Volume and Surface Elements

Important special cases are obtained by letting F be a scalar, vector, and tensor.

Let F be a scalar ψ. Then Green's theorem becomes

$$\iiint_V \psi_{,i}\, d\tau = \iint_S \psi n_i\, dA \qquad\qquad \text{[C.2]}$$

which is written in symbolic notation as

$$\iiint_V \operatorname{grad} \psi\, d\tau = \iint_S \psi \mathbf{n}\, dA \qquad\qquad \text{[C.3]}$$

Next let F be a vector v_p. For this case [C.1] becomes

$$\iiint_V v_{p,i}\, d\tau = \iint_S v_p n_i\, dA$$

Letting $p = i$ gives the familiar divergence theorem

$$\iiint_V v_{i,i}\, d\tau = \iint_S v_i n_i\, dA \qquad\qquad \text{[C.4]}$$

or, in symbolic notation

$$\iiint_V \operatorname{div} \mathbf{v}\, d\tau = \iint_S \mathbf{v} \cdot \mathbf{n}\, dA \qquad\qquad \text{[C.5]}$$

Finally, let F be the tensor $\epsilon_{ris}v_s$. For this case [C.1] becomes

$$\iiint_V \epsilon_{ris}v_{s,i}\, d\tau = \iint_S \epsilon_{ris}v_s n_i\, dA \qquad\qquad \text{[C.6]}$$

which, in symbolic notation, is

$$\iiint_V \operatorname{curl} \mathbf{v}\, d\tau = \iint_S \mathbf{n} \times \mathbf{v}\, dA \qquad\qquad \text{[C.7]}$$

From the preceding examples we note that the "rule" in applying Green's theorem is to replace the $_{,i}$ in a volume integral by n_i in a surface integral. Care must be taken to insure that the $_{,i}$ operates on all of the integrand of the volume integral.

STOKES' THEOREM

Let ds_i be a differential element of the closed curve C bounding the surface S as in Figure C.2. The normal n_i to the surface S is related to ds_i in a right-handed sense.

Stokes' theorem then states that

$$\oint_C u_i\, ds_i = \iint_S \epsilon_{ijk}u_{k,j}n_i\, dA \qquad\qquad \text{[C.8]}$$

which can be written in symbolic notation as

$$\oint_C \mathbf{u}\cdot d\mathbf{s} = \iint_S (\nabla \times \mathbf{u})\cdot \mathbf{n}\, dA \qquad\qquad \text{[C.9]}$$

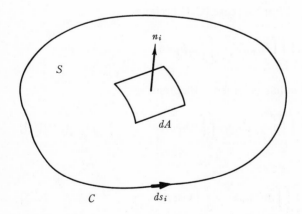

FIGURE C.2 Surface and Line Elements

D

TRANSFORMATION OF MULTIPLE INTEGRALS— JACOBIANS

Consider the multiple integral $\iint \cdots \int F(u_1, u_2, \ldots, u_N)\, du_1\, du_2 \cdots du_N$ where the integration is extended over any range of the variables u. If the variables of integration $u_1, u_2, \ldots, u_N$ are changed to a different set $v_1, v_2, \ldots, v_N$, then the integral is transformed to

$$\iint \cdots \int G(v_1, v_2, \ldots, v_N)\, |J|\, dv_1\, dv_2 \cdots dv_N$$

where

$$G(v_1, v_2, \ldots, v_N) \equiv F(u_1, u_2, \ldots, u_N)$$

and J is the Jacobian determinant:

$$J = \frac{\partial(u_1, u_2, \ldots, u_N)}{\partial(v_1, v_2, \ldots, v_N)} = \begin{vmatrix} \dfrac{\partial u_1}{\partial v_1} & \dfrac{\partial u_2}{\partial v_1} & \cdots & \dfrac{\partial u_N}{\partial v_1} \\[2mm] \dfrac{\partial u_1}{\partial v_2} & \dfrac{\partial u_2}{\partial v_2} & \cdots & \dfrac{\partial u_N}{\partial v_2} \\[2mm] \cdot & \cdot & \cdot & \cdot \\[2mm] \dfrac{\partial u_1}{\partial v_N} & \dfrac{\partial u_2}{\partial v_N} & \cdots & \dfrac{\partial u_N}{\partial v_N} \end{vmatrix} \qquad \text{[D.1]}$$

The new integration is extended over the values of v which correspond to the range of values of the original variables u.

    Example   Two-dimensional polar coordinates.
  Transform the integral

$$\int_0^\infty \int_0^\infty e^{-(x_1^2 + x_2^2)}\, dx_1\, dx_2$$

to polar coordinates (r, θ).

$$x_1 = r \cos \theta$$
$$x_2 = r \sin \theta$$
$$x_1^2 + x_2^2 = r^2$$
$$dx_1\, dx_2 = |J|\, dr\, d\theta$$

Thus, the new integral is

$$\int_0^{\pi/2} \int_0^\infty e^{-r^2}\, |J|\, dr\, d\theta$$

where

$$J = \frac{\partial(x_1, x_2)}{\partial(r, \theta)} = \begin{vmatrix} \dfrac{\partial x_1}{\partial r} & \dfrac{\partial x_2}{\partial r} \\[2mm] \dfrac{\partial x_1}{\partial \theta} & \dfrac{\partial x_2}{\partial \theta} \end{vmatrix} = \begin{vmatrix} \cos \theta & \sin \theta \\[2mm] -r \sin \theta & r \cos \theta \end{vmatrix}$$

$$= r \cos^2 \theta + r \sin^2 \theta = r$$

Therefore, the new integral is

$$\int_0^{\pi/2} \int_0^\infty e^{-r^2}\, r\, dr\, d\theta$$

E

TAYLOR SERIES EXPANSIONS

A function $f(x)$ can be expanded in a Taylor series about x_0

$$f(x) = f(x_0) + \frac{\partial f}{\partial x}(x - x_0) + \frac{1}{2!}\frac{\partial^2 f}{\partial x^2}(x - x_0)^2 + \cdots \qquad [E.1]$$

where the derivatives are evaluated at $x = x_0$. In a similar manner a function of two variables $F(x, y)$ can be expanded about a point x_0, y_0 as follows

$$F(x, y) = F(x_0, y_0) + \left[\frac{\partial F}{\partial x}(x - x_0) + \frac{\partial F}{\partial y}(y - y_0)\right]$$
$$+ \frac{1}{2!}\left[\frac{\partial^2 F}{\partial x^2}(x - x_0)^2 + 2\frac{\partial^2 F}{\partial x \partial y}(x - x_0)(y - y_0) + \frac{\partial^2 F}{\partial y^2}(y - y_0)^2\right] + \cdots$$
$$[E.2]$$

487

where the derivatives are evaluated at (x_0, y_0). From [E.2], the function $F(x + h, y + k)$ expanded about $F(x, y)$ is

$$F(x + h, y + k) = F(x, y) + \left[\frac{\partial F(x, y)}{\partial x} h + \frac{\partial F(x, y)}{\partial y} k \right]$$
$$+ \frac{1}{2!} \left[h^2 \frac{\partial^2 F(x, y)}{\partial x^2} + 2hk \frac{\partial^2 F(x, y)}{\partial x\, \partial y} + k^2 \frac{\partial^2 F(x, y)}{\partial y^2} \right] + \cdots$$

F

INTEGRALS CONTAINING EXPONENTIALS

Consider the integral

$$I = \int_0^\infty w^2 e^{-\alpha w^2}\, dw \qquad \text{[F.1]}$$

If we integrate by parts by letting $u = w$ and $dv = we^{-\alpha w^2}\, dw$ then we obtain

$$I = uv \bigg|_0^\infty - \int_0^\infty v\, du$$

$$= \frac{1}{2\alpha} \int_0^\infty e^{-\alpha w^2}\, dw \qquad \text{[F.2]}$$

Now, the integral in [F.2] may be evaluated in the following way: Changing the variable of integration we square the integral and obtain

$$I^2 = \frac{1}{4\alpha^2} \int_0^\infty e^{-\alpha x^2}\, dx \int_0^\infty e^{-\alpha y^2}\, dy$$

$$= \frac{1}{4\alpha^2} \int_0^\infty \int_0^\infty e^{-\alpha(x^2+y^2)}\, dx\, dy \qquad [F.3]$$

We thus have a "double integral" where the integration extends over the first quadrant. We change to polar coordinates:

$$x = r \cos\theta$$

$$y = r \sin\theta$$

$$x^2 + y^2 = r^2$$

Making the change of variables, [F.3] becomes

$$I^2 = \frac{1}{4\alpha^2} \int_0^\infty \int_0^{\pi/2} e^{-\alpha r^2}\, r\, d\theta\, dr$$

$$= \frac{\pi}{8\alpha^2} \int_0^\infty r e^{-\alpha r^2}\, dr$$

We can readily evaluate

$$\int_0^\infty r e^{-\alpha r^2}\, dr = \frac{1}{2\alpha}$$

so that

$$I^2 = \frac{\pi}{16\alpha^3}$$

from which

$$I = \frac{1}{4} \sqrt{\frac{\pi}{\alpha^3}}$$

or

$$\int_0^\infty w^2 e^{-\alpha w^2}\, dw = \frac{1}{4} \sqrt{\frac{\pi}{\alpha^3}} \qquad [F.4]$$

Consider now the more general integral

$$\int_0^\infty w^r e^{-\alpha w^2}\, dw \qquad\qquad [\text{F.5}]$$

This integral may be conveniently expressed in terms of the Gamma function. The Gamma function is defined as

$$\Gamma(x) = \int_0^\infty e^{-t} t^{x-1}\, dt \qquad x > 0 \qquad [\text{F.6}]$$

The Gamma function has the following important properties

$$\Gamma(x + 1) = x!$$
$$\Gamma(x) = (x - 1)\Gamma(x - 1)$$
$$\Gamma(\tfrac{1}{2}) = \sqrt{\pi} \qquad\qquad [\text{F.7}]$$

In equation [F.5] let

$$s = \alpha w^2 \qquad ds = 2\alpha w\, dw$$

so that [F.5] becomes

$$\tfrac{1}{2}\alpha^{-(r+1)/2} \int_0^\infty e^{-s} s^{(r-1)/2}\, ds = \tfrac{1}{2}\alpha^{-(r+1)/2}\, \Gamma\!\left(\frac{r+1}{2}\right) \qquad r > -1 \quad [\text{F.8}]$$

For the case when r is an integer, we have, using the relations of [F.7] with [F.8]

$$\int_0^\infty w^r e^{-\alpha w^2}\, dw = \tfrac{1}{2}\alpha^{-(r+1)/2}\left(\frac{r-1}{2}\right)\cdots\frac{5}{2}\cdot\frac{3}{2}\cdot\frac{1}{2}\sqrt{\pi} \qquad \text{for } r \text{ even}$$

$$[\text{F.9}]$$

or

$$\int_0^\infty w^r e^{-\alpha w^2}\, dw = \tfrac{1}{2}\alpha^{-(r+1)/2}\left(\frac{r-1}{2}\right)! \qquad \text{for } r \text{ odd} \qquad [\text{F.10}]$$

G

ELASTIC COLLISION
CROSS SECTIONS

Figure G.1 shows values of elastic collision cross sections for six common gases. The relationship between the probability of collision P_c and the cross section Q can be shown as follows.

Consider a beam of electrons of intensity I incident upon a gas with a particle number density of N_G. Then the reduction in the intensity of the beam dI due to scattering in a distance dx is given by

$$\frac{dI}{I} = -N_G Q \, dx \qquad \text{[G.1]}$$

so that

$$I = I_0 e^{-N_G Q x} \qquad \text{[G.2]}$$

where we will assume that the electron energy is sufficiently low so that only elastic scattering occurs and Q is the cross section for elastic scattering. I_0 is the value of I for $x = 0$.

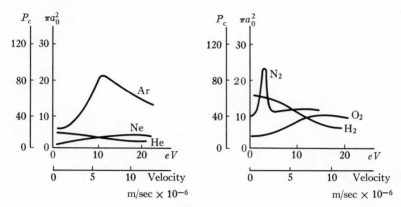

FIGURE G.I Elastic Collision Cross Sections Ar, Ne, N_2, O_2, H_2: R. B. Brode, *Rev. Mod. Phys.* **5**, 257 (1933). He: A. V. Phelps, O. T. Fundingsland, S. C. Brown, *Phys. Rev.* **84**, 559 (1951)

The product $N_G Q$ is called the *absorption coefficient* α, and the *probability of collision* P_c is defined as the value of α at a pressure of 1 Torr and a temperature of 0°C. P_c is therefore the fraction of particles scattered out of a collimated beam in unit distance per Torr at 0°C.

The number of gas molecules per c.c. at normal temperature and pressure is Loschmidt's number $L = 2.687 \times 10^{19}$ cm^{-3} so the number of gas molecules at a pressure of p Torr at 0°C is $pL/760 = 3.536 \times 10^{16}p$. The absorption coefficient α is therefore $\alpha = N_G Q = 3.536 \times 10^{16}pQ$ and the probability of collision P_c is

$$P_c = 3.536 \times 10^{16}Q \qquad \text{[G.3]}$$

for P_c in units of cm^{-1} and Q in cm^2.

The radius of the first Bohr orbit of the hydrogen atom $a_0 = 0.53 \times 10^{-8}$ cm. The corresponding orbital area is $\pi a_0^2 = 0.88 \times 10^{-16}$ cm^2 so that

$$P_c = 4.0Q \qquad \text{[G.4]}$$

for P_c in units of cm^{-1} and Q in units of πa_0^2 cm^2.

H

EIGENVALUES
AND EIGENVECTORS

We have seen that, in general, the second order tensor M_{ij} transforms the vector A_j into a vector B_i which differs from A_j in both magnitude and direction. However, in particular cases, it is found that the operation $M_{ij}A_j$ results in a vector B_i which differs from A_j in magnitude only, so that we can write

$$M_{ij}A_j = \lambda A_i \qquad \text{[H.1]}$$

where λ is a scalar quantity.

Equation [H.1] can be rewritten as

$$(M_{ij} - \lambda\delta_{ij})A_j = 0 \qquad \text{[H.2]}$$

A non-trivial solution of [H.2] exists when

$$\det(M_{ij} - \lambda\delta_{ij}) = 0 \qquad \text{[H.3]}$$

that is

$$\begin{vmatrix} M_{11} - \lambda & M_{12} & M_{13} \\ M_{21} & M_{22} - \lambda & M_{23} \\ M_{31} & M_{32} & M_{33} - \lambda \end{vmatrix} = 0$$

The resulting equation in λ is of third order giving in general three permissible values of λ. These roots may be complex. They are called the eigenvalues of the matrix M. Inserting these values of λ into [H.1] will give corresponding values of A_j which are called the eigenvectors of the matrix M.

EIGENVALUES AND EIGENVECTORS
FOR THE PLASMA DIELECTRIC TENSOR

It is shown in Section 7.2 that the dielectric tensor for a plasma, κ_{ij}, can be written in the form

$$\kappa_{ij} = \begin{bmatrix} S & -iD & 0 \\ iD & S & 0 \\ 0 & 0 & T \end{bmatrix}$$

where S, D, and T are defined in that section. Let us find the eigenvalues and eigenvectors of this tensor.

For this case equation [H.3] can be written

$$\begin{vmatrix} S - \lambda & -iD & 0 \\ iD & S - \lambda & 0 \\ 0 & 0 & T - \lambda \end{vmatrix} = 0$$

or

$$(T - \lambda)(\lambda^2 - 2S\lambda + S^2 - D^2) = 0$$

The three solutions are

$$\lambda^{(1)} = S + D$$
$$\lambda^{(2)} = S - D \qquad\qquad \text{[H.4]}$$
$$\lambda^{(3)} = T$$

These are the eigenvalues of κ_{ij}. To determine the values of A_j which are the corresponding eigenvectors, we write [H.2] using the dielectric tensor κ_{ij} as follows

$$
\begin{bmatrix}
S - \lambda & -iD & 0 \\
iD & S - \lambda & 0 \\
0 & 0 & T - \lambda
\end{bmatrix}
\begin{bmatrix}
A_1 \\
A_2 \\
A_3
\end{bmatrix} = 0
\qquad \text{[H.5]}
$$

Now inserting the value for $\lambda^{(1)}$ from [H.4] in this equation we obtain the three equations

$$
-DA_1^{(1)} - iDA_2^{(1)} = 0
$$

$$
iDA_1^{(1)} - DA_2^{(1)} = 0
$$

$$
(T - S - D)A_3^{(1)} = 0
$$

Because $(T - S - D)$ is not zero, $A_3^{(1)} = 0$. Also we have that $iA_1^{(1)} = A_2^{(1)}$. Thus

$$
A_i^{(1)} = (g, ig, 0)
$$

where g is any scalar. If we desire that the eigenvector $A_i^{(1)}$ have a magnitude of unity, we can write it as $e_i^{(1)}$ where

$$
e_i^{(1)} = \frac{1}{\sqrt{2}}(1, i, 0)
\qquad \text{[H.6]}
$$

Similarly by inserting $\lambda^{(2)} = S - D$ in [H.5] we find that the corresponding eigenvector $A_i^{(2)}$ normalized to unity is

$$
e_i^{(2)} = \frac{1}{\sqrt{2}}(1, -i, 0)
\qquad \text{[H.7]}
$$

and for the eigenvalue $\lambda^{(3)} = T$ we obtain the normalized value of $A_i^{(3)}$ as

$$
e_i^{(3)} = (0, 0, 1)
\qquad \text{[H.8]}
$$

COMPLEX VECTORS
AND PROJECTION OPERATORS

Since the eigenvectors $e_i^{(1)}$ and $e_i^{(2)}$ given by [H.6] and [H.7] have complex components, we will find it convenient to introduce the following notation.

Let $|e^{(1)}\rangle$ represent the eigenvector $e_i^{(1)}$ written as a column matrix. That is

$$|e^{(1)}\rangle = \frac{1}{\sqrt{2}}\begin{bmatrix} 1 \\ i \\ 0 \end{bmatrix} \qquad \text{[H.9]}$$

Then let $\langle e^{(1)}|$ represent the corresponding row matrix formed by taking the complex conjugates of the elements in [H.9]. That is,

$$\langle e^{(1)}| = \frac{1}{\sqrt{2}}\begin{bmatrix} 1 & -i & 0 \end{bmatrix} \qquad \text{[H.10]}$$

Similarly, we can write the eigenvectors $e_i^{(2)}$ and $e_i^{(3)}$ as

$$|e^{(2)}\rangle = \frac{1}{\sqrt{2}}\begin{bmatrix} 1 \\ -i \\ 0 \end{bmatrix} \quad \text{and} \quad \langle e^{(2)}| = \frac{1}{\sqrt{2}}\begin{bmatrix} 1 & i & 0 \end{bmatrix} \qquad \text{[H.11]}$$

and

$$|e^{(3)}\rangle = \begin{bmatrix} 0 \\ 0 \\ 1 \end{bmatrix} \quad \text{and} \quad \langle e^{(3)}| = \begin{bmatrix} 0 & 0 & 1 \end{bmatrix} \qquad \text{[H.12]}$$

It is clear that two types of products can be formed from the matrices $|e^{(\beta)}\rangle$ and $\langle e^{(\alpha)}|$. Thus, if we multiply the row matrix $\langle e^{(\alpha)}|$ into the column matrix $|e^{(\beta)}\rangle$, we will obtain a scalar quantity which we will denote by $\langle e^{(\alpha)}|e^{(\beta)}\rangle$. From [H.9] to [H.12] we see that the eigenvectors are orthonormal in the sense that

$$\langle e^{(\alpha)}|e^{(\beta)}\rangle = \delta_{\alpha\beta} \qquad \text{[H.13]}$$

On the other hand if we multiply the column matrix $|e^{(\alpha)}\rangle$ into the row matrix $\langle e^{(\alpha)}|$ we obtain a 3×3 matrix, often called an *operator*, which we will denote by $P^{(\alpha)}$ and write as

$$P^{(\alpha)} = |e^{(\alpha)}\rangle\langle e^{(\alpha)}| \qquad \text{[H.14]}$$

Using [H.13] we see that if we operate on $P^{(\alpha)}$ by itself we obtain

$$P^{(\alpha)}P^{(\alpha)} = |e^{(\alpha)}\rangle\langle e^{(\alpha)}|e^{(\alpha)}\rangle\langle e^{(\alpha)}| = |e^{(\alpha)}\rangle\langle e^{(\alpha)}| = P^{(\alpha)} \qquad \text{[H.15]}$$

Such an operator which, when operating on itself, yields itself again, is called a *projection operator*.

From [H.9] to [H.12] we see that we can form the three projection operators

$$P^{(1)} = \left| e^{(1)} \right\rangle \left\langle e^{(1)} \right| = \tfrac{1}{2} \begin{bmatrix} 1 & -i & 0 \\ i & 1 & 0 \\ 0 & 0 & 0 \end{bmatrix} \qquad \text{[H.16]}$$

$$P^{(2)} = \left| e^{(2)} \right\rangle \left\langle e^{(2)} \right| = \tfrac{1}{2} \begin{bmatrix} 1 & i & 0 \\ -i & 1 & 0 \\ 0 & 0 & 0 \end{bmatrix} \qquad \text{[H.17]}$$

$$P^{(3)} = \left| e^{(3)} \right\rangle \left\langle e^{(3)} \right| = \begin{bmatrix} 0 & 0 & 0 \\ 0 & 0 & 0 \\ 0 & 0 & 1 \end{bmatrix} \qquad \text{[H.18]}$$

If we add the matrices in [H.16], [H.17], and [H.18], we note that

$$\sum_{\alpha=1}^{3} P^{(\alpha)} = P^{(1)} + P^{(2)} + P^{(3)} = \begin{bmatrix} 1 & 0 & 0 \\ 0 & 1 & 0 \\ 0 & 0 & 1 \end{bmatrix} = \mathsf{I} \qquad \text{[H.19]}$$

We also note that $P^{(1)}$, $P^{(2)}$, and $P^{(3)}$ are mutually exclusive projection operators. That is,

$$P^{(\alpha)}P^{(\beta)} = \left| e^{(\alpha)} \right\rangle \left\langle e^{(\alpha)} \middle| e^{(\beta)} \right\rangle \left\langle e^{(\beta)} \right|$$
$$= \left| e^{(\alpha)} \right\rangle \delta_{\alpha\beta} \left\langle e^{(\beta)} \right|$$

from which we have that

$$P^{(\alpha)}P^{(\alpha)} = P^{(\alpha)}$$

and

$$P^{(\alpha)}P^{(\beta)} = 0 \qquad \text{if } \alpha \neq \beta$$

THE DIELECTRIC TENSOR
IN THE PRINCIPAL COORDINATE SYSTEM

We now wish to determine how the components of an arbitrary vector referred to the physical coordinate system transform when referred to the principal coordinate system in which the unit vectors are the three eigenvectors.

Consider a vector whose components in the physical coordinate system are given by the column matrix

$$|A\rangle = \begin{bmatrix} A_1 \\ A_2 \\ A_3 \end{bmatrix} \qquad \text{[H.20]}$$

Since $|A\rangle = 1 \, |A\rangle$, we have using [H.19] that

$$|A\rangle = 1 \, |A\rangle = P^{(1)}|A\rangle + P^{(2)}|A\rangle + P^{(3)}|A\rangle$$
$$= |e^{(1)}\rangle\langle e^{(1)}|A\rangle + |e^{(2)}\rangle\langle e^{(2)}|A\rangle + |e^{(3)}\rangle\langle e^{(3)}|A\rangle$$

or

$$|A\rangle = |e^{(1)}\rangle \, \tilde{A}_1 + |e^{(2)}\rangle \, \tilde{A}_2 + |e^{(3)}\rangle \, \tilde{A}_3 \qquad \text{[H.21]}$$

where $\tilde{A}_1$, $\tilde{A}_2$, and $\tilde{A}_3$ are the components of the vector $|A\rangle$ when referred to the principal coordinate system with unit vectors $|e^{(1)}\rangle$, $|e^{(2)}\rangle$, and $|e^{(3)}\rangle$. From [H.21], [H.20], and [H.9] to [H.12] we see that

$$\tilde{A}_1 = \langle e^{(1)}|A\rangle = \frac{1}{\sqrt{2}}\,(A_1 - iA_2)$$

$$\tilde{A}_2 = \langle e^{(2)}|A\rangle = \frac{1}{\sqrt{2}}\,(A_1 + iA_2) \qquad \text{[H.22]}$$

$$\tilde{A}_3 = \langle e^{(3)}|A\rangle = A_3$$

We can write [H.22] as a matrix equation

$$\begin{bmatrix} \tilde{A}_1 \\ \tilde{A}_2 \\ \tilde{A}_3 \end{bmatrix} = \frac{1}{\sqrt{2}} \begin{bmatrix} 1 & -i & 0 \\ 1 & i & 0 \\ 0 & 0 & \sqrt{2} \end{bmatrix} \begin{bmatrix} A_1 \\ A_2 \\ A_3 \end{bmatrix} \qquad \text{[H.23]}$$

or

$$|\tilde{A}\rangle = \mathsf{U}\,|A\rangle \qquad \text{[H.24]}$$

where

$$\mathsf{U} = \frac{1}{\sqrt{2}} \begin{bmatrix} 1 & -i & 0 \\ 1 & i & 0 \\ 0 & 0 & \sqrt{2} \end{bmatrix} \qquad \text{[H.25]}$$

If we premultiply [H.24] by the inverse of U, we find that

$$|A\rangle = U^{-1}|\tilde{A}\rangle \qquad \text{[H.26]}$$

Taking the inverse of [H.25], we obtain

$$U^{-1} = \frac{1}{\sqrt{2}}\begin{bmatrix} 1 & 1 & 0 \\ i & -i & 0 \\ 0 & 0 & \sqrt{2} \end{bmatrix} \qquad \text{[H.27]}$$

Note from [H.27] and [H.25] that the inverse of U is equal to the Hermitian conjugate $U^\dagger$ of U formed by transposing and taking the complex conjugate of the matrix elements. A matrix with the property $U^{-1} = U^\dagger$ is termed *unitary*. Also notice that the columns of the matrix U^{-1} are the eigenvectors.

From [H.26] and [H.27] we can write the components of $|A\rangle$ in terms of the components of $|\tilde{A}\rangle$. Thus

$$A_1 = \frac{1}{\sqrt{2}}(\tilde{A}_1 + \tilde{A}_2)$$

$$A_2 = \frac{1}{\sqrt{2}}i(\tilde{A}_1 - \tilde{A}_2) \qquad \text{[H.28]}$$

$$A_3 = \tilde{A}_3$$

Now let K be the matrix representing the dielectric tensor referred to the physical coordinate system. That is,

$$K = \begin{bmatrix} S & -iD & 0 \\ iD & S & 0 \\ 0 & 0 & T \end{bmatrix} \qquad \text{[H.29]}$$

where the values of the elements are given in Section 7.2. We can write the relationship between the electric displacement and the electric field intensity as

$$|D\rangle = \epsilon_0 K|\tilde{E}\rangle \qquad \text{[H.30]}$$

Let $\tilde{K}$ be the matrix representing the dielectric tensor referred to the principal coordinate system. That is, it satisfies the matrix equation

$$|\tilde{D}\rangle = \epsilon_0\tilde{K}|\tilde{E}\rangle \qquad \text{[H.31]}$$

Now $|D\rangle = \mathsf{U}^{-1}|\tilde{D}\rangle$ and $|E\rangle = \mathsf{U}^{-1}|\tilde{E}\rangle$ so that [H.30] can be written

$$\mathsf{U}^{-1}|\tilde{D}\rangle = \epsilon_0 \mathsf{K}\mathsf{U}^{-1}|\tilde{E}\rangle$$

which becomes, upon premultiplying by U,

$$|\tilde{D}\rangle = \epsilon_0 \mathsf{U}\mathsf{K}\mathsf{U}^{-1}|\tilde{E}\rangle \qquad \text{[H.32]}$$

Comparing [H.31] with [H.32] we see that

$$\tilde{\mathsf{K}} = \mathsf{U}\mathsf{K}\mathsf{U}^{-1} \qquad \text{[H.33]}$$

Performing this matrix multiplication, we find that

$$\tilde{\mathsf{K}} = \begin{bmatrix} R & 0 & 0 \\ 0 & L & 0 \\ 0 & 0 & T \end{bmatrix} \qquad \text{[H.34]}$$

where

$$R = S + D$$
$$L = S - D \qquad \text{[H.35]}$$

We see that when referred to the principal coordinate system the dielectric tensor assumes a diagonal form and that the diagonal elements are the three eigenvalues given by [H.4].

AUTHOR INDEX

TO CHAPTER REFERENCES

503

INDEX

MAXWELL'S EQUATIONS

$\nabla \times \mathbf{E} = -\dot{\mathbf{B}} \quad \epsilon_{ijk}E_{k,j} = -\dot{B}_i$ [3.34]

$\nabla \times \mathbf{H} = \mathbf{J} + \dot{\mathbf{D}} \quad \epsilon_{ijk}H_{k,j} = J_i + \dot{D}_i$

[3.35]

$\nabla \cdot \mathbf{B} = 0 \quad B_{i,i} = 0$ [3.37]

$\nabla \cdot \mathbf{D} = \eta \quad D_{i,i} = \eta$ [3.38]

COLLISION FREQUENCY

$\nu_{\text{EN}} = N_N Q g$ [4.1]

MEAN FREE PATH

$L = 1/N_N Q$ [4.2]

SCATTERING CROSS SECTION

$Q = 2\pi \int_0^\pi S(\chi) \sin \chi \, d\chi$ [4.62]

SCATTERING CROSS SECTION FOR MOMENTUM TRANSFER

$Q_M = 2\pi \int_0^\pi (1 - \cos \chi) S(\chi) \sin \chi \, d\chi$ [4.74]

PARTICLE NUMBER DENSITY

$N = \int f \, dc$ [5.1]

MEAN VALUE OF A FUNCTION

$\phi = \phi(v)$

$\langle \phi \rangle = \dfrac{1}{N} \int \phi f \, dc$ [5.3]

PECULIAR VELOCITY

$V_i = v_i - \langle v_i \rangle$ [5.5]

PRESSURE

$P_j = \rho n_i \langle V_i V_j \rangle$ [5.8]

PRESSURE TENSOR

$\Psi_{ij} = \rho \langle V_i V_j \rangle$ [5.10]

KINETIC THEORY DEFINITION OF TEMPERATURE

$\tfrac{1}{2}m\langle V_i V_i \rangle = \tfrac{3}{2}kT$ [5.14]

THE BOLTZMANN EQUATION

$\dfrac{\partial f}{\partial t} + v_i \dfrac{\partial f}{\partial x_i} + R_i \dfrac{\partial f}{\partial v_i}$

[5.32]

$= \int (\tilde{f}\tilde{f}^B - ff^B)gp \, dp \, d\psi \, dc^B$ [5.33]

MAXWELLIAN DISTRIBUTION FUNCTION

$f = N \left(\dfrac{m}{2\pi kT} \right)^{3/2} e^{-(mW^2/2kT)}$ [5.61]

MOMENT EQUATIONS FOR A SINGLE SPECIES

THE CONTINUITY EQUATION

$\dfrac{\partial N^{(s)}}{\partial t} + \dfrac{\partial}{\partial x_i}(N^{(s)}\langle v_i^{(s)} \rangle) = 0$ [6.16]

THE MOMENTUM EQUATION

$\dfrac{\partial \langle v_i^{(s)} \rangle}{\partial t} + \langle v_j^{(s)} \rangle \dfrac{\partial \langle v_i^{(s)} \rangle}{\partial x_j}$

$+ \dfrac{1}{N^{(s)}m^{(s)}} \dfrac{\partial \Psi_{ij}^{(s)}}{\partial x_j}$

$- \dfrac{q^{(s)}}{m^{(s)}}(E_i + \epsilon_{ijk}\langle v_j^{(s)} \rangle B_k)$

$= \nu_{\text{SN}}(\langle v_i^N \rangle - \langle v_i^{(s)} \rangle)$ [6.37]